Microbial Enzymes

Microbial Enzymes

Production, Purification, and Industrial Applications

Volume 1

Edited by Dinesh Yadav, Pankaj Chowdhary, Gautam Anand, and Rajarshi Kumar Gaur

WILEY-VCH

Editors

Dr. Dinesh Yadav
Deen Dayal Upadhyaya Gorakhpur University
Department of Biotechnology
Civil Lines
Gorakhpur, Uttar Pradesh 273009
India

Dr. Pankaj Chowdhary
Society for Green Environment
New Delhi 110067
India

Dr. Gautam Anand
Agricultural Research Organization
Volcani Institute
Department of Plant Pathology and Weed Research
Rishon LeZion 7505101
Israel

Dr. Rajarshi Kumar Gaur
Deen Dayal Upadhyaya Gorakhpur University
Department of Biotechnology
Gorakhpur, Uttar Pradesh 273009
India

Cover Image: © Christoph Burgstedt/Shutterstock

Library of Congress Card No.: applied for

British Library Cataloguing-in-Publication Data
A catalogue record for this book is available from the British Library.

Bibliographic information published by the Deutsche Nationalbibliothek The Deutsche Nationalbibliothek lists this publication in the Deutsche Nationalbibliografie; detailed bibliographic data are available on the Internet at <http://dnb.d-nb.de>.

Print ISBN: 978-3-527-35291-3
ePDF ISBN: 978-3-527-84435-7
ePub ISBN: 978-3-527-84436-4
oBook ISBN: 978-3-527-84434-0

Typesetting Straive, Chennai, India
Printing and Binding CPI Group (UK) Ltd, Croydon, CR0 4YY

C9783527352913_021024

Contents

About the Editors

Dr. Dinesh Yadav is Professor of the Department of Biotechnology and currently the Director of the Research and Development Cell at DDU Gorakhpur University. He has served as the Dean of the Faculty of Rural Sciences, Head of the Department of Biotechnology, Nodal Officer of the IPR Cell and Coordinator of Centre for Genomics and Bioinformatics at D.D.U. Gorakhpur University. He has also served as Associate Professor of the Department of Molecular Biology and Genetic Engineering at G.B. Pant University of Agriculture and Technology, Pantnagar, from 2006 to 2009. He completed his master's degree in biotechnology from Devi Ahilya University, Indore, in 1996 and PhD from G.B. Pant University of Agriculture and Technology, Pantnagar, in 2002. He has more than 23 years of teaching and research experience.

He has availed the DST-BOYSCAST Fellowship at the Australian Centre for Plant Functional Genomics (ACPFG), University of Adelaide, South Australia, from 3 May 2012 to 12 April 2013. He was awarded for Excellence in Teaching and Research in Higher Education by the University on Teacher's Day, 5 September 2021. He received Dr. Pushpendra Kumar Gupta Vishisht Krishi Vaigyanik Puraskar (2015) in the field of agricultural sciences by Uttar Pradesh Academy of Agricultural Sciences (UPAAS), Lucknow, and the Young Scientist Award (2008) by the Uttarakhand State Council of Science & Technology in the discipline of biotechnology, biochemistry, and microbiology.

His areas of specialization include molecular biology, bioinformatics, plant biotechnology, and enzyme technology. He has published more than 150 research papers, including reviews, books, book chapters, and conference proceedings, and has more than 300 GenBank accession numbers. A total of 48 indigenously isolated microbial strains (fungal and bacterial) have been deposited in several culture collection centers in India. He has carried out nine projects with support from funding agencies such as DBT, UGC, UP Council of Agricultural Research, Lucknow, and DST as PI/Co-PI and Mentor. Presently, he is involved in three projects funded by CST (UP) and UPCAR (Lucknow).

He has guided 12 students to PhD in biotechnology, and four students have submitted PhD thesis. He has also supervised more than 114 students for MSc dissertations and short project works in biotechnology. He has been a mentor for five postdoctoral fellowships, namely UGC-Dr. D.S. Kothari (twice), DST-Women Scientist-A, DST-Women Scientist-B, and SERB National PDF.

He is a life member of various scientific societies such as BRSI, Trivandrum; SBC(I), Bangalore; Indian Science Congress Association, Calcutta; Society of Plant Biochemistry and Biotechnology, IARI, New Delhi, Association of Microbiologists of India (AMI), New Delhi; and UPAAS, Lucknow.

He has delivered more than 100 invited talks and lectures at conferences and symposiums and served as Mentor for the DST-INSPIRE Science Internship Camp and Inspire Awards. Currently, he is working on plant-specific transcription factor-DOF (DNA binding with one finger) and nuclear factor-Y (NF-Y) for developing biotic and abiotic stress tolerance crops and pectinases group of enzymes with potential applications in different industries.

His research works have been published in journals of national and international repute, including *Journal of Experimental Botany, Cellulose, World Journal of Microbiology and Biotechnology, Environmental Science and Pollution Research, Theoretical and Applied Genetics, Cellulose, Frontiers in Microbiology, Planta, World Journal of Microbiology and Biotechnology, Process Biochemistry, Molecular Biology Reports, Plant Systematics and Evolution, Molecular Biotechnology, Applied Biochemistry and Biotechnology, Annals of Microbiology, Journal of Basic Microbiology, 3 Biotech, Biologia, Journal of Cereal Sciences, Physiology and Molecular Biology of Plants, Biochemistry (Moscow), Current Proteomics, Interdisciplinary Sciences: Computational Life Sciences, Biocatalysis and Agricultural Biotechnology, Cell Biochemistry and Biophysics, Online Journal of Bioinformatics, Chemistry and Ecology, African Journal of Biotechnology, Applied Biochemistry and Microbiology, Sugar Tech,* and *Enzyme Research*.

Dr. Pankaj Chowdhary is President of the Society for Green Environment (SGE), New Delhi, India. He completed his PhD in 2018 in the area of microbiology from the Department of Environmental Microbiology at Babasaheb Bhimrao Ambedkar University, Lucknow, Uttar Pradesh, India. His doctorate work was mainly focused on the role of ligninolytic-enzyme-producing bacterial strains in the decolorization and degradation of coloring compounds from distillery wastewater. His main research areas include microbial biotechnology, biodegradation and bioremediation of environmental contaminants in industrial wastewaters, metagenomics, and lignocellulosic waste valorization. He has edited eight international books and authored two books. He has published more than 60 research and review papers in national and international peer-reviewed journals with a high impact factor, published by Springer, Elsevier, Royal Society of Chemistry (RSC), Taylor & Francis Group, and Frontiers. He has also published many national and international book chapters and magazine articles on the biodegradation and bioremediation of environmental pollutants. He has presented many posters and papers relevant to research areas in national and international conferences. He has actively worked as a potential reviewer for various SCI journals published by reputed international publishers (Springer, Elsevier, RSC, Taylor & Francis Group, Wiley, and Frontiers). He is a life member of the Association of Microbiologists of India (AMI) and the Indian Science Congress Association (ISCA), Kolkata, India".

Dr. Gautam Anand is a postdoctoral fellow at the Department of Plant Pathology and Weed Research, Agricultural Research Organization (ARO) – Volcani Institute, Israel. He obtained his MSc and PhD degrees in biotechnology from Deen Dayal Upadhyaya Gorakhpur University, India. During his PhD, he worked on an industrially important microbial enzyme of the pectinases group, namely polygalacturonase. He was selected for the Agricultural Research Organization – Postdoctoral Fellowship, Israel, for the year 2020–2021 and the Valazzy Pikovsky Fellowship for postdoctoral research at the Hebrew University of Jerusalem, Israel, for the year 2018–2019. He has also worked as a postdoctoral fellow at the Robert H. Smith Faculty of Agriculture, Food and Environment, Hebrew University of Jerusalem, Israel. He has worked extensively on plant–fungus interactions. His main area of research is characterizing the importance of trafficking pathways in fungal virulence using deletion mutagenesis and cell biology techniques. Dr. Anand has also worked on fungal pectinases, particularly polygalacturonases and pectin lyases. He has published more than 30 papers in reputable international journals and 14 book chapters.

Dr. Rajarshi Kumar Gaur earned his PhD in 2005. Currently, he is Professor at the Department of Biotechnology, Deen Dayal Upadhyaya Gorakhpur University, Gorakhpur, Uttar Pradesh, India. His PhD focused on the molecular characterization of sugarcane viruses, namely, mosaic, streak mosaic, and yellow luteovirus. He received the MA SHAV Fellowship from the Israel government for his postdoctoral studies and joined the Volcani Centre, Israel, and Ben-Gurion University, Negev, Israel. In 2007, he received a Visiting Scientist Fellowship from the Swedish Institute Fellowship, Sweden, to work at Umeå University, Umeå, Sweden. He received a Postdoctoral Fellowship from ICGEB, Italy, in 2008. He has made significant contributions to the study on sugarcane viruses and has published 135 national and international papers, authored 27 edited books, and presented about 50 papers in national and international conferences. He is an honored Fellow of Linnean Society, Royal Society of Biology, Society of Plant Research, Society of Applied Biology (FSAB), International Society of Biotechnology (FISBT), and Indian Virological Society (FIVS). He has received awards such as Prof. B.M. Johri Memorial Award, Society of Plant Research (SPR); Excellent Teaching Award by Astha Foundation, Meerut; UGC-Research Teacher Award; Young Scientist Award-2012 in Biotechnology by Society of Plant Research

(SPR), Meerut; and Scientific & Applied Research Centre Gold Medal Award (2011) for outstanding contribution in the field of biotechnology. He has visited several laboratories in the United States, Canada, New Zealand, the United Kingdom, Thailand, Sweden, and Italy. Currently, he is handling national and international grants and international collaborative projects on plant viruses and disease management.

Preface

The book *Microbial Enzymes: Production, Purification, and Industrial Applications* provides an insight into diverse aspects of microbial enzymes, highlighting strategies for their production, purification, manipulation, and elucidating multifarious industrial applications. Microbial enzymes have played a pivotal role in several industries, and over the years, substantial efforts have been made to reveal the hidden potential of untapped microbial diversity in search of a repertoire of enzymes. A plethora of microbial enzymes have been reported so far, and efforts have been made to incorporate many of these enzymes in this book authored by experts. An emphasis has also been placed on discussing the recent technological interventions in microbial enzyme technology, such as metagenomics, system biology, molecular biology, genomics, directed evolution, and bioinformatics, in this book. The important microbial enzymes highlighted in this book include xylanases, ureases, methane monooxygenase, polyhydroxyalkanoates, pectinases, peroxidases, α-L-rhamnosidase, alkane hydroxylases, laccases, proteases, gallic acid decarboxylase, chitinases, beta-glucosidase, lipases, inulinases, tannase, mycozyme, ACC deaminase, and ligninolytic enzymes, among others. Few chapters are exclusively focused on microbial enzyme intervention as an eco-friendly approach in diverse industrial applications.

From an environmental point of view, all the recent and classic microbial treatment technologies should be amplified to make them more viable and feasible. Contaminate mitigation or removal using enzyme technology has become an attractive and potential alternative in recent days. Further, recent developments in the fields of biotechnology, molecular biology, ecology, and microbiology have been applied to develop different novel treatment methods involving novel strains of microorganisms with desirable properties that would be applicable in the process of bioremediation. Various types of beneficial microbes are present in the ecosystem, and they can play a key role in mitigating climate concern, improving green production technology, enhancing agriculture productivity, and providing a means of earning a livelihood. A few chapters have highlighted the omics-driven research in microbial enzyme technology.

This book is a good collection of chapters reflecting multidimensional aspects of microbial enzyme technology, and it will be of immense importance for students, scientists, biotechnologists, microbiologists, and policymakers working in environmental microbiology, biotechnology, and environmental sciences with the basics and advanced enzyme technology. Moreover, readers can also get state-of-the-art or background information on existing technologies, their challenges, and future prospects.

The editors express sincere thanks to the contributors for submitting their work in a timely and proper manner. The editors are also thankful to national and international reviewers for their evaluation and valuable suggestions and comments to heighten the book's quality for readers. Further, editors also acknowledge the cooperation received from the Wiley team for their guidance in finalizing this book.

2024, Gorakhpur

Dinesh Yadav, PhD
Deen Dayal Upadhyaya Gorakhpur University
Department of Biotechnology, Civil Lines
Gorakhpur, Uttar Pradesh 273009, India

Pankaj Chowdhary, PhD
Society for Green Environment
New Delhi 110067, India

Gautam Anand, PhD
Agricultural Research Organization
Volcani Institute
Department of Plant Pathology and Weed Research
Rishon LeZion 7505101, Israel

Rajarshi Kumar Gaur, PhD
Deen Dayal Upadhyaya Gorakhpur University
Department of Biotechnology
Gorakhpur, Uttar Pradesh 273009, India

1

Xylanases: Sources, Production, and Purification Strategies

Mariana Delgado-Garcia[1], *Lizeth G. Campos-Muzquiz*[2], *Rocio G. Castillo-Godina*[2], *Sendar D. Nery-Flores*[2], *Lissethe Palomo-Ligas*[2], *Adriana C. Flores-Gallegos*[2], *Beatriz del C. Cutiño-Laguna*[2], and *Raul Rodriguez-Herrera*[2]

[1] *Technological Institute of Superior Studies of Monterrey, Campus Guadalajara, School of Engineering and Sciences, Av. General Ramón Corona 2514, Nuevo México, Zapopan, 45138 Jalisco, México*
[2] *Universidad Autónoma de Coahuila, School of Chemistry, Blvd. V. Carranza y Jose Cárdenas s/n, Col. Republica, Saltillo, Coahuila 25280, México*

1.1 Introduction

The cell wall of the plant is composed of different lignocellulosic compounds, being the xylan the main compound of hemicellulose. This structure consists of xylose united by β-1,4-glycosidic bonds and different branches of α-D-glucuronide, arabinose, galactose, acetate, methyl glucuronic acid, and other simple sugars [1, 2]. Xylanase is a group of hydrolytic enzymes involved in the hydrolysis of xylan to convert it into monosaccharides and xylooligosaccharides. The xylanase system is constituted by glycosyl hydrolases (*endo*-xylanases, *exo*-xylanases, β-D-xylosidases, α-glucuronidase, and α-L-arabinofuranosidases) and esterases [3].

The heterogeneous composition of hemicellulose hampers the complete depolymerization by a single enzyme, requiring the action of both glycosyl hydrolases and esterases [4]. Each enzyme of the xylanase group contributes to xylan degradation in a specific way: *endo*-xylanase randomly cleaves the xylan; *exo* and *endo* xylanases acting on the xylan backbone and producing short-chain oligomers; β-D-xylosidases cleaves xylose monomers, α-L-arabinofuranosidases removes the side groups, α-D-glucuronidases, and acetylxylan esterases remove acetyl and phenolic side branches and act synergistically on the complex polymer [4, 5]. The most common natural sources of xylanases are produced by different biological systems such as bacteria, protozoans, fungi, plants, and mollusks. Actually, it has been reported that xylanases have been identified from lignocellulose-degrading microbiota from cow rumen and, the termite hindgut. There are two strategies applied to date for microbial xylanase production, either using native microorganisms or genetic engineering modified microorganisms [3, 4].

Microbial Enzymes: Production, Purification, and Industrial Applications, First Edition.
Edited by Dinesh Yadav, Pankaj Chowdhary, Gautam Anand, and Rajarshi Kumar Gaur.

Xylanase production from nonmodified fungi and bacteria must use proper microorganisms, which should produce acceptable yields and should not produce toxins or any other unsought products [6]. Xylanases can be produced by hydrolysis of xylan by the microorganisms that express the enzyme gene. Nonetheless, due to the xylan complexity, the production of this enzyme from different microorganisms on a large-scale is hard because one of the main problems is the presence of other enzymes. This problem is also present during the purification steps, increasing costs. Hence, one alternative is the use of modified strains for large-scale xylanase production [7, 8].

In the case of bacteria, the alkaline-thermostable xylanase-producing trait is useful in most industrial applications since it reduces the steps due to the higher pH level required for the optimal growth and activity of the microorganism [9]. Xylanases require *N*-glycosylation as one of the most important posttranslational modifications; therefore, not all bacterial expression hosts are suitable, such as *Escherichia coli*, which lacks the *pgl* gene, to produce this modification. Because of this, other alternative expression hosts are *Bacillus subtilis* and *Lactobacillus* sp. [10, 11].

Filamentous fungi are an important option to produce high amounts of xylanases in comparison to yeast and bacteria [12]. A problem associated with fungal xylanases is cellulase excretion; therefore, an operational process to obtain xylanolytic systems free of cellulases is very important in this case [13]. Another major problem associated with fungi is the reduced xylanase yield in fermenter studies, principally for the agitation that promotes fungal disruption, leading to low productivity [14].

Some examples of xylanases-producing fungus used in industry are *Penicillium canescens, Streptomyces* sp. P12–137, *Thermomyces lanuginosus* SD-21, *Penicillium fellutanum, Penicillium sclerotiorum, Acremonium furcatum, Aspergillus niger* PPI, *Neocallimastix* sp. Strain L2, *Cochliobolus sativus* Cs6, *Bacillus circulans* D1, *Streptomyces* sp. strain Ib 24D, and *Paecilomyces themophila* J18. The substrate used by these microorganisms for fermentation is derived from cereals as soya, wheat, corn, and oat [15–25]. On the other hand, yeasts are good expression hosts due to their ability to perform eukaryotic posttranslational modifications, high cell density growth, and secretion of proteins into fermentation media [26, 27]. Some yeasts used for xylanase production are *Saccharomyces cerevisiae* and *Pichia pastoris* [28, 29]

Plants are also used for xylanases production, using bio-farming. The requirements for this objective are (i) high-level expression, (ii) stability and functionality of enzymes to be expressed, and (iii) easy purification. *In planta* expression of lignocellulose-digesting enzymes from mesophilic bacteria and fungi can compromise plant biomass production because of autohydrolysis of cell walls and others such as growth, yield, germination, fertility and susceptibility of the host to disease [30]. There are enzymes that can be used during the lignocellulose pretreatment without losing their enzymatic activity for their hypo-thermophilic capacity [31].

Recently, there has been much industrial interest on xylanases, from native microorganisms and recombinant hosts for different applications. For example, in the baking industry, *endo*-1,4-β-xylanase from *Aspergillus oryzae, B. subtilis*, and *Trichoderma longibrachiatum* is used for bread making, the production of maize starch and alcohol through fermentation. Particularly, in the bread industry, the uses of xylanase are intended for flexibility and stabilization of dough (breaking down polysaccharides) and improve gluten strength. This impacts the sensory perception of bread [32].

In the animal nutrition industry, xylanases from *Acidothermus cellulolyticus* and *Neocallimastix patriciarum* are used to reduce feed conversion rate and enhance the digestibility of cereal feeds in poultry and ruminant [33, 34]. *Lactobacillus* xylanases depolymerize hemicellulose, making silage more stable and digestible by cattle [35]. The most common uses of xylanases have been used in the paper and pulp industry for the benefits of the quality of the products as purity, bright, and more permeability of fiber surface and diffusion during the bleaching processes [36–38]. Due to the current crisis of energy, the utilization of lignocellulosic agents is considered as sustainable biomass to produce nonfossil fuels. These biomasses should be hydrolyzed for bioethanol production from agricultural waste such as corncob, chili residue, rice straw, banana peel, apple pomace, and others [3, 39–42].

Xylanases have an important role in hydrolyzing the xylan and generate value-added products, such as xylitol. Xylitol is a sweetener used in soft drinks, candies, ice cream, chewing gum, and various pharmaceutical products as a natural sweetener in toothpaste [43]. Other uses have been explored, e.g., extracellular xylanase from a culture of *Aspergillus carneus* M34 and used to treat xylooligosaccharide. Feruloyl xylooligosaccharides showed antioxidative capacity in a cell model of ultraviolet B (UVB)-induced oxidative damage, demonstrating the potential of xylanases use in photo-protectant preparation [44].

1.2 Sources, Production, and Purification Strategies

Xylanases can be obtained in a large number of biologic systems such as fungi, bacteria (*Bacillus pumilus, B. subtilis, Bacillus amyloliquefaciens, Bacillus cereus, B. circulans, Bacillus megatorium, Bacillotherus licheniformis, Bacillotherus* sp., *Streptomyces roseiscleroticus, Streptomyces cuspidosporus, Streptomyces actuosus, Pseudonomas* sp., *Clostridium absonum,* and *Thermoactinomyces thalophilus*), yeasts, and seaweed [45]. Some other organisms such as mycorrhizae, actinomycetes, protozoa, insects, crustaceans, snails, and some plant seeds during the germination phase have been identified as xylanase sources [46]. Filamentous fungi being the main producers of xylanolytic enzymes, compared to other microorganisms [47]. In this way, xylanases have different applications, according to the source of production and some studies have focused on optimizing enzyme production, mainly from more powerful fungal and bacterial strains or through mutant strains for higher enzyme production [26, 48–50].

Fungal strains are important producers of xylanases due to their high yield and extracellular release of enzymes. They also show greater xylanase activity than yeast and bacteria. However, they present some characteristics that make them little available for use in industry. Fungal xylanases cannot be used in the pulp and paper industry because they need an alkaline pH and a temperature higher than 60 °C [45]. These xylanases are efficient at temperatures below 50 °C and a pH range of 4–6. The fungal sources of xylanases are *A. niger, Aspergillus fetidus, Aspergillus brasiliensis, Aspergillus flavus, Aspergillus nidulans, Aspergillus terreus Penicillium* sp., *Trichoderma reesei, T. longibrachiatum, Trichoderma harzianum, Trichoderma viride, Trichoderma atroviride, Fusarium oxysporum, T. lanuginosus, Alternaria* sp., *Talaromyces emersonii, Schizophyllum commune*, and *Piromyces* sp. [47]. Although many of the reports focus on studies of xylanolytic systems from filamentous fungi mainly, and by bacteria, there are some reports on obtaining xylanases from yeasts [51, 52]. Two *Cryptococcus* yeast strains had been identified as producers of xylanases with a thermostable behavior [52]. Other reports are on the identification of yeast strains able to produce cellulase-free xylanases to solve the most common problem during the search of biologic systems for xylanase production [53].

From the great variety of xylanase-producing microorganisms, some thermophilic microorganisms have been isolated, which grow at an optimal temperature between 50 and 80 °C, and extremophiles or hyperthermophiles, which grow at temperatures above 80 °C [54]. Thermophilic microorganisms are sources of enzymes with greater activity at high temperatures [55]; these sources are important because xylanolytic enzymes are required to be able to withstand aggressive working conditions, such as acidic or alkaline environments and high temperatures, this due to its various industrial applications. For this reason, xylanases have been isolated from extremophilic bacteria and fungi. According to the analyses of genomic and transcriptomic profiles of xylanase-producing extremophilic fungi, it is argued that the discovery of new sources of thermostable xylanases, using molecular tools such as directed evolution, can satisfy the growing demand for thermostable xylanases. Table 1.1 shows a list of xylanases that come from thermophilic and hyperthermophilic microorganisms [61, 62].

Recent studies have focused on xylanase production optimization, for which they have used new strains of endophytic fungi, which were good producers of xylanases when solid-state fermentation (SSF) is used [63]. In the past, about 80–90% of commercial xylanases have been produced by submerged fermentation (SmF); however, SSF has a great option, such as less space requirement, low cost, and the

Table 1.1 Thermophilic and hyper-thermophilic microorganisms producing thermostable xylanases.

Source	Specie	GH family	References
Bacteria	*Caldicellulosiruptor* sp.	10	[56]
Bacteria	*Caldicoprobacter algeriensis*	11	[56]
Bacteria	*Dictyoglomus thermophilum*	11	[57]
Bacteria	*Microcella alkaliphila*	10	[58]
Hongo	*Aspergillus niger*	11	[59]
Hongo	*Malbranchea cinnamomea*	11	[44]
Hongo	*Thermomyces lanuginosus*	11	[60]

application of circular economy for the use of agricultural waste as a substrate for enzyme production. Therefore the xylanase production process has been optimized by *Fusarium solani*, using SSF. This fungal strain produces xylanases with low cellulolytic activity [64].

The catalytic function of xylanases, in general, the xylan hydrolysis, which is one of the polysaccharide's components of hemicellulose, mainly hydrolyzes the xylan bond that is composed of various xylose residues, through β-1,4 bonds-glycosidic. Xylanases differ not only in size and shape but also in their physicochemical properties; these will be classified based on their catalytic differences and the type of microorganism source, i.e., if they work better at a low pH, they are called acidophilic xylanases, if they work at an alkaline pH they are called alkaliphilic xylanases and neutral xylanases at a neutral pH, in a range of 5–7 [65]. Various studies have shown the catalytic properties of the xylanases of different microorganisms, finding the most efficient conditions of humidity, pH, and temperature of two species of the *Trichoderma* genus, and the extracts obtained showed good production of xylooligosaccharides and low cellulase activity [66]. Other authors have reported the catalytic diversity of two subfamilies of GH30 bacterial xylanases, both of which break the β-1,4-D-xylosidic bond; their study offers a broader panorama of their enzymatic activity and their mechanism of recognition of substrate. It was suggested to use genetic engineering techniques to create specific xylanases, from regions of some already known xylanase genes [65, 67].

1.3 Structure

Xylanases if endohydrolytic breaks 1,4-β-D-xylosidic linkages in xylan; thus they mediate the xylan degradation to simpler utilizable units generating simple xylan units. Currently, in the CAZy database (http://cazy.org), xylanase activity (EC 3.2.1.8) has been classified under glycoside hydrolase (GH) families 5, 7, 8, 9, 10, 11, 12, 16, 26, 30, 43, 44, 51, and 62 [2]. Most β-1,4-xylanases are classified into the groups GH10 (formerly F) and GH11 (formerly G) and represent the best studies of xylanase families. Furthermore, xylanase varieties are related to physicochemical properties, chemical structure, substrate specificity, and their mechanism of action.

The hydrolysis of xylan by xylanase may occur by two different mechanisms: retention or inversion of stereochemical configuration at the anomeric carbon. Enzymes of families 5, 7, 10, and 11 mostly are the most studied and have an interesting retention mechanism [3]. The retention mechanism is a process given by a covalent glycosyl enzyme intermediate that is formed in the glycosylation step and subsequently hydrolyzed in the deglycosylation step via transition states, including substrate distortion and electrophilic migration of C1. The glutamate residues in the catalytic site are essential, as they act as a nucleophile and an acid/base catalyst. Two carboxylic acid residues present in the active site (approximately 5.5 Å apart) are involved in the formation of the α-glycosyl intermediate. The intermediated formation is for substrate protonation, where a carboxylic acid residue acts and the departure of the leaving group. This resulted in β to α inversion. In the second step, the carboxylate group takes a proton from a nucleophilic water molecule and attacks the anomeric carbon. Then, a second substitution in which anomeric carbon again passes via an oxocarbenium-ion-like transition state to give rise to a product with the β configuration (α to β inversion). This second substitution generates a product with the same stereochemistry as the substrate, thus retaining the anomeric configuration [5, 68, 69].

The enzymes of families 8 and 43 have a catalytic mechanism given by an inversion of the anomeric center with glutamate and aspartate as the major catalytic residue where a single displacement reaction is generated, where only one carboxylate ion offers for overall acid-catalyzed group departure. This enzyme xylanase can act as the base for activating a nucleophilic water molecule to attack the anomeric carbon for breaking the glycosidic bonds and causing an inversion of anomeric carbon configuration [5, 69, 70].

GH10 family are represented by cellobiohydrolases (exocellulases) and *endo*-1,3-xylanases besides xylanases (*endo*-1,4-β-xylanases), while family 11 is solely xylanases. The CAZy database lists 358 xylanases of the GH10 family as well as 55 3D structure entries [71]. A characteristic of GH10 xylanase is its wide spectrum of xylan source specificity. In mixed linkage xylan, GH10 family hydrolyzes β-1,3-linkages flanked on both sides by β-1,4-linkages. These xylanases can tolerate the replacement of one or two consecutive xylose residues by glucose residues in the substrate [50]. Also, some GH10 family members are efficient in hydrolyzing the aryl β-glycosides of xylobiose and xylotriose at the aglyconic bond [2]. Most of the GH10 xylanases have high molecular mass (>30 kDa), low isoelectric point, and $(\alpha/\beta)_8$-barrel fold or "salad bowl" shape with extended loops, creating a catalytic cleft that contains at least four to seven xylose-binding subsites. The catalytic residues are two glutamate residues in C-terminal ends of β-strands 4 (acid/base) and 7 (nucleophile) [72]. For example, xylanase Xys1 from *Streptomyces halstedii* folds in an $(\alpha/\beta)_8$ barrel. Eight parallel twisted β-strands (β1–β8) are surrounded by eight major α-helices (α1–α8) in a right-handed β–α–β motif. Long βα loops at the carbonyl side of the β-barrel confer "salad-bowl" shape to the molecule (Figure 1.1). The active site glutamate residues appear at the C terminus of the strands β4 and β7, Glu127 in loop β4α4 is the acid/base catalyst, while Glu235 in strand β7

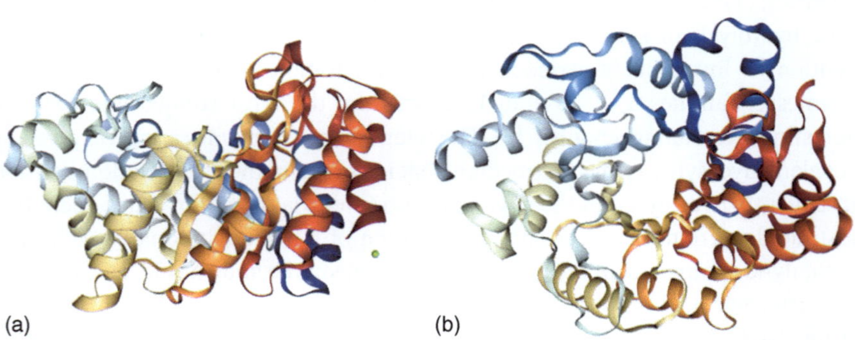

Figure 1.1 3D structure representation of Xys1 from *Streptomyces halstedii*. (a) Side view of the catalytic domain. (b) Top view of the catalytic domain.

is the nucleophile [73]. Another example is *Thermoascus aurantiacus* xylanase, which shows a long polypeptide chain with an $(\alpha/\beta)_8$ triose-phosphate-isomerase (TIM) barrel fold. The catalytic residues consist of two glutamate residues located at the C terminus end of the β-barrel (Glu131 and Glu237). A salt bridge in Arg124-Glu232, which is almost buried, bridges the β-strands β4 and β7 where the catalytic glutamate residues reside, and it may play a key role in the stability and activity at elevated temperatures [74].

GH family 11 xylanases are called "true xylanases" for their specificity on D-xylose-containing substrates, and the products from its activities such as xylobiose and xylotriose usually required further hydrolysis by other xylanase enzymes. The CAZy database lists 294 xylanases of the GH10 family as well as 36 3D structure entries. These enzymes have a small molecular weight (<30 kDa) and a conserved β-jelly roll fold, whose catalytic cleft is almost 30–35 Å long, which can accommodate six xylose moieties at most [75]; the subclassification if often acidic and alkaline xylanases based on their pH-optima. In xylanases that function optimally under acidic conditions (pH < 5), this residue is Asp, whereas in alkaline xylanases (pH > 5) is an Asn [76, 77]. In general, GH11 xylanases consist of a single catalytic domain with an all β-strand "sandwich-like" fold containing two β-sheets forming a large cleft that can accommodate the xylan polymers [78–80]. The catalytic site is composed of two glutamate residues, acting as a nucleophile and an acid/base catalyst, located in the middle of the long cleft [81]. For example, xylanase from *T. lanuginosus* is a compact, globular protein with a prominent long cleft spanning the whole molecule and containing the active site (Figure 1.2). The structure consists of two β-sheets and sheet A forms the "outer" surface of the enzyme Sheet B if formed by nine antiparallel strands. The catalytic site has as active residues of Glu86 and Glu178, but Glu86 should be unprotonated while Glu178 should be protonated. An extra disulfide bridge in this xylanase is responsible for its thermostability and connects the C-terminus (catalysis β-strand) catalysis with the N-terminus (α-helix). On the other hand, the rest of the xylanase types have a hydrogen bond in this position [82].

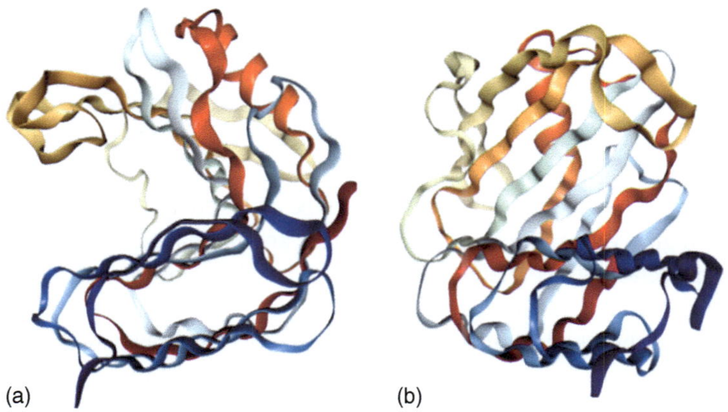
(a) (b)

Figure 1.2 3D structure representation of xylanase from *Thermomyces lanuginosus*. (a) Side view of the catalytic domain. (b) Front view of the catalytic domain.

1.4 Xylanases as Biocatalyst

1.4.1 Properties Relationship of Xylanases for Hydrolysis Catalytic Reaction

To carry out a hydrolysis reaction using xylanases as a biocatalyst and to obtain biotechnological products like xylooligosaccharides, some catalytic characteristics of xylanases are important. Of all the families of GH, the most studied and important are GH10 and GH11 families of enzymes to obtain xylooligosaccharides. The characteristics of reaction media are important in that the xylanase can or not act efficiently, one of them is the high temperature that is important in industrial applications. As a biocatalyst, the thermostability allows it to resist the changes in viscosity of the reaction-mix, having a great impact on the enzyme–substrate interaction as changes in the solubility and accessibility of the xylan, increasing the half-life and the hydrolysis capacity of the xylanase [3, 83, 84]. Thermostability property is due to the presence of disulfide bridges and aromatics patch content, high ratio of Tyr and Trp in their structures, where some bacterial xylanases, especially GH11 of *B. subtilis* strain 168, *T. lanuginosus* have this structural property [84]. Some xylanases of *Bacillus* sp. are thermostable at 60–70 °C values [85].

An important aspect is that the hydrolysis capacity of xylanases is related also to the botanical origin, tissue localization of the substrate used, structural similarity, or alternative catalytic reactions with a range of substrates [3, 86]. Commonly, the terrestrial xylan is chemical structure of D-xylose linked by β-1,4 glycosidic and L-arabinose traces inside of the heteropolymeric structure, allowing xylanases to hydrolyze it with retention or inversion catalytic mechanism. Both catalytic mechanisms are carried out by different amino acids; in the case of the retention catalytic mechanism, glutamate plays an important role, while inversion catalytic mechanism is carried out by glutamate and aspartate. These amino acids are important because their carboxyl groups are part of a catalytic reaction intermediary [3, 83]. In addition, the catalytic capacity is given by the specificity, selectivity, affinity, and other typical characteristics of the xylanases described as K_{cat}/K_m and K_m values. In bacteria it is possible to obtain xylanases with high affinity to substrate showing a K_m (mg/ml) range of 0.4–0.6 in reports of *Bacillus* sp. SN5 and *Panebacillus barcinonensis*. In fungi, it is possible to observe a major affinity with values of 0.2 km (mg/ml) value in *A. oryzae* LC1 or *Streptomyces griseorubens* LH-3 1.44 km (mg/ml) [3, 87, 88].

GH11 xylanase family has high selectivity for a type of heteroxylan, where the substitutions are highly variable like galactose, xylose, arabinose, ferulic, and glucuronic acids. This selectivity is related by the structural planes of the carboxylic groups and the Val or Leu in 35 positions in substitute (−1) both for the orientation of acid/base, and also, the sterical hindrances and the absence of possible hydrogen bond with the O6 of glucose residue. The selectivity in GH11 is given for the decoration in the heteroxylan backbone due to the high degree of substitutions, which can complicate the hydrolysis capacity of this group of xylanases [79]. GH10 xylanase family is versatile and involved in the cleavage of the nonreducing side of substituted xylose residues of the xylan backbone; also it can catalyze cellulose; their selectivity and specificity are low compared to the GH11 xylanase family. However, this family can tolerate glucose but has a low capacity to catalyze insoluble xylan [84, 89].

Xylanase is a good catalyst for the proprieties mentioned, but also is important as the noncatalytic carbohydrate-binding molecules (CBMs), an auxiliary autonomous module to recognize the complex and heterogeneous xylan and the with domains impact in the stability of the xylanase. These CBMs allow to xylanases increase the enzyme quantity on the surface of the substrate, catalysis of substrate disruption, and interfacial/surface modifications. Generally, this capacity is located both N-terminal and/or C-terminal and is rich in serine or threonine. The CBMs are so important that they allow classification in CAZy into 64 families according to the amino acid sequence. The selectivity of the xylanases has also been given by CBMs for their capacity to link to xylan or have a low affinity for acid-swollen cellulose, but this depends on the interaction of their aromatic residues and sugars. Also CBMs contribute to the thermostability [79].

All these catalytic properties mentioned allow having xylooligosaccharides (XOS) of different degree of polymerization (DP), where the xylanases first decrease the polymerization structure with the formation of short XOS. For example, the thermos-alkali-stable xylanase released XOS with DP of 2 and 6 units, xylobiose (X2), xylotriose (X3), and xylotetraose (X4) from different terrestrial xylan substrates, this is typical of the degradation model of the xylanases like non-arabinose liberating *endo*-xylanases, arabinose liberating xylanases and β-xylosidase [86, 90]. Generally, the GH10 xylanases family results in short XOS with low DP (X2–X5), but GH11 xylanases until X6 units due to the capacity to access to larger and complex xylan associated with the single and smaller domain [84].

1.4.2 Inhibition and Synergism During Hydrolysis Catalytic Reaction

During the hydrolysis process, two effects can be present. First, the catalytic activity of xylanases can act with other enzymes, simulating the natural processes of xylan degradation. The synergy allows have a total activity of the combination of various enzymes with xylanases such as arabinofuranosidases that help in the hydrolysis α-1,2 and α-1,3 and, together with endoxylanases, can hydrolyze efficiently the xylan. In this way, it is possible to obtain different XOS in one catalytic reaction. There are few studies of the "synergistic catalytic reaction" of the xylanases and other accessory enzymes, but it had been referenced that acetylxylan esterases of *Thermobifida fusca*, glucuronidases of *Pichia stipis* CBS 6054, arabinofuranosidases, pectin esterases, cellulases, proteases, mannanase are reported that can allow major access of the endoxylanase to xylan hydrolysis. For the synergy, choice of the raw material, pretreatment, selection of enzymes, and the type of synergism [91, 92]. Homeosynergy is a cooperative catalysis between two or more different main-chain or chain cleaving enzymes, while in heterosynergy catalysis, reaction between side-chain and main-chain cleaving enzymes occur [86].

Second, although there is a wide variety of xylan substrates, consider the great possibility of other obstacles during the catalysis mechanism of xylanases is possible. Different molecules of the plant as a source of xylan are important to hydrolysis obstacles. The phenolic compounds as cinnamic acid, ferulic acid, caffeic acid, and chlorogenic acid affect the acid residues of the surface and internal aromatic residues, decreasing in some cases the K_m value [86]. The plants protect themselves by producing different inhibitors of phytopathogenic microorganisms of protein character, some called XIP (xylanase inhibitor protein), (*Triticum aestivum* xylanase inhibitor), and TXLI (Thaumatin-like xylanase inhibitor). The inhibition of XIP is competitive between fungal GH10 and GH11 xylanases, affecting the thumb-loop into the active site. On the other hand, TAXI inhibitors, both in GH10 and GH11 xylanases, are competitive; it has been suggested that the TAXI site covers the xylanase thumb and cleft in the catalytic site. In the case of TXLl, it is a noncompetitive inhibition where the His22 of the xylanase GH11 interacts outside of the active site [86].

1.4.3 Catalytic Mechanisms of Synthesis of XOS and Alkyl Glycosides

The search for new opportunities of the GH enzymes has allowed the possibility of their use in the production of XOS for trans-glycosylation and obtain a variety of XOS with defined-length is possible. In addition, the major studies of the catalytic mechanism of the xylanases consist of hydrolysis reaction, but the glycosyl hydrolases are able to synthesize different compounds like mannosides or alkyl xylosides with an important application in the detergents for the surfactant property, bioavailability of therapeutic agents, etc. [93]. For this to be possible, a catalytic mechanism of retention for catalyzing transglycosylation reactions or transxylosylation using glycosyl hydrolases or β-xylosidases. During the synthesis reactions, some aspects are important to select in front of chemical synthesis. The most important is a unique single step for the reaction while chemical synthesis requires steps of protection, activation, glycosylation, and deactivation for the reaction. To carry out the enzymatic reactions, there are some important elements for enzymatic reactions. The transglycosylation which is an acceptor is necessary commonly a saccharide molecule, and a hydroxyl group as a nucleophilic acceptor, that can be an alcohol present in the aglycone subsite and essential for the catalysis. In the case of transxylosylation is important the presence of polyphenolic acceptors for the necessity of two hydroxyl groups both for interaction and correct orientation of the active site [94]. For the "perfect reaction" although less extent compared with hydrolysis reaction is necessary a thermodynamic equilibrium and control reduce the amount of water; however, protein engineering and directed evolution are possible to reduce the catalytic activity, modifying the active site that influences the synthesis reaction [93]. Until now, the major use of GH is the production of alkyl xylosides, a potential opportunity for GH enzyme applications.

1.4.4 Trends of Xylanases as Biocatalyst

The common carbon sources and the catalytic mechanisms and action of xylanase action had been studied from terrestrial xylan derivative from agro-wastes of wheat bran, wheat husk, rice husk, sugarcane bagasse, coconut coir, coconut oil cake, groundnut shell, wood pulp, sawdust. In addition, industrial or domestic organic wastes like molasses, sugar beet pulp fruit, vegetable, and pulp industry wastes [45, 54, 95, 96]. However, the marine environment is also rich in "nonconventional" xylan sources, allowing a new approach to xylanases. Mangrove forests are among these sources, rich in nutrients, salinity, humidity, and organic matter; it is a uniquely dynamic environment. The seaweed also is a potential xylan source, but is different from the terrestrial xylan due to the low lignin content and β-1,3 xylan and it has been suggested that is possible the presence of combined-linkage xylans (1,3; 1,4-β-D-xylan) but are still a largely unexplored field [97].

The approach of different nonconventional substrates for xylanases is an opportunity to explore new sources or the possibility of creating multifunctional enzymes like chimeric xylanases and potentiate their catalysis using in silico analysis of proteins. Chimeric xylanases are artificial enzymes designed for market sales, which generated gains above 8.3 million dollars in 2010. These enzymes have the property to catalyze consecutive reactions as a behavior of synergism for the transference of the intermediate to the next active site; this is a possibility to substitute the xylanosomes formed with many enzymes of microorganisms to degrade a complex substrate. The most common strategy is by tandem domain fusion of various sequences that encode proteins with a linker or without to produce one polypeptide chain [98]. Xylanase and arabinosidase had shown an increase in the specificity, specific activity, optimum temperature, and storage capability of the enzyme. Another strategy is based on the domain insertion in a place that is not directly involved in enzyme activity that can become the penetration in complex substrates. A chimeric enzyme is built by xylanase and laccase from *B. subtilis*, showing a major thermostability and resistance to proteolytic activity [99]. It is important to mention that to build a chimeric enzyme, we need to consider the elasticity of the connecting domains, structure, conformation, and physicochemical properties of each parent protein [100].

1.5 Genomics Studies on Xylanases

Xylanases are principally members of two glycosyl hydrolases GH10 and 11 based on their protein sequences. The major action mechanism of xylan hydrolysis is given by *endo*-1,4-beta-xylanase and beta-xylosidase present in all biologic systems, being the fungi most common [12, 101].

1.5.1 Expression of Xylanases

Most of the studies and development around the xylanases are based on improving the gene characteristic by DNA technology [85]. In nature, the xylanase complex is activated under catabolic repression by glucose. However, xylan is the major inductor of the xylanases and their fragments such as xyloboiose, xylotrose, xylooligosaccharides, and heterodisaccharides. Sources rich in xylan particularly grains and seeds, are the most inducers of xylanases. Other reports have demonstrated that organic sources of nitrogen such as tryptone, yeast extract, peptone, and soymeat, among others, have a high influence on the enhancement of xylanases production. Trace elements, vitamins, and amino acids are important for enhanced production [2, 101]. Both, xylan as the natural source and physiochemical conditions allow the optimal xylanase activity of different biological systems [9].

1.5.2 Genetic Significance

It had been reported a unique xylanase gene can encode multiple xylanases, acting as a genic operon, where during the expression and posttranslational modification is possible glycosylation, proteolysis, or both [4]. In the searching for genes producing xylanases, several studies showed that the genes which encode putative xylanases are obtained from grass, compost soil, and cow dung compost. These genes were cloned, obtained, and proved their efficiency by techniques as site-directed mutagenesis [102–104]. Other examples of identification are projects of sequencing, xylanase Y from the alkaliphile *Bacillus halodurans* C-125 which was identified during its genome sequencing [5]. It had been reported the homology between several xylanases sequences (94–99%) like JX030400 and JX030401 was identified from *Caldicellulosiruptor* sp. F32 [56]. The advances in omics have allowed to know the microbial adaptation in front of different conditions and building enzymatic libraries [54].

1.5.3 Strains Improvement

The isolation and cloning of the xylanases gene are important to obtain the most efficient microorganism. By cloning it is possible for the introduction of novel genes and the amplification of existing expression. For heterologous expression of xylanases several biologic systems are used both eukaryotic and prokaryotic in nature, being an excellent option; however, one of the reasons to select it is the posttranslational machinery. For this reason, some microorganisms, especially *Saccharomyces* sp. *Bacillus* sp., and *Lactobacillus* sp. have been considered an excellent source of potent biomass-degrading enzymes and Generally Regarded as Safe and improved by DNA recombinant technology [65, 105].

Strategies used to increase the production of xylanases are named strain improvement. Most of the processes that use xylanases are aggressive, particularly alkaline conditions, so genomic strategies are an option for retrieving alkali-xylanase genes. The use of recombinant DNA techniques like protoplast fusion in eukaryotic systems or phage vectors in prokaryotic systems, as an example to resolve the principal problems in xylanases production, like low yield [100]. There is a huge demand for thermostable and alkali-stable xylanases, expectant to adapt various innovative genomic strategies for retrieving genes that encode thermostable and alkali-stable xylanases with high activity [54]. Other methods to generate modified microorganisms are the mutagenesis, where the use of inducers, radiation, and others have been effective in creating mutant strains. These options of modification methods promote thermostability, pH tolerance, and other extreme conditions, allowing desired strains [106]. There are numerous reports of heterologous systems for xylanases. Genes like XynAM6, using DNA recombinant construction in *P. pastoris*, allowed having microbes with a high-temperature range of tolerance and protease resistance [107]. Protein engineering is another strategy used to improve new characteristics in xylanases. Particularly, the alteration of the amino acid sequence is one of the strategies used to generate protein with new catalytic properties such as thermostability, which is enhanced by the insertion of disulfide bridges, increasing intra-hydrogen bonding, and surface modification of the enzyme molecules. It has been observed that enhancing cysteine pairs in an *endo*-β-1,4-xylanase from the termite gut impacts its thermostability with catalytic efficiency at 60 °C and pH 9.0 [108]. Considering the prospects of xylanases for biotechnological exploitations, it is very important to analyze the chemical properties of xylanases with respect to the regulation of biosynthesis and catalytic action with their cloning, sequencing, mutagenesis, and crystallographic analysis.

1.6 Xylanases as a Promising Enzyme for Industrial Applications

Currently, one of the main concerns of the growing world population is the increase in demand for functional foods, as well as producing new foods with better quality and facilitating the production process. For this reason, it is imperative to look for alternatives that allow the use of various enzymes such as proteases, lipases, cellulases, and xylanases [109].

Among the various sources of enzymes, the xylanases (*endo*-1,4-β-xylanase) stand out, which are an important group of biocatalysts involved in random hydrolytic reactions and breaks the β-(1 → 4) glucosidic bonds of the polysaccharide complex xylan to produce shorter xylooligosaccharides that will give rise to xyloses [5, 109] a major source of carbon in plant cell metabolism [2]. Xylanases are generated by different organisms such as algae, fungi, protozoa, bacteria, yeast, and actinomycetes [2, 5, 109]. Xylanases, being biocatalytic enzymes of microbial origin, are ideal for various industrial applications, and these processes are carried out under hostile conditions such as extreme pH changes, with the presence of enzyme inhibitors in some cases, high temperatures, so the enzymes to be used must be strong enough to survive in such an environment, and in effect, xylanases have a unique place since these enzymes can possess properties desired by the different processes [110, 111]. It is said that these enzymes have received appreciable attention in biotechnology due to their vast potential in various industries such as the paper industry, biofuels, and others [109], food processing such as bread, biscuits, cereals, juice clarification, dairy, fermentation [111, 112], the biofuels industry (bioethanol), and the pharmaceutical industry [57, 95].

1.7 Industrial Food Applications

1.7.1 Bakery and Drinks

Manufactured bread uses wheat flour and is one of the world's staple foods. Regarding the wheat grain, it contains hydrophobic peripheral tissues and is composed of lignocelluloses complex. Likewise, the internal tissues of the wheat grain contain arabinoxylan and β-D-glucans present in their two forms (soluble and insoluble in water) [109]. Xylanases have been widely used in the bread and bakery industry to improve the properties of dough and bread [109]. Since xylanases transform insoluble arabinoxylans into soluble arabinoxylans, which interact with water during the preparation of the dough, creating more uniform and finer crumbs, as well as increasing the volume and decreasing the firmness of the dough in such a way that does not adhere to the walls of the material in which the dough is made [110, 112]. Also, the addition of xylanases provides extraordinary tolerance to the dough against variation and processing parameters with a significant increase in the baked bread since it creates thin and more uniform lumps and better resistance to fermentation [111]. Indeed, the dough and baked bread increase their quality and shelf life. For these reasons, xylanases have also been combined and used with other accessory enzymes such as amylases, laccases, glucanases, and others, to improve the quality of bread and bakery products [112].

Xylanases are also used to clarify wines and juices (fruits or vegetables) because these enzymes, together with amylases, pectinases, and cellulases, promote an improvement in juices through liquefaction, increasing the recovery of aromas, stabilizing the food pulp, and reducing viscosity [113]. It is worth mentioning that clarification of fruit juices is caused by the presence of various polysaccharide components such as hemicelluloses, cellulose, and pectin, which is why xylanases increase the quality and performance of the juices as they degrade carbohydrates adequate [111]. As mentioned in various studies on the extraction of pulp juices, it was treated with xylanases from *Bacillus licheniformis*, improving the content of reducing sugars in the juices (apple: 750–1320 mg/ml; pineapple: 375–700 mg/ml; mousambi: 300–620 mg/ml), and the turbidity of the juices was reduced by more than 70% [114]. Likewise, the treatment with xylanases of *A. terreus* S9 in orange juice, mousambi, and pineapple juices, resulting in a clarification of the juices thanks to the degradation of carbohydrates, which increases the yield, clarification, and quality characteristics of fruits treated with xylanases [113].

1.7.2 Animal Feed Industry

One of the sectors of agribusiness in which enzymes are also used is in the production of feed and forages where xylanases are used alone or mixed with other enzymes such as proteases, amylases, glucanases, and pectinases [57]. The use of xylanases for animal feed is mainly to improve digestion which will allow better use of energy [50]. Under the above, grains such as sorghum, corn and cereals constitute the basis of the diet and the main nutritional and energy contribution for the animals. However, grains contain arabinoxylan, which is considered an antinutritional component present in the cell walls of grains and cereals [57, 115]. Likewise, arabinoxylans are partially water-soluble polysaccharide compounds, so when mixing grains and cereals with water [116], Therefore, the decrease in viscosity in grains (corn and sorghum) and cereals is attributed to their arabinoxylan content, making grains and cereals unmanageable for animal feed [57]. However, arabinoxylans improve gel formation, viscosity, water absorption, stabilization of emulsions, etc., in processes based on cereals and grains, with an impact on the quality of cereals, offering soluble and insoluble fibers and antioxidant properties due to its phenolic remains in its configuration [116]. In this sense, the addition of xylanases to this type of food will increase the use of energy [50], because xylanases separate arabinoxylans into nutrients, helping to promote the fluency of the raw material and generating its nutritional value [57].

Several studies have indicated that the addition of xylanases in the treatment of grains (they contain arabinoxylan) in the form of a substrate allows solving the problem of viscosity [113]. Some authors [117] recorded that the apparent absorption of nitrogen and fiber was improved, as was the diffusion time of the feed, due to the addition of β-xylanase in the poultry feed. In this sense, the presence of β-xylanase decreases the fluency of the feed and improves the digestion capacity of the nutrients. On the other hand, the addition of xylanases in rye-based feeds for broilers in effect reduces intestinal viscosity and increases weight gain [26]. In addition, combining xylanases with enzymes such as phytase and β-glucanase improves the performance of broilers due to the reduction of the viscosity of the digesta, the reduction of the relative weight, the increase of the apparent metabolizable energy, and the length of the small intestine [50].

On the other hand, the combination of xylanases with cellulases produces better silage that increases the rate of digestion of the feed in ruminants. Xylanases increase the amount of nutritive sugar, which is beneficial for ruminants, among other animals [57]. Finally, it should be mentioned that the addition of thermostable xylanases before the granulation process, which is operated at high temperatures (70–95 °C), will be of benefit given the conditions of the digestive tract, which has a pH of 4.8 and a temperature of 40 °C [5].

1.7.3 Pharmaceutical Industry

The risk of suffering from various diseases associated with digestive metabolism (intestines) and associated dysfunctions at different ages of the population has led to the search to disseminate and overcome the causes of diseases associated with digestion this problem has based its attention on obtaining prebiotics [112]. In this sense, as the most important products obtained by xylan hydrolysis are XOS. According to the number of xylose residues, they are called xylotetrose, xylobiose, xylotriose, among others [50]. XOS are ideal as probiotics that can be applied in food since they exert this effect, thanks to the fact that they are not hydrolyzed or absorbed in the organs of the upper gastrointestinal tract and, therefore, selectively stimulate development or activity in the host of various healthy bacteria in the intestine improving the health of the host since it reduces cholesterol, improves the biological availability of calcium, reduces the maintenance of gastrointestinal health, and improves the nutritional properties of foods [113].

XOS are obtained from xylan containing lignocellulosic complex (LCC) by various methods such as chemical, enzymatic, or combined methods [50]. However, the enzymatic process through the hydrolysis of heteroxylan by xylanases avoids the production of high amounts of xylose since it has inhibitory effects on the production of XOS. Los XOS have a big commercial market because it is a nutraceutical produced by enzymes and has health-promoting properties [50, 113].

1.7.4 Bio-bleaching of Paper Pulp Industry

The cell wall of plants is mainly composed of lignin (20–30%), cellulose (35–50%), and hemicellulose (20–30%, with mainly xylan) [2]. Xylan is a complex heteropolysaccharide, highly branched, and is the main hemicellulosic constituent that has a linear skeleton of xyloses with β-1,4 bonds. The xylan is at the interface of cellulose (1,4-β-glucan) and the phenolic lignin residues linked by a covalent interaction, being the lignocellulosic complex, the main polymeric elements in the cell walls of plants. In addition, xylan is considered essential for fiber cohesion and the integrity of the plant [2, 5]. Due to the complex and heterogeneous characteristics of xylan, it is necessary to carry out complete hydrolysis, which is why the use of enzymes capable of carrying out this process is required [5]. In this sense, various xylanases of microbial origin are capable of degrading xylan to be used in the pulp and paper industry since they report that xylanases can easily hydrolyze xylan by producing β-xylosidases (EC 3.2.1.37) and 1,4-β-Dendoxylanases (EC 3.2.18) [2].

Concerning the cellulosic material constituting plants, it can be said that 15–30% are possessed by grass plants, 7–12% are contained in gymnosperms (softwoods) [118], while 15–30% are contained by angiosperms (hardwoods), and <30% content in annual plants [5]. With these data, for the paper industry, it is necessary to consider a profitable and environmentally friendly biotechnological method, which is why pretreatment with xylanase has been chosen in the traditional pulping process because it expands the dissemination of sodium hydroxide in soft and hardwoods [2], also considering, having a bio-bleaching in which it is necessary to use xylanases free of cellulolytic enzymes to preserve the cellulose fibers [50], thermostable, wide alkaline pH range, alkaline and dynamic at high temperatures (55–70 °C) [118, 119], that allow the enzymatic elimination of lignin bound to hemicellulose with minor damage to the pulp and expand the fibrillation of the pulp. In addition, using xylanases in these processes increases the chemical extraction of lignin from the pulp, improves the thickness of the dough, the quality of the paper, the length of tear, and it would allow to reduce the release of volatile organic compounds at the same time that it reduces the use of chlorine dioxide (ClO_2) [2]. In this sense, xylanases can also be used successfully in the treatment of recycled paper [118].

In this way, xylanases are very important to this industry, since they are an ecological alternative for the application of green biotechnology since they reduce pollution and increase the quality of the products obtained, compared to polluting chemical technologies that use toxic chlorinated compounds (ClO_2) causing environmental hazards and some diseases, becoming a safer option for substituting dangerous chlorinated compounds [2, 118] sodium carbonate, chelating agents, peroxide hydrogen, sodium hydroxide, hypo-chlorites, and sodium silicate [50].

1.7.5 Biofuel Production

In recent years, the production of biofuels is an option to substitute the fossil fuels [26]. Therefore, viable alternatives are being sought to improve energy security and produce fuels that are friendly to the environment. It is a good alternative to use waste from agriculture or industry to produce ethanol or lignocellulosic biomass by incorporating treatment with xylanases alone or in combination with other hydrolytic lignocellulosic enzymes such as cellulases and laccases. However, one of the limitations is the difficult structure of the plant cell wall, the majority composed of lignocellulosic compounds, where xylanases have a role to generate alternatives of biofuels from lignocellulosic biomass [50]. It is worth mentioning that to obtain bioethanol, the degradation of lignocellulose must first occur to release hemicellulose and cellulose from their complex with lignin, followed by depolymerization of the carbohydrate polymers to produce free sugars, and finally, the fermentation of the mixture must occur of pentose and hexose sugar to obtain bioethanol [113].

1.7.6 Other Applications of Xylanases

Xylanases from microorganisms have exorbitant potential at different industrial levels. Therefore, apart from the promising applications mentioned above, they can also be applied in other industries such as obtaining inexpensive products among which unicellular proteins, gaseous and liquid fuels, sugar syrups, degumming fibers (bast, hemp, jute, and ramie), the debarking process in wood processing, in the detergent industry, etc. [118].

1.8 Future Trends

After cellulose, xylan is the most abundant polysaccharide abundant in the nature [50], composed in some cases of different sugars and organic acids [3]. This compound has β-1,4-glycoside linkages, which are hydrolyzed by xylanases [120], and classified into different glycoside hydrolase families (GH) [43]. For these reasons, xylanases are used as biocatalytic components of different compounds and technology applied in the food, biofuel, pulp, paper, and agricultural industries [121]. According to the literature consulted, some trends in xylanase research can be seen; the immobilization of this enzyme is important for obtaining different compounds, including ionone and vitamins, that can be used in the cosmetic and food industries [122]. Thus, more research on this topic will appear in the next years.

Some industrial processes are performed under high-temperatures, alkaline conditions, or require high substrate specificity. In the last two decades, research has focused on bacterial xylanases because they have a wide tolerance under alkaline and high-temperature conditions than fungal xylanases. Thermostable xylanases can be produced by different microorganisms such as *T. reesei* or *Bacillus firmus* [106]. In addition, bacterial xylanases have low cellulase activity, high specificity of carbohydrate, and can selectively solubilize arabinoxylan [50]. In addition, xylanases have high specificity and can be used for prebiotic xylooligosaccharides [120]. These bacterial xylanase properties are a great option for industrial processes such as bio-bleaching industry, increasing pulp brightness, and reducing environmental pollution [2]. Identification and purification of new and high-quality microbial thermostable xylanase could reduce costs [106].

Traditional production of xylanases has been performed by mutation, using physical or chemical agents in order to reduce or inhibit an undesirable trait [50]. In the last three decades, this enzyme production has been enhanced using recombinant DNA technology [106]. Xylanase has been expressed using several host organisms, being *E. coli,* and *P. pastoris*, the most suitable hosts for xylanase expression [43]. Another DNA recombinant technology that could be used is the production of fusion xylanases, e.g., that with both cellulolytic and lignolytic activities, which could be used for biofuel production [50]. One strategy with potential is to isolate novel xylanase genes from extreme microorganisms and improve them by recombinant DNA technologies for specific industrial requirements [43]. Recently, techniques such as drug designing such as *in silico* directed mutagenesis or simulation of molecular behavior have been used to design better xylanases [50]. However, there is still a lack of information about the whole process of xylan degradation by xylanases [2].

Microorganisms are the most important source of xylanase; some of the advantages of enzymes are that they show specificity for diverse substrates and present different biochemical properties; because of these characteristics, microbial enzymes can be used in different industrial processes [3]. However, distinctive differences were reported between fungal and bacterial xylanases, especially for substrate recognition [120]. Isolation of bacteria with novel genes and yielding xylanases is still one of the foremost challenges [50].

Industrial processes performed at high temperatures have given rise to increasing research on thermophilic microorganisms, which not only are able to grow to high temperatures, but also tolerate a wide range of pH [43], or other denaturing factors and produce stable xylanases [121]. Thermophilic xylanolytic enzymes can be produced from bacteria [123]. Different sources for thermophilic enzymes that have been mentioned are volcanic craters, submarine volcanoes, hot springs, and deep-sea troughs [123]. However, the production of thermophilic xylanases has some drawbacks because of the high temperatures for fermentation processes [107]. In addition, xylanase from fungal (*Aspergillus fumigates*) and bacterial (*B. pumilus* and *B. firmus*) strains, which are free from cellulase have been reported for increased xylan hydrolysis [106].

The fermentation parameters for microbial growth are fundamental to obtaining high amount of native xylanase produced [106]. In addition, the presence of xylan-binding domains in some xylanases may affect their thermostability and how they bind to insoluble substrates [43]. Different recombinant xylanases have been developed with improved enzyme activity; examples are an *endo*-1,4-β-xylanase from *Neurospora sitophila* [124], putative xylanase from *Thermothelomyces thermophila* in *P. pastoris*, thermostable xylanase from a *Thermoanaero* bacterium [121] or recombinant xylanase from *A. oryzae* and expressed in *A. niger* [125]. However, the expression of the xylanase with improved activity may affect substrate specificity and enzyme stability at high temperatures and pH [43]. For these reasons, different expression techniques have been performed in order to overcome these disadvantages, among them, cloning and expression of xylanase with partial identity to the known xylanases [121], the addition of different reagents such as Tween 80 to enhance xylanase activity [125], changing the catalytic mechanism (xylobiohydrolase) of *endo*-1,4-β-xylanase [121], or *exo*-acting catalytic activity [120, 121] increasing enzyme stability at high temperature or presence of metal ions and denaturing [121] or purifying recombinant xylanases by His-tag column [125].

On the other hand, different thermophilic xylanases have been reported, one xylanase with an optimal temperature of 55 °C and pH of 6.5 [125], another with optimal activity at pH 5.5 and 55 °C xylanase with stability at 60 °C for six hours with a pH range between 4 and 10 [123], and that with the most tolerance to high temperatures, an *endo*-1,4-β-xylanase with an optimal temperature of 65–75 °C and pH 7.5 [121]. The future trends on this topic will deal with xylanase tolerance to high temperature, enzymatic stability different types of catalysis and elimination of the cellulase activity of this enzyme.

1.9 Conclusions

The most important relevant aspects of the xylanases, both molecular analysis and the potential industrial applications, are presented. The future trends based on different contexts of the ecological balance and the efficiency to satisfy the necessity of diverse processes is the way to create new knowledge and strategies for the economical utilization of xylan sources, where the generation of innovative products with these enzymes is essential. However, the previous knowledge about xylanases is related to biological sources, type, behavior, success processes, etc. Based on xylanases and their accessory enzymes and to change their perspective and related information, prospects for targeted engineering of the xylanase to create enzymes with desired properties in both industrial and science sectors have been discussed.

Acknowledgments

RGCG, SDNF, and LPL thank the National Council of Science and Technology (CONACyT) Mexico for the financial support during their postdoctoral training. BCCL thanks CONACyT for a scholarship for her PhD degree program in Food Science and Technology at the Autonomous University of Coahuila, Saltillo Campus, Mexico.

References

1 Houfani, A.A., Anders, N., Spiess, A.C. et al. (2020). Insights from enzymatic degradation of cellulose and hemicellulose to fermentable sugars – a review. *Biomass Bioenergy* 134: 105481. https://doi.org/10.1016/j.biombioe.2020.105481.

2 Walia, A., Guleria, S., Mehta, P. et al. (2017). Microbial xylanases and their industrial application in pulp and paper biobleaching: a review. *3 Biotech* 7 (1): 1–12. https://doi.org/10.1007/s13205-016-0584-6.

3 Bhardwaj, N., Kumar, B., and Verma, P. (2019). A detailed overview of xylanases: an emerging biomolecule for current and future prospective. *Bioresour. Bioprocess.* 6 (40): https://doi.org/10.1186/S40643-019-0276-2.

4 Juturu, V. and Wu, J.C. (2012). Microbial xylanases: engineering, production and industrial applications. *Biotechnol. Adv.* 30 (6): 1219–1227. https://doi.org/10.1016/j.biotechadv.2011.11.006.

5 Collins, T., Gerday, C., and Feller, G. (2005). Xylanases, xylanase families and extremophilic xylanases. *FEMS Microbiol. Rev.* 29 (1): 3–23. https://doi.org/10.1016/j.femsre.2004.06.005.

6 Uday, U.S.P., Choudhury, P., Bandyopadhyay, T.K., and Bhunia, B. (2016). Classification, mode of action and production strategy of xylanase and its application for biofuel production from water hyacinth. *Int. J. Biol. Macromol.* 82: 1041–1054. https://doi.org/10.1016/j.ijbiomac.2015.10.086.

7 Kimura, I., Sasahara, H., and Tajima, S. (1995). Purification and characterization of two xylanases and an arabinofuranosidase from *Aspergillus sojae*. *J. Ferment. Bioeng.* 80 (4): 334–339. https://doi.org/10.1016/0922-338X(95)94200-B.

8 Kormelink, F., Leeuwen, M.S., Wood, T., and Voragen, A. (1993). Purification and characterization of three endo-(1,4)-β-xylanases and one β-xylosidase from *Aspergillus awamori*. *J. Biotechnol.* 27: 249–265.

9 Subramaniyan, S. and Prema, P. (2002). Biotechnology of microbial xylanases: enzymology, molecular biology, and application. *Crit. Rev. Biotechnol.* 22 (1): 33–64. https://doi.org/10.1080/07388550290789450.

10 Kulkarni, N., Shendye, A., and Rao, M. (1999). Molecular and biotechnological aspects of xylanases. *FEMS Microbiol. Rev.* 23 (4): 411–456. https://doi.org/10.1016/S0168-6445(99)00006-6.

11 Ding, N., Yang, C., Sun, S. et al. (2017). Increased glycosylation efficiency of recombinant proteins in *Escherichia coli* by auto-induction. *Biochem. Biophys. Res. Commun.* 485 (1): 138–143. https://doi.org/10.1016/j.bbrc.2017.02.037.

12 Polizeli, M.L.T.M., Rizzatti, A.C.S., Monti, R. et al. (2005). Xylanases from fungi: properties and industrial applications. *Appl. Microbiol. Biotechnol.* 67 (5): 577–591. https://doi.org/10.1007/s00253-005-1904-7.

13 Biely, P. (1991). Biotechnological potential and production of xylanolytic systems free of cellulases. In: *Enzymes in Biomass Conversion* (ed. T. Page), 408–416. American Chemical Society https://doi.org/10.1021/bk-1991-0460.ch031.

14 Palma, M.B., Milagres, A.M.F., Prata, A.M.R., and De Mancilha, I.M. (1996). Influence of aeration and agitation rate on the xylanase activity from *Penicillium janthinellum*. *Process Biochem.* 31 (2): 141–145. https://doi.org/10.1016/0032-9592(95)00042-9.

15 Antoine, A.A., Jacqueline, D., and Thonart, P. (2010). Xylanase production by *Penicillium canescens* on soya oil cake in solid-state fermentation. *Appl. Biochem. Biotechnol.* 160 (1): 50–62. https://doi.org/10.1007/s12010-008-8496-5.

16 Arabi, M.I.E., Jawhar, M., and Bakri, Y. (2011). Effect of additional carbon source and moisture level on xylanase production by *Cochliobolus sativus* in solid fermentation. *Microbiology* 80 (2): 150–153. https://doi.org/10.1134/S0026261711010024.

17 Bocchini, D.A., Oliveira, O.M.M.F., Gomes, E., and Da Silva, R. (2005). Use of sugarcane bagasse and grass hydrolysates as carbon sources for xylanase production by *Bacillus circulans* D1 in submerged fermentation. *Process Biochem.* 40 (12): 3653–3659. https://doi.org/10.1016/j.procbio.2005.02.021.

18 Coman, G. and Bahrim, G. (2011). Optimization of xylanase production by *Streptomyces* sp. P12-137 using response surface methodology and central composite design. *Ann. Microbiol.* 61 (4): 773–779. https://doi.org/10.1007/s13213-010-0195-0.

19 Dijkerman, R., Ledeboer, J., Op Den Camp, H.J.M. et al. (1997). The anaerobic fungus *Neocallimastix* sp. strain L2: growth and production of (hemi)cellulolytic enzymes on a range of carbohydrate substrates. *Curr. Microbiol.* 34 (2): 91–96. https://doi.org/10.1007/s002849900150.

20 Knob, A. and Carmona, E.C. (2008). Xylanase production by *Penicillium sclerotiorum* and its characterization. *World Appl. Sci. J.* 4 (2): 277–283. http://www.idosi.org/wasj/wasj4(2)/19.pdf.

21 Palaniswamy, M., Pradeep, B.V., Sathya, R., and Angayarkanni, J. (2008). Isolation, identification and screening of potential xylanolytic enzyme from litter degrading fungi. *Afr. J. Biotechnol.* 7 (12): 1978–1982. https://doi.org/10.5897/ajb2008.000-5045.

22 Pandey, P. and Pandey, A.K. (2002). Production of cellulase-free thermostable xylanases by an isolated strain of *Aspergillus niger* PPI, utilizing various lignocellulosic wastes. *World J. Microbiol. Biotechnol.* 18 (3): 281–283. https://doi.org/10.1023/A:1014999728406.

23 Rawashdeh, R., Saadoun, I., and Mahasneh, A. (2005). Effect of cultural conditions on xylanase production by *Streptomyces* sp. (strain Ib 24D) and its potential to utilize tomato pomace. *Afr. J. Biotechnol.* 4: 251–255. https://www.ajol.info/index.php/ajb/article/view/15089.

24 Yang, G., Hou, L.L., and Zhang, F.L. (2011). Study on the solid-state fermentation conditions for producing thermostable xylanase feed in a pressure pulsation bioreactor. *Adv. Mater. Res.* 236–238: 72–76. https://doi.org/10.4028/http://www.scientific.net/AMR.236-238.72.

25 Yang, S.Q., Yan, Q.J., Jiang, Z.Q. et al. (2006). High-level of xylanase production by the thermophilic *Paecilomyces themophila* J18 on wheat straw in solid-state fermentation. *Bioresour. Technol.* 97 (15): 1794–1800. https://doi.org/10.1016/j.biortech.2005.09.007.

26 Burlacu, A., Cornea, C.P., and Israel-Roming, F. (2016). Microbial xylanase: a review. *Sci. Bull. Ser. F. Biotechnol.* 20: 335–342.

27 Buckholz, R. and Gleeson, M.A.G. (1991). Yeast systems for commercial production of heterologous proteins. *Nat. Biotechnol.* 9: 1067–1071. https://doi.org/10.1038/nbt1191-1067.

28 Cheng, Y.F., Yang, C.H., and Liu, W.H. (2005). Cloning and expression of *Thermobifida xylanase* gene in the methylotrophic yeast *Pichia pastoris*. *Enzym. Microb. Technol.* 37 (5): 541–546. https://doi.org/10.1016/j.enzmictec.2005.04.006.

29 Pérez-González, J.A., De Graaff, L.H., Visser, J., and Ramön, D. (1996). Molecular cloning and expression in *Saccharomyces cerevisiae* of two *Aspergillus nidulans* xylanase genes. *Appl. Environ. Microbiol.* 62 (6): 2179–2182. https://doi.org/10.1128/aem.62.6.2179-2182.1996.

30 Kim, J.Y., Nong, G., Rice, J.D. et al. (2017). In planta production and characterization of a hyperthermostable GH10 xylanase in transgenic sugarcane. *Plant Mol. Biol.* 93 (4): 465–478. https://doi.org/10.1007/s11103-016-0573-5.

31 Mir, B.A., Myburg, A.A., Mizrachi, E., and Cowan, D.A. (2017). In planta expression of hyperthermophilic enzymes as a strategy for accelerated lignocellulosic digestion. *Sci. Rep.* 7: 11462. https://doi.org/10.1038/s41598-017-11026-1.

32 Haertlé, T. (2016). Enzymes: analysis and food processing. In: *Encyclopedia of Food and Health* (ed. T. Page), 524–531. Academic Press.

33 Cheng, K.-J., Chen, Y.-C., Cheng, H.-L. et al. (2009). Xylanase gene sequences from the genomic DNA of unpurified rumen microorganisms. US Patent 2008/0118491A1, issue 22 May 2008.

34 Zhi, C.W., Clarkson, K.A., and Morgan, A.J. (1999). Xylanase from *Acidothermus cellulolyticus*. US Patent 590258, issue 11 May 1999.

35 Evans, T., Christopher, P., Mann, P. et al. (1995). Formulation for treating silage containing beta-1,4-xylanase and beta-1,3-xylosidase but essentially free of beta-1,4-glucanase and beta-1,4-cellobiohydrolase, and one or more lactic acid-producing bacteria. US Patent 5432074, filed 13 August 1993 and issue 11 July 1995.

36 Archana, A. and Satyanarayana, T. (2003). Purification and characterization of a cellulase-free xylanase of a moderate thermophile *Bacillus licheniformis* A99. *World J. Microbiol. Biotechnol.* 19 (1): 53–57. https://doi.org/10.1023/A:1022527702400.

37 Archana, G., Amit, K., and Dharm, D. (2017). Production and characterization of cellulase-free xylanase by *Aspergillus flavus* ARC-12 and its application in pre-bleaching of ethanol-soda pulp of *Eulaliopsis binata*. *Res. J. Biotechnol.* 12 (8): 63–71.

38 Lu, Q., Lu, J., Ma, H. et al. (2019). The effect of lanthanum (III) on the activity of xylanase by *Penicillium* and its influence on brightness in the paper pulp bleaching. *3 Biotech* 9 (12): 452. https://doi.org/10.1007/s13205-019-1977-0.

39 Boonchuay, P., Techapun, C., Leksawasdi, N. et al. (2018). An integrated process for xylooligosaccharide and bioethanol production from corncob. *Bioresour. Technol.* 256: 399–407. https://doi.org/10.1016/j.biortech.2018.02.004.

40 Kumar, D., Surya, K., and Verma, R. (2020). Bioethanol production from apple pomace using co-cultures with *Saccharomyces cerevisiae* in solid-state fermentation. *J. Microbiol. Biotechnol. Food Sci.* 9 (4): 742–745. https://doi.org/10.15414/jmbfs.2020.9.4.742-745.

41 Prakash, H., Chauhan, P.S., General, T., and Sharma, A.K. (2018). Development of eco-friendly process for the production of bioethanol from banana peel using inhouse developed cocktail of thermo-alkali-stable depolymerizing enzymes. *Bioprocess Biosyst. Eng.* 41 (7): 1003–1016. https://doi.org/10.1007/s00449-018-1930-3.

42 Bhardwaj, N., Kumar, B., Agrawal, K., and Verma, P. (2020). Bioconversion of rice straw by synergistic effect of in-house produced ligno-hemicellulolytic enzymes for enhanced bioethanol production. *Bioresour. Technol. Rep.* 10: 100352. https://doi.org/10.1016/j.biteb.2019.100352.

43 Basit, A., Jiang, W., and Rahim, K. (2021). Xylanase and its industrial applications. In: *Biotechnological Applications of Biomass* (ed. T. Page). IntechOpen https://doi.org/10.5772/intechopen.92156.

44 Fang, H.-Y., Chang, S.-M., Lan, C.-H., and Fang, T.J. (2008). Purification and characterization of a xylanase from *Aspergillus carneus* M34 and its potential use in photoprotectant preparation. *Process Biochem.* 43 (1): 49–55. https://doi.org/10.1016/j.procbio.2007.10.015.

45 Sindhu, R., Binod, P., Mathew, A.K. et al. (2017). Development of a novel ultrasound-assisted alkali pretreatment strategy for the production of bioethanol and xylanases from chili post harvest residue. *Bioresour. Technol.* 242: 146–151. https://doi.org/10.1016/j.biortech.2017.03.001.

46 BBL, C. (2013). Enzimas xilanolíticas bacterianas y sus aplicaciones industriales. *Rev. Esp. Cienc. Salud.* 16 (1): 19–22.

47 Izidoro, S.C. and Knob, A. (2014). Production of xylanases by an *Aspergillus niger* strain in wastes grain. *Acta Sci. Biol. Sci.* 36 (3): 313–319. https://doi.org/10.4025/actascibiolsci.v36i3.20567.

48 Vásquez Vanegas, A.M. (2013). Producción de xilanasas por aspergillus sp: en fermentación sumergida y fermentación en medio sólido. Master thesis. Universidad Iberoamericana.

49 Dutta, B., Banerjee, A., Chakraborty, P., and Brandopadhyay, R. (2018). In silico studies on bacterial xylanases enzyme: structural and functional insight. *J. Genet. Eng. Biotechnol.* 16 (2): 749–756. https://doi.org/10.1016/j.jgeb.2018.05.003.

50 Chakdar, H., Kumar, M., Pandiyan, K. et al. (2016). Bacterial xylanases: biology to biotechnology. *3 Biotech* 6 (2): 1–15. https://doi.org/10.1007/s13205-016-0457-z.

51 Lara, C.A., Santos, R.O., Cadete, R.M. et al. (2014). Identification and characterisation of xylanolytic yeasts isolated from decaying wood and sugarcane bagasse in Brazil. *Antonie Van Leeuwenhoek* 105: 1107–1119. https://doi.org/10.1007/s10482-014-0172-x.

52 Lopes, F., Motta, F., Andrade, C.C.P. et al. (2011). Thermo-stable xylanases from non conventional yeasts. *J. Microb. Biochem. Technol.* 3: 36–42. https://doi.org/10.4172/1948-5948.1000049.

53 Otero, D.M., Cadaval, C.L., Teixeira, L.M. et al. (2015). Screening of yeasts capable of producing cellulase-free xylanase. *Afr. J. Biotechnol.* 14 (23): 1961–1969. https://doi.org/10.5897/AJB2015.14476.

54 Kumar, V., Dangi, A.K., and Shukla, P. (2018). Engineering thermostable microbial xylanases toward its industrial applications. *Mol. Biotechnol.* 60 (3): 226–235. https://doi.org/10.1007/S12033-018-0059-6.

55 Basit A, Liu J, Rahim K, Jiang W, Lou H (2018) Thermophilic xylanases: from bench to bottle. *Crit. Rev. Biotechnol.* 38: 1–15. https://doi.org/10.1080/07388551.2018.1425662

56 Ying, Y., Meng, D., Chen, X., and Li, F. (2013). An extremely thermophilic anaerobic bacterium *Caldicellulosiruptor* sp. F32 exhibits distinctive properties in growth and xylanases during xylan hydrolysis. *Enzym. Microb. Technol.* 53 (3): 194–199. https://doi.org/10.1016/j.enzmictec.2013.04.004.

57 Kumar, V. and Shukla, P. (2016). Functional aspects of xylanases toward industrial applications. In: *Frontier Discoveries and Innovations in Interdisciplinary Microbiology* (ed. T. Page), 157–165. New Delhi: Springer.

58 Kuramochi, K., Uchimura, K., and Kurata, A. (2016). High-molecular-weight, alkaline, and thermostable β-1,4-xylanase of a subseafloor *Microcella alkaliphila*. *Extremophiles* 20: 471–478. https://doi.org/10.1007/s00792-016-0837-7.

59 Zhang, S., Zhao, S., Shang, W. et al. Synergistic mechanism of GH11 xylanases with different action modes from *Aspergillus niger* An76. *Biotechnol. Biofuels* (14): 118. https://doi.org/10.1186/s13068-021-01967-1.

60 Bassit, A., Liu, J., Rahim, K. et al. (2018). Thermophilic xylanases: from bench to bottle. *Crit. Rev. Biotechnol.* 38 (7): 989–1002. https://doi.org/10.1080/07388551.2018.1425662.

61 Chadha, B.S., Kaur, B., Basotra, N. et al. (2019). Thermostable xylanases from thermophilic fungi and bacteria: current perspective. *Bioresour. Technol.* 277: 195–203. https://doi.org/10.1016/j.biortech.2019.01.044.

62 Cuevas Crisóstomo, C.V. (2021). Enzimas xilanolíticas provenientes de microorganismos termófilos para aplicaciones industriales. http://repositorio.udec.cl/xmlui/handle/11594/5103 (accessed 20 August 2021).

63 Marques, N. P., de Cassia Pereira, J., Gomes, E., da Silva, R., Araújo, A. R., Ferreira, H., Bocchini, D. A. (2018). Cellulases and xylanases production by endophytic fungi by solid state fermentation using lignocellulosic substrates and enzymatic saccharification of pretreated sugarcane bagasse. *Ind. Crop. Prod.* 122: 66–75. https://doi.org/10.1016/j.indcrop.2018.05.022.

64 Martínez-Pacheco, M.M., Flores-García, A., Zamudio-Jaramillo, M.A. et al. (2020). Optimization of production of xylanases with low cellulases in *Fusarium solani* by means of a solid state fermentation using statistical experimental design. *Rev. Argent. Microbiol.* 52 (4): 328–338. https://doi.org/10.1016/j.ram.2019.12.003.

65 Dey, P. and Roy, A. (2018). Molecular structure and catalytic mechanism of fungal family G acidophilic xylanases. *3 Biotech* 8 (2): 78. http://doi.org/10.1007/s13205-018-1091-8.

66 Costa, A.C., Cavalheiro, G.F., de Queiroz Vieira, E.R. et al. (2019). Catalytic properties of xylanases produced by *Trichoderma piluliferum* and *Trichoderma viride* and their application as additives in bovine feeding. *Biocatal. Agric. Biotechnol.* 19: 101161. https://doi.org/10.1016/j.bcab.2019.101161.

67 Suchová, K., Puchart, V., Spodsberg, N., Mørkeberg Krogh, K. B., Biely, P. (2021). Catalytic diversity of GH30 xylanases. *Molecules* 26(15): 4528. https://doi.org/10.3390/molecules26154528

68 Javier, P.F.I., Óscar, G., Sanz-Aparicio, J., and Díaz, P. (2007). Xylanases: molecular properties and applications. In: *Industrial Enzymes: Structure, Function and Applications* (ed. T. Page), 65–82. Dordrecht: Springer Netherlands.

69 Pollet, A., Delcour, J.A., and Courtin, C.M. (2010). Structural determinants of the substrate specificities of xylanases from different glycoside hydrolase families. *Crit. Rev. Biotechnol.* 30 (3): 176–191. https://doi.org/10.3109/07388551003645599.

70 Dodd, D., Cann, I. K. O. (2009). Enzymatic deconstruction of xylan for biofuel production. *Glob. Change Biol. Bioenergy.,* 1(1): 2–17. https://doi.org/10.1111/j.1757-1707.2009.01004.x

71 Nguyen, S.T.C., Freund, H.L., Kasanjian, J., and Berlemont, R. (2018). Function, distribution, and annotation of characterized cellulases, xylanases, and chitinases from CAZy. *Appl. Microbiol. Biotechnol.* 102 (4): 1629–1637. https://doi.org/10.1007/s00253-018-8778-y.

72 Henrissat, B., Callebaut, I., Fabrega, S., Lehn, P., Mornon, J. P., Davies, G. (1995). Conserved catalytic machinery and the prediction of a common fold for several families of glycosyl hydrolases. *Proc. Natl. Acad. Sci.* 92(15):7090–7094. https://doi.org/10.1073/pnas.92.15.7090

73 Canals, A., Vega, M.C., Gomis-Rüth, F.X. et al. (2003). Structure of xylanase Xys1Δ from *Streptomyces halstedii*. *Acta Crystallogr. Sect. D* 59 (8): 1447–1453. https://doi.org/10.1107/S0907444903012629.

74 Natesh, R., Bhanumoorthy, P., Vithayathil, P.J. et al. (1999). Crystal structure at 1.8 Å resolution and proposed amino acid sequence of a thermostable xylanase from *Thermoascus aurantiacus*. *J. Mol. Biol.* 288 (5): 999–1012. https://doi.org/10.1006/jmbi.1999.2727.

75 Wu, X., Zhang, S., Zhang, Q. et al. (2020). The contribution of specific subsites to catalytic activities in active site architecture of a GH11 xylanase. *Appl. Microbiol. Biotechnol.* 104 (20): 8735–8745. https://doi.org/10.1007/s00253-020-10865-9.

76 Andaleeb, H., Ullah, N., Falke, S., Perbandt, M., Brognaro, H., Betzel, C. (2020). High-resolution crystal structure and biochemical characterization of a GH11 endoxylanase from *Nectria haematococca*. *Sci. Rep.* 10:15658. https://doi.org/10.1038/s41598-020-72644-w.

77 El Enshasy, H.A., Kandiyil, S.K., Malek, R., and Othman, N.Z. (2016). Microbial xylanases: sources, types, and their applications. In: *Microbial Enzymes in Bioconversion of Biomass*, vol. 3, 151–213. Springer https://doi.org/10.1007/978-3-319-43679-1-7.

78 Tahir, T.A., Berrin, J.-G., Flatman, R. et al. (2002). Specific characterization of substrate and inhibitor binding sites of a glycosyl hydrolase family11 xylanase from *Aspergillus niger*. *J. Biol. Chem.* 277 (46): 44035–44043. https://doi.org/10.1074/jbc.M205657200.

79 Paës, G., Berrin, J.-G., and Beaugrand, J. (2012). GH11 xylanases: structure/function/properties relationships and applications. *Biotechnol. Adv.* 30 (3): 564–592. https://doi.org/10.1016/j.biotechadv.2011.10.003.

80 Paës, G., Cortés, J., Siméon, T. et al. (2012). Thumb-loops up for catalysis: a structure/function investigation of a functional loop movement in a Gh11 xylanase. *Comput. Struct. Biotechnol. J.* 1 (2): e201207001. https://doi.org/10.5936/csbj.201207001.

81 Sermsathanaswadi, J., Pianwanit, S., Pason, P. et al. (2014). The C-terminal region of xylanase domain in Xyn11A from *Paenibacillus curdlanolyticus* B-6 plays an important role in structural stability. *Appl. Microbiol. Biotechnol.* 98 (19): 8223–8233. https://doi.org/10.1007/s00253-014-5748-x.

82 Gruber, K., Klintschar, G., Hayn, M., Schlacher, A., Steiner, W., Kratky, C. (1998). Thermophilic xylanase from *Thermomyces lanuginosus*: high-resolution X-ray structure and modeling studies. *Biochemistry* 37(39): 13475–13485. https://doi.org/10.1021/bi980864l

83 Lombard, V., Ramulu, H.G., Drula, E., and Coutinho, B.H. (2014). The carbohydrate-active enzymes database (CAZy). *Nucleic Acids Res.* 42 (1): D490–D495. https://doi.org/10.1093/nar/gkt1178.

84 Linares-Pasten, J., Arosson, A., and Karlsson, E.N. (2018). Structural considerations on the use of endo-xylanases for the production of prebiotic xylooligosaccharides from biomass. *Curr. Protein Pept. Sci.* 19 (1): 48–67. https://doi.org/10.2174/1389203717666160923155209.

85 Thomas, L., Ushasree, M., Pander, A. (2014). An alkali-thermostable xylanase from *Bacillus pumilus* functionally expressed in *Kluyveromyces lactis* and evaluation of its deinking efficiency *Biosour. Technol.*165:309–313. https://doi.org/10.1016/j.biortech.2014.03.037.

86 Moreira, L.R.S. and Filho, E.X.F. (2016). Insights into the mechanism of enzymatic hydrolysis of xylan. *Appl. Microbiol. Biotechnol.* 100: 5205–5214. https://doi.org/10.1007/s00253-016-7555-z.

87 Bai, W., Xue, Y., Zhou et al. (2012). Cloning, expression and characterization of a novel salt-tolerant xylanase from *Bacillus* sp. SN5. *Biotechnol. Lett.* 34 (11): 2093–2099. https://doi.org/10.1007/s10529-012-1011-7.

88 Wu, H., Cheng, X., Zhu, Y. et al. (2018). Purification and characterization of a cellulase-free, thermostable endo-xylanase from *Streptomyces griseorubens* LH-3 and its use in biobleaching on eucalyptus kraft pulp. *J. Biosci. Bioeng.* 125 (1): 46–51. https://doi.org/10.1128/AEM.02970-18.

89 Fredriksen, L., Stokke, R., Jensen, M.S. et al. (2019). Discovery of a thermostable GH10 xylanase with broad substrate specificity from the Arctic Mid-Ocean Ridge vent system. *Appl. Environ. Microbiol.* 85 (6): https://doi.org/10.1128/AEM.02970-18.

90 Marcolongo, L., La Cara, F., Morana, A. et al. (2015). Properties of an alkali-thermo stable xylanase from *Geobacillus thermodenitrificans* A333 and applicability in xylooligosaccharides generation. *World J. Microbiol. Biotechnol.* 31 (4): 633–648. https://doi.org/10.1007/S11274-015-1818-1.

91 Weng, X.Y., Huang, Y.-Y., Gao, H., and Sun, J.-Y. (2010). Characterization of a xylanase inhibitor TAXI-I from wheat. *Biol. Plant.* 54 (1): 154–158. https://doi.org/10.1007/S10535-010-0025-Z.

92 Ryabova, O., Vršanská, M., Kaneko, S. et al. (2009). A novel family of hemicellulolytic α-glucuronidase. *FEBS Lett.* 583 (9): 1457–1462. https://www.sciencedirect.com/science/article/pii/S001457930900249X.

93 Kazi, Z. (2020). Novel retaining glycoside hydrolases: potential candidates for transglycosylation and hydrolysis. Ph.D. thesis. Lund University.

94 Brusa, C., Belloy, N., Gérard, D. et al. (2018). Exploring the aglycone subsite of a GH11 xylanase for the synthesis of xylosides by transglycosylation reactions. *J. Biotechnol.* 20 (272): 56–63. https://www.sciencedirect.com/science/article/pii/S0168165618300646.

95 Bajaj, P. and Mahajan, R. (2019). Cellulase and xylanase synergism in industrial biotechnology. *Appl. Microbiol. Biotechnol.* 21 (103): 8711–8724. https://doi.org/10.1007/s00253-019-10146-0.

96 Rosmine, E., Edassery Sainjan, N.C., Silvester, R., and Varghese, S.A. (2019). Utilisation of agrowaste xylan for the production of industrially important enzyme xylanase from aquatic *Streptomyces* sp. and potential role of xylanase in deinking of newsprint. *Int. J. Curr. Microbiol. App. Sci.* 8: 2061–2076. https://doi.org/10.20546/ijcmas.2019.801.216.

97 Qeshmi, F., Homaei, A., Fernandes, P. et al. (2020). Xylanases from marine microorganisms: a brief overview on scope, sources, features and potential applications. *Biochim. Biophys. Acta, Proteins Proteomics* 1868 (2): 140312. https://www.sciencedirect.com/science/article/pii/S1570963919301980.

98 Martins, M., Dinamarco, T., and Goldbeck, R. (2020). Recombinant chimeric enzymes for lignocellulosic biomass hydrolysis. *Enzym. Microb. Technol.* 140: 109647. https://doi.org/10.1016/j.enzmictec.2020.109647.

99 Ribeiro, L., Furtado, G., Lourenzoni, M.R. et al. (2011). Engineering bifunctional laccase-xylanase chimeras for improved catalytic performance. *J. Biol. Chem.* 286 (50): 43026–43038. https://www.jbc.org/article/S0021-9258(20)87018-5/abstract.

100 Thomas, L., Joseph, A., Arumugam, M., and Pandey, A. (2013). Production, purification, characterization and over-expression of xylanases from actinomycetes. *Indian J. Exp. Biol.* 51 (11): 875–884.

101 Beg, Q. K., Kapoor, M., Mahajan, L., Hoondal, G. S. (2001). Microbial xylanases and their industrial applications: a review. *Appl. Microbiol. Biotechnol.* 56(3–4): 326–338. https://doi.org/10.1007/s002530100704.

102 Gong, X., Gruniniger, R. J., Forster, R. J., Teather, R. M., & McAllister, T. A. (2013). Biochemical analysis of a highly specific, pH stable xylanase gene identified from a bovine rumen-derived metagenomic library. *Appl. Microbiol. Biotechnol.* 197(6): 2423–2431. https://doi.org/10.1007/s00253-012-4088-y

103 Jeong, Y. S., Na, H. B., Kim, S. K., Kim, Y. H., Kwon, E. J., Kim, J., Kim, H. (2012). Characterization of xyn10J, a novel family 10 xylanase from a compost metagenomic library. *Appl. Biochem. Biotechnol.* 166(5): 1328–1339. https://doi.org/10.1007/s12010-011-9520-8

104 Sun, M.Z., Zheng, H.C., Meng, L.C. et al. (2015). Direct cloning, expression of a thermostable xylanase gene from the metagenomic DNA of cow dung compost and enzymatic production of xylooligosaccharides from corncob. *Biotechnol. Lett.* 37 (9): 1877–1886. https://doi.org/10.1007/s10529-015-1857-6.

105 Sá-Pereira, P., Paveia, H., Costa-Ferreira, M., and Aires-Barros, M. (2003). A new look at xylanases: an overview of purification strategies. *Mol. Biotechnol.* 24 (3): 257–281. https://doi.org/10.1385/mb:24:3:257.

106 Selvarajan, E. and Veena, R. (2017). Recent advances and future perspectives of thermostable xylanase. *Biomed. Pharmacol. J.* 10 (1): 261–279. https://doi.org/10.13005/bpj/1106.

107 Qiu, Z., Shi, P., Luo, H. et al. (2010). A xylanase with broad pH and temperature adaptability from *Streptomyces megasporus* DSM 41476, and its potential application in brewing industry. *Enzym. Microb. Technol.* 46 (6): 506–512. https://doi.org/10.1016/j.enzmictec.2010.02.003.

108 Boonyapakron, K., Jaruwat, A., Liwnaree, B. et al. (2017). Structure-based protein engineering for thermostable and alkaliphilic enhancement of endo-β-1,4-xylanase for applications in pulp bleaching. *J. Biotechnol.* 259: 95–102. https://doi.org/10.1016/j.jbiotec.2017.07.035.

109 De Queiroz Brito Cunha, C.C., Gama, A.R., Cintra, L.C. et al. (2018). Improvement of bread making quality by supplementation with a recombinant xylanase produced by *Pichia pastoris*. *PLoS One* 13 (2): 1–14. https://doi.org/10.1371/journal.pone.0192996.

110 Yegin, S., Altinel, B., and Tuluk, K. (2018). A novel extremophilic xylanase produced on wheat bran from *Aureobasidium pullulans* NRRL Y-2311-1: effects on dough rheology and bread quality. *Food Hydrocoll.* 81: 389–397. https://doi.org/10.1016/j.foodhyd.2018.03.012.

111 Sharma, S., Sharma, V., Nargotra, P., and Bajaj, B.K. (2020). Bioprocess development for production of a process-apt xylanase with multifaceted application potential for a range of industrial processes. *SN Appl. Sci.* 2 (4): 1–15. https://doi.org/10.1007/s42452-020-2541-6.

112 Sharma, K., Thakur, A., and Goyal, A. (2019). Xylanases for food applications. In: *In Green Bio-Processes* (ed. T. Page), 99–118. Springer Singapore.

113 Shahi, N., Hasan, A., Akhtar, S. et al. (2016). Xylanase: a promising enzyme. *J. Chem. Pharm. Res.* 8 (3): 334–339.

114 Bajaj, B.K. and Manhas, K. (2012). Production and characterization of xylanase from *Bacillus licheniformis* P11(C) with potential for fruit juice and bakery industry. *Biocatal. Agric. Biotechnol.* 1 (4): 330–337. https://doi.org/10.1016/j.bcab.2012.07.003.

115 Demuth, T., Betschart, J., and Nyström, L. (2020). Structural modifications to water-soluble wheat bran arabinoxylan through milling and extrusion. *Carbohydr. Polym.* 240: 116328. https://doi.org/10.1016/j.carbpol.2020.116328.

116 Izydorczyk, S.M. (2021). Arabinoxylans. In: *Handbook of Hydrocolloids* (ed. T. Page), 399–461. Elsevier Ltd. All rights reserved.

117 Babalola, T.O.O., Apata, D.F., and Atteh, J.O. (2006). Effect of β-xylanase supplementation of boiled castor seed meal-based diets on the performance, nutrient absorbability and some blood constituents of pullet chicks. *Trop. Sci.* 46 (4): 216–223. https://doi.org/10.1002/ts.181.

118 Dhiman, S.S., Sharma, J., and Battan, B. (2008). Industrial applications and future prospects of microbial xylanases: a review. *Bioresources* 3 (4): 1377–1402. https://doi.org/10.15376/biores.3.4.1377-1402.

119 Walia, A., Mehta, P., Guleria, S., Shirkot, K.C., (2015). Modification in the properties of paper by using cellulase-free xylanase in biobleaching of wheat straw pulp produced from alkalophilic *Cellulosimicrobium cellulans* CKMX1. *Can. J. Microbiol.* 61 (9): 671–81.https://doi.org/10.1139/cjm-2015-0178

120 Katsimpouras, C., Dedes, G., Thomaidis, N.S., and Topakas, E. (2019). A novel fungal GH30 xylanase with xylobiohydrolase auxiliary activity. *Biotechnol. Biofuels* 12: 120. https://doi.org/10.1186/s13068-019-1455-2.

121 Zarafeta, D., Galanopoulou, A.P., Leni, M.E. et al. (2020). XynDZ5: a new thermostable GH10 xylanase. *Front. Microbiol.* 11: 545. https://doi.org/10.3389/fmicb.2020.00545.

122 Cortez-Ávila, M.G., Ardilas-Arias, A.N., Salgado-Román, J.M. et al. (2016). Actividad enzimática de xilanasa inmovilizada en perlas de alginato de sodio en la hidrogenación de citral en medio líquido. *Acta Univ.* 26 (1): 48–55. https://doi.org/10.15174/au.2016.852.

123 Damayanti, M., Purwani, N.N., Purwadi, N.M.D., and Fithri, L. (2019). Identification, characterization, and purification of xylanase PC-01 isolated from Pacet hot spring. *Opción* 24: 1074–1091.

124 Escalante-Garcia, Z., Gomez-Angulo, J.H., Flores-Cosio, G. et al. (2017). Cloning, expression and hydrolytic characterization of the new xylanase nsi xyn11a from *Neurospora sitophila* BDJ1I. *Rev. Mex. Ing. Chim.* 16 (2): 385–397.

125 Tuyen, D.T., Cuong, N.T., Thanh, N.S. et al. (2021). Cloning, expression, and characterization of xylanase G2 from *Aspergillus oryzae* VTCC-F187 in *Aspergillus niger* VTCC-F017. *Biomed. Res. Int.* https://doi.org/10.1155/2021/8840038.

2

Exploration of the Microbial Urease and Their Industrial Applications

Jackson Khedia[1], *Rupali Gupta*[2], *and Gautam Anand*[2]

[1]*Agricultural Research Organization, Volcani Institute, Department of Plant Pathology and Weed Research, Rishon LeZion 7505101, Israel*
[2]*Volcani Institute, Department of Plant Pathology and Weed Research, Agricultural Research Organization, Rishon LeZion 7505101, Israel*

2.1 Urease Enzyme and Its History

Urease enzyme is ubiquitous metalloenzyme, which catalyzes the hydrolysis of urea into carbon dioxide and ammonia. It has been shown that urease is a highly abundant enzyme in plants (Fabaceae and Curcubitaceae family), and furthermore, it is found in several eukaryotic microorganisms and bacteria as well. In 1864, van Tieghem obtained the first ureolytic bacterium, *Micrococcus ureae*, and in 1874, Musculus identified the first ureolytic enzyme from rotten urine. Miquel proposed the term "urease" in 1890 [1]. Its discovery is intertwined with the understanding of urea hydrolysis and the role of microorganisms in this process. Here are two key milestones in history: ureases have made significant contributions to biochemistry, since it was the first ever enzyme to be crystallized from jack bean (*Canavalia ensiformis*) seeds by James B. Sumner (1926), which proved that enzymes are proteinaceous and was awarded the 1946 Nobel Prize in Chemistry [2]. In another study, nickel ions were identified in the active site of the jack bean urease and concluded the importance of these ions for the enzyme's catalytic activity, thereby recognizing the biological relevance of nickel [3]. In their active regions, ureases contain two Ni^{2+} ions [1, 4], with a few documented outliers [5, 6]. As a substrate-specific enzyme, this enzyme only catalyzes the hydrolysis of urea, which is a common diagnostic criterion for many urease-producing pathogenic bacteria [7].

2.2 Urea Hydrolysis

Urease, urea amidohydrolase; EC 3.5.1.5, affiliated to the class hydrolases and phosphotriesterases [8], hydrolyzes urea to form ammonia and carbamate, then the

Microbial Enzymes: Production, Purification, and Industrial Applications, First Edition.
Edited by Dinesh Yadav, Pankaj Chowdhary, Gautam Anand, and Rajarshi Kumar Gaur.

carbamate spontaneously breaks down to release another ammonia molecule and carbonic acid:

$$\underset{\text{Urea}}{NH_2\text{-}CO\text{-}NH_2} + H_2O \xrightarrow{\text{Urease}} \underset{\text{Ammonia}}{NH_3} + NH_2\text{-}COOH$$

$$NH_2\text{-}COOH + H_2O \longrightarrow \underset{\text{Ammonia}}{NH_3} + H_2CO_3$$

The resulted products of these enzymatic reactions lead to enhancement in pH through the equilibrium of their deprotonated and protonated forms [9].

$$2NH_3 + 2H_2O \leftrightarrow 2NH_4^+ + 2OH^-$$

$$H_2CO_3 \leftrightarrow H^+ + HCO_3^-$$

The abrupt increase in alkalinity in the soil can reduce its agricultural applicability by up to 50%. This is especially the case in calcareous, high-organic carbon, and soils with limited buffer capacity. Nitrogen is the most important element required for the growth and development of the crops. Urea is a relevant nitrogen source for plants and is utilized as a soil fertilizer all over the world. The soil is rich in urease, which is found in bacteria and fungi as well as extracellular urease that is attached to humic materials and clays [10, 11]. Cell-free ureases ureolyze soil, which causes the precipitation of calcium carbonate and alters the availability of minerals when soil is alkaline [12, 13]. Furthermore, elevated soil urease levels diminish the effectiveness of urea fertilization, resulting in ammonia leakage into the atmosphere and phytotoxicity caused by ammonia [14, 15].

2.3 Sources and Molecular Attributes of Urease Enzyme

The urease orthologs share approximately 55% of translational similarities derived from different sources, indicating divergence from a common ancestor. The amino acid sequences of the smaller prokaryotic urease subunits coincide with those of the single chain of eukaryotic ureases. A monomer, or functional unit, is composed of varied polypeptide chains depending on the source of urease. Ureases produced by fungi and plants are comprised of one polypeptide chain (α). X-ray crystallography studies have demonstrated that bacterial and plant ureases have similar trimeric structures [1, 16]. To constitute a bacterial urease, two subunits (α and β, which are currently exclusive to *Helicobacter*) or three types (α, β, and γ) of polypeptide chains are needed. The most common structure of plant ureases, besides the dimeric, trimeric, and tetrameric ones, is a homo-hexameric proteins (α3)2. Unlike bacterial ureases, which crystallize multimers of three subunit complexes as trimers ([αβγ]3), *Helicobacter pylori* urease crystallizes as multimers of dimers ([αβ]3)4 [16, 17].

Urease enzymes are widely distributed in nature, and various microorganisms have been identified as potent sources of this important enzyme. Upon release, urease is attached to both organic and inorganic soil components (clays and humic substances) in the soil where it is shielded from external proteolytic enzymes and microorganisms that break it down. The microbial sources of urease mostly include bacteria and fungi. Bacteria employ urease as a nitrogen source to convert urea to ammonia [18]. Bacteria such as *Lactobacillus* [19], *Bacillus* [20–22], *Staphylococcus* [23–25] and fungi such as *Rhizopus* [26], *Aspergillus* [27, 28], *Cryptococcus* [29, 30], *Coccidioides* [31, 32], and *Schizosaccharomyces* [33] are among the numerous microbial sources for urease enzyme. Roughly 40% of all urease enzymes are derived from filamentous fungus [34]. A number of bacterial ureases, including those from *Morganella morganii*, *Klebsiella aerogenes*, *Ureaplasma ureolyticum*, *Proteus mirabilis*, and *H. pylori*, are significant players in the pathophysiology of illnesses in both humans and animals. Microbial urease sources have been discussed in detail in Table 2.1.

2.4 Urease Purification

Purifying microbial urease enzyme is a crucial step in obtaining a high-quality enzyme preparation for various applications and research. Several methods are employed to purify microbial urease, each tailored to the characteristics of the source organism and the desired end use. One common method for purifying microbial urease involves precipitation techniques, such as ammonium sulfate or acetone precipitation. By carefully adjusting the concentrations of the solvents, proteins in the crude extract are differentially precipitated, and the urease enzyme can be selectively isolated [36]. Chromatographic techniques, such as ion exchange chromatography, can further refine the purification process by exploiting the differences in charge among proteins [40, 52]. Gel filtration chromatography is effective for separating proteins based on their size and molecular weight. By passing the crude enzyme extract through a gel filtration column, smaller proteins are excluded from the gel pores, while larger urease molecules pass through, resulting in purification based on size [39, 41]. Other Modern techniques, such as high-performance liquid chromatography (HPLC) and fast protein liquid chromatography (FPLC), have also been employed for the purification of microbial urease [43, 47]. Another widely used method is affinity chromatography, where a substrate analog, such as ligands with free NH_2 [27], monoclonal antibodies (against urease enzyme) [53], hydroxyurea [54], and L-tyrosine-*p*-aminobenzene sulfonamide [22] were utilized for the urease specific interaction and purification. The enzyme binds selectively to the immobilized substrate, allowing for its isolation and subsequent elution under controlled conditions. This method provides a high degree of specificity and purity. All chromatographic techniques together allow for high-resolution separation of proteins and can be particularly useful in achieving high purity levels for specific applications [31, 46, 55, 56]. In summary, the purification of microbial urease enzyme involves a combination of precipitation, chromatography, and other advanced techniques, each chosen based on the unique properties of the source organism and the intended application of the purified enzyme preparation (Figure 2.1). These methods contribute to obtaining highly pure and active urease enzymes for scientific, medical, and industrial purposes.

Table 2.1 Urease-producing microbial sources and their habitat.

	Microbial sources	Habitat	References
Bacteria	*Aerobacter aerogenes*	Human gastrointestinal tract, in numerous wastes and soil	[35]
	Arthrobacter oxydans	Soil	[36]
	Bacillus halodurans	Soil and sediments	[22]
	Bacillus paramycoides	Soil, oceans, and many geological formations	[21]
	Bacillus megaterium	Soil, seawater, sediments, rice paddies, dried food, honey, and milk	[20]
	Brevibacterium ammoniagenes	Soil, water, and food products	[37]
	Brucella suis	Sty for domestic pigs	[38]
	Citrobacter sedlakii	Water, soil, food, and the intestinal tracts of animals and humans	[21]
	Enterobacter bugandensis	Soil, water, sewage, feces and gut environments	[21]
	Haloarcula aidinensis, Haloarcula hispanica, Haloarcula japonica, and *Haloarcula marismortui*	Hypersaline environments	[39]
	Helicobacter pylori	Acidic gastric mucosa in human stomach	[40, 41]
	Klebsiella aerogenes	Human gastrointestinal tract	[42]
	Lactobacillus reuteri	Gastrointestinal tract, urinary tract, skin, and breast milk	[19]
	Morganella morganii	Feces and intestines of humans, dogs, and other mammals	[43, 44]
	Prochlorococcus marinus	Oligotrophic ocean in tropical and subtropical regions	[45]
	Proteus mirabilis	Gastrointestinal tracts of humans and animals, soil, water sources, and sewage	[44]

	Providencia rettgeri	Soil, water, and sewage	[44]
	Providencia stuartii	Soil, water, and sewage	[44, 46]
	Selenomonas ruminantium	Rumens of livestock	[47]
	Sporosarcina pasteurii	Alkaline lake soil	[48, 49]
	Staphylococcus leei	Human stomach	[24]
	Staphylococcus saprophyticus	Perineum, rectum, urethra, cervix, and gastrointestinal tract	[25]
	Staphylococcus xylosus	Skin and the mucous membranes of mammals and birds	[23]
	Ureaplasma ureolyticum	Lower urogenital tract	[50, 51]
Fungi	*Aspergillus nidulans*	Soil	[27]
	Aspergillus niger	Soil, seeds, plant litter, plant rhizospheres, dried fruit, and nuts	[28]
	Coccidioides immitis	Soil	[31]
	Coccidioides posadasii	Soil	[32]
	Cryptococcus gattii	Soil	[30]
	Cryptococcus neoformans	Soil, on decaying wood, in tree hollows, or in bird droppings	[29]
	Rhizopus oryzae	Soil, dung, and rotting vegetation	[26]
	Schizosaccharomyces pombe	Fruits such as apples and grapes, various alcoholic beverages, and fermented tea	[33]

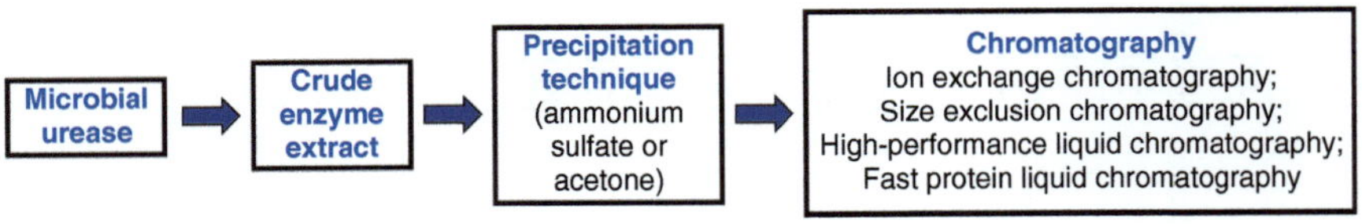

Figure 2.1 General scheme for urease enzyme purification.

Chromatography is a versatile technique used for separating and analyzing enzymes in a mixture based on their physicochemical properties. Ion exchange chromatography, hydrophobic interaction chromatography, and size exclusion chromatography were used to purify urease from bacterial sources such as *K. aerogenes* (224 kDa) [42]; *Staphylococcus saprophyticus* (420 kDa) [25]; *Providencia stuartii* (337 ± 18 kDa) and *M. morganii* (712 kDa) [44] along with fungi *Coccidioides immitis* (445 kDa) [31] and *Aspergillus niger* (250 kDa) [28]. Urease was precipitated and fractions were collected through ultrafiltration from the crude extracts of *Arthrobacter oxydans* (242 kDa) [36] and *Schizosaccharomyces pombe* (212 kDa) [33] together with size exclusion chromatography and ion exchange chromatography, respectively. FPLC was one of the techniques utilized to purify urease from *Selenomonas ruminantium* (360 ± 50 kDa) [47]; *Staphylococcus xylosus* (300 kDa) [23]; *U. ureolyticum* (190 ± 10 kDa) [51], and *S. pombe* (212 kDa) [33], whereas HPLC was performed on *Staphylococcus leei* (480 kDa) [24] extract. Affinity chromatography has been used to purify urease from *Bacillus halodurans* (size not mentioned) [22], *Brevibacterium ammoniagenes* (200 kDa) [37], and *Aspergillus nidulans* (40 kDa per subunit of hexamer) [27].

2.5 Applications of Urease Enzyme

2.5.1 Urea Biosensor for Determination of Urea Level in Dialysate

Over the past few decades, there has been significant progress in the development of enzyme-based biosensing tools. These tools have emerged as revolutionary tools for both qualitative and quantitative analysis of different target substrates across a diverse range of applications [57, 58]. Enzyme-based biosensors offer numerous advantages, including their remarkable sensitivity and accuracy, compactness, cost-effectiveness, and miniature functionality. These features, coupled with their suitability for point-of-care diagnostic tests, have contributed to their growing popularity in clinical research, food-protection regulation, and intent-testing monitoring [59].

Urea biosensor is an absorbance-based flow-through system for measuring urea, particularly in the spent dialysate. Calcium alginate microspheres encapsulating urease enzyme constitute the bio-recognition element of the biosensor whereas cresol red dye encapsulated within polyelectrolyte nanofilms assembled on calcium alginate microspheres via Layer-by-Layer (LbL) self-assembly technique plays the role of the transducer. The enzymatic catalysis of urea by enzyme urease results in the production of ammonium ions that cause the change in pH of the aqueous environment, which is immediately detected by cresol red [60]. The change in absorbance of the dye recorded by the UV/VIS spectrophotometer is proportional to the urea concentration present in the dialysate [61].

2.5.2 Application of Acid Urease to Reduce Urea in Commercial Wines

Urease is used in wine industries for the removal of urea from wine [62]. Numerous studies have been conducted to highlight the practicality of utilizing acid urease for eliminating urea from various wine varieties [63, 64]. Fidaleo and colleagues conducted a study to evaluate the rate of urea degradation using acid urease from *Lactobacillus fermentum* in both simulated wine solutions and actual wines. In addition, they estimated the costs associated with the enzyme preparation required for urea degradation. The results of their estimation indicated that the costs were relatively high, which could explain the limited implementation of free acid urease treatment on an industrial scale. The effectiveness of urease treatment varied depending on the specific type of wine, the presence of inhibiting factors, and the conditions of application. Notably, the most potent inhibitors of urease in wines were identified as fluoride, malate, ethanol, and phenolic compounds as reported by researchers [65, 66]. In a subsequent study by Cerreti et al., using a purified acid urease preparation from *L. fermentum*, it was discovered that total phenols significantly reduced the efficacy of the enzymatic therapy, especially when applied at the highest dosage permitted. This effect was predominantly noticeable in red wines, which had a polyphenol content ranging from 1640 to 1663 mg of gallic acid equivalent (GAE) per dm^3 of treated wine [65].

2.5.3 Microbiologically Induced Sealant for Concrete Crack Remediation

Urease-producing microbes have the ability to facilitate the formation of calcium carbonate, a type of cementing material, through a process known as microbially induced carbonate precipitation. This biocement process has been extensively studied in recent years [67]. In summary, the urea is hydrolyzed by the microbial urease to produce carbon dioxide and ammonia. The ammonia released into the environment raises pH, which causes a deposit of insoluble $CaCO_3$. Ammonia raises the pH of the surroundings, which causes $CaCO_3$ to precipitate, mostly in the form of calcite. Microorganisms that exhibit a significant level of urease activity would lead to a substantial production of microbial $CaCO_3$. The precipitation of calcium carbonate ultimately enhances both the compressive strength and durability of cementitious materials and structures by reducing water permeability and the ingress of aggressive ions. Hence, it becomes crucial to augment the urease activity of bacteria.

$$\text{Urea} + \text{Calcium substrate} \xrightarrow{\text{Bacterial urease}} CaCO_3$$

Its potential uses include surface soil consolidation, in-base and sub-base stabilization, and the repair of surface fissures and cracks in a variety of structural formations. For instance, *Sporosarcina pasteurii*, a type of bacterial strain that is tolerant to alkali and possesses ureolytic properties, is commonly used for microbial self-healing applications [68]. This particular strain is well studied for self-healing concrete owing to its ability to form spores and produce intracellular urease [69]. In order to ensure the survival of the bacteria in the harsh alkaline environment of concrete, dormant spores are typically used instead of living cells, as spores exhibit greater resistance and longevity [70]. One simple method for preparing self-healing concrete is to combine the nutrients, urea, bacterial culture, and calcium source directly with new concrete mixtures. Even in their dormant state, there is still a chance that the bacterial spores could be harmed during the mixing and curing process. The cells may suffer as a result of the mixing beater's high shear stress. Furthermore, when the cement continues to hydrate, a thick structure is formed, with the majority of the pores being smaller than 0.5 μm in size. Furthermore, the strength, durability, and setting time of concrete can all be negatively impacted by specific nutrients [71]. To address these challenges, one feasible solution is to encapsulate the healing agents within carriers. These carriers need to meet a number of requirements, such as, giving the bacteria a protective role, providing enough room for nutrients, and having few detrimental effects on the characteristics of concrete [72]. Thus, biogenic $CaCO_3$ offers a distinct advantage in terms of being environment friendly when compared to conventional technologies for repairing cracks. Urease-producing fungal and bacterial microorganisms are useful in healing cracks in cementitious composites.

2.5.4 Urease Conductometric Biosensors for Detection of Heavy Metal Ions

Nowadays, the issue of environmental pollution caused by heavy metals has become a worldwide concern. Heavy metals are extensively used in industries such as textiles, agriculture, and other fields [73]. However, the production and release of these heavy metals inevitably lead to pollution. Owing to their nondegradable nature, heavy metal ions can cause severe damage to both humans and other organisms [73]. The toxicity of these metals resulted in various disorders and damage caused by oxidative stress triggered by the metal ions [74]. Therefore, it is of utmost importance to develop effective techniques for determining the levels of heavy metal contamination in different mediums. Conductometric methods, among various electrochemical biosensors, offer a straightforward, user-friendly, and precise approach to address several important scientific and technological challenges [75].

The quantitative assessment of heavy-metal ion pollution in general water has been conducted using urease conductometric biosensors, which are equipped with gold electrodes and enzyme membranes for heavy-metal ion detection [76]. Urease residual activity was measured in Tris-HNO_3 buffer following a preincubation period in a model metal–salt solution. In model solutions of heavy-metal ions, the detection limits have been found to vary on preincubation time and dynamic ranges. The order of metal ions in relation to urease toxicity is: $Hg^{2+} > Cu^{2+} > Cd^{2+} > Co^{2+} > Pb^{2+} > Sr^{2+}$. A thorough assessment of the requirements for the biosensors' real-world applications has been conducted with the objective of optimizing their performance. It has been shown that EDTA can reactivate urease after heavy metal ions have inhibited it [77].

2.5.5 Biomimetic Hydroxyapatite (HA) Powder Synthesis via an Enzyme Reaction of Urea with Urease

Calcium hydroxyapatite (HA): $Ca_{10}(PO_4)_6(OH)_2$) bioceramics have attracted significant interest in orthopedic and dental applications due to their resemblance to the minerals found in human bone and dentin. In contrast, biological apatites have been observed to contain carbonate substitutions and calcium deficiencies [78]. Typically, HA powders for bioceramic purposes are chemically synthesized through aqueous solutions [79, 80]. It is well known that HA exhibits the least solubility and highest stability among calcium phosphate phases in aqueous solutions [81]. HA powders synthesized in highly alkaline media ($pH > 7$) are often characterized by their remarkable thermal stability and phase purity, even after undergoing high-temperature sintering processes at 1100–1300 °C. On the other hand, it is acknowledged that the process of forming HA powders in neutral or slightly acidic aqueous medium is more complex and difficult [82].

In a prior study, calcium nitrate tetrahydrate and di-ammonium hydrogen phosphate salts mixed in synthetic bodily fluid solutions rather than distilled water were used to create biomimetic HA powders [83]. The synthesis process was conducted under physiological conditions of 37 °C and pH 7.4. Throughout the precipitation process, a controlled and constant supply of a base, such as diluted NH_4OH solutions, was needed to keep the pH level at or slightly above 7.4. However, the addition of urea (H_2NCONH_2) into the body fluids just before the HA precipitation experiments was found to significantly reduce the amount of base needed to be continuously added to maintain the pH at 7.4 [83]. After being dried overnight at 90 °C, calcium phosphate precipitates that had developed in bodily fluids containing urea and the enzyme urease at 37 °C and pH 7.4 were discovered to be amorphous. These precursors started to crystallize at temperatures higher than 300 °C, and they fully converted into single-phase HA after six hours of calcination at 1100 °C. In recent years, biological synthesis has garnered increased attention owing to its compatibility with human safety [84].

2.5.6 Application of Urease in Urinary Drainage Bags

Urinary drainage bags are commonly used in medical settings to assist patients with urinary drainage catheters. These bags are designed with additional features that allow for drainage without disconnecting the catheter, enabling the bag to be emptied and refilled over an extended period without the need for bag replacement [85]. However, there is a potential risk associated with the use of drainage bags, as pathogenic bacteria can inadvertently contaminate the stored urine, leading to bacterial multiplication. Despite the presence of a drip chamber and a dry-wall gap in most urinary drainage bags, which serve as barriers to prevent bacteria movement, there is still a possibility of bacterial growth. In this regards, the growth and proliferation of bacteria in the stored urine can be inhibited by introducing the enzyme urease into the drainage container [86]. Urease acts by hydrolyzing urea in the presence of water, resulting in the formation of carbon dioxide (CO_2) and ammonia. The ammonia then dissolves in water as ammonium hydroxide, causing an increase in pH toward the alkaline direction, approximately pH 9.0. Bacterial growth is significantly reduced at pH levels above 8.0 [87]. Notably, urease activity is most efficient at pH 7.0, but as the pH rises to 9.0, the action of urease tends to be inhibited. However, when fresh urine is added to the drainage container, the pH drops, reactivating the urease activity. This process continues until the pH once again reaches approximately 9.0, at which point the reaction is halted once more [87, 88].

2.6 Conclusion and Future Aspects

The history of urease reflects its significance in biological processes, microbial physiology, and its practical applications in various fields. Figure 2.2 provides a schematic representation of some of the modern applications of microbial ureases. The discovery and characterization of microbial urease have paved the way for advancements in biotechnology, medicine, and environmental science. Researchers continue to explore the enzymatic properties, structural features, and applications of microbial urease, seeking to enhance its efficiency and uncover new potential uses. As an enzyme with both ecological and practical significance, microbial urease remains a subject of ongoing scientific investigation and technological innovation. The goal of this chapter is to highlight the beneficial aspects of this metalloenzyme and, perhaps most importantly, to stimulate curiosity and drive for more research into the field of biochemistry and its potential applications.

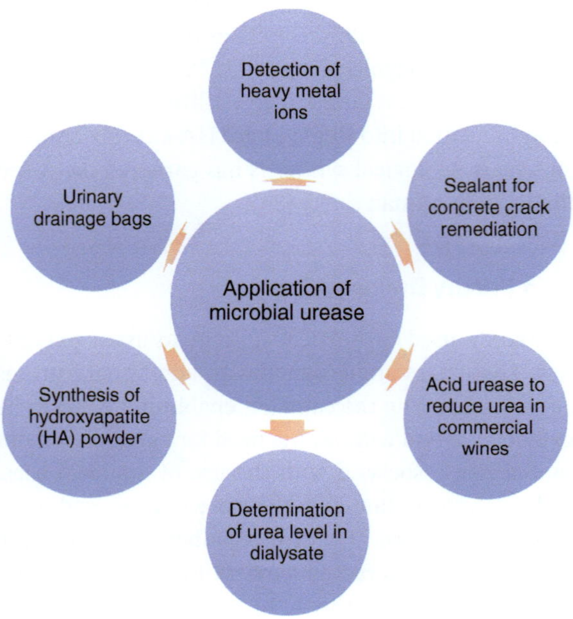

Figure 2.2 Schematic representations of some applications of urease.

References

1 Krajewska, B. (2009). Ureases I. Functional, catalytic and kinetic properties: a review. *J. Mol. Catal. B: Enzym.* 59 (1–3): 9–21.

2 Sumner, J.B. (1968). The isolation and crystallization of the enzyme urease. Preliminary paper. In: *Source Book in Chemistry, 1900–1950* (ed. H.M. Leicester), 322–327. Cambridge, MA and London, England: Harvard University Press.

3 Dixon, N.E., Gazzola, C., Blakeley, R.L., and Zerner, B. (1975). Jack bean urease (EC 3.5.1.5). Metalloenzyme. Simple biological role for nickel. *J. Am. Chem. Soc.* 97 (14): 4131–4133.

4 Zambelli, B., Musiani, F., Benini, S., and Ciurli, S. (2011). Chemistry of Ni^{2+} in urease: sensing, trafficking, and catalysis. *Acc. Chem. Res.* 44 (7): 520–530.

5 Carter, E.L., Tronrud, D.E., Taber, S.R. et al. (2011). Iron-containing urease in a pathogenic bacterium. *Proc. Natl. Acad. Sci. U.S.A.* 108 (32): 13095–13099.

6 Follmer, C., Carlini, C.R., Yoneama, M.L., and Dias, J.F. (2002). PIXE analysis of urease isoenzymes isolated from *Canavalia ensiformis* (jack bean) seeds. *Nucl. Instrum. Methods Phys. Res., Sect. B* 189 (1–4): 482–486.

7 Menegassi, A., Wassermann, G.E., Olivera-Severo, D. et al. (2008). Urease from cotton (*Gossypium hirsutum*) seeds: isolation, physicochemical characterization, and antifungal properties of the protein. *J. Agric. Food Chem.* 56 (12): 4399–4405.

8 Holm, L. and Sander, C. (1997). An evolutionary treasure: unification of a broad set of amidohydrolases related to urease. *Proteins Struct. Funct. Bioinf.* 28 (1): 72–82.

9 Mobley, H.L. and Hausinger, R.P. (1989). Microbial ureases: significance, regulation, and molecular characterization. *Microbiol. Rev.* 53 (1): 85–108.

10 Ciurli, S., Marzadori, C., Benini, S. et al. (1996). Urease from the soil bacterium *Bacillus pasteurii*: immobilization on Ca-polygalacturonate. *Soil Biol. Biochem.* 28 (6): 811–817.

11 Kumar, V. and Wagenet, R.J. (1984). Urease activity and kinetics of urea transformation in soils. *Soil Sci.* 137 (4): 263–269.

12 Bachmeier, K.L., Williams, A.E., Warmington, J.R., and Bang, S.S. (2002). Urease activity in microbiologically-induced calcite precipitation. *J. Biotechnol.* 93 (2): 171–181.

13 Sondi, I. and Salopek-Sondi, B. (2005). Influence of the primary structure of enzymes on the formation of $CaCO_3$ polymorphs: a comparison of plant (*Canavalia ensiformis*) and bacterial (*Bacillus pasteurii*) ureases. *Langmuir* 21 (19): 8876–8882.

14 Bremner, J.M. and Krogmeier, M.J. (1989). Evidence that the adverse effect of urea fertilizer on seed germination in soil is due to ammonia formed through hydrolysis of urea by soil urease. *Proc. Natl. Acad. Sci. U.S.A.* 86 (21): 8185–8188.

15 Krogmeier, M.J., McCarty, G.W., and Bremner, J.M. (1989). Phytotoxicity of foliar-applied urea. *Proc. Natl. Acad. Sci. U.S.A.* 86 (21): 8189–8191.

16 Mazzei, L., Musiani, F., and Ciurli, S. (2017). *The Biological Chemistry of Nickel* (ed. D. Zamble, M. Rowińska-Żyrek, and H. Kozlowski), 60–97. The Royal Society of Chemistry.

17 Carlini, C.R. and Ligabue-Braun, R. (2016). Ureases as multifunctional toxic proteins: a review. *Toxicon* 110: 90–109.

18 Benini, S. (2000). Structure and function relationships of urease and cytochrome c-553 from *Bacillus pasteurii*. Doctoral dissertation. University of York.

19 Kakimoto, S., Sumino, Y., Ichi Akiyama, S., and Nakao, Y. (1989). Purification and characterization of acid urease from *Lactobacillus reuteri*. *Agric. Biol. Chem.* 53 (4): 1119–1125.

20 Jiang, N.J., Yoshioka, H., Yamamoto, K., and Soga, K. (2016). Ureolytic activities of a urease-producing bacterium and purified urease enzyme in the anoxic condition: implication for subseafloor sand production control by microbially induced carbonate precipitation (MICP). *Ecol. Eng.* 90: 96–104.

21 Mekonnen, E., Kebede, A., Nigussie, A. et al. (2021). Isolation and characterization of urease-producing soil bacteria. *Int. J. Microbiol.* 2021: 1–11.

22 Nathan, V.K., Vijayan, J., and Parvathi, A. (2020). Optimization of urease production by *Bacillus halodurans* PO_{15}: a mangrove bacterium from Poovar mangroves, India. *Mar. Life Sci. Technol.* 2: 194–202.

23 Christians, S., Jose, J., Schäfer, U., and Kaltwasser, H. (1991). Purification and subunit determination of the nickel-dependent *Staphylococcus xylosus* urease. *FEMS Microbiol. Lett.* 80 (2–3): 271–275.

24 Jin, M., Rosario, W., Watler, E., and Calhoun, D.H. (2004). Development of a large-scale HPLC-based purification for the urease from *Staphylococcus leei* and determination of subunit structure. *Protein Expression Purif.* 34 (1): 111–117.

25 Schäfer, U.K. and Kaltwasser, H. (1994). Urease from *Staphylococcus saprophyticus*: purification, characterization and comparison to *Staphylococcus xylosus* urease. *Arch. Microbiol.* 161: 393–399.

26 Farley, P.C. and Santosa, S. (2002). Regulation of expression of the *Rhizopus oryzae* uricase and urease enzymes. *Can. J. Microbiol.* 48 (12): 1104–1108.

27 Creaser, E.H. and Porter, R.L. (1985). The purification of urease from *Aspergillus nidulans*. *Int. J. Biochem.* 17 (12): 1339–1341.

28 Smith, P.T., King, A.D. Jr., and Goodman, N. (1993). Isolation and characterization of urease from *Aspergillus niger*. *Microbiology* 139 (5): 957–962.

29 Cox, G.M., Mukherjee, J., Cole, G.T. et al. (2000). Urease as a virulence factor in experimental cryptococcosis. *Infect. Immun.* 68 (2): 443–448.

30 Feder, V., Kmetzsch, L., Staats, C.C. et al. (2015). *Cryptococcus gattii* urease as a virulence factor and the relevance of enzymatic activity in cryptococcosis pathogenesis. *FEBS J.* 282 (8): 1406–1418.

31 Mirbod, F., Schaller, R.A., and Cole, G.T. (2002). Purification and characterization of urease isolated from the pathogenic fungus *Coccidioides immitis*. *Med. Mycol.* 40 (1): 35–44.

32 Mirbod-Donovan, F., Schaller, R., Hung, C.Y. et al. (2006). Urease produced by *Coccidioides posadasii* contributes to the virulence of this respiratory pathogen. *Infect. Immun.* 74 (1): 504–515.

33 Lubbers, M.W., Rodriguez, S.B., Honey, N.K., and Thornton, R.J. (1996). Purification and characterization of urease from *Schizosaccharomyces pombe*. *Can. J. Microbiol.* 42 (2): 132–140.

34 Archer, D.B. and Peberdy, J.F. (1997). The molecular biology of secreted enzyme production by fungi. *Crit. Rev. Biotechnol.* 17 (4): 273–306.

35 Kamel, M.Y. and Hamed, R.R. (1975). *Aerobacter aerogenes* PRL-R3 urease. Purification and properties. *Acta Biol. Med. Ger.* 34 (6): 971–979.

36 Schneider, J. and Kaltwasser, H. (1984). Urease from *Arthrobacter oxydans*, a nickel-containing enzyme. *Arch. Microbiol.* 139: 355–360.

37 Nakano, H., Takenishi, S., and Watanabe, Y. (1984). Purification and properties of urease from *Brevibacterium ammoniagenes*. *Agric. Biol. Chem.* 48 (6): 1495–1502.

38 Bandara, A.B., Contreras, A., Contreras-Rodriguez, A. et al. (2007). *Brucella suis* urease encoded by *ure* 1 but not *ure* 2 is necessary for intestinal infection of BALB/c mice. *BMC Microbiol.* 7 (1): 1–14.

39 Mizuki, T., Kamekura, M., DasSarma, S. et al. (2004). Ureases of extreme halophiles of the genus *Haloarcula* with a unique structure of gene cluster. *Biosci. Biotechnol. Biochem.* 68 (2): 397–406.

40 Dunn, B.E., Campbell, G.P., Perez-Perez, G.I., and Blaser, M.J. (1990). Purification and characterization of urease from *Helicobacter pylori*. *J. Biol. Chem.* 265 (16): 9464–9469.

41 Mobley, H.L., Cortesia, M.J., Rosenthal, L.E., and Jones, B.D. (1988). Characterization of urease from *Campylobacter pylori*. *J. Clin. Microbiol.* 26 (5): 831–836.

42 Todd, M.J. and Hausinger, R.P. (1987). Purification and characterization of the nickel-containing multicomponent urease from *Klebsiella aerogenes*. *J. Biol. Chem.* 262 (13): 5963–5967.

43 Hu, L.T., Nicholson, E.B., Jones, B.D. et al. (1990). *Morganella morganii* urease: purification, characterization, and isolation of gene sequences. *J. Bacteriol.* 172 (6): 3073–3080.

44 Jones, B.D. and Mobley, H.L. (1987). Genetic and biochemical diversity of ureases of Proteus, Providencia, and Morganella species isolated from urinary tract infection. *Infect. Immun.* 55 (9): 2198–2203.

45 Zhang, X., Zhao, S., He, Y. et al. (2020). Pipeline for targeted meta-proteomic analyses to assess the diversity of cattle rumen microbial urease. *Front. Microbiol.* 11: 573414.

46 Mulrooney, S.B., Lynch, M.J., Mobley, H.L., and Hausinger, R.P. (1988). Purification, characterization, and genetic organization of recombinant *Providencia stuartii* urease expressed by *Escherichia coli*. *J. Bacteriol.* 170 (5): 2202–2207.

47 Hausinger, R.P. (1986). Purification of a nickel-containing urease from the rumen anaerobe *Selenomonas ruminantium*. *J. Biol. Chem.* 261 (17): 7866–7870.

48 Benini, S., Rypniewski, W.R., Wilson, K.S. et al. (1998). The complex of *Bacillus pasteurii* urease with β-mercaptoethanol from X-ray data at 1.65-Å resolution. *J. Biol. Inorg. Chem.* 3: 268–273.

49 Ma, L., Pang, A.P., Luo, Y. et al. (2020). Beneficial factors for biomineralization by ureolytic bacterium *Sporosarcina pasteurii*. *Microb. Cell Fact.* 19 (1): 1–12.

50 Eng, H., Robertson, J.A., and Stemke, G.W. (1986). Properties of urease from *Ureaplasma urealyticum*: kinetics, molecular weight, and demonstration of multiple enzyme isoelectric point forms. *Can. J. Microbiol.* 32 (6): 487–493.

51 Thirkell, D., Myles, A.D., Precious, B.L. et al. (1989). The urease of *Ureaplasma urealyticum*. *Microbiology* 135 (2): 315–323.

52 Gang, J.G., Yun, S.K., and Hwang, S.Y. (2009). *Helicobacter pylori* urease may exist in two forms: evidence from the kinetic studies. *J. Microbiol. Biotechnol.* 19 (12): 1565–1568.

53 Turbett, G.R., Høj, P.B., Horne, R., and Mee, B.J. (1992). Purification and characterization of the urease enzymes of *Helicobacter* species from humans and animals. *Infect. Immun.* 60 (12): 5259–5266.

54 Wong, B.L. and Shobe, C.R. (1974). Single-step purification of urease by affinity chromatography. *Can. J. Microbiol.* 20 (4): 623–630.

55 Geweely, N.S. (2006). Purification and characterization of intracellular urease enzyme isolated from *Rhizopus oryzae*. *Biotechnology* 5 (3): 358–364.

56 Lee, M.H., Mulrooney, S.B., and Hausinger, R.P. (1990). Purification, characterization, and in vivo reconstitution of *Klebsiella aerogenes* urease apoenzyme. *J. Bacteriol.* 172 (8): 4427–4431.

57 Hussain, A., Rafeeq, H., Afsheen, N. et al. (2022). Urease-based biocatalytic platforms—a modern view of a classic enzyme with applied perspectives. *Catal. Lett.* 152 (2): 414–437.

58 Pérez, J.A.C., Sosa-Hernández, J.E., Hussain, S.M. et al. (2019). Bioinspired biomaterials and enzyme-based biosensors for point-of-care applications with reference to cancer and bio-imaging. *Biocatal. Agric. Biotechnol.* 17: 168–176.

59 Nguyen, H.H., Lee, S.H., Lee, U.J. et al. (2019). Immobilized enzymes in biosensor applications. *Materials* 12 (1): 121.

60 Pundir, C.S., Jakhar, S., and Narwal, V. (2019). Determination of urea with special emphasis on biosensors: a review. *Biosens. Bioelectron.* 123: 36–50.

61 Singh, S., Sharma, M., and Singh, G. (2021). Recent advancements in urea biosensors for biomedical applications. *IET Nanobiotechnol.* 15 (4): 358–379.

62 Fidaleo, M. and Tavilli, E. (2021). Urea removal in rosé and red wines by immobilised acid urease in a packed bed reactor. *Food Bioprod. Process.* 126: 42–50.

63 Fidaleo, M., Esti, M., and Moresi, M. (2006). Assessment of urea degradation rate in model wine solutions by acid urease from *Lactobacillus fermentum*. *J. Agric. Food Chem.* 54 (17): 6226–6235.

64 Liu, Q., Chen, Y., Yuan, M. et al. (2017). A *Bacillus paralicheniformis* iron-containing urease reduces urea concentrations in rice wine. *Appl. Environ. Microbiol.* 83: e01258-17–e01258-17.

65 Cerreti, M., Fidaleo, M., Benucci, I. et al. (2016). Assessing the potential content of ethyl carbamate in white, red, and rosé wines as a key factor for pursuing urea degradation by purified acid urease. *J. Food Sci.* 81 (7): C1603–C1612.

66 Yang, L.Q., Wang, S.H., and Tian, Y.P. (2010). Purification, properties, and application of a novel acid urease from *Enterobacter* sp. *Appl. Biochem. Biotechnol.* 160: 303–313.

67 Wang, X., Xu, J., Wang, Z., and Yao, W. (2022). Use of recycled concrete aggregates as carriers for self-healing of concrete cracks by bacteria with high urease activity. *Constr. Build. Mater.* 337: 127581.

68 Chen, B., Sun, W., Sun, X. et al. (2021). Crack sealing evaluation of self-healing mortar with *Sporosarcina pasteurii*: influence of bacterial concentration and air-entraining agent. *Process Biochem.* 107: 100–111.

69 Garg, R., Garg, R., and Eddy, N.O. (2023). Microbial induced calcite precipitation for self-healing of concrete: a review. *J. Sustain. Cem.-Based Mater.* 12 (3): 317–330.

70 Zhu, X., Mignon, A., Nielsen, S.D. et al. (2021). Viability determination of *Bacillus sphaericus* after encapsulation in hydrogel for self-healing concrete via microcalorimetry and in situ oxygen concentration measurements. *Cem. Concr. Compos.* 119: 104006.

71 Bundur, Z.B., Kirisits, M.J., and Ferron, R.D. (2015). Biomineralized cement-based materials: impact of inoculating vegetative bacterial cells on hydration and strength. *Cem. Concr. Res.* 67: 237–245.

72 Tang, Y. and Xu, J. (2021). Application of microbial precipitation in self-healing concrete: a review on the protection strategies for bacteria. *Constr. Build. Mater.* 306: 124950.

73 Vardhan, K.H., Kumar, P.S., and Panda, R.C. (2019). A review on heavy metal pollution, toxicity and remedial measures: current trends and future perspectives. *J. Mol. Liq.* 290: 111197.

74 Mishra, S., Bharagava, R.N., More, N. et al. (2019). Heavy metal contamination: an alarming threat to environment and human health. In: *Environmental Biotechnology: For Sustainable Future* (ed. R.C. Sobti et al.), 103–125. Springer Nature Singapore Pte Ltd.

75 Sarkar, A., Sarkar, K.D., Amrutha, V., and Dutta, K. (2019). An overview of enzyme-based biosensors for environmental monitoring. In: *Tools, Techniques and Protocols for Monitoring Environmental Contaminants* (ed. S.K. Brar et al.), 307–329. Amsterdam, The Netherlands: Elsevier.

76 Velusamy, K., Periyasamy, S., Kumar, P.S. et al. (2022). Biosensor for heavy metals detection in wastewater: a review. *Food Chem. Toxicol.* 168: 113307.

77 Arkhypova, V., Soldatkin, O., Soldatkin, A., and Dzyadevych, S. (2023). Electrochemical biosensors based on enzyme inhibition effect. *Chem. Rec.* e202300214.

78 Kono, T., Sakae, T., Nakada, H. et al. (2022). Confusion between carbonate apatite and biological apatite (carbonated hydroxyapatite) in bone and teeth. *Minerals* 12 (2): 170.

79 Hoque, M.E., Sakinah, N., Chuan, Y.L., and Ansari, M.N.M. (2014). Synthesis and characterization of hydroxyapatite bioceramic. *Int. J. Sci. Eng. Technol.* 3 (5): 458–462.

80 Kaimonov, M.R., Safronova, T.V., Filippov, Y.Y. et al. (2021). Calcium phosphate powder for obtaining of composite bioceramics. *Inorg. Mater. Appl. Res.* 12: 34–39.

81 Glazov, I.E., Krut'ko, V.K., Musskaya, O.N., and Kulak, A.I. (2022). Calcium phosphate apatites: wet formation, thermal transformations, terminology, and identification. *Russ. J. Inorg. Chem.* 67 (2): 173–182.

82 Fiume, E., Magnaterra, G., Rahdar, A. et al. (2021). Hydroxyapatite for biomedical applications: a short overview. *Ceramics* 4 (4): 542–563.

83 Bayraktar, D. and Tas, A.C. (2001). Formation of hydroxyapatite precursors at 37 °C in urea-and enzyme urease-containing body fluids. *J. Mater. Sci. Lett.* 20 (5): 401–403.

84 Emtiazi, G., Shapoorabadi, F.A., and Mirbagheri, M. (2019). Chemical and biological synthesis of hydroxy apatite: advantage and application. *Int. J. Microbiol. Curr. Res.* 1 (1): 20–22.

85 Harrison, J.M., Dick, A.W., Madigan, E.A. et al. (2022). Urinary catheter policies in home healthcare agencies and hospital transfers due to urinary tract infection. *Am. J. Infect. Control* 50 (7): 743–748.

86 Yang, W., Li, J., and Yang, X. (2021). Features and applications of urine stabilization methods: a review. *Front. Sustainability* 2: 710739.

87 Qin, Y. and Cabral, J.M. (2002). Review properties and applications of urease. *Biocatal. Biotransform.* 20 (1): 1–14.

88 Siddiq, D.M. and Darouiche, R.O. (2012). New strategies to prevent catheter-associated urinary tract infections. *Nat. Rev. Urol.* 9 (6): 305–314.

3

Methane Monooxygenase Production and Its Limitations

Gaurav S. Rana, Neetika Naudiyal, Vaibhav Badoni, Amit S. Rana, Ashutosh Dubey, and Ashok K. Verma

G. B. Pant University of Agriculture and Technology, Department of Biochemistry, College of Basic Sciences and Humanities, Pantnagar, Uttarakhand 263145, India

3.1 Introduction

Methane possesses approximately 84 times the potency of carbon dioxide as a greenhouse gas [1, 2]. It is commonly employed as a raw material for producing liquid fuels using the Fischer–Tropsch method, which involves substantial financial investment, risks, and adverse impacts on the environment and society [3]. The pursuit of environmentally sustainable and economically viable methane utilization has prompted scientists to explore alternative catalysts.

Methanotrophic bacteria have the ability to utilize methane as their primary source of carbon and energy, converting it into valuable chemicals. These bacteria are studying over 110 years and have found capable of oxidizing methane [4–6]. Methanotrophs belong to a broad group of Gram-negative bacteria that can survive in extreme conditions such as high temperatures, salinity, and pH levels. They can adapt to either facultative or obligate lifestyles, relying on C-1 compounds like methane for their survival [7–9]. Most of the methanotrophs known today are mesophiles found in environments with near neutral pH levels. However, more recently, methanotrophs have been discovered in extreme environments including hot springs [10], acidic peat bogs [11], soda lakes [12], and the Antarctic [13], suggesting their widespread presence in nature. While some methanotrophs can also survive on methanol, none have been observed to grow using multicarbon compounds. Methanotrophs have been found for various applications, such as the production of single-cell protein (SCP) and bulk chemicals like propylene oxide. They have also investigated their potential for bioremediation by oxidizing alkanes, alkenes, and substituted aliphatic compounds [14]. Methanotrophs possess a strong affinity for methane and are capable of oxidizing even trace amounts of this greenhouse gas (e.g., 1–2 ppm), thereby reducing its impact on global warming [15]. Methanotrophs are classified into two classes: Type I and Type II. Type I methanotrophs are classified within the Proteobacteria family and comprise various genera, including *Methylomonas, Methylobacter, Methylomicrobium, Methylococcus,*

Microbial Enzymes: Production, Purification, and Industrial Applications, First Edition.
Edited by Dinesh Yadav, Pankaj Chowdhary, Gautam Anand, and Rajarshi Kumar Gaur.

Methylocaldum, and *Methylosphaera*. These bacteria have intracytoplasmic membrane bundles, predominantly use 16-carbon fatty acids, and absorb formaldehyde produced during the oxidation of methane through the ribulose monophosphate (RuMP) cycle (via methanol). Type II methanotrophs, which are α-proteobacteria of the *Methylosinus* and *Methylocystis* genera, have intracytoplasmic membranes arranged around the cell's periphery. They primarily use 18-carbon fatty acids in their membranes and assimilate formaldehyde into cellular carbon using the serine cycle [16].

Methanotrophs possess a C-1 metabolism based on tetrahydromethanopterin and require the enzyme methane monooxygenase (MMO) to initiate the methane oxidation pathway [17]. MMO is the first enzyme involved in this process.

3.2 Classes of MMO

MMO enzymes can be categorized into two groups: one consists of soluble enzyme complexes that are found in the cytoplasm (known as soluble methane monooxygenase [sMMO]), while the other includes membrane-bound enzyme systems that are associated with particles (known as particulate methane monooxygenase [pMMO]).

3.2.1 Soluble Methane Monooxygenase (sMMO)

The enzyme has been found in two types of methanotrophs: *Methylococcus capsulatus* from the Methanotrophs type I genus, and *Methylosinus* and *Methylocystis* from the type II genus (Figure 3.1). However, recent studies have also identified sMMO in one marine species of *Methylomicrobium* [18] and one species of *Methylomonas* [19]. Compared to pMMO, sMMO exhibits a much wider range of substrate specificity. It can efficiently oxidize various nongrowth substrates such as alkanes, alkenes, and aromatic chemicals. This characteristic makes sMMO particularly appealing for co-oxidation reactions and bioremediation processes [14].

The genes that are responsible for encoding the sMMO are arranged in a six-gene operon called mmoXYBZDC (Figure 3.2). To be more precise, mmoX, mmoY, and mmoZ are responsible for encoding the α-, β-, and γ-subunits of the hydroxylase enzyme, respectively [20]. Within this operon, mmoB and mmoC encode MMOB and MMOR proteins, while mmoD (previously known as orfY) is an open reading frame which is a regulatory protein that directly interacts with methane monooxygenase hydroxylase (MMOH) [9, 21].

3.2.2 Particulate Methane Monooxygenase (pMMO)

pMMO, which is present in nearly all examined methanotrophs, is absent in strain K. Strain K is an acidophilic methanotroph derived from a northern wetland peat and belongs to the Proteobacteria α-subclass [11]. Although this strain possesses a sMMO similar to type II methanotrophs, it lacks a pMMO. Methanotrophs express pMMO when they grow in conditions with a high ratio of copper to biomass.

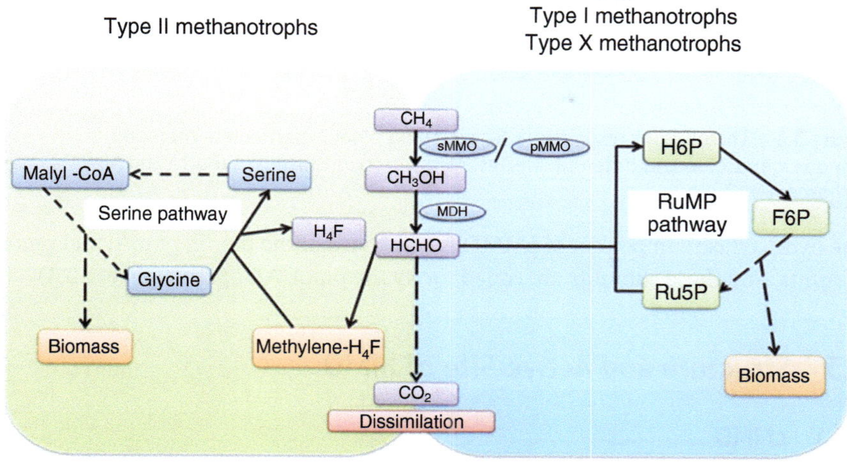

Figure 3.1 Different metabolic pathways employed by methanotrophs (organisms capable of utilizing methane as a carbon and energy source) for the conversion of methane into biomass. There are three main pathways depicted: Pathways I, II, and X. In Pathways I and X, methane is first converted to methanol, a process facilitated by either soluble methane monooxygenase (sMMO) or particulate methane monooxygenase (pMMO). Methanol is then transformed into formaldehyde with the help of an enzyme called methanol dehydrogenase (MDH). Subsequently, formaldehyde is incorporated into biomass by type I and X methanotrophs through the ribulose monophosphate (RuMP) route. On this route, formaldehyde is converted to hexulose-6-phosphate (H6P), which further undergoes transformations to fructose-6-phosphate (F6P), ribulose-5-phosphate (Ru5P), tetrahydrofolate (H4F), and finally malyl coenzyme A (malyl-CoA). Type II methanotrophs, on the other hand, utilize the serine route for the assimilation of formaldehyde. In this pathway, formaldehyde is incorporated into biomass via the conversion of serine, an amino acid, ultimately leading to the formation of complex biomolecules. All methanotrophs possess dissimilation pathways for formaldehyde, which allow them to break down formaldehyde back into simpler compounds. To summarize, methanotrophs employ various metabolic pathways, such as RuMP and serine routes, for the assimilation of formaldehyde and conversion of methane to biomass. The mentioned abbreviations in the figure represent different compounds involved in these pathways, including ribulose monophosphate (RuMP), hexulose-6-phosphate (H6P), fructose-6-phosphate (F6P), ribulose-5-phosphate (Ru5P), tetrahydrofolate (H4F), and malyl coenzyme A (malyl-CoA).

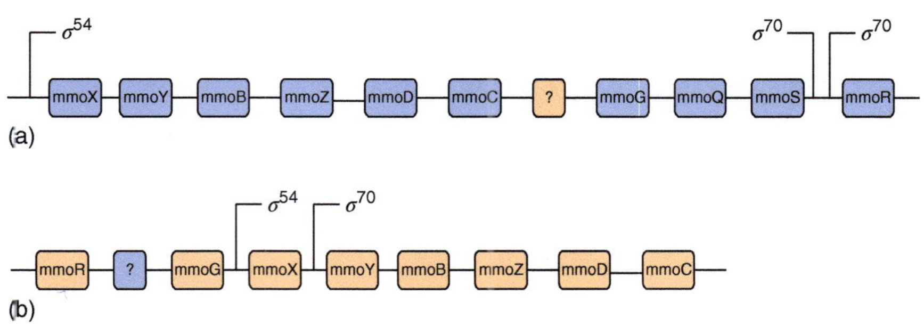

Figure 3.2 Structural arrangement of the operon responsible for encoding soluble methane monooxygenase (sMMO) in two different species, namely (a) *Methylococcus capsulatus* (Bath) and (b) *Methylosinus trichosporium* OB3b.

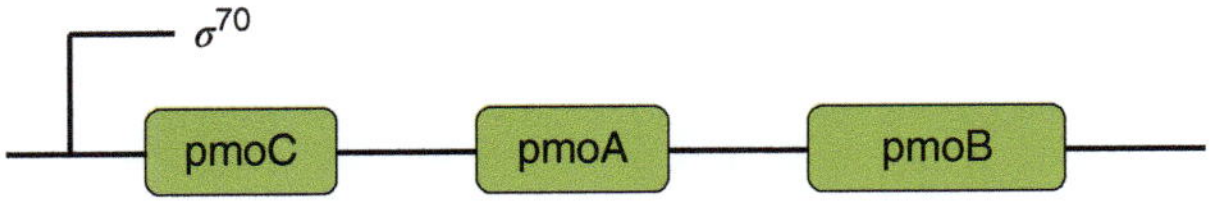

Figure 3.3 The operons responsible for encoding pMMO (particulate methane monooxygenase) in two different species: *Methylococcus capsulatus* (Bath) and *Methylosinus trichosporium* OB3b.

The hydroxylase component of pMMO is composed of the pmoB, pmoA, and pmoC subunits, and these subunits are coded for by the pmoCAB operon (Figure 3.3).

3.3 Structure and Active Site of MMO

3.3.1 sMMO

A total of 28 crystal structures of MMOH, primarily derived from *M. capsulatus* (Bath), have been identified. The first crystal structure of MMOH was established in 1993 with a resolution of 1.7 Å [22, 23]. This structure consists of two α subunits with 60.6 kDa each, two β subunits with 45.1 kDa each, and two γ subunits with 19.8 kDa each. These subunits are arranged in the form of an $\alpha_2\beta_2\gamma_2$ dimer, predominantly composed of α-helices, with the exception of two β hairpins located in the α and γ subunits (Figure 3.4).

MMOB is a protein that does not have cofactors. Its structure consists of 7β strands arranged in 2β sheets and 3α helices. On the other hand, MMOR contains two domains, each composed of both α and β structures. These domains bind to FAD and NADH and transfer electrons to a ferredoxin domain containing a [2Fe–2S] cluster, which then transfers the electrons to the active site of MMOH [24, 25]. Within MMOH, there is a diiron metal center situated at the active site, present in each α subunit of the $\alpha_2\beta_2\gamma_2$ dimer. This diiron center is situated within a 4-helix bundle, with helices E and F on its surface. These helices undergo conformational changes during catalysis [24].

The two iron ions in the diiron center are connected by the residue Glu144 and two hydroxides. When the center is reduced, the distance between the iron ions increases from approximately 3.1 Å to around 3.3 Å. Additionally, Glu243 undergoes a carboxylate shift, replacing one of the bridging hydroxide ions as a ligand to the diiron center [23, 26]. This shift creates a reactive site for interaction with dioxygen. In its oxidized form, MMOH contains an antiferromagnetically coupled diiron(III) site, while in its reduced form, it possesses a weakly ferromagnetically coupled diiron(II) center [27]. The activity of sMMO can be determined by measuring the epoxidation of propylene. Propylene oxide, a product of this reaction, is not further oxidized by methanotroph cells and extracts [28].

3.3.2 pMMO

The initial crystal structure of pMMO from *M. capsulatus* (Bath) was determined with a resolution of 2.8 Å [29]. Within the pMMO structure, the subunits pmoB,

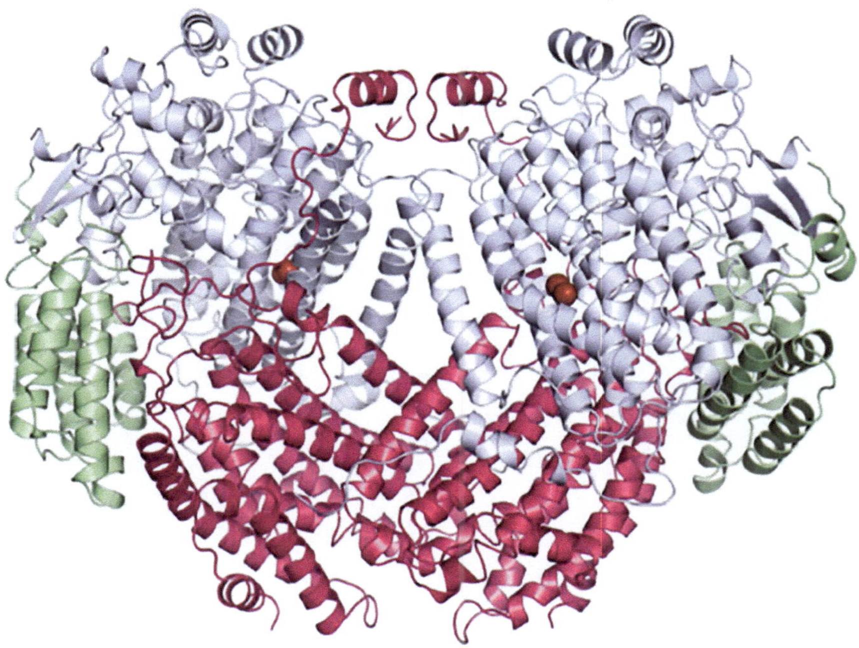

Figure 3.4 sMMO (soluble methane monooxygenase) of *Methylococcus capsulatus* (Bath), with the α subunits represented in gray, β subunits in magenta, and γ subunits in green. The iron ions within the structure are highlighted in a red-brown color.

pmoA, and pmoC form a trimer with a total molecular weight of 300 kDa, consisting of three $\alpha_3\beta_3\gamma_3$ units [30] (Figure 3.5). The pmoB subunit encompasses two cupredoxin-like domains connected by two transmembrane helices, while the pmoA and pmoC subunits are made up of transmembrane helices [31–33].

Unlike MMOH, pMMO structures display the presence of multiple metal centers. All pMMO structures feature a copper binding site located at the N-terminus of the pmoB subunit, with ligands consisting of His33, His137, and His139 in *M. capsulatus* (Bath). In the structures of *M. capsulatus* (Bath) [29] and *Methylosinus trichosporium* OB3b [31], two copper ions were observed at a distance of approximately 2.5 Å. However, in *Methylocystis* sp. str. Rockwell pMMO, a monocopper site was identified through crystallographic resolution at a range of 2.6–3.9 Å [33]. After purification and concentration of the enzyme, both of these pMMOs exhibit low copper binding stoichiometries. The 1.8 Å resolution structure of the soluble domain of the amoB subunit from ammonia Monooxygenase (AMO) enzyme of *Nitrosocaldus yellowstonii* also contains a monocopper site at the corresponding position, indicating the conservation of this site throughout the extensive pMMO/AMO superfamily. However, in this structure, the copper ion participates in a crystal lattice contact, and the N-terminal histidine ligand is disordered [34]. Additionally, in the *M. capsulatus* (Bath) pmoB subunit, there is an additional copper ion situated at the interface of the two cupredoxin domains, coordinated by His48 and His72. The presence of the His48 ligand is not conserved

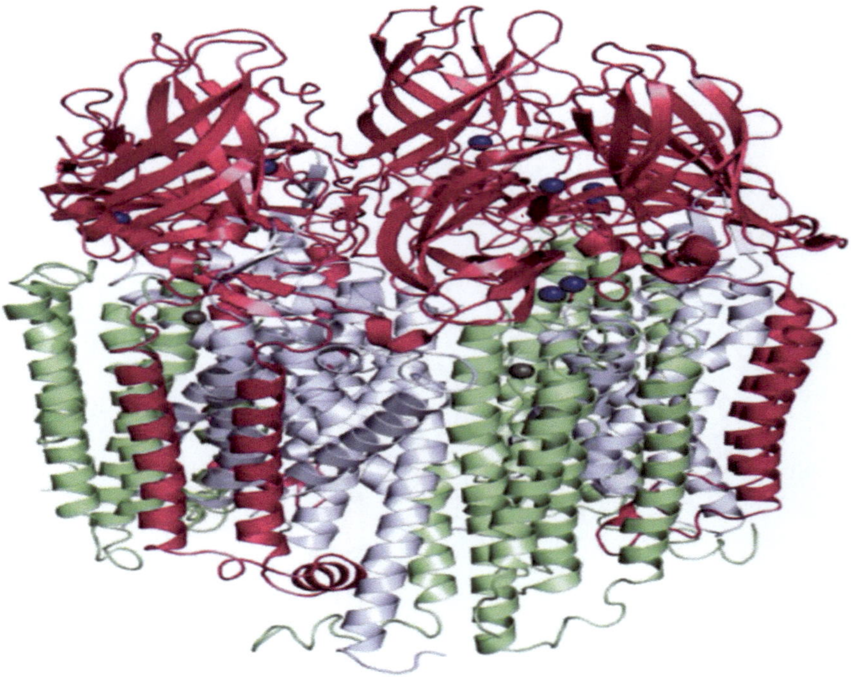

Figure 3.5 The representation of *Methylococcus capsulatus* (Bath) pMMO (PDB accession code 3RGB), showcasing the PmoC subunits highlighted in green, the PmoB subunits displayed in magenta, and the PmoA subunits depicted in gray. The copper ions are represented by a dark blue color, while the zinc ions are represented by a gray color.

in other pMMO sequences, and this site is not observed in the other pMMO structures [31–33].

3.4 Mechanism of Action

In the process of methane oxidation performed by methanotrophs, a crucial chemical bond between dioxygen and the C—H bond in methane, was broken by the MMO enzyme. This breakdown occurred through a sequence of steps and intermediates [35].

3.4.1 Soluble MMO

Initially, the reduced diiron(II) MMOH interacts with O_2 in the presence of two equivalents of MMOH, leading to the formation of a species referred to as "O." In this particular state, O_2 is bound, although not directly to the diiron cluster (Figure 3.6). Following this, the intermediate "O" undergoes a transformation into peroxo intermediates identified as P* and P. In the case of *M. capsulatus* (Bath) MMOH, P* is characterized as a diiron(III) site, with the only distinction from the subsequent intermediate P being the arrangement of ligands [36]. Subsequently, intermediate

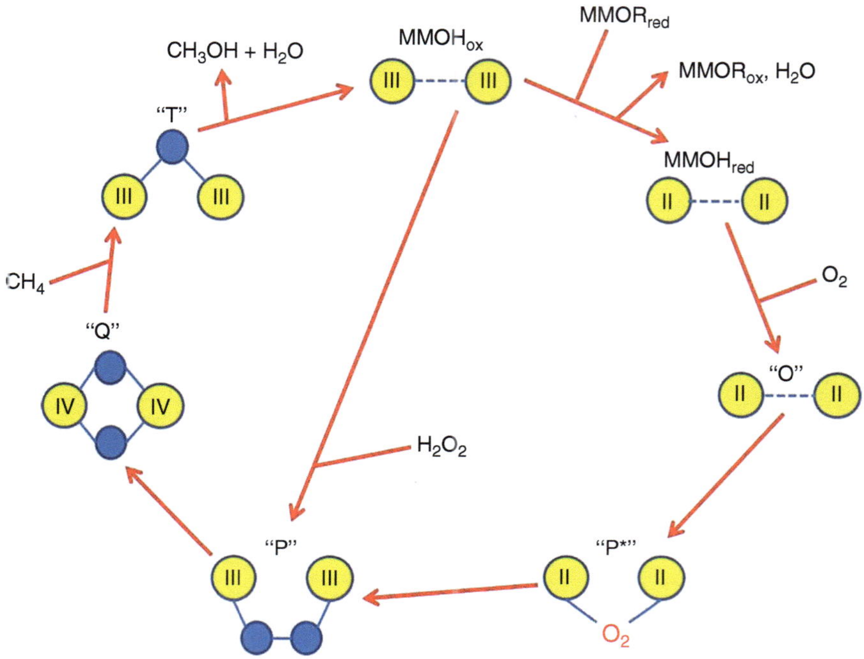

Figure 3.6 Catalytic process of soluble methane monooxygenase (sMMO), depicting the iron ions highlighted in yellow and indicating their respective oxidation states. The blue circles represent oxygen atoms, except for intermediate P*, where the specific binding of O_2 to the active site is uncertain. Another pathway to produce intermediate P involves the reaction of $MMOH_{ox}$ with H_2O_2, referred to as the peroxide shunt mechanism.

P undergoes a process dependent on protons to transform into Q, which entails the cleavage of the O—O bond. Intermediate Q is the species that engages with methane to break the C—H bond. After the oxidation of methane, Q undergoes a transition into the product complex known as T, which is hypothesized to have a structure featuring a mono-μ-oxo bridge [37].

3.4.2 Particulate MMO

In the pMMO enzyme, the catalytic reaction occurs at the CuC site within the PmoC subunit, while the monocopper CuB site in the PmoB subunit does not participate in the activation of O_2 [38] (Figure 3.7). The catalytic process begins with the coordination of a proton-transfer coupled DQH^- to Cu_C(II), resulting in the formation of a Cu_C(II)-DQH^- species (labeled as 1). Subsequently, O_2 binds to this species ($1 \rightarrow 2$), and a hydrogen atom abstraction (HAA) takes place from the DQH$^{\cdot}$ molecule ($2 \rightarrow 3$), generating the Cu_C(II)-DQH^- species (labeled as 3). This species then undergoes further HAA ($3 \rightarrow 4$) with a new DQH_2 molecule, leading to the production of H_2O_2 and the Cu_C(II)-DQH- species (labeled as 4). The subsequent dissociation of DQH$^{\cdot}$($4 \rightarrow 5$) and O—O homolysis catalyzed by CuC(I) ($5 \rightarrow 6$) generate the HO$^{\cdot}$ radical, which forms a hydrogen bond with Cu_C(II)-OH^-, resulting in the formation of species 6. Following this, HO$^{\cdot}$ coordinates with Cu_C(II)

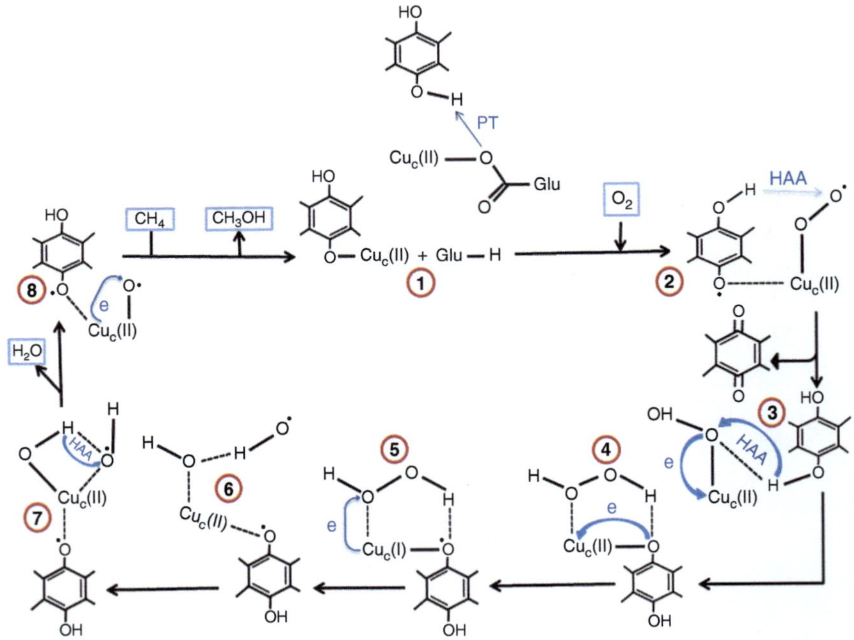

Figure 3.7 Catalytic cycle of pMMO in the presence of DQH_2; PT, proton transfer; DQH_2, duroquinol; HAA, hydrogen atom abstraction.

(6 → 7), and another HAA occurs (7 → 8), producing the Cu_C(II)-$O^{\bullet -}$active species responsible for C—H oxidations (8 → 1) [39, 40].

3.5 Regulation of MMO

Methanotrophs like *M. trichosporium* OB3b and *M. capsulatus* (Bath) possess two types of enzyme systems, sMMO and pMMO. They exhibit a unique metabolic shift triggered by copper ions (Figure 3.8). When these cells grow in an environment with a high copper-to-biomass ratio, they express the pMMO enzyme and do not show any detectable expression of sMMO. However, when the cells experience copper deprivation, resulting in a low copper-to-biomass ratio (<0.2 μM Cu^{2+} in a typical flask batch culture of *M. trichosporium* OB3b), they start expressing the sMMO enzyme. This phenomenon, known as the "copper switch," is solely regulated by the presence of copper ions [41]. Copper ions irreversibly inhibit the activity of sMMO both *in vivo* and *in vitro* by deactivating its reductase component [42].

3.6 Sources of MMO

The sMMO enzyme is only found in specific categories of bacteria categorized as Gram-negative. Examples of such bacteria include *Methylococcus* spp., *Methylosinus*

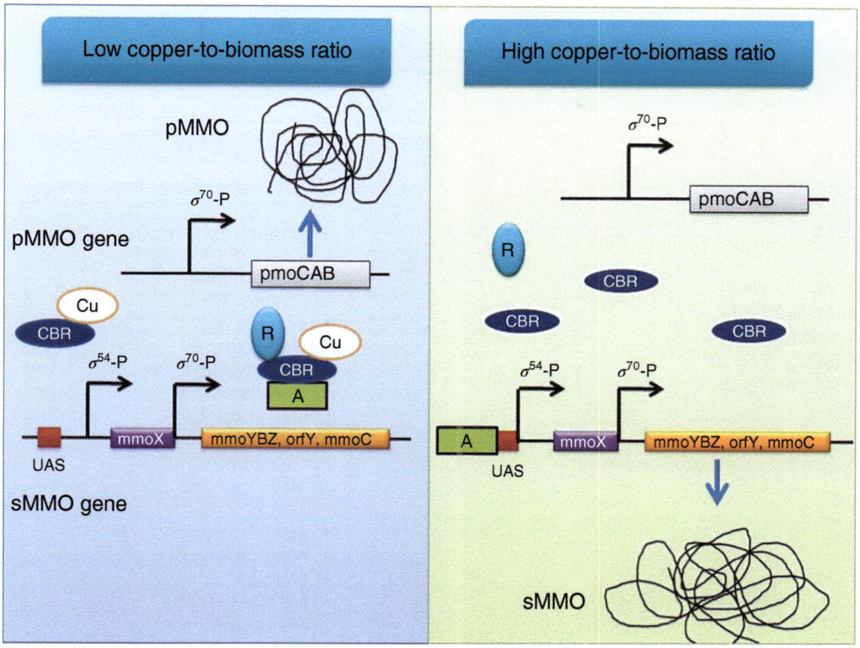

Figure 3.8 Regulation of the MMO genes in *Methylosinus trichosporium* OB3b by copper. In conditions where there is a high ratio of copper to biomass, the pMMO enzyme complex is produced. Conversely, when the copper-to-biomass ratio is low, the sMMO is expressed. This regulation is mediated by the Copper-Binding Regulator (CBR). Under high copper-to-biomass ratios, the CBR binds to copper, causing a change in its structure. This altered conformation allows the CBR to bind to both R and A. This interaction prevents R from repressing the pmo genes and also prevents A from activating the smo genes. However, when the copper-to-biomass ratio is low, the CBR is unable to form a complex with R and/or A. Consequently, R actively represses the transcription of the pmo genes. In contrast, A activates the smo genes by binding to a hypothetical Upstream Activating Sequence (UAS). This binding enables σ54-associated RNA polymerase to initiate the transcription process.

spp., and certain strains of *Methylocystis* and *Methylomonas* spp. The genes responsible for producing this enzyme complex have been effectively replicated, and their sequences have been elucidated from *M. capsulatus* (Bath) and *M. trichosporium* OB3b. Additionally, the sMMO enzyme has been isolated and recognized in various methanotrophic bacterial species (Figure 3.9).

3.7 Genetic Engineering of MMOs

3.7.1 Expression in Heterologous Host

The gene cluster of *M. trichosporium* sMMO was successfully expressed in different host organisms such as*Pseudomonas putida*, *Agrobacterium tumefaciens*, and *Rhizobium meliloti*. These organisms demonstrated the ability to degrade trichloroethylene (TCE) [42, 43]. Currently, efforts have been made to engineer various microbial

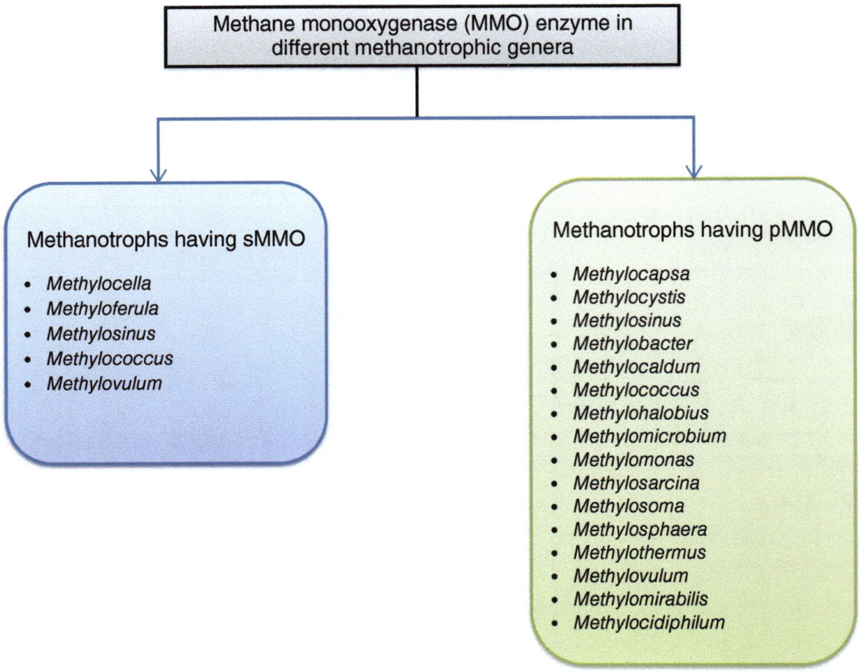

Figure 3.9 Distribution of sMMO and pMMO among different types of methane-utilizing organisms.

strains like *Escherichia coli*, *Bacillus subtilis*, and *Corynebacterium glutamicum* by cloning the MMO gene [44–46].

However, the recombinant expression of pMMO, has been challenging due to the lack of understanding regarding the role of the intracytoplasmic membrane in its activity. Moreover, expressing the pmo gene cluster in *E. coli* has been found to have harmful effects, and producing pMMO heterologously is difficult due to its known toxicity and membrane-bound nature.

Nonetheless, a recombinant version of the soluble enzyme of sMMO has been created, which exhibits activity in oxidizing propylene and methane in the presence of copper ions. This finding suggests that copper is present in the enzyme's active site [47]. The cloned subunit also displays activity similar to duroquinol, an artificial electron donor, which is capable of oxidizing methane through a series of chemical processes based on Fenton and Haber–Weiss chemistry [48]. However, when pMMO is isolated from its natural membranes and subjected to lysis, solubilization, and purification processes, it experiences a significant loss of activity, ranging from 10 to 100 times [33, 40]. After separating pMMO from its original membranes, a reduction in activity by 17% was observed. This loss is attributed to a change in the crucial metallocofactor of the enzyme [48].

3.7.2 Expression in Homologous Host

In the mutant strain F of *M. trichosporium*, a system was established to express the wild-type sMMO hydroxylase. This system involved producing recombinant sMMO genes, resulting in highly active sMMO [49]. Mutant F was able to grow using methane as the substrate due to its ability to oxidize methane with pMMO at a high copper-to-biomass ratio. By introducing a plasmid carrying the sMMO operon through conjugation and culturing the resulting strain at a low copper-to-biomass ratio, pMMO was suppressed while recombinant sMMO was expressed from its natural copper-repressed promoter [49, 50]. This demonstrated the potential of using a homologous expression system to express mutant sMMO genes. To facilitate the expression of mutant MmoX derivatives in sMMOs, a simple approach was taken to create plasmids that allowed the cloning of mutant mmoX genes into a 10-kb region containing the sMMO-encoding operon and adjacent sequences. This region was known to direct the functional expression of the sMMO complex in *M. trichosporium* mutant F [49].

sMMO is an enzyme that can oxidize TCE, a commonly detected pollutant, at least 50 times faster than other enzymes. However, the use of this bacterium is limited due to the slow growth of the strain, strong competition between TCE and methane for sMMO, and the repression of the smmo locus by low copper ion concentrations. To overcome these limitations, the 5.5-kb smmo locus from *M. trichosporium* OB3b was cloned into a plasmid vector with a wide range of hosts and introduced into *P. putida* through electroporation. This engineered strain contained all the necessary subunits to efficiently degrade TCE, with a maximum reaction rate (V_{max}) of 5 nmol/min/mg [43].

3.8 MMO Production

The activity of the MMO in the obligatory methanotroph *M. trichosporium* OB3b can vary depending on the developmental conditions. When there is an adequate amount of copper in the culture medium, the MMO takes on a particulate form pMMO. However, when there is a severe shortage of copper, the MMO assumes a soluble form sMMO [41, 51].

3.8.1 Batch Culture Method

A significant lack of copper is needed to produce only sMMO through batch manufacturing. Even at low cell densities, a copper concentration as low as 1 pM is sufficient to transform all MMO activity from being soluble to being in particulate form. *M. trichosporium* cells linked to diethylaminoethyl (DEAE)-cellulose, which exhibited a high specific activity of methane mono-oxygenase (66 pmol methane oxidized/h mg cells), were employed in the conversion of methane derived from biogas into methanol using both a batch and a continuous cell reactor. The optimal ratio of cells to carrier was found to be 0.5 g cells per gram of dry weight cellulose. Batch experiments revealed that a phosphate ion concentration of 100 mM was necessary to prevent further oxidation of methanol. An excess supply of oxygen favored the accumulation of methanol and increased the efficiency of methane conversion to 27%. To sustain the activity of methane mono-oxygenase, a pulse of 40 mM sodium format administered at the end of six hours regenerated the required $NADH_2$, thereby restoring methanol accumulation. In the batch reactor, the maximum level of methanol achieved was 50 pmol/mg cells [52].

3.8.2 Continuous Culture Method

The cells attached together through covalent bonds produced methanol consistently at a rate of 100 pmol/h for the initial 10 hours in a standard 50 ml ultrafiltration continuous reactor. However, the rate of methanol accumulation decreased afterward due to a depletion of $NADH_2$. The highest rate of methanol accumulation, reaching 267 pmol/h, was achieved when 20 mM formate was introduced into the feed stream along with 100 mM phosphate ions. This level of methanol biosynthesis was maintained for more than 72 hours. The half-life ($t_{1/2}$) and thermal denaturation rate constant (K_d) were calculated to be 108 hours and 6.42×10^{-3} h^{-1}, respectively [52].

3.9 Applications of MMO and Methanotrophs

Methanotrophs equipped with pMMO possess the metabolic ability to accumulate lipids for the production of liquid fuels [53, 54]. These microorganisms form a distinct group, and among them, *Methylocystis parvus* OBBP, which expresses MMO, has been the only documented bacteria capable of utilizing biogas successfully [55]. The monooxygenase mechanism of these particular bacteria shows assure for converting methane into biofuel in an environmentally sustainable manner. Methanotrophic bacteria have long been studied for their exceptional catalytic abilities through the pMMO and sMMO systems, making them valuable biocatalysts for synthetic chemistry and bioremediation. The exploration of biological pathways for synthesizing biofuels and other valuable products from methane, including methanol, biodiesel, SCP, biopolymers, pigments, organic acids, ectoine, farnesene, vitamin B12, and exopolysaccharides, is gaining attractiveness [56].

3.9.1 Single-cell Protein

A method invented in the 1970s allows for the creation of SCPs using methane. In 2010, significant advancements were made in synthesizing industrial SCPs from methane found in natural gas, utilizing a combination of bacteria called methanotrophic bacterial consortia. These SCPs can be used as a well-balanced amino acid diet for fish and other animals [57]. The European Union has approved the use of SCPs generated from a mixed culture dominated by *M. capsulatus* Bath for protein-rich animal feeds, including salmon, pigs, poultry, and cattle [56]. This methanotrophic conversion process offers the advantage of controlling greenhouse gas emissions in disturbed aquatic ecosystems, both natural and human-made, while contributing to the overall economic sustainability of the process.

3.9.2 Isoprenoid Compounds and Carotenoid Pigments

Methanotrophs have been discovered to contain isoprenoid chemicals and carotenoid pigments of different carbon lengths. In the United States, numerous patents have been filed for producing isoprene (2-methyl-1,3-butadiene) from methane gas or methanol. The genes responsible for the biosynthesis of isoprenoids have been identified in *Methylomonas* sp. By introducing an isoprene synthase gene from *Ipomoea batatas*, *Methylomicrobium alcaliphilum*, a methylotroph, was able to undergo a transformation that allowed it to accumulate isoprene solely from methane, which served as its carbon source.

3.9.3 Osmoprotectants

Moderately halotolerant methanotrophs and methylotrophs contain osmoprotectants such as 5-Oxoproline (pyrrolidone carboxylic acid), ectoine (1,4,5,6-tetrahydro-2-methyl-4-pyrimidine carboxylate), and its derivative hydroxyectoine. These compounds serve to stabilize enzymes, nucleic acids, and DNA-protein complexes, while also safeguarding cells from the detrimental effects of various physical and chemical factors like temperature, dehydration, UV radiation, and chemotherapeutic agents (e.g. drugs used in cancer treatment) [58]. For instance, the species *M. alcaliphilum* 20Z and other related strains are capable of accumulating ectoine, which can constitute up to 20% of their cell weight. These organisms exhibit rapid and reliable growth on methane or high concentrations of methanol under varying conditions of salinity (0–10% NaCl) and pH (pH 7–10) [12, 59, 60]. The attractiveness of utilizing methylotrophs lies in their ability to produce ectoine, which is a valuable substance with a market value of approximately US$ 1000/kg. Ectoine can find application as a moisturizer in cosmetics, thereby adding to its commercial value.

3.9.4 Lactic Acid

Lactic acid is a widely used chemical component in various industries such as cosmetics, pharmaceuticals, and chemicals. It can be produced through chemical or biological methods. Recently, there has been increasing attention given to utilizing lactic acid in the production of polylactic acid, which is a sustainable alternative to petrochemical resources and is used as a raw material for bioplastics. Certain microorganisms like *Methylomicrobium buryatense* with MMO have the ability to biocatalyze the conversion of methane into lactate [61]. In 2014, Calysta Inc. filed a US patent that demonstrates the potential for overproduction of lactic acid. They genetically modified two different methanotrophs, *M. capsulatus* Bath and a *Methylomicrobium* sp., to enhance the expression of lactate dehydrogenase, an enzyme that converts pyruvate into lactate, which is a chemical precursor for polymer production from methane-derived lactate monomer on a large scale [53].

3.9.5 Methanobactin

Methanobactins are copper-binding high affinity peptides produced by methanotrophs. They are employed as the pMMO for catalytic activity that needs copper [62]. Methanobactins protect methanotrophs from copper toxicity and may extract copper from insoluble minerals due to their copper chelating properties [63]. Methanobactins might also be employed in environmental remediation (solubilization or immobilization of various metals *in situ*) and metal recovery from mining leachates, as well as therapies, due to their capacity to bind other metals such as gold, iron, nickel, zinc, cobalt, cadmium, mercury, and uranium [56].

3.9.6 Carbohydrates

Methanotrophic cells have the ability to transform the byproducts of methane oxidation, namely methanol and formaldehyde, into various complex substances such as carbohydrates, lipids, SCP, carotenoids, and isoprenes. When methanotrophs are exposed to high rates of methane flow along with limited nitrogen or oxygen, they are known to produce exopolysaccharides [64, 65]. It has found that exopolysaccharides generated from a culture enriched with methylotrophs using methane as the sole carbon source contained important components like glucose, galactose, mannose, fucose, and rhamnose [66].

3.9.7 Biopolymers

It has been shown that certain methanotrophic bacteria that utilize the serine C1 metabolism, in addition to producing exopolysaccharides, can accumulate significant quantities of a biopolymer called polyhydroxyalkanoate (PHA) from methane. These methanotrophic genera show promise in the production of biodegradable plastics. For example, in the case of the type II methanotroph *M. parvus* OBBP, the accumulation of approximately 70% PHA (by weight) has been demonstrated. It has reported that this methanotroph able to synthesize PHAs which contains repeating units beyond 3HB (3-hydroxybutyrate) and 3HV (3-hydroxyvalerate) [55, 67].

3.9.8 Gas-to-Liquid (GTL) Conversion

Methane can be converted to methanol through an expensive and inefficient chemical process conducted at normal temperature and pressure. This process relies on the use of MMOs [53, 54, 61, 68]. However, an alternative approach called Bio-GTL (biological gas-to-liquids) utilizes methanotrophs, which naturally produce MMOs, as biological catalysts. In Bio-GTL, the activity of methanol dehydrogenase (MDH), which converts methanol to formaldehyde, needs to be inhibited to allow methanol accumulation [69]. However, this inhibition can negatively affect the growth of facultative methanotrophs [21, 59]. To address this issue, a multistage reactor can be employed, where biomass growth prioritized in the first stage, and MDH activity inhibited in the second stage to enable methanol accumulation.

3.10 Limitations in MMO Production

The slow growth rate (0.3–0.4 h^{-1}) of methanotrophs compared to *E. coli* (0.4–0.7 h^{-1} on minimal media) and their limited ability to grow in pure cultures compared to mixed cultures with heterotrophs have also posed challenges for using methanotrophs [62].

The presence of copper not only inhibits the expression of genes that encode the enzyme responsible for methane oxidation (sMMO), but also affects the enzymatic activity of sMMO itself. This copper sensitivity can hamper the production of heterologous sMMO. Given that copper is commonly found in growth media, it is necessary to conduct growth experiments with low copper levels to assess the viability of a particular host organism.

The encoding of the methane monooxygenase enzyme (MMO) involves a complex operon with multiple genes, some of which have auxiliary functions that may have been overlooked in previous attempts. The existence of numerous subunits within MMO may contribute to difficulties in expressing the enzyme properly, affecting its maturation and functionality. There is a proposition suggesting that the maturation and effective production of sMMO require the presence of a chaperone protein known as mmoG-encoded GroEL-like chaperone [55]. A similar chaperonin protein was also required for the production of a binuclear iron monooxygenase in a strain of mycobacteria [63, 70].

The poor growth rates and biomass output of synthetic methanotrophs pose a significant barrier to their development. However, the incorporation of the C1 assimilation route can enhance both biomass production and the synthesis of valuable chemicals in native and synthetic methylotrophs engineered for methane utilization. The production of sufficient levels of MMO is crucial for efficient methane utilization. Limitations in MMO activity would result in poor growth rates and biomass formation. Despite the challenges, the development of synthetic methanotrophs through heterologous MMO synthesis seems to be a promising alternative to current methane utilization methods.

The fact that certain methanotrophs can survive on methanol and other sources with multiple carbon compounds, although they are primarily dependent on them, has hindered the advancement of their engineering tools, leading to slow progress [12, 61].

3.11 Conclusion

MMOs have a unique capability to produce a powerful oxidant suitable for methane, making them particularly important in the field of O_2 activation. It is remarkable that two distinct biological solutions to this difficult reaction have evolved, sometimes coexisting within the same organism despite differences in other metabolic processes. Hence, instead of wasting large amounts of high-energy methane gas, converting it into valuable fuels products through methanotrophic processes offers a way to reduce greenhouse gas emissions. However, the low productivity and limited genetic manipulability of natural methane-consuming bacteria have hindered progress in methane biocatalysis thus far. The extensive research conducted on these exceptional methanotrophic bacteria demonstrates their significant potential for biologically producing important commercial goods.

References

1 Kvalevag, M.M., Samset, B.H., and Myhre, G. (2013). Hydrological sensitivity to greenhouse gases and aerosols in a global climate model. *Geophys. Res. Lett.* 40 (7): 1432–1438.

2 Bibler, C.J., Marshall, J.S., and Pilcher, R.C. (1998). Status of worldwide coal mine methane emissions and use. *Int. J. Coal Geol.* 35 (1–4): 283–310.

3 Bentlage, B., Peterson, A.T., Barve, N., and Cartwright, P. (2013). Plumbing the depths: extending ecological niche modelling and species distribution modelling in three dimensions. *Global Ecol. Biogeogr.* 22 (8): 952–961.

4 Hutton, W.E. and ZoBell, C.E. (1949). The occurrence and characteristics of methane-oxidizing bacteria in marine sediments. *J. Bacteriol.* 58 (4): 463–473.

5 Kaserer, H. (1905). *Uber die Oxydation des Wasserstoffes und des Methans durch Mikroorganismen*. Hartleben.

6 Sohngen, N.L. (1906). Bacteria which use methane as a carbonaceous energy sources. *Zentr. Bakt. Parasitenk. Abt.* II (15): 513–517.

7 Dedysh, S.N. and Knief, C. (2018). Diversity and phylogeny of described aerobic methanotrophs. In: *Methane Biocatalysis: Paving the Way to Sustainability* (ed. M.G. Kalyuzhnaya and X.-H. Xing), 17–42. Cham: Springer.

8 Jiang, H., Chen, Y., Jiang, P. et al. (2010). Methanotrophs: multifunctional bacteria with promising applications in environmental bioengineering. *Biochem. Eng. J.* 49 (3): 277–288.

9 Choi, D.W., Bandow, N.L., McEllistrem, M.T. et al. (2010). Spectral and thermodynamic properties of methanobactin from γ-proteobacterial methane oxidizing bacteria: a case for copper competition on a molecular level. *J. Inorg. Biochem.* 104 (12): 1240–1247.

10 Csaki, R., Bodrossy, L., Klem, J. et al. (2003). Genes involved in the copper-dependent regulation of soluble methane monooxygenase of *Methylococcus capsulatus* (Bath): cloning, sequencing and mutational analysis. *Microbiology* 149 (7): 1785–1795.

11 Dedysh, S.N., Panikov, N.S., Liesack, W. et al. (1998). Isolation of acidophilic methane-oxidizing bacteria from northern peat wetlands. *Science* 282 (5387): 281–284.

12 Khmelenina, V.N., Kalyuzhnaya, M.G., Sakharovsky, V.G. et al. (1999). Osmoadaptation in halophilic and alkaliphilic methanotrophs. *Arch. Microbiol.* 172 (5): 321–329.

13 Bowman, J.P., McCammon, S.A., and Skerrat, J.H. (1997). *Methylosphaera hansonii* gen. nov., sp. nov., a psychrophilic, group I methanotroph from Antarctic marine-salinity, meromictic lakes. *Microbiology* 143 (4): 1451–1459.

14 Sullivan, J.P., Dickinson, D., and Chase, H.A. (1998). Methanotrophs, *Methylosinus trichosporium* OB3b, sMMO, and their application to bioremediation. *Crit. Rev. Microbiol.* 24 (4): 335–373.

15 Dunfield, P.F., Liesack, W., Henckel, T. et al. (1999). High-affinity methane oxidation by a soil enrichment culture containing a type II methanotroph. *Appl. Environ. Microbiol.* 65 (3): 1009–1014.

16 Hanson, R.S. and Hanson, T.E. (1996). Methanotrophic bacteria. *Microbiol.Rev.* 60 (2): 439–471.

17 Vorholt, J.A., Chistoserdova, L., Stolyar, S.M. et al. (1999). Distribution of tetrahydromethanopterin-dependent enzymes in methylotrophic bacteria and phylogeny of methenyl tetrahydromethanopterin cyclohydrolases. *J. Bacteriol.* 181 (18): 5750–5757.

18 Fuse, H., Ohta, M., Takimura, O. et al. (1998). Oxidation of trichloroethylene and dimethyl sulfide by a marine *Methylomicrobium* strain containing soluble methane monooxygenase. *Biosci., Biotechnol., Biochem.* 62 (10): 1925–1931.

19 Shigematsu, T., Hanada, S., Eguchi, M. et al. (1999). Soluble methane monooxygenase gene clusters from trichloroethylene-degrading *Methylomonas* sp. strains and detection of methanotrophs during in situ bioremediation. *Appl. Environ. Microbiol.* 65 (12): 5198–5206.

20 Jiang, Y., Wilkins, P.C., and Dalton, H. (1993). Activation of the hydroxylase of sMMO from *Methylococcus capsulatus* (Bath) by hydrogen peroxide. *Biochim. Biophys. Acta,Protein Struct. Mol. Enzymol.* 1163 (1): 105–112.

21 Kim, H.J., Huh, J., Kwon, Y.W. et al. (2019). Biological conversion of methane to methanol through genetic reassembly of native catalytic domains. *Nat. Catal.* 2 (4): 342–353.

22 Rosenzweig, A.C., Frederick, C.A., Lippard, S.J., and Nordlund, P. (1993). Crystal structure of a bacterial non-haem iron hydroxylase that catalyses the biological oxidation of methane. *Nature* 366 (6455): 537–543.

23 Rosenzweig, A.C., Nordlund, P., Takahara, P.M. et al. (1995). Geometry of the soluble methane monooxygenase catalytic diiron center in two oxidation states. *Chem. Biol.* 2 (6): 409–418.

24 Sazinsky, M.H. and Lippard, S.J. (2006). Correlating structure with function in bacterial multicomponent monooxygenases and related diiron proteins. *Acc. Chem. Res.* 39 (8): 558–566.

25 Merkx, M., Kopp, D.A., Sazinsky, M.H. et al. (2001). Dioxygen activation and methane hydroxylation by soluble methane monooxygenase: a tale of two irons and three proteins. *Angew. Chem. Int. Ed.* 40 (15): 2782–2807.

26 Whittington, D.A. and Lippard, S.J. (2001). Crystal structures of the soluble methane monooxygenase hydroxylase from *Methylococcus capsulatus* (Bath) demonstrating geometrical variability at the dinuclear iron active site. *JACS* 123 (5): 827–838.

27 Fox, B.G., Surerus, K.K., Münck, E., and Lipscomb, J.D. (1988). Evidence for a mu-oxo-bridged binuclear iron cluster in the hydroxylase component of methane monooxygenase. Mössbauer and EPR studies. *J. Biol. Chem.* 263 (22): 10553–10556.

28 Colby, J., Stirling, D.I., and Dalton, H.O. (1977). The soluble methane monooxygenase of *Methylococcus capsulatus* (Bath). Its ability to oxygenate n-alkanes, n-alkenes, ethers, and alicyclic, aromatic and heterocyclic compounds. *Biochem. J.* 165 (2): 395–402.

29 Lieberman, R.L. and Rosenzweig, A.C. (2005). Crystal structure of a membrane-bound metalloenzyme that catalyses the biological oxidation of methane. *Nature* 434 (7030): 177–182.

30 Kitmitto, A., Myronova, N., Basu, P., and Dalton, H. (2005). Characterization and structural analysis of an active particulate methane monooxygenase trimer from *Methylococcus capsulatus* (Bath). *Biochemistry* 44 (33): 10954–10965.

31 Hakemian, A.S., Kondapalli, K.C., Telser, J. et al. (2008). The metal centers of particulate methane monooxygenase from *Methylosinus trichosporium* OB3b. *Biochemistry* 47 (26): 6793–6801.

32 Smith, S.M., Rawat, S., Telser, J. et al. (2011). Crystal structure and characterization of particulate methane monooxygenase from *Methylocystis* species strain M. *Biochemistry* 50 (47): 10231–10240.

33 Sirajuddin, S., Barupala, D., Helling, S. et al. (2014). Effects of zinc on particulate methane monooxygenase activity and structure. *J. Biol. Chem.* 289 (31): 21782–21794.

34 Lawton, T.J., Ham, J., Sun, T., and Rosenzweig, A.C. (2014). Structural conservation of the B subunit in the ammonia monooxygenase/particulate methane monooxygenase superfamily. *Proteins Struct. Funct. Bioinf.* 82 (9): 2263–2267.

35 Tinberg, C.E. and Lippard, S.J. (2011). Dioxygen activation in soluble methane monooxygenase. *Acc. Chem. Res.* 44 (4): 280–288.

36 Tinberg, C.E. and Lippard, S.J. (2009). Revisiting the mechanism of dioxygen activation in soluble methane monooxygenase from *M. capsulatus* (Bath): evidence for a multi-step, proton-dependent reaction pathway. *Biochemistry* 48 (51): 12145–12158.

37 Banerjee, R., Proshlyakov, Y., Lipscomb, J.D., and Proshlyakov, D.A. (2015). Structure of the key species in the enzymatic oxidation of methane to methanol. *Nature* 518 (7539): 431–434.

38 Solomon, E.I., Heppner, D.E., Johnston, E.M. et al. (2014). Copper active sites in biology. *Chem. Rev.* 114 (7): 3659–3853.

39 Wang, B., Walton, P.H., and Rovira, C. (2019). Molecular mechanisms of oxygen activation and hydrogen peroxide formation in lytic polysaccharide monooxygenases. *ACS Catal.* 9 (6): 4958–4969.

40 Yoshizawa, K. and Shiota, Y. (2006). Conversion of methane to methanol at the mononuclear and dinuclear copper sites of particulate methane monooxygenase (pMMO): a DFT and QM/MM study. *JACS* 128 (30): 9873–9881.

41 Stanley, S.H., Prior, S.D., Leak, D.J., and Dalton, H. (1983). Copper stress underlies the fundamental change in intracellular location of methane monooxygenase in methane-oxidizing organisms: studies in batch and continuous cultures. *Biotechnol. Lett.* 5 (7): 487–492.

42 Jahng, D., Kim, C.S., Hanson, R.S., and Wood, T.K. (1996). Optimization of trichloroethylene degradation using soluble methane monooxygenase of

Methylosinus trichosporium OB3b expressed in recombinant bacteria. *Biotechnol. Bioeng.* 51 (3): 349–359.

43 Jahng, D. and Wood, T.K. (1994). Trichloroethylene and chloroform degradation by a recombinant pseudomonad expressing soluble methane monooxygenase from *Methylosinus trichosporium* OB3b. *Appl. Environ. Microbiol.* 60 (7): 2473–2482.

44 Heux, S., Brautaset, T., Vorholt, J.A. et al. (2018). Synthetic methylotrophy: past, present, and future. In: *Methane Biocatalysis: Paving the Way to Sustainability* (ed. M.G. Kalyuzhnaya and X.-H. Xing), 133–151. Cham: Springer.

45 Antoniewicz, M.R. (2019). Synthetic methylotrophy: strategies to assimilate methanol for growth and chemicals production. *Curr. Opin. Biotechnol.* 59: 165–174.

46 Wang, C.C., Li, C.H., and Yang, C.F. (2019). Acclimated methanotrophic consortia for aerobic co-metabolism of trichloroethene with methane. *Int. Biodeterior. Biodegrad.* 142: 52–57.

47 Balasubramanian, R., Smith, S.M., Rawat, S. et al. (2010). Oxidation of methane by a biological dicopper centre. *Nature* 465 (7294): 115–119.

48 Ross, M.O., MacMillan, F., Wang, J. et al. (2019). Particulate methane monooxygenase contains only mononuclear copper centers. *Science* 364 (6440): 566–570.

49 Lloyd, J.S., De Marco, P., Dalton, H., and Murrell, J.C. (1999). Heterologous expression of soluble methane monooxygenase genes in methanotrophs containing only particulate methane monooxygenase. *Arch. Microbiol.* 171 (6): 364–370.

50 Cardy, D.L., Laidler, V., Salmond, G.P., and Murrell, J.C. (1991). The methane monooxygenase gene cluster of *Methylosinus trichosporium*: cloning and sequencing of the mmoC gene. *Arch. Microbiol.* 156 (6): 477–483.

51 Park, S., Hanna, L., Taylor, R.T., and Droege, M.W. (1991). Batch cultivation of *Methylosinus trichosporium* OB3b. I: production of soluble methane monooxygenase. *Biotechnol. Bioeng.* 38 (4): 423–433.

52 Mehta, P.K., Ghose, T.K., and Mishra, S. (1991). Methanol biosynthesis by covalently immobilized cells of *Methylosinus trichosporium*: batch and continuous studies. *Biotechnol. Bioeng.* 37 (6): 551–556.

53 Haynes, C.A. and Gonzalez, R. (2014). Rethinking biological activation of methane and conversion to liquid fuels. *Nat. Chem. Biol.* 10 (5): 331–339.

54 Fei, Q., Guarnieri, M.T., Tao, L. et al. (2014). Bioconversion of natural gas to liquid fuel: opportunities and challenges. *Biotechnol. Adv.* 32 (3): 596–614.

55 Myung, J., Flanagan, J.C., Waymouth, R.M., and Criddle, C.S. (2017). Expanding the range of polyhydroxyalkanoates synthesized by methanotrophic bacteria through the utilization of omega-hydroxyalkanoate co-substrates. *AMB Express* 7 (1): 118.

56 Strong, P.J., Kalyuzhnaya, M., Silverman, J., and Clarke, W.P. (2016). A methanotroph-based biorefinery: potential scenarios for generating multiple products from a single fermentation. *Bioresour. Technol.* 215: 314–323.

57 Hamer, G. (2010). Methanotrophy: from the environment to industry and back. *Chem. Eng. J.* 160 (2): 391–397.

58 Khmelenina, V.N., Rozova, O.N., But, S.Y. et al. (2015). Biosynthesis of secondary metabolites in methanotrophs: biochemical and genetic aspects. *Appl. Biochem. Microbiol.* 51 (2): 150–158.

59 Cantera, S., Lebrero, R., Rodríguez, E. et al. (2017). Continuous abatement of methane coupled with ectoine production by *Methylomicrobium alcaliphilum* 20Z in stirred tank reactors: a step further towards greenhouse gas biorefineries. *J. Cleaner Prod.* 152: 134–141.

60 Hwang, I.Y., Lee, S.H., Choi, Y.S. et al. (2014). Biocatalytic conversion of methane to methanol as a key step for development of methane-based biorefineries. *J. Microbiol. Biotechnol.* 24 (12): 1597–1605.

61 Henard, C.A., Smith, H., Dowe, N. et al. (2016). Bioconversion of methane to lactate by an obligate methanotrophic bacterium. *Sci. Rep.* 6 (1): 1–9.

62 Bowman, J. (2006). The methanotrophs—the families Methylococcaceae and Methylocystaceae. *Prokaryotes* 5: 266–289.

63 Balasubramanian, R. and Rosenzweig, A.C. (2008). Copper methanobactin: a molecule whose time has come. *Curr. Opin. Chem. Biol.* 12 (2): 245–249.

64 Chiemchaisri, W., Wu, J.S., and Visvanathan, C. (2001). Methanotrophic production of extracellular polysaccharide in landfill cover soils. *Water Sci. Technol.* 43 (6): 151–159.

65 Wilshusen, J.H., Hettiaratchi, J.P., De Visscher, A., and Saint-Fort, R. (2004). Methane oxidation and formation of EPS in compost: effect of oxygen concentration. *Environ. Pollut.* 129 (2): 305–314.

66 Huq, M.N., Ralph, B.J., and Rickard, P.A. (1978). The extracellular polysaccharide of a methylotrophic culture. *Aust. J. Biol. Sci.* 31 (3): 311–316.

67 Asenjo, J.A. and Suk, J.S. (1986). Microbial conversion of methane into poly-β-hydroxybutyrate (PHB): growth and intracellular product accumulation in a type II methanotroph. *J. Ferment. Technol.* 64 (4): 271–278.

68 Pieja, A.J., Morse, M.C., and Cal, A.J. (2017). Methane to bioproducts: the future of the bioeconomy? *Curr. Opin. Chem. Biol.* 41: 123–131.

69 Hwang, I.Y., Nguyen, A.D., Nguyen, T.T. et al. (2018). Biological conversion of methane to chemicals and fuels: technical challenges and issues. *Appl. Microbiol. Biotechnol.* 102 (7): 3071–3080.

70 Furuya, T., Hayashi, M., Semba, H., and Kino, K. (2013). The mycobacterial binuclear iron monooxygenases require a specific chaperonin-like protein for functional expression in a heterologous host. *FEBS J.* 280 (3): 817–826.

4

Polyhydroxyalkanoates: An Eco-sustainable Development Toward a Green World

Abhijeet W. Singh[1], Ramendra Soni[1], Arun K. Pal[1], Jayant Kashyap[2], Pooja Tripathi[3], and Vijay Tripathi[4]

[1] *Sam Higginbottom University of Agriculture, Technology and Sciences, Jacob Institute of Biotechnology and Bioengineering, Department of Molecular and Cellular Engineering, Rewa Road, Prayagraj, Uttar Pradesh 211007, India*
[2] *Sam Higginbottom University of Agriculture, Technology and Sciences, Jacob Institute of Biotechnology and Bioengineering, Department of Industrial Microbiology, Rewa Road, Prayagraj, Uttar Pradesh 211007, India*
[3] *Sam Higginbottom University of Agriculture, Technology and Sciences, Jacob Institute of Biotechnology and Bioengineering, Department of Computational Biology and Bioinformatics, Rewa Road, Prayagraj, Uttar Pradesh 211007, India*
[4] *Graphic Era Deemed to be University, Department of Microbiology, Bell Road, Clement Town, Dehradun, Uttarakhand 248002, India*

4.1 Introduction

Proper municipal solid waste (MSW) administration and disposal is a crucial environmental and economic issue of the modern world [1, 2]. Currently, 56% of the total world population resides in urban areas and accounts for generating a substantial volume of MSW [3]. In the present scenario, MSW is being generated from various sources, viz. agro-waste, industrial waste, sewage waste, plastic waste, animal waste, and food and vegetable waste [4]. As per a report, the amount of MSW generated on a global scale was 2.02 billion metric tons in 2016 and by 2050, it is expected to observe an annual increment of 70% (3.4 billion metric tons) [5]. Environmental harm is caused by a remarkable increase in waste production, inadequacy in sustainable waste management strategies, and their implementation laws [6]. The World Health Organization (WHO) has drawn attention to the concerns connected with improper solid waste disposal with regard to soil and water quality and related health implications for populations living around the affected areas [7]. It is, therefore, important that waste generation be minimized and the recovery of wastes maximized for environmental and economic sustainability [3]. The proper management and refinement of MSW in the landfills can be a bipolar process to balance the ecosystem in reducing the organic pollution load and creating some value-added products such as enzymes, chemicals, fertilizer, simple sugars, and energy fuels. These products are also very cost-effective, eco-friendly and sustainably an alternative by-product [3].

A few decades ago, the discovery of plastics revolutionized the world, but scientists were unaware of the associated growing plastic pollution and distribution

Microbial Enzymes: Production, Purification, and Industrial Applications, First Edition.
Edited by Dinesh Yadav, Pankaj Chowdhary, Gautam Anand, and Rajarshi Kumar Gaur.

of plastic waste. The scientific description of the existence of polymeric materials by Staudinger [8] marked the beginning of the success story of plastics approximately a century ago. However, in the current scenario, plastic waste increased to 353 million tons in the past decade, out of which only 9% get completely recycled, whereas 19% is incinerated, 50% is dumped in landfills, and the remaining 22% is left over from waste management channels. The leftover wastes can be accumulated in unregulated dump yards, burnt in the open environment, or released into the aquatic ecosystems ([9]).

A wide range of naturally occurring biopolymers has recently attracted a lot of attention as a means of overcoming the drawbacks of plastics and the depletion of petroleum resources. An extensive variety of microorganisms, including *Cupriavidus necator* (*Ralstonia eutropha*), accumulate numerous natural polymers for intracellular carbon and energy storage. Polyhydroxyalkanoates (PHAs), which belong to the biodegradable polyesters class, are also used by microorganisms [10] (Figure 4.1a).

Due to their nontoxic and biodegradable qualities, natural polymers are considered viable substitutes for petrochemical nonrenewable plastics. As a consequence, PHAs have gained applications in medical, industrial, and agricultural sectors. Given that it lowers the cost of operation and provides a pathway for their utilization, wastes produced from MSW can be viewed as a source of inexpensive raw materials for the manufacturing of PHAs [3]. Lemoigne discovered PHA granules in the bacterium *Bacillus megaterium* in 1926, and 300 different bacterial species have since been found to intracellularly store PHAs [11, 12].

This chapter provides insight into the production and characteristics of PHAs as a value-added product for a sustainable and positive environment. The biodegradability and biocompatibility aids significance to the properties of PHAs have found use in a variety of fields, including agriculture, industry, and medicine. Wastes

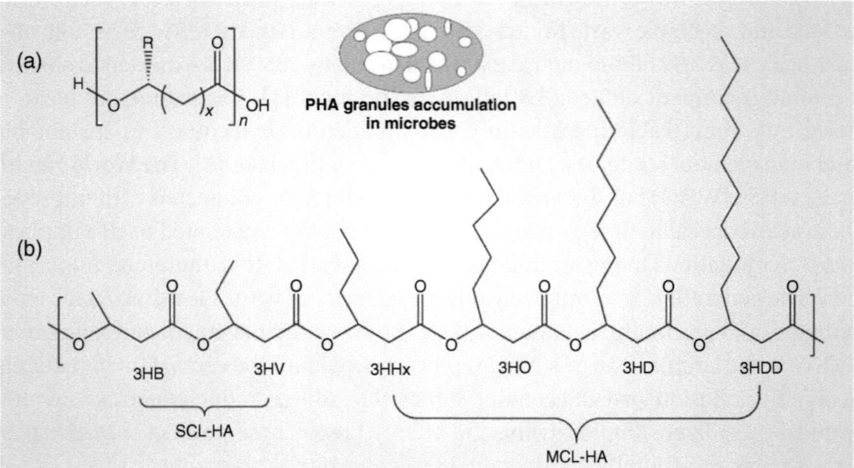

Figure 4.1 Structure of PHAs. (a) Structure of PHAs and accumulation of PHAs in microorganisms and (b) classification of PHAs.

generated from MSW can be seen as a source of cheap raw materials for the manufacturing of PHAs since it lowers operational costs and provides a technique for the utilization of MSW wastes.

4.2 Structure, Classification, and Properties of PHAs

Figure 4.1b shows the general molecular structure of PHAs. Based on carbon numbers PHAs are categorized into two different groups. Based on carbon numbers attached to the side chain, PHAs can be classified into three classes, mainly short-, medium-, or long-chain lengths [13]. The short-chain-length PHAs (SCL-PHAs) structure has less than five carbon atoms, and medium-chain-length PHAs (MCL-PHAs) have 5–14 carbon atoms, while long-chain-length PHAs (LCL-PHAs) have more than 14 carbon atoms. The SCL-PHAs include analog of 3-hydroxyvalerate and 3-hydroxybutyrate, while 3-hydroxyhexanoate and 3-hydroxytetradecanoate belong to MCL-PHAs consisting of 6–14 carbon atoms attached to their side chain [14]. The examples for LCL PHAs are 3-hydroxypentadecanoate and 3-hydroxyoctadecanoate, which consist of 15–18 carbon atoms (Figure 4.1b). The flexibility of PHA biosynthesis helps in constructing and designing biopolymers having distinct physical properties, such as hardness, malleability, robustness, confrontation, or elastic properties [15, 16] (Table 4.1).

Structural variations in PHA monomers generally change their properties and chemical composition as homopolymers and copolymers. They are miscible in chloroform and other chlorinated solvents but immiscible in water and are UV-resistant, biocompatible, and biodegradable materials [20]. Biodegradation of these materials is affected by polymer group and constituent, microorganisms (that produce different PHA-degrading compounds such as PHA-depolymerase) and environmental conditions [21].

Table 4.1 Types of PHAs.

S. no.	PHAs type	No. of carbon atoms	Type of polymer	Microorganisms	Applications	References
1.	Short-chain-length PHA [poly (SCL-PHAs)]	C_3–C_5	Poly(3HB), poly(3HV)	*Cupriavidus necator*	Packaging materials, biomaterials, fiber materials	Wang et al. [17]
2.	Medium-chain-length PHA [poly (MCL-PHAs)]	C_6–C_{14}	Poly(3HHx), poly(3HHp)	*Pseudomonas aeruginosa*	Thermoplastic elastomers, biomedical applications	Tanikkul et al. [18]
3.	Long-chain-length PHA [poly (LCL-PHAs)]	C_{15}–C_{18}	Poly(3HHD), poly(3HOD)	*Pseudomonas putida*	Biodegradable polyesters, packaging industry	Licciardello et al. [19]

4.3 Production and Synthesis of PHAs

The biosynthesis of PHA bioplastics occurs in both prokaryotic and eukaryotic microorganisms in the environment, including cyanobacteria and archaebacteria. The production conditions of PHA polymers essentially depend on the different bacterial strains and the types of carbon sources available. A list of various microorganisms producing PHAs is presented in Table 4.2. Generally, SCL-PHAs are the most common form of PHAs which are produced by various microbes such as *C. necator*. However, MCL-PHAs are mostly biosynthesized by the *Pseudomonas* strains [18]. The *Pseudomonas putida* is very advantageous for the synthesis of different PHAs, which are linked with various functional groups [35]. In a previous study, it was reported that 36 different carbon sources are involved in the synthesis and production of a variety of PHAs via *P. putida* [36]. Besides *P. putida*, there are many microbial species such as *Enterobacter*, *Aeromonas* sp., *Bacillus*, and *Clostridium*, which are also used to accumulate PHAs. Recently, in experiments using gamma-rays muted *Pseudomonas aeruginosa* and soybean oil, a large production of PHA was found [37]. Therefore, the yield of PHAs is mainly influenced by the selection of a broad variety of carbon sources as a substrate. *C. necator* is another microorganism that has been used extensively for PHA production.

Numerous studies have documented the utilization of food industry wastes to produce molecules with significant added value, including lactic acid, starch, citric acid, cellulose, lipids, organic acid enzymes, and polymers (PHAs). It has been suggested that PHAs, a collection of exciting bio-polyesters accumulated by various bacterial

Table 4.2 List of microorganisms producing PHAs.

Bacterial strain	Type of PHAs	References
Bacillus firmus	PHB	Sindhu et al. [22]
Ralstonia eutropha	PHB	Yu and Stahl [23]
Halomonas boliviensis	PHB	Van-Thuoc et al. [24]
Mixed culture from activated sludge	PHA	Waller et al. [25]
Bacillus megaterium	PHB	Zhang et al. [26]
Saccharophagus degradans	PHA	Alva Munoz and Riley [27]
Pseudomonas sp.	MCL-PHAs	Możejko and Ciesielski [28]
Pseudomonas putida	MCL-PHAs	Ruiz et al. [29]
Pseudomonas putida	Elastomeric MCL-PHAs	Kang et al. [30]
Pseudomonas oleovorans	P(3HB-*co*-3HV)	Allen et al. [31]
Cupriavidus *nector* H16	P(3HB-*co*-3HHx)	Zainab-l et al. [32]
Burkholderia thailandensis	P(3HB)	Kourmentza et al. [33]
Salinivibrio sp. M318	P(3HB)	Van Thuoc et al. [34]

cells, can be produced from the organic fraction of municipal solid waste (OFMSW). Various types of PHAs can be synthesized utilizing OFMSW as substrate. The studies have also reported that OFMSW can be first processed through fermentation and can get OA (organic acid), and then OA can be further processed for PHAs [38]. PHA production from sources like leachate [38] and percolate [39], which make up the OFMSW, and a combination of primary sludge and OFMSW [40] has also been the subject of some research.

All the aforementioned research and studies supported and suggested that OFMSW can be a competitive, economical, and sustainable approach for producing PHAs.

4.4 Applications of PHAs in the Health Sector

PHAs are widely used in many areas because of their biocompatibility and biodegradability [41]. The polymers of PHAs can be used for the manufacture of medical equipment and instruments such as surgical instruments, wound dressing, heart valves, bones, and drug carriers. Some of the major applications of PHAs in the medical sector are listed (Table 4.3) and explained below.

4.5 Tissue Engineering

PHAs have been widely utilized in biomedical tissue engineering because of the diversity in their structural makeup and physical–chemical characteristics. A wide range of PHAs comprising poly(3-hydroxybutyrate) and 3-hydroxybutyrate are being employed for the *in vitro* propagation of human cells. Numerous research has documented the application of PHAs in tissue engineering for organ, bone, nerve, and tissue repair. Initially, during the investigation of the application of PHAs in bone

Table 4.3 List of PHAs producing microorganisms having clinical importance.

S. No.	Microorganism	Source	Clinical application	References
1.	*Staphylococcus aureus*	Polyhydroxybutyrate	Peripheral nerve guide	Mosahebi et al. [42]
2.	*Bacillus cereus*	PHB	Drug carrier	Pradhan et al. [43]
3.	*Aeromonas caviae*	P(3HB-*co*-3HHx)	Sutures	Ali and Jamil [44]
4.	*Cupriavidus necator* DSM 545	P(3HB)	Wound management	Berezina [45]
5.	*Pseudomonas fluorescens*	Polyhydroxyalkanoate (MCL)	Drug delivery, antibody immobilization	Ihssen et al. [46]
6.	*Pseudomonas putida* KT2442, *Pseudomonas putida* KT2442 fadB and *Pseudomonas fluorescens* GK13	Poly-3-hydroxy-acetyllthioalkanoate-*co*-3-hydroxyalkanoate	Antibacterial activity against MRSA (methicillin-resistant *Staphylococcus aureus*)	Martínez-Sanz et al. [47]; Dinjaski et al. [48]

tissue engineering, it was observed that bone formation happened rapidly near the polyhydroxybutyrate (PHB) complex constituents utilized for bone tissue rejuvenation, and there was no lethal inflammation observed despite the duration of a year of treatment with PHAs [49]. PHB materials can be utilized for hard tissue replacements since they have hardness and tensile strength because of the addition of nontoxic material, hydroxyapatite (HA) [50].

PHB has also been mentioned in relation to tissue engineering of heart valves. Extensive research is being performed to develop biodegradable scaffolds using these PHA polymers for the synthesis and bioengineering of live tissue of heart valves. Further, the scaffolds are utilized to replace heart valves that may be unhealthy [51].

4.6 Bio-implantation Patches

PHAs are employed as bio-transplant scaffolds for wound treatment because of their biocompatibility, low detrimental response, decomposition, and application in tissue regeneration. The transmural abnormalities in the gastrointestinal system are frequently treated with local excision and closure by suture. Such closure may be accomplished using PHB-based bio-implanted patches [52, 53]. The use of PHB-based orthopedic implants in cats has been documented [54], and PHB and HA-based composites for bone replacement in rabbits have also been documented [55].

4.7 Drug Delivery

Due to the biodegradability and biocompatibility of PHAs, there is a great deal of consideration in employing PHAs as drug delivery carriers [56]. Different drugs are coated on the micro- and nanospheres of PHAs for sustained and targeted drug release within the *in vivo* systems. Application of PHAs as drug carriers has been successfully achieved on rats, sheep, dogs, cattle, rabbits, and humans, even for treating the disease of gingivitis [57]. On the other hand, PHBs, along with polyamidoamine dendrimers, have been frequently reported for transdermal medication administration or drug delivery. The introduction of dendrimers to the PHBs enhanced the transcutaneous permeability of the medicine named tamsulosin [58]. These PHBs are bioengineered as bioactive beads for numerous biomedical applications.

4.8 Surgical Applications

PHAs have been extensively used in medicine since the 1970s. As a result, the first Vicryl surgical sutures made of biodegradable polymers were introduced to the pharmaceutical market in 1974 [59]. Due to the piezoelectric properties of PHAs, they are being used to heal the injured nerves [60]. In rats, the PHB was used as a substitute, widely used for nerve grafting, and showed outstanding efficacy for nerve regeneration [61]. PHAs are also utilized in scaffolds [62] and wound dressings [63]. The scaffolds made using PHAs have been shown to hold enhanced tensile strength and provide nutrients to the cells, aiding cell proliferation. These items can be found in the form of screws, staples, sutures, plates, etc., which support the propagation of stem cells and cell adhesion, and, further, have been used to make fiber meshes. SCL and MCL PHAs can be used as scaffolds for liver tissue grafting. Alternatively, PHA nanofibers have been used to create 3D scaffolds. P(3HB-3HO) has been used to create scaffolds for cartilage repair [64].

4.9 Orthopedic Applications

In humans, a build-up of a high quantity of 3HB causes a metabolic condition known as ketoacidosis, which is characterized by pathologically high ketone body concentrations in the urine and serum. 3HB oligomer compounds get diffused rapidly in peripheral tissues, as these have properties that make them captivating energy sources for patients. Through its fast calcium deposition and potent serum alkaline phosphatase activity, 3HB promotes osteoblast development and antiosteoporosis activity. It aids in preventing bone mineral density loss and lowering serum osteocalcin levels [65].

4.10 Industrial Applications of PHAs

Due to their high biodegradability, high deformability, high heat resistance, resistance to hydrolysis, environment-friendly makeup, and potential to replace polymers made from fossil fuels, PHAs are a promising material for the polymer industry. Applications of PHA cover an extensive range of industrial sectors, for example, food packaging, biofuels, biorefinery, bioplastics, PHA-coated papers, and antimicrobial packaging.

4.10.1 Food Packaging

A food product's shelf life is significantly influenced by the design and structure of the food package. The quality and freshness of the product are maintained throughout the distribution and storage with the appropriate packaging materials and technologies. Different packaging materials such as Glass, various metals (aluminum, tinplate, and electrolytic chromium-coated steel), kraft paper, parchment paper, numerous paperboards, and food-grade plastics are all historically well-known materials employed for food packaging.

Alternative plastics are being sought after due to the rise in food consumption brought on by an expanding population. Conventional plastics are understood to be petroleum-based synthetic plastics [66]. Despite having several advantages, such as lightweight, flexibility, durability, etc., the usage of plastics has severely polluted the environment. According to reports, 22% and 43% of plastics are disposed of in landfills, which leach toxic or harmful chemicals that pollute groundwater [67]. Using eatable or decomposable components, such as plant fibers, grain powders, and nanomaterials, as an alternative and sustainable approach to food packaging systems can reduce the ecological burden of conventional food packaging [68].

PHAs are regarded as environmentally friendly materials having biodegradable qualities that have been used as bioplastic for packaging. PHAs have several characteristics, including being insoluble in water and resistant to UV light. They are also nontoxic and nonsticky and have a low tendency to hydrolyze and decompose in the soil, even in anaerobic conditions. Polyhydroxybutyrate has a low elongation capacity, is stiff, brittle, and has a breakpoint below 15% [20]. In the 1980s, Imperial Chemical Industries (ICI, now Zeneca) commercially released Biopol, a thermoplastic resin made of P(3HB) and a variety of copolymer loadings of (3HV), demonstrating the promising application of PHAs as widely accepted packaging material. PHAs were first introduced as humidity blockades in sanitary products by Wella, Germany [69], packaging materials [70], and containers for commonly used products such as soap decanters [71]. Including food packaging materials such as paperboards and veneers, PHAs are being widely used as wrapping sheets, carry bags, sanitary napkins, beauty & healthcare products and their containers, fabric material, medical aprons, floor mats, rugs, and a plethora of other products of everyday needs [72].

4.10.2 PHA as Coating Agent

The invention of veneers made of PHA layer or coating for wrapping food products might be an exciting and innovative concept in the food packaging industry. Recently, a patent has been granted to Danimer Bioplastics Inc. [73] for the invention titled "Biodegradable coatings based on aqueous PHA dispersions," which is aimed to develop a biodegradable substrate made up of 35–75% of water and 25–65% of PHA to cover up the food items. Due to the excellent fire retardancy and aquaphobic characteristics, PHA coatings are also used to synthesize biodegradable polyester-based fireproof fabrics [74]. Other applications of PHAs include coating material in the paint industry as PHA-based nanoparticles [75]. These properties make PHAs a promising polymer in packaging industries with more reliability, focusing on sustainable and cost-effective approaches [76].

4.10.3 Biorefinery and Biofuels

The best substitute for biofuels and petrochemical plastics is thought to be bio-based polymers. Additionally, PHAs represent a viable future substitute for plastics made from fossil fuels among the numerous biopolymers [77]. Numerous bacteria and archaea produce structurally varied microbial polyesters known as PHAs as water-insoluble inclusions in their cytoplasm [78]. Furthermore, because of their structural diversity, PHAs may easily be converted into methyl ester and used as biofuels, expanding their potential uses. Like biodiesel, PHA-based biofuels have a high oxygen concentration but no nitrogen or sulfur [79]. The potential of PHA-synthesized materials as biofuels was initially suggested by [80]. They introduced two novel biofuels from bacterial PHAs, hydroxyalkanoates methyl ester (HAME) and hydroxybutyrate methyl ester (HBME). Chemically, hydroxyalkanoates esters are composed of the methyl ester of long-chain fatty acids, just like biofuels, particularly biodiesel. PHA-based biofuels' production costs are comparatively higher than the conventional fossil fuels [81]. In a study reported by Zhang et al. [80], blending of HBME with gasoline resulted in enhanced oxygen content, viscosity, and boiling point in comparison to conventional fossil fuels.

Several whole crops are used as bioenergy feedstocks, such as rye, switchgrass, wheat, stover, sugarcane, maize, and corn [82]. Among these, various crops can simultaneously produce PHAs. A bioengineered system is constructed in a crop as part of the crop-based synthesis method or approach for PHAs, and simultaneously, another cost-efficient and nonpatent technology is developed that may be applied to a diverse biomass crop. As a result, additional harvests will be gathered and sold in various areas according to demand, leading to improved commercialization [83, 84]. The first biorefinery to produce PHAs was the sugarcane industry. The main benefit of sugarcane is that around half of the trunk's dry weight may be converted into fermentable sugar. Switchgrass, however, which is a different bioenergy crop, can coproduce PHAs using multigene expression systems. Additionally, switchgrass has an advantage over sugarcane because it can be processed throughout the year and can be cultivated in less humid settings, improving total investment productivity. Switchgrass is also a high-produce crop, allowing it to be grown on land that is intended for negligible use by other crops, requires little in the way of chemical inputs, possibly reduces runoff from topsoil, pesticides, and fertilizers, and fixes carbon dioxide in its root systems [85].

The feedstock used in biorefineries and the generation of biofuels can be great sources of PHAs. Managing and recovering these feedstocks and using them for PHAs can contribute to the creation of products with value added.

4.11 Agricultural Applications

Numerous agricultural operations necessitate the extensive usage of plastic. Researchers have introduced the PHA to minimize the use of conventional plastics in agriculture. According to Voĭnova et al. [86], pesticides like alpha-hexachlorocyclohexane and lindane can be delivered to the soil in a designated and regulated approach using PHAs as a vehicle. The pesticides contained in the PHA carrier were released slowly and steadily without any interruption as the polymer was broken down by the soil microflora. When the PHA-pesticide composite was introduced as a new nutrient substrate, the microbial soil component actively reacted; later, it was broken down and subsequently used. The necessity for repeated treatments and the influence of the herbicides on non-target bacterial classes may be lessened via controlled release [87]. An herbicide called ametryn's controlled release formulation utilized PHB and poly β-hydroxybutyrate-co-β-hydroxy valerate (PHBV) micro- and nanoparticles [87]. Prudnikova et al. [88] used P(3HB/3HV) to produce micro granules and films that are controlled-release drug formulations of the herbicide. They discovered that PHAs can be utilized successfully to create sustainable release systems composed of PHA and herbicides that can be sown with seeds [89]. In a study, Boyandin et al. [90] reported that the P3HB/PEG carrier is an efficient agent for the targeted delivery of encapsulated metribuzin.

In the agriculture industry, mulch is an essential tool for crop protection and to enhance crop yield. Mulching is applied to preserve healthy soil properties, avoid pollution, prevent soil erosion, retain humidity, and manage weeds [91]. Mulch mostly comes in two different kinds: natural mulch and synthetic mulch. Synthetic mulch is preferable for use on a broad scale in agriculture due to the absence of weed control and insufficient material requirements for natural mulch manufacturing. Plastic is a synthetic mulch utilized extensively, along with paper and other materials [92]. According to [93], in 2012, when agricultural mulch was reported for 40% of plastic usage, agricultural plastic film was predicted to rise from 4.4 to 7.4 million tons globally by 2019. Environmental concerns have been raised in relation to the disposal of used plastic mulch. In recent years, research into creating mulch that degrades quickly has gathered significant impetus. The application of materials, including polybutylene succinate, polylactic acid (PLA), ethylene vinyl acetate, and maize starch-based polymers, was the focus of the research [94]. Products made of PHA are not offered for sale. This could result from high production costs, poor mechanical qualities, and variable degradation rates [94]. Danimer Scientific holds the patent for the biodegradable poly(3-hydroxybutyrate-*co*-3-hydroxyhexanoate) copolymer known as Nodax [95]. This company used Nodax to create customized agricultural mulch.

Grow bags are one of the most common plastic goods used in agriculture. However, these bags degrade and dissolve very slowly and are hazardous to the environment. The use of PHA grow bags in agriculture offers several benefits. First off, unlike nonbiodegradable plastic, which, when recycled or burned, produces dangerous organic matter and poisonous emissions [96], PHA grow bags are nontoxic in nature and decompose through composting faster than traditional plastic [97]. PHA products that have been abandoned can be planted and buried to help the soil nutrient cycle by enhancing nitrogen fixation [98]. At present, Greenpoly Co. Ltd. company deals in the production and export of fiber pots and uses PHAs such as PHA, P(3HB-*co*-3HV), and PLA, in the process of making natural vegetable fiber pots, which are completely biodegradable.

In conclusion, PHAs and PHA-based polymers, can be implemented in selected agricultural applications, and PHA usage in agriculture is economical, sustainable, and environmentally friendly. These biopolymers will be sustainable for the soil and will support the nutrient cycle and balance the soil composition being decomposed without any toxicity (Figure 4.2).

4.12 Conclusion and Future Prospective

The economic analysis of MSW management found that because there was a lack of available space due to the rise in MSW production over the past 10 years,

Figure 4.2 Graphical representation of the diverse applications of PHAs in various sectors.

traditional solutions such as integrated waste conversion and landfilling were very expensive. Uncontrolled population growth is primarily responsible for producing a sizable amount of MSW. The desire to reduce waste and increase recovery has been motivated by an awareness of economic and environmental sustainability. MSW is valued for creating new, high-value goods like bioplastics and biomaterials (PHAs), enzymes, and surfactants. Due to their biodegradability and biocompatibility, PHAs are intriguing intracellular biopolymers that have garnered considerable interest as a competitive alternative to replace petroleum-based conventional plastics in various applications. The attributes of green materials have led to their widespread use in the industrial, agricultural, and medical fields. Due to advantages including low operational costs, affordable raw materials, and sustainability, recent developments in the microbial synthesis of PHAs using MSW as the carbon source are becoming more popular. Due to the high manufacturing and downstream processing costs connected with PHA extraction, industrialization, and commercialization of PHAs have not yet been accomplished. The final use of the output heavily influences the choice and cost of the downstream. PHAs, however, could still be a viable substitute for plastics with more improvements to the upstream and downstream processes for a higher output.

Acknowledgments

The authors are highly grateful to the authority of the respective departments and universities for their support in doing this research.

References

1 FAOSTAT Food and Agriculture Organization of the United Nations (2013). http://faostat3.fao.org/faostat-gateway/go/to/home/E (accessed 14 December 2021).

2 OECD (2021). Environment at a glance: circular economy, waste and materials, Environment at a Glance: Indicators, http://www.oecd.org/environment-at-a-glance (accessed 6 September 2023).

3 Kaur, P., Kaur, G.J., Routray, W. et al. (2021). Recent advances in utilization of municipal solid waste for production of bioproducts: a bibliometric analysis. *Case Stud. Chem. Environ. Eng.* 4: 100164. http://doi.org/10.1016/j.cscee.2021.100164.

4 OECD (Organisation for Economic Co-operation and Development) (2003). OECD environmental indicators. Development, measurement and use. OECD Environment Directorate; Paris, France. http://www.oecd.org/env (accessed 14 December 2021).

5 Kaza, S., Yao, L.C., Bhada-Tata, P., and Van Woerden, F. (2018). What a waste 2.0: a global snapshot of solid waste management to 2050. Urban Development. © Washington, DC: World Bank. http://hdl.handle.net/10986/30317 License: CC BY 3.0 IGO. http://hdl.handle.net/10986/30317.

6 Mani, S. and Singh, S. (2016). Sustainable municipal solid waste management in India: a policy agenda. *Procedia Environ. Sci.* 35: 150–157. http://doi.org/10.1016/j.proenv.2016.07.064.

7 World Health Organization (2021). Solid waste. *Compendium of WHO and Other UN Guidance on Health and Environment*. Geneva (WHO/HEP/ECH/EHD/21.02). https://cdn.who.int/media/docs/default-source/who-compendium-on-health-and-environment/who_compendium_chapter4_v2_01092021.pdf?sfvrsn=b4e99edc_5 (accessed 17 April 2024).

8 Staudinger, H. (1920). Über Polymerisation. *Ber. Dtsch. Chem. Ges.* 53 (6): 1073–1085.

9 Global Plastics Outlook (2022). Economic drivers, environmental impacts and policy options. https://www.oecd-ilibrary.org/environment/global-plastics-outlook_de747aef-en (accessed 6 September 2023).

10 Clarinval, A.M. and Halleux, J. (2005). Classification of biodegradable polymers. In: *Biodegradable Polymers for Industrial Applications* (ed. R. Smith), 3–56. Boca Raton: CRC.

11 Grigore, M.E., Grigorescu, R.M., Iancu, L. et al. (2019). Methods of synthesis, properties and biomedical applications of polyhydroxyalkanoates: a review. *J. Biomater. Sci., Polym. Ed.* 30: 695–712. http://doi.org/10.1080/09205063.2019.1605866.

12 Lemoigne, M. (1926). Produit de de'shydratation et de polyme'risation de l'acide β-oxybutyrique. *Bull. Soc. Chim. Biol.* 8: 770–782.

13 Kunasundari, B. and Sudesh, K. (2011). Isolation and recovery of microbial polyhydroxyalkanoates. *Exp. Polym. Lett.* 5 (7).

14 Puppi, D., Pecorini, G., and Chiellini, F. (2019). Biomedical processing of polyhydroxyalkanoates. *Bioengineering* 6: 108. http://doi.org/10.3390/bioengineering6040108.

15 Amstutz, V., Hanik, N., Pott, J. et al. (2019). Tailored biosynthesis of polyhydroxyalkanoates in chemostat cultures. In: *Methods in Enzymology*, vol. 627, 99–123. Academic Press http://doi.org/10.1016/bs.mie.2019.08.018.

16 McAdam, B., Brennan Fournet, M., McDonald, P., and Mojicevic, M. (2020). Production of polyhydroxybutyrate (PHB) and factors impacting its chemical and mechanical characteristics. *Polymers* 12 (12): 2908. http://doi.org/10.3390/polym12122908.

17 Wang, S., Chen, W., Xiang, H. et al. (2016). Modification and potential application of short-chain-length polyhydroxyalkanoate (SCL-PHA). *Polymers* 8 (8): 273. http://doi.org/10.3390/polym8080273.

18 Tanikkul, P., Sullivan, G.L., Sarp, S., and Pisutpaisal, N. (2020). Biosynthesis of medium chain length polyhydroxyalkanoates (MCL-PHAs) from palm oil. *Case Stud. Chem. Environ. Eng.* 2: 100045. http://doi.org/10.1016/j.cscee.2020.100045.

19 Licciardello, G., Catara, A.F., and Catara, V. (2019). Production of polyhydroxyalkanoates and extracellular products using *Pseudomonas corrugata* and *P. mediterranea*: a review. *Bioengineering* 6 (4): 105. http://doi.org/10.3390/bioengineering6040105.

20 Bugnicourt, E., Cinelli, P., Lazzeri, A., and Alvarez, V. (2014). Polyhydroxyalkanoate (PHA): review of synthesis, characteristics, processing and potential applications in packaging. *eXPRESS Polym. Lett.* 8 (11): 791–808. http://doi.org/10.3144/expresspolymlett.2014.82.

21 Masood, F., Yasin, T., and Hameed, A. (2014). Comparative oxo-biodegradation study of poly-3-hydroxybutyrate-*co*-3-hydroxyvalerate/polypropylene blend in controlled environments. *Int. Biodeterior. Biodegrad.* 87: 1–8. http://doi.org/10.1016/j.ibiod.2013.09.023.

22 Sindhu, R., Silviya, N., Binod, P., and Pandey, A. (2013). Pentose-rich hydrolysate from acid pretreated rice straw as a carbon source for the production of poly-3-hydroxybutyrate. *Biochem. Eng. J.* 78: 67–72. http://doi.org/10.1016/j.bej.2012.12.015.

23 Yu, J. and Stahl, H. (2008). Microbial utilization and biopolyester synthesis of bagasse hydrolysates. *Bioresour. Technol.* 99: 8042–8048. http://doi.org/10.1016/j.biortech.2008.03.071.

24 Van-Thuoc, D., Quillaguamán, J., Mamo, G., and Mattiasson, B. (2007). Utilization of agricultural residues for poly(3-hydroxybutyrate) production by *Halomonas boliviensis LC1. J. Appl. Microbiol.* 104 (2): 420–428. http://doi.org/10.1111/j.1365-2672.2007.03553.x.

25 Waller, J.L., Green, P.G., and Loge, F.J. (2012). Mixed-culture polyhydroxyalkanoate production from olive oil mill pomace. *Bioresour. Technol.* 99 (3): 285–289. http://doi.org/10.1016/j.biortech.2012.06.024.

26 Zhang, Y., Sun, W., Wang, H., and Geng, A. (2013). Polyhydroxybutyrate production from oil palm empty fruit bunch using *Bacillus megaterium* R11. *Bioresour. Technol.* 147: 307–314. http://doi.org/10.1016/j.biortech.2013.08.029.

27 Alva Munoz, L.E. and Riley, M.R. (2008). Utilization of cellulosic waste from tequila bagasse and production of polyhydroxyalkanoate (PHA) bioplastics by *Saccharophagus degradans*. *Biotechnol. Bioeng.* 100 (5): 882–888. http://doi.org/10.1002/bit.21854.

28 Możejko, J. and Ciesielski, S. (2013). Saponified waste palm oil as an attractive renewable resource for MCL-polyhydroxyalkanoate synthesis. *J. Biosci. Bioeng.* 116 (4): 485–492. http://doi.org/10.1016/j.jbiosc.2013.04.014.

29 Ruiz, C., Kenny, S.T., Narancic, T. et al. (2019). Conversion of waste cooking oil into medium chain polyhydroxyalkanoates in a high cell density fermentation. *J. Biotechnol.* http://doi.org/10.1016/j.jbiotec.2019.08.020.

30 Kang, D.K., Lee, C.R., Lee, S.H. et al. (2017). Production of polyhydroxyalkanoates from sludge palm oil using *Pseudomonas putida* S12. *J. Microbiol. Biotechnol.* 27: 990–994. http://doi.org/10.4014/jmb.1612.12031.

31 Allen, A.D., Anderson, W.A., Ayorinde, F.O., and Eribo, B.E. (2010). Biosynthesis and characterization of copolymer poly(3HB-*co*-3HV) from saponified *Jatropha curcas* oil by *Pseudomonas oleovorans*. *J. Microbiol. Biotechnol.* 37 (8): 849–856. http://doi.org/10.1007/s10295-010-0732-7.

32 Zainab-L, I., Uyama, H., Li, C. et al. (2018). Production of polyhydroxyalkanoates from underutilized plant oils by *Cupriavidus necator*. *CLEAN - Soil Air Water* http://doi.org/10.1002/clen.201700542.

33 Kourmentza, C., Costa, J., Azevedo, Z. et al. (2018). *Burkholderia thailandensis* as a microbial cell factory for the bioconversion of used cooking oil to polyhydroxyalkanoates and rhamnolipids. *Bioresour. Technol.* 247: 829–837. http://doi.org/10.1016/j.biortech.2017.09.138.

34 Van Thuoc, D., My, D.N., Loan, T.T., and Sudesh, K. (2019). Utilization of waste fish oil and glycerol as carbon sources for polyhydroxyalkanoate (PHA) production by *Salinivibrio* sp. M318. *Int. J. Biol. Macromol.* 141: 885–892. http://doi.org/10.1016/j.ijbiomac.2019.09.063.

35 Poblete-Castro, I., Escapa, I.F., Jäger, C. et al. (2012). The metabolic response of *P. putida* KT2442 producing high levels of polyhydroxyalkanoate under single- and multiple-nutrient-limited growth: highlights from a multi-level omics approach. *Microb. Cell Fact.* 11 (1): 34. http://doi.org/10.1186/1475-2859-11-34.

36 Kim, D.Y., Kim, Y.B., and Rhee, Y.H. (2000). Evaluation of various carbon substrates for the biosynthesis of polyhydroxyalkanoates bearing functional groups by *Pseudomonas putida*. *Int. J. Biol. Macromol.* 28: 23–29. http://doi.org/10.1016/s0141-8130(00)00150-1.

37 Abid, S., Raza, Z.A., and Hussain, T. (2016). Production kinetics of polyhydroxyalkanoates by using *Pseudomonas aeruginosa* gamma ray mutant strain EBN-8 cultured on soybean oil. *3 Biotech* 6 (2): http://doi.org/10.1007/s13205-016-0452-4.

38 Korkakaki, E., Mulders, M., Veeken, A. et al. (2016). PHA production from the organic fraction of municipal solid waste (OFMSW): overcoming the inhibitory matrix. *Water Res.* 96: 74–83. http://doi.org/10.1016/j.watres.2016.03.033.

39 Colombo, B., Favini, F., Scaglia, B. et al. (2017). Enhanced polyhydroxyalkanoate (PHA) production from the organic fraction of municipal solid waste by using mixed microbial culture. *Biotechnol. Biofuels* 10: 201. http://doi.org/10.1186/s13068-017-0888-8.

40 Basset, N., Katsou, E., Frison, N. et al. (2016). Integrating the selection of PHA storing biomass and nitrogen removal via nitrite in the main wastewater treatment line. *Bioresour. Technol.* 200: 820–829. http://doi.org/10.1016/j.biortech.2015.10.063.

41 Chen, G. and Dai, Z. (2010). Anti-adhesion gel containing polyhydroxyalkanoates (PHA) and hydrophilic organic solvent, and application thereof, CN101618045A, Shantou University, People's Republic of China, 28.

42 Mosahebi, A., Fuller, P., Wiberg, M., and Terenghi, G. (2002). Effect of allogeneic Schwann cell transplantation on peripheral nerve regeneration. *Exp. Neurol.* 173: 213–223. http://doi.org/10.1006/exnr.2001.7846.

43 Pradhan, S., Dikshit, P.K., and Moholkar, V.S. (2018). Production, ultrasonic extraction, and characterization of poly(3-hydroxybutyrate) (PHB) using *Bacillus megaterium* and *Cupriavidus necator*. *Polym. Adv. Technol.* 29: 2392–2400. http://doi.org/10.1002/pat.4351.

44 Ali, I. and Jamil, N. (2016). Polyhydroxyalkanoates: current applications in the medical field. *Front. Biol.* 11 (1): 19–27. http://doi.org/10.1007/s11515-016-1389-z.

45 Berezina, N. (2013). Novel approach for productivity enhancement of polyhydroxyalkanoates (PHA) production by *Cupriavidus necator DSM 545*. *New Biotechnol.* 30: 192–195. http://doi.org/10.1016/j.nbt.2012.05.002.

46 Ihssen, J., Magnani, D., Thöny-Meyer, L., and Ren, Q. (2009). Use of extracellular medium chain length polyhydroxyalkanoate depolymerase for targeted binding of proteins to artificial poly[(3-hydroxyoctanoate)-*co*-(3-hydroxyhexanoate)] granules. *Biomacromolecules* 10 (7): 1854–1864. http://doi.org/10.1021/bm9002859.

47 Martínez-Sanz, M., Villano, M., Oliveira, C. et al. (2014). Characterization of polyhydroxyalkanoates synthesized from microbial mixed cultures and of their nanobiocomposites with bacterial cellulose nanowhiskers. *New Biotechnol.* 31 (4): 364–376. http://doi.org/10.1016/j.nbt.2013.06.003.

48 Dinjaski, N., Fernández-Gutiérrez, M., Selvam, S. et al. (2014). PHACOS, a functionalized bacterial polyester with bactericidal activity against methicillin-resistant *Staphylococcus aureus*. *Biomaterials* 35 (1): 14–24. http://doi.org/10.1016/j.biomaterials.2013.09.059.

49 Wei, S., Ma, J.X., Xu, L. et al. (2020). Biodegradable materials for bone defect repair. *Mil. Med. Res.* 7 (1): http://doi.org/10.1186/s40779-020-00280-6.

50 Ni, J. and Wang, M. (2002). In vitro evaluation of hydroxyapatite reinforced polyhydroxybutyrate composite. *Mater. Sci. Eng., C* 20 (1–2): 101–109. http://doi.org/10.1016/s0928-4931(02)00019-x.

51 Hong, H., Dong, N., Shi, J. et al. (2009). Fabrication of a novel hybrid heart valve leaflet for tissue engineering: an in vitro study. *Artif. Organs* 33: 554–558. http://doi.org/10.1111/j.1525-1594.2009.00742.x.

52 Baptist, J.N. and Ziegler, J.B. (1965). Methods of making absorbable surgical sutures from poly beta hydroxy acids. US Patent 3,225,766.

53 Pulingam, T., Appaturi, J.N., Parumasivam, T. et al. (2022). Biomedical applications of polyhydroxyalkanoate in tissue engineering. *Polymers* 14: 2141. http://doi.org/10.3390/polym14112141.

54 Alves, E.G.L., Rezende, C.M.d.F., Serakides, R. et al. (2011). Orthopedic implant of a polyhydroxybutyrate (PHB) and hydroxyapatite composite in cats. *J. Feline Med. Surg.* 13 (8): 546–552. http://doi.org/10.1016/j.jfms.2011.03.002.

55 Masaoka, T., Yamada, T., Yuasa, M. et al. (2016). Biomechanical evaluation of the rabbit tibia after implantation of porous hydroxyapatite/collagen in a rabbit model. *J. Orthop. Sci.* 21: 230–236. http://doi.org/10.1016/j.jos.2015.11.008.

56 Lu, X.Y., Wu, D.C., Li, Z.J. et al. (2011). Polymer nanoparticles. *Prog. Mol. Biol. Transl. Sci.* 104: 299–323. http://doi.org/10.1016/B978-0-12-416020-0.00007-3.

57 Valappil, S.P., Misra, S.K., Boccaccini, A.R., and Roy, I. (2006). Biomedical applications of polyhydroxyalkanoates, an overview of animal testing and in vivo responses. *Expert Rev. Med. Devices* 3 (6): 853–868. http://doi.org/10.1586/17434440.3.6.853.

58 Wang, Z., Itoh, Y., Hosaka, Y. et al. (2003). Mechanism of enhancement effect of dendrimer on transdermal drug permeation through polyhydroxyalkanoate matrix. *J. Biosci. Bioeng.* 96 (6): 537–540. http://doi.org/10.1016/s1389-1723(04)70146-2.

59 Bonartsev, A.P., Bonartseva, G.A., Reshetov, I.V. et al. (2019). Application of polyhydroxyalkanoates in medicine and the biological activity of natural poly(3-hydroxybutyrate). *Acta Nat.* 11 (2): 4–16. http://doi.org/10.32607/20758251-2019-11-2-4-16.

60 Pryadko, A., Surmeneva, M.A., and Surmenev, R.A. (2021). Review of hybrid materials based on polyhydroxyalkanoates for tissue engineering applications. *Polymers* 13 (11): 1738. http://doi.org/10.3390/polym13111738.

61 Karimi, M., Biazar, E., Keshel, S.H. et al. (2014). Rat sciatic nerve reconstruction across a 30 mm defect bridged by an oriented porous PHBV tube with Schwann cell as artificial nerve graft. *ASAIO J.* 60 (2): 224–233. http://doi.org/10.1097/mat.0000000000000044.

62 Dwivedi, R., Pandey, R., Kumar, S., and Mehrotra, D. (2020). Poly hydroxyalkanoates (PHA): role in bone scaffolds. *J. Oral Biol. Craniofacial Res.* 10 (1): 389–392. http://doi.org/10.1016/j.jobcr.2019.10.004.

63 De Souza, L. and Shivakumar, S. (2019). Polyhydroxyalkanoates (PHA) – applications in wound treatment and as precursors for oral drugs. In: *Biotechnological Applications of Polyhydroxyalkanoates* (ed. V. Kalia), 227–270. Singapore: Springer http://doi.org/10.1007/978-981-13-3759-8&uscore;9.

64 Mikova, G. and Chodak, I. (2006). Properties and modification of poly(3-hydroxybutanoate). *Chem. Listy* 100: 1075–1083.

65 Raza, Z.A., Khalil, S., and Abid, S. (2020). Recent progress in development and chemical modification of poly(hydroxybutyrate)-based blends for potential medical applications. *Int. J. Biol. Macromol.* 160: 77–100. http://doi.org/10.1016/j.ijbiomac.2020.05.114.

66 Xanthos, D. and Walker, T.R. (2017). International policies to reduce plastic marine pollution from single-use plastics (plastic bags and microbeads):

a review. *Mar. Pollut. Bull.* 118 (1–2): 17–26. http://doi.org/10.1016/j.marpolbul.2017.02.048.

67 Dietrich, O., Fahle, M., and Seyfarth, M. (2016). Behavior of water balance components at sites with shallow groundwater tables: possibilities and limitations of their simulation using different ways to control weighable groundwater lysimeters. *Agric. Water Manage.* 163: 75–89. http://doi.org/10.1016/j.agwat.2015.09.005.

68 Han, J.W., Ruiz-Garcia, L., Qian, J.P., and Yang, X.T. (2018). Food packaging: a comprehensive review and future trends. *Compr. Rev. Food Sci. Food Saf.* 17: 860–877. http://doi.org/10.1111/1541-4337.12343.

69 Lauzier, C.A., Monasterios, C.J., Saracovan, I. et al. (1993). Film formation and paper coating with poly(β-hydroxyalkanoate), abiodegradable latex. *Tappi J.* 76: 71–77.

70 Weiner, R.M. (1997). Biopolymers from marine prokaryotes. *Trends Biotechnol.* 15: 390–394. http://doi.org/10.1016/S0167-7799(97)01099-8.

71 Hocking, P.J. and Marchessault, R.H. (1994). Biopolyesters. In: *Chemistry, Technology of Biodegradable Polymers* (ed. G. Griffin), 48–96. London: Blackie Academic & Professional.

72 Naser, A.Z., Deiab, I., and Darras, B.M. (2021). Poly(lactic acid) (PLA) and polyhydroxyalkanoates (PHAs), green alternatives to petroleum-based plastics: a review. *RSC Adv.* 11 (28): 17151–17196. http://doi.org/10.1039/D1RA02390J.

73 Danimer Bioplastics Inc. (2020). Biodegradable coatings based on aqueous PHA dispersions. World Intellectual Property Organization (WIPO). Patent No. WO 2020/036843 A1.

74 Vahabi, H., Rohani Rad, E., Parpaite, T. et al. (2019). Biodegradable polyester thin films and coatings in the line of fire: the time of polyhydroxyalkanoate (PHA)? *Prog. Org. Coat.* 133: 85–89. http://doi.org/10.1016/j.porgcoat.2019.04.044.

75 Samrot, A.V., Samanvitha, S.K., Shobana, N. et al. (2021). The synthesis, characterization and applications of polyhydroxyalkanoates (PHAs) and PHA-based nanoparticles. *Polymers* 13: 3302. http://doi.org/10.3390/polym13193302.

76 Shen, Z., Simon, G.P., and Cheng, Y.B. (2002). Comparison of solution intercalation and melt intercalation of polymer–clay nanocomposites. *Polymer* 43: 4251–4260. http://doi.org/10.1016/S0032-3861(02)00230-6.

77 Raza, Z.A., Abid, S., and Banat, I.M. (2018). Polyhydroxyalkanoates: characteristics, production, recent developments and applications. *Int. Biodeterior. Biodegrad.* 126: 45–56. http://doi.org/10.1016/j.ibiod.2017.10.001.

78 Surendran, A., Lakshmanan, M., Chee, J.Y. et al. (2020). Can polyhydroxyalkanoates be produced efficiently from waste plant and animal oils? *Front. Bioeng. Biotechnol.* 8: http://doi.org/10.3389/fbioe.2020.00169.

79 Riaz, S., Rhee, K.Y., and Park, S.J. (2021). Polyhydroxyalkanoates (PHAs): biopolymers for biofuel and biorefineries. *Polymers* 13 (2): 253. http://doi.org/10.3390/polym13020253.

80 Zhang, X., Luo, R., Wang, Z. et al. (2009). Application of (*R*)-3-hydroxyalkanoate methyl esters derived from microbial polyhydroxyalkanoates as novel biofuels. *Biomacromolecules* 10: 707–711. http://doi.org/10.1021/bm801424e.

81 Gutschmann, B., Huang, B., Santolin, L. et al. (2022). Native feedstock options for the polyhydroxyalkanoate industry in Europe: a review. *Microbiol. Res.* 264: 127177. http://doi.org/10.1016/j.micres.2022.127177.

82 Badgujar, K.C. and Bhanage, B.M. (2018). Dedicated and waste feedstocks for biorefinery: an approach to develop a sustainable society. In: *Waste Biorefinery* (ed. T. Bhaskar, A. Pandey, S.V. Mohan, et al.), 3–38. http://doi.org/10.1016/b978-0-444-63992-9.00001-x.

83 Calvo, V.M., Colombo, B., Corno, L. et al. (2018). Bioconversion of giant cane for integrated production of biohydrogen, carboxylic acids, and polyhydroxyalkanoates (PHAs) in a multistage biorefinery approach. *ACS Sustainable Chem. Eng.* 6: 15361–15373. http://doi.org/10.1021/acssuschemeng.8b03794.

84 de Jong, E., Higson, A., Walsh, P., and Wellisch, M. (2012). Product developments in the bio-based chemicals arena. *Biofuels, Bioprod. Biorefin.* 6: 606–624. http://doi.org/10.1002/bbb.1360.

85 Chobchuenchom, W. and Tanadchangsaeng, N. (2019). Production of medium chain length polyhydroxyalkanoates by *Pseudomonas putida* ATCC47054 using glycerol and sodium octanoate as substrates. *Proceedings of the RSU International Research Conference*, Riga, Latvia, 29–31, March 2023, pp. 1–3.

86 Voĭnova, O.N., Kalacheva, G.S., Grodnitskaia, I.D., and Volova, T.G. (2009). Microbial polymers as a degradable carrier for pesticide delivery [Article in Russian]. *Prikl. Biochim. Microbiol.* 45 (4): 427–431. http://doi.org/10.1134/S0003683809040061.

87 Grillo, R., dos Santos, N.Z.P., Maruyama, C.R. et al. (2012). Poly(-caprolactone) nanocapsules as carrier systems for herbicides: physico-chemical characterization and genotoxicity evaluation. *J. Hazard. Mater.* 231–232: 1–9. http://doi.org/10.1016/j.jhazmat.2012.06.019.

88 Prudnikova, S.V., Boyandin, A.N., Kalacheva, G.S., and Sinskey, A.J. (2012). Degradable polyhydroxyalkanoates as herbicide carriers. *J. Polym. Environ.* 21 (3): 675–682. http://doi.org/10.1007/s10924-012-0561-z.

89 Tharanathan, R. (2003). Biodegradable films and composite coatings: past, present and future. *Trends Food Sci. Technol.* 14 (3): 71–78. http://doi.org/10.1016/s0924-2244(02)00280-7.

90 Boyandin, A.N., Zhila, N.O., Kiselev, E.G., and Volova, T.G. (2016). Constructing slow-release formulations of Metribuzin based on degradable poly(3-hydroxybutyrate). *J. Agric. Food. Chem.* 64: 5625–5632. http://doi.org/10.1021/acs.jafc.5b05896.

91 El-Beltagi, H.S., Basit, A., Mohamed, H.I. et al. (2022). Mulching as a sustainable water and soil saving practice in agriculture: a review. *Agronomy* 12 (8): 1881. http://doi.org/10.3390/agronomy12081881.

92 Dagnon, K.L., Thellen, C., Ratto, J.A., and D'Souza, N.A. (2010). Physical and thermal analysis of the degradation of poly(3-hydroxybutyrate-*co*-4-hydroxybutyrate) coated paper in a constructed soil medium. *J. Polym. Environ.* 18 (4): 510–522. http://doi.org/10.1007/s10924-010-0231-y.

93 Sintim, H.Y. and Flury, M. (2017). Is biodegradable plastic mulch the solution to agriculture's plastic problem? *Environ. Sci. Technol.* 51 (3): 1068–1069. http://doi.org/10.1021/acs.est.6b06042.

94 Niaounakis, M. (2015). Definitions of terms and types of biopolymers. In: *Biopolymers: Applications and Trends*, 1–90. William Andrew. http://doi.org/10.1016/b978-0-323-35399-1.00001-6.

95 Hassan, M.K., Abou-Hussein, R., Zhang, X. et al. (2006). Biodegradable copolymers of 3-hydroxybutyrate-*co*-3-hydroxyhexanoate (NodaxTM), including recent improvements in their mechanical properties. *Mol. Cryst. Liq. Cryst.* 447 (1): 341–362. http://doi.org/10.1080/15421400500380028.

96 Kolybaba, M., Tabil, L.G., Panigrahi, S. et al. (2003). Biodegradable polymers: past, present, and future. *ASABE/CSBE North Central Intersectional Meeting*. http://doi.org/10.13031/2013.41300.

97 Catarci Carteny, C. and Blust, R. (2021). Not only diamonds are forever: degradation of plastic films in a simulated marine environment. *Front. Environ. Sci.* 9: 662844. http://doi.org/10.3389/fenvs.2021.662844.

98 Huang, J.C., Shetty, A.S., and Wang, M.S. (1990). Biodegradable plastics: a review. *Adv. Polym. Technol.* 10: 23–30. http://doi.org/10.1002/adv.1990.060100103.

5

An Insight into Production Strategies for Microbial Pectinases: An Overview

Shruti Dwivedi[1], *Gautam Anand*[1], *Sangeeta Yadav*[1], *and Dinesh Yadav*[1]

[1]*Deen Dayal Upadhyaya Gorakhpur University, Department of Biotechnology, Gorakhpur, Uttar Pradesh 273009, India*
[2]*Agricultural Research Organization, Volcani Institute, Department of Plant Pathology and Weed Research, Rishon LeZion 7505101, Israel*

5.1 Introduction

Human civilization is dependent on more than a hundred industrial processes and products. These industries' processes require enzymatic catalysts for efficient industrial processing. These catalysts lack enantiomeric specificities, and are inefficient at high temperatures, extreme pH, and high-pressure conditions [1, 2]. Microbes are the producers of enzymes that act as biocatalysts with higher catalytic efficiency, low production costs, longer shelf life, and stronger stereoselectivity. These microbial enzymes can act on natural substrates or nonnatural substrates, highly specific and selective in nature, and have easy modification ability for genetic engineering to enhance their activities [3]. Thus, empowers the industrial processes and makes them sustainable [4–6].

In 1930, pectinase was used for the first time in a commercial setting to prepare wine and fruit juices. It was not until the 1960s that the chemical makeup of plant tissues became clear, and as a result, researchers were able to use a wider variety of enzymes more effectively. Pectinases are currently one of the upcoming enzymes in the industry [7, 8]. Plant cell walls and middle lamella contain structural polysaccharides called pectin, which are primarily degraded by these enzymes. Pectin is a lengthy and intricate molecule. They are polysaccharides with many functions that are frequently employed in the food business as an emulsifying, gelling, stabilizing, and thickening agent [9–11]. Their chemical structure aids in the pharmaceutical industry by controlling the delivery of bioactive compounds through the pectin-made matrix. These pectin matrices or colloids can also withstand acidic conditions of the human colon [12]. Due to its superior stability, low cost, nontoxicity, and effective gelation, this polymer has great importance. Pectins are obtained easily from dicot plants, fruit baggases, apple pomaces, rice husks, and other agro-wastes. The diverse and easy bioavailability of pectin's natural sources makes the occurrence of industrial potent pectinase mining easy [12–14].

Microbial Enzymes: Production, Purification, and Industrial Applications, First Edition.
Edited by Dinesh Yadav, Pankaj Chowdhary, Gautam Anand, and Rajarshi Kumar Gaur.

It can also be employed as a blood pressure stabilizer, cholesterol controller, and detoxifier in the pharmaceutical sector. Renewable and biocompatible materials are becoming increasingly popular in the pharmaceutical industry [15]. Research into pectin-degrading enzymes and their characteristics has helped to better understand the complex heterogeneity of this polysaccharide and to continue exploring new uses for pectin outside of its conventional uses in food, textile, paper, and pulp [16–18].

The extraction and treatment of natural fibers by bioscouring, retting and degumming, fermentation of tea and coffee, oil-extractions, and fruit juice clarifications is industrially enhanced by pectinases [2, 19]. Pectinases also help in waste management by their valorization and saccharifications. They also assist in the remediation of pectic-rich wastewater, and waste lands. In pulp and textile industries, they are used for bio-bleaching, producing effluents with fewer pollutants. These enhance animal feed productions and assist in protoplast fermentation [20, 21]. Pectinases are a common type of industrial enzyme, but like many other industrial enzymes, they are limited by their low productivity and yield during manufacture. Due to both their stability and catalytic activity, microbial pectinases have seen a sharp rise in utilization in bioprocesses over the past few decades. For isolation, purification, characterization, and applications, microorganism-produced pectinases have received substantial research on a global scale. Numerous recombinant pectinases from bacteria and fungi are employed commercially in a variety of bioprocesses [12, 22].

Pectinases have so been the focus of research efforts to increase production levels to commercial levels. Due to its simplicity of manufacture and distinctive physicochemical features, microbial pectinases are one of the most commonly used pectinases from natural sources [2, 13, 23]. The creation of pectinase enzymes from various microbial sources is the main topic of this chapter, along with several types of tactics used to optimize their production and increase production. Pectinase production is continually being improved through the use of methods including bioreactor-based production, resonance surface methodology (RSM)-based analysis, and immobilization. The improved pectinases can aid in bioprocessing of pectinolytic applications.

5.2 Microbial Pectinases

The group of enzymes known as pectinases react with pectic acid, galacturonate, protopectin, and pectin. Kertz made the first of these observations in 1930. The polymer of pectin has xylose, arabinose, galactose, and L-rhamnose molecules, which serve as their side chains of D-galacturonic acid residues linked together by 1,4-glycosidic connections. These are located in plant cells' middle lamella [24, 25]. These share the wide family of pectinolytic microbial enzymes based on mode of action, specificity of substrate, and cleavage mechanism [26]. Pectinases are enzymes that can be found within and outside of cells. The demand for microbial pectinase has rapidly increased due to its wide variety of uses and excellent catalytic efficiency [19, 27]. Pectinases, which are frequently used because of their ease of production and unique physicochemical characteristics, are produced naturally by microbes [23]. The pectinases family, with a total of 25% market share in the food and beverage enzymes market, is biotechnologically very important [9, 28, 29].

Pectin serves as the carbon source for a large number of microorganisms that make pectinases. Pectin is a negatively charged, high-molecular-weight heteropolysaccharide made up primarily of monomers of the D-galacturonic acid whose 1,4 links are broken ([30–32]. Plant tissues gain their tensile strength and stiffness from the naturally occurring pectin carbohydrate. Numerous bacteria that degrade pectins provide a wide range of compounds and enzymes that are employed in numerous industrial processes [14, 20].

5.3 Microbial Pectinases: Mode of Action and Classifications

Various pectic compounds, reaction mechanisms, and the degradation of the hairy and smooth regions have all been used to classify pectinases or pectinolytic enzymes [9, 11, 33]. The pectinolytic enzymes have been divided into three broader categories as follows:

A) **Protopectinases:** they are responsible for the degradation of insoluble protopectin. The degradation results in increasing highly polymerized soluble pectin.
B) **Esterases:** they are responsible for the removal of methoxyl esters. This process of catalyzation is termed the de-esterification of pectin. These include pectin esterase (PE) (EC 3.1.1.11).
C) **Depolymerases:** they are responsible for cleaving α (1,4)-glycosidic bonds in the D-galacturonic acid moieties of the pectic substances. Catalysis reaction of hydrolysis either at hydrolyzing pectin or pectic acid (polygalacturonic acid). They can be catalyzed using a trans-elimination reaction on unsaturated polymethyl digalacturonates or pectic acid [9]. These are subclassified into hydrolases, which include polygalacturonase (PG) (EC 3.2.1.15); (2) lyase/transaminases, which include pectinase (PNL) (EC 4.2.2.10) and pectate lyase (PL) (EC 4.2.2.2) [29, 34] Figure 5.1 shows sources of microbial pectinases and their mechanism on pectin.

5.4 Sources of Microbial Pectinases

About 85% of the industrial enzymes are primarily derived from microorganisms such as yeast, fungi, and bacteria, while about 15% are obtained from either plants or algae. Lower output, longer processing times, and inadequacy of producing pectinase under a variety of environmental circumstances make plants and animals less preferred sources [35]. The production of pectinase from diseased plant and

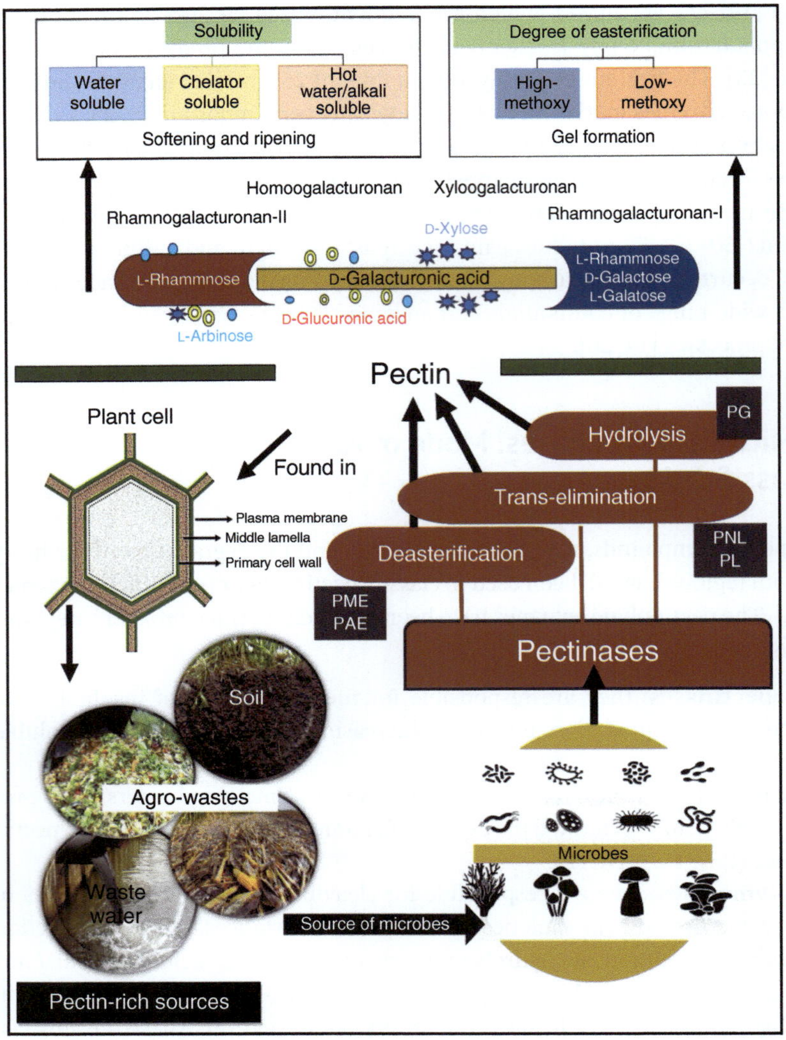

Figure 5.1 Pectin and microbial pectinases.

animal sources carries a high risk of disease contamination and has difficulty being isolated and purified. Additionally in animal tissue, certain inhibitors, and proteases are found in plant tissue [36, 37]. All these limitations make microbes as the most prominent sources of pectinolytic enzymes. Among the microorganisms that are capable of decomposing the pectin components and generating pectinases are bacteria, fungus, and yeasts. Microbes also have a shorter lifespan, are easy to modify genetically, and are environment-friendly [3, 4].

Bacteria are easy to grow under a variety of laboratory environmental conditions, such as temperature and pH. Bacterial pectinases often have a neutral or slightly alkaline pH. *Bacillus, Pseudomonas, Staphylococcus,* and *Enterobacter* [38, 39] are well-known bacteria that can produce pectinases. The longer shelf life and greater catalytic effectiveness of fungal pectinases frequently overshadow bacterial pectinases [40]. The fungi can use decomposing wastes as a substrate and can make both extracellular and intracellular enzymes. Fungi feed on carbon sources like pectin and assist in their breakdown. Pectins are among macromolecules that are tough to break into micro-molecules for further usage [41]. The extraction of extracellularly secreted enzymes is easier compared to intracellular enzymes and requires lesser time and cost. Ninety percent of the enzymes in the culture medium are secreted by the filamentous fungus of the genus *Aspergillus*, which is principally responsible for creating the most economically useful pectinases [6, 42].

The fungi most frequently used for the production of pectinases include *Aspergillus*, *Rhizopus*, and *Penicillium* species, *Aspergillus awamori*, *Aspergillus niger*, *Trichoderma viride*, *Penicillium restrictum*, *Yarrowia lipolytica*, and *Mucor piriformis* [29, 43].

Wickerhamomyces anomalus, *Saccharomycopsis fibuligera*, *Papiliotrema flavescens*, *Aureobasidium pullulans*, *Metschnikowia pulcherrima*, *Pichia kudriavzevii*, *Saccharomyces cerevisiae*, and *Metschnikowia fructicola* are among the yeast species that serve as a source of pectinases [14, 37, 44].

These microbial sources of pectinases have been exploited from known microbial isolates and also been mined from different natural sources. Natural sources like soil, water, vegetable wastes, and fruit wastes grow microbes naturally. Pectinases from such microbial origin will be stable, have better catalytic efficiencies and can also be produced cost effectively. Some of the natural sources of microbial pectinases have been summarized in Table 5.1.

The following are some prominent sources of microbes for pectinolytic mining.

5.4.1 Soil

Microbes like bacteria, fungi, algae, protozoa, nematodes, and actinomycetes constitute the soil microbial community. Soil includes a substantial amount of living microorganisms as well as their dead fractions, in addition to the remains of dead plants or animals. The humus fraction, which contributes to the long-lasting carbon pool in soil and is resistant to microbial degradation, lasts for thousands of years [14, 47, 58]. The decomposition of soil organic matter is facilitated by soil microorganisms, and the pace of decomposition is influenced by the types of microorganisms present in the soil as well as the sources of the organic matter. In addition to the humification process, soil microbes are also engaged in the mineralization, which causes soils to lose carbon. Carbon stabilization is helped by soil microbes [43].

The functioning of grassland ecosystems depends heavily on the soil microflora, yet soil pH has an impact on the variety, functionality, and composition of the soil microbes [60]. The use of fertilizer, soil tiling activities, and crop-rotational practices influence the microflora of the top layer of soil. These are key members that absorb organic matter and nutrients affecting the soil ecology [1, 59]. Soil enzymes of extracellular origin behave as mediators and catalysts in a variety of biochemical processes in the soil. These biochemical processes include mineralization and

Table 5.1 The sources of microbial pectinases.

S. No.	Source	Microbes	Enzyme	References
1.	Vegetable dump soil	*Bacillus tropicus*	Pectinase	[45]
2.	Pineapple stem extract	*Bacillus*	Pectinase	[46]
3.	Vegetable dump soil	*Chryseobacterium indologenes*	Pectinase	[40]
4.	Coffee pulp	*Bacillus*	Pectinase	[47]
5.	Soil	*Bacillus tequilensis*	Pectinase	[38]
6.	Soil and effluent from decorted wood	*Sphingobacterium* sp.	Pectinase	[48]
7.	Soil	*Streptomyces, Cellulomonas* sp. and *Bacillus* sp.	Pectinase	[14]
8.	Horticulture field	*Bacillus subtilis*	Pectinase	[49]
9.	Fruit waste soil	*Bacillus*	Pectinase	[39]
10.	Coffee wet-processing wastewater	*Kluyveromyces marxianus*	Polygalacturonase	[50]
11.	Deseeded sunflower head	*Aspergillus niger*	Pectinases	[51]
12.	Soil sample and plant wastes	*Microspores* var. *rhizopodiformis*	Pectinase	[52]
13.	Lemon peel pomace	*Aspergillus niger*	Pectinase	[44]
14.	Desert sand sample	*Achaetomium*	Polygalacturonase	[53]
15.	Soil	*Aspergillus niger*	Pectinase	[54]
16.	Soil	*Aspergillus tubingensis*	Pectin methylesterases	[36]
17.	Kenaf water retting tank	*Aspergillus fumigatus* R6	PG	[43]
18.	Wuhan textile industry water	RAMCD407 stable microbial consortium	Pectinase	[55]
19.	Soil	*Aspergillus fumigatus*	Pectinase	[56]
20.	Mangrove soils	*Aspergillus nomius*	Polygalacturonase	[57]

21.	Agriculture soil	*Fusarium oxysporum* M1-EGY	Pectinase	[41]
22.	Orange peel	*Aspergillus awamori* 2B.361 U2/1	*Exo*-PG	[58]
23.	Orange peel	*Aspergillus* species NCIM-1432	Pectinase	[32]
24.	Coffee pulp	*Aspergillus* sp. *VTM5*	Pectinase	[3]
25.	Soil isolate	*Aspergillus fumigatus* SKF2	Pectinase	[59]
26.	Banana peels	*Fusarium proliferatum*	Polygalacturonase	[7]
27.	Soil	*Aspergillus parvisclerotigenus*	Pectinase	[37]
28.	Soils	*Aspergillus niger*	Pectinase	[60]
29.	Compost soil	*Aspergillus terreus*	Pectinase	[42]
30.	Soil sample	*Aspergillus oryzae* and *Aspergillus niger*	Pectinase	[61]
31.	Soil	*Aspergillus japonicus*	Polygalacturonase	[62]
32.	Sugarcane liquid Vat	*Saccharomyces cerevisiae*	PL	[63]
33.	Soil sample	*Aspergillus aculeatus*	Pectinase	[64]

cycling of soil nutrients, and decomposition and the synthesis of soil organic matter. The soil holds the leaf litters, wastes rich in pectin, and makes a prominent source for pectin-rich biomass. The microbes so isolated act as a source of broad-range catalytic pectinases [6].

5.4.2 Agro-wastes

A wide range of waste materials from the agriculture and food industries fall under the umbrella of "agro-industrial residues" [65]. The phrase "agricultural waste" refers to any lignocellulosic residue produced by the agro-food sector during routine activities, including leaves, stalks, bagasse, roots, bark, bagasse, seeds, straw residues, wood residues, and animal feces [66]. Cellulose, hemicellulose, lignin, moisture, ash, carbon, nitrogen, and other components are found in various fruit industry waste compositions. The robust enzymatic system of microorganisms allows them to digest lignocellulosic and starchy materials [67]. Both the hydrolytic system, which breaks down polysaccharides, and the extracellular enzymatic systems, which break down lignin and open phenyl rings, are present in microorganisms. Agro-waste is easily available, inexpensive, and useless. Their high lignocellulosic-rich biomass provides an ideal habitat for microbial development. The ratio of dry to moist components is ideal since these are good for growth production and easily granulated. Cellulases and hemicellulases stand out among the diverse array of enzymes that bacteria use to enzymatically degrade vegetable biomass [67, 68].

5.4.3 Wastewater

Waste management and collection have grown to be serious issues as a result of insufficient treatment facilities [69, 70]. The aquatic microflora is affected by dissolved oxygen and nutrients. Additionally, the salinity, the availability of nutrients, heavy metals, and human-made land use, particularly the introduction of chemical contaminants, affect the microflora and its diversity. According to changes in species richness, which are frequently followed by changes in dominance/evenness, the presence of specific pollutants in the environment may contribute to significant adjustments in the organization of the native microbial community [71].

Pollutants like strong acids, polyaromatic hydrocarbons, metallic ions, and heavy metals are among the contaminants included in the effluents that are produced. Some microbes have been discovered to live in these settings, despite the fact that most living forms cannot survive such polluting conditions. The pollutants act as a source of carbon for these microbes. Microbial enzymes bio-transform these carbon sources into organic and inorganic matters for further being used up in other reactions. However, what counts most is whether these contaminants have the capacity to put selection pressure on the microbial communities of receiving habitats. Pectinases from microorganisms that are the source of industrial effluents, such as retting water and coffee pulp processing, have been identified for possible uses [69, 72].

5.5 Production of Microbial Pectinases

Fermentation process is utilized by microorganisms such as bacteria and fungi to produce pectinase. The ability of the microbial world to develop a wide range of pectolytic enzymes with different modes of action and biochemical characteristics has shown it to be highly diverse [73]. The various fermentation methods may alter the rate of enzyme synthesis to increase the yield. Since the 1940s, microbes have been raised in liquid broth while being constantly stirred in order to produce antibiotics, metabolites, and commercial enzymes on a large scale. The predominance of solid-state fermentation (SSF)-based fermentation is due to its ability to utilize the solid substrates that closely mirror the natural habitat of fungal strains and supply enough nutrients to support both the growth and production of microorganisms [24]. Historically, the majority of enzyme manufacturing companies have used the submerged fermentation (SmF) process to produce their enzymes. The production method using SSF is more productive, ecologically friendly, and cost-effective. It also has a high biomass yield, which improves the quality of the final product [2, 74, 75]. Figure 5.2 shows an overall representation of production strategies for pectinases.

5.5.1 Modes of Microbial Fermentation

SSF is the name given to microbial fermentation that takes place with substrates to provide solid ground for mycelium to grow with lesser moisture content. The chosen microorganisms, especially fungus, are well adapted to this environment because it is similar to their natural habitat [29]. Throughout history, SSF has been widely used. In the East, the traditional production of fermented foods and in the West, cheese that has aged because of mold, both use this process. As a system, it can be described as one in which a certain bacterium (or microorganisms) thrives on solid materials with low moisture concentrations [60, 67]. Filamentous fungi have been reported to be the major producers of pectinases using SSF and is preferred as it is cost-effective [7, 32, 76].

SmFs are used by the majority of enzyme companies to create their biocatalysts since it is regarded to be easier to control. SSF technology, on the other hand, might be an attractive and underutilized alternative method for creating enzyme complexes. A primary benefit of SSF is that it triggers the production of various enzymes directly from raw materials rich in lignocellulose [25, 71]. Further, its low water and energy consumption is also a major benefit and its yield is also better as compared to SmF. Bacteria prefer to grow in liquid media; thus, SmF is the best choice. However, fungi, because of their mycelia nature, need less water and can flourish in SSF. The synergistic impact of multiple enzymes may be demonstrated during SmF, resulting in better biomass utilization and higher enzyme activity [66].

High maintenance expenses, high energy consumption, and a complicated downstream are some of the limitations of SmF that limit its industrial adoption. According to recent trends, SSF's output is likewise gaining popularity. Low cultivation, operating, and capital expenditures, as well as a decreased incidence of contamination, simple enzyme recovery, and high output per reactor volume, are just a few

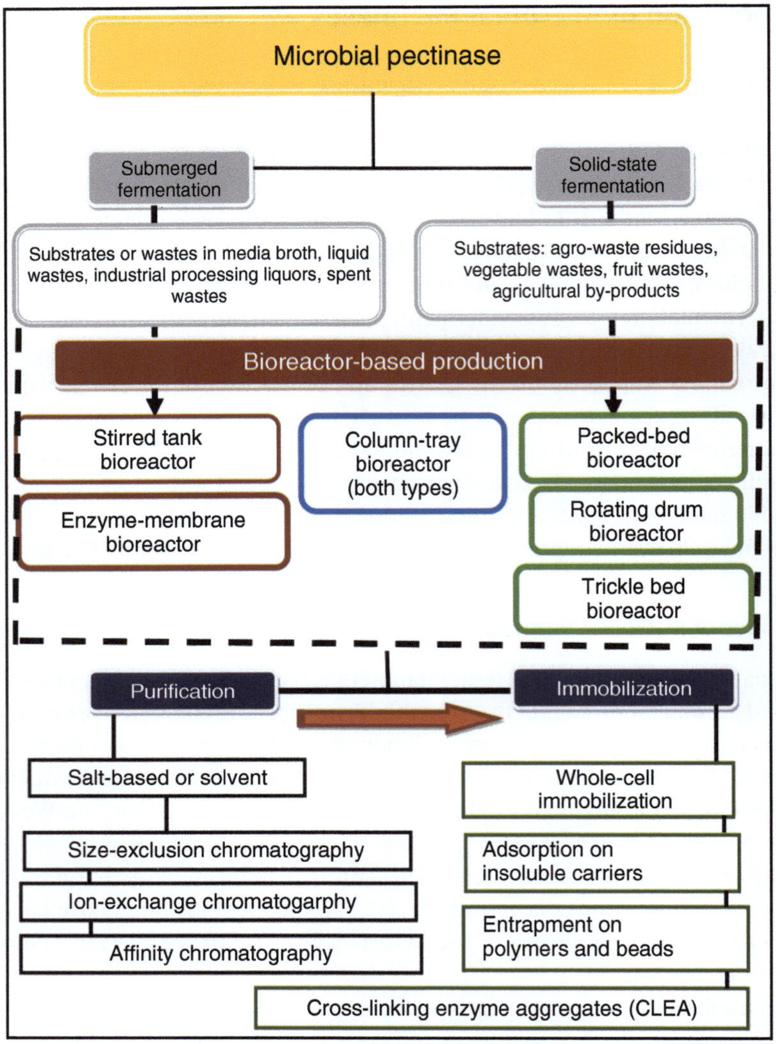

Figure 5.2 Flowchart of bioprocessing of pectinases.

of its advantages. SSF has some drawbacks, such as the fact that not all bacteria can use it, but the fungal system can, and it requires correct aeration and humidity management. Lastly, the scaling up of SSF is a lengthy process [39].

5.6 Bioreactors-based Production of Microbial Pectinases

High-density bioreactors have been used to get the best possible fungal pectinase output. Lignocellulosic wastes and agricultural wastes have been employed in bioreactors for fungal pectinases as substrates for industry-effective, scalable enzyme production [59, 77]. These bioreactors or fermenters are made to process biological products in a precisely controlled environment. Table 5.2 lists reports on the generation of microbial pectinases in bioreactors.

5.6.1 Submerged Fermenters

There are two major categories of submerged bioreactors viz.; stirred tank (STR) and plug flow reactors. As a result of their versatility, STRs are by far the most popular [85]. These bioreactors provide proper mixing of nutrients, maintenance and regulation of temperature, pH, and dissolved oxygen. Additionally, they contain feed ports that enable the constant supply of oxygen and other gases, nutrients for feeding groups of animals, alkaline and acidic solutions to maintain the pH at the right level, and antifoaming agents to maintain the appropriate level.

Plug flow reactors are chiefly used for the total conversion of the substrate, such as the remediation of calcitrant wastewater. In these circumstances, a STR is used as pretreatment prior to the plug flow reactor [21, 57]. Other STR fermenter models that use pneumatic agitation rather than mechanical agitation include the fluidized bed reactor, tower fermenter, airlift fermenter, and bubble column reactor.

5.6.2 Solid-state Fermenters

There are four common types of fermenters utilizing solid-sate fermentation method: fluidized bed reactors, horizontal drums, packed bed reactors, and trays. The methods used for aeration and agitation in these fermenters vary [73, 84]. Tray fermenters are the most basic solid-state fermenters. In these fermenters, the substrates are thinly spread (5–10 cm) over trays made of stainless steel, plastic, or wood that are stacked on top of one another and kept in a space with constant temperature and humidity using continuous airflow. The bottom and sides of the trays are often perforated to allow air to flow through.

The drum-type fermenter normally comprises a cylindrical drum that is parallelly positioned, partly filled with a substrate bed, and powered by air being pushed out from the top. To mix the bed, the drum in rotating drum fermenters rotates about its axis. In stirred-type drum fermenters, blades straddling on a shaft running along the drum's center axis rotate while the drum body remains stationary to mix the bed [86, 87].

In the past, open wood or concrete fermentation tanks had flat bottoms. They have been mostly replaced in recent years, nevertheless, with fiberglass-reinforced plastic tanks with a 15–20 ton capacity. Historically, fermentation tanks were open, flat-bottomed wooden or concrete structures [88]. However, fiberglass-reinforced plastic tanks of a comparable design and a 15–20 tonne capacity have mainly replaced them. The substrates are submerged in the tanks under wood planks or semicircular fiberglass covers with openings for the brine to pass freely. In small-scale operations, the loading of fresh cucumbers into the tanks and the unloading of fermented substrates is done by hand, whereas they are mostly mechanized in large-scale operations [89].

Table 5.2 Bioreactor based production of microbial pectinases.

S. no.	Source of microbe	Microbe	Enzyme	Bioreactor type	Characteristics	References
1.	Agricultural wastes	*Aspergillus niger*	*Exo* and *endo* PG	Surface culture bioreactor	Activity enhanced up to 1.5 and 0.014 U/ml	[78]
2.	Semi-dessert plant	*Penicillium Aspergillus niger*	Pectinases	Column-tray	Activity increases up to 2181 U/l	[44]
3.	Tea	*Penicillium brasilianum*	*Exo*-PG	Agitated	Increased activity up to 53.8 U/ml in 36 h	[79]
4.	Randon mutation	*Aspergillus sojae*	*Exo*-PG	Submerged fed-batch	Enhanced activity 244.0 U/ml in 127.5 h	[80]
5.	Decomposing passion fruit peels	*Aspergillus oryzae*	Pectinases	Pilot-scale packed-bed	Activity increases 33–41 U/g	[74]
6.	Saharan soil	*Aureobasidium pullulans*	PG	Batch bioreactor	Activity increases up to 25.75 U/ml	[81]
7.	—	*Aspergillus niger*	Pectinase	Mixed packed-bed bioreactors	average pectinase activity increased up to 22 U/g	[82]
8.	Mexican rotten tomatoes	*Aspergillus flavipes*	*Endo* and *exo* pectinases	Stirred tank bioreactor	Activity increases up to 7- and 40-fold	[83]
9.	Citrus fruit	*Aspergillus niger*	Pectinases	Fed-batch submerged	Activity increases up to 450 U/ml after 126 h	[75]
10.	Rotten orange	*Aspergillus niger*	PG	Tray and rotating drum	Activity increases up to 45% and 37% higher of tray bioreactor	[84]
11.	Genetically engineered	*Yarrowia lipolytica*	Pectinase	Baffled stirred-tank	Enhanced activity by 9.23%	[73]

5.7 Response Surface Methodology for Enhancing Production of Microbial Pectinases

The RSM) is a collection of mathematical and statistical techniques to create careful experiment design seeks to optimize an outcome variable (response), which is influenced by a variety of independent variables (input variables). In an experiment, runs are used to perform a number of tests in order to adjust the input variables and identify the reasons why the output response fluctuates [77, 90, 91]. A series of tests, referred to as runs, are used in an experiment to alter the input variables and discover the causes of changes in the output response. RSM was initially created by Box and Draper in 1987 to model experimental reactions, but it has since expanded to simulate numerical experiments. The difference is in the kind of error that the response produces.

It is standard procedure to change one parameter while holding the others constant to find the best operating circumstances [85]. The primary drawback of this single-variable optimization is that it does not account for interactive effects between the variables, and as a result, does not show the overall impact of different parameters on the reaction. The RSM has been used in optimization studies to address this issue. RSM requires fewer experimental trials to examine various parameters and their interactions, making it less time- and labor-intensive than other methods. The food sector has used RSM extensively to improve procedures [92].

The goal of RSM's application to design optimization is to reduce the cost of pricey analysis methods (such as the finite element method or CFD analysis) and the numerical noise they produce. The investigation of production parameter selection is aided by studies utilizing the RSM. The use of the response surface approach in research and business has several benefits, including the optimization of production systems, processes, and products, as well as the design and layout of experimental setups. Clear curves and other visual aids make it simple to present how variables interact, and surface plots, graphs, etc., are excellent for visualizing responses or results. They have been heavily utilized in developing the ideal production parameter to improve the utilization of pectinases [92, 93]. Table 5.3 shows reports of RSM in microbial pectinase studies.

It can be used in a variety of significant ways to develop and formulate new products, as well as to improve the appearance of ones that currently exist. Optimizing processes, interpreting experimental data, and designing experiments may all be done with the help of RSM. As determined by the factors, the objective is to maximize the reaction [108]. Response surface technique primarily uses the central composite design (CCD) and the Box–Behnken design. Face central composite design and central composite rotatable design have both recently been employed in optimization studies. RSM relies heavily on the design of experiments, or DoE for short. These techniques can be used with numerical experiments as well; they were initially developed for the model fitting of physical experiments [91, 108]. The process's mathematical model is linked to the majority of the criteria for the best experiment design. The tests that correlate to these mathematical models are typically polynomials with unknown structures; thus, each specific topic has a unique set of experiments.

Table 5.3 RSM-based enhancement of production of microbial pectinases.

S. no.	Source	Microbe	Enzymes	RSM method	Application	References
1.	Lab procured	*Aspergillus niger*	Pectinase	Second-order central composite rotatable design	Mousambi juice extraction	[94]
2.	Commercial by Novozymes	*Aspergillus aculeatus*	Pectinex Ultra SP-L	Central composite design	Clarification of carambola fruit juice	[95]
3.	Lab procured	*Aspergillus sojae*	PG	RSM	Optimization of enzyme production	[96]
4.	Soil	*Bacillus pumilus*	Pectinase	Plackett–Burman design	Degumming of ramie fibers	[97]
5.	Commercial	*Aspergillus niger*	Pectinex	Two-factor central composite design	Clarification of sapodilla juice	[98]
6.	Lab procured	*Bacillus subtilis*	Pectinase	A second-order polynomial regression model	Bio scouring of cotton knitted fabrics	[99]
7.	Lab procured	*Aspergillus awamori*	Pectinase	Central composite rotatable design	Optimization of enzyme production	[100]
8.	Lab procured	*Aspergillus niger*	Pectinase	Central composite rotatable design	Guava juice clarification	[101]
9.	Spoiled fruits	*Aspergillus niger*	*Endo* pectinase	Fractional factorial design	Optimization of enzyme production	[102]
10.	Lab procured	*Tricholoma matsutake*	Pectinase	central composite design	Optimization of enzyme production	[103]
11.	Recombinant	*Penicillium griseoroseum*	PG, PL	RSM	Optimization of enzyme production	[104]
12.	Lab procured	*Bacillus pumilus*	*exo*-pectinase	Central composite design	Optimization of enzyme production	[105]
13.	Lab procured	*Penicillium oxalicum*	*exo*-pectinase	Plackett–Burman factorial design	Optimization of enzyme production	[106]
14.	Lab procured	*Bacillus subtilis*	PG	Box–Behnken	Optimization of enzyme production	[107]
15.	Commercial by Himedia	*Aspergillus niger*	Pectinase	Rotatable central composite design	Extraction of Chironji fruit juice	[93]
16.	Lab procured	*Aspergillus fumigatus*	Pectinase	Face centered central composite design	Optimization of enzyme production	[92]
17.	Red seawater	*Penicillium chrysogenum*	Pectinase	Plackett-Burman design	Optimization of enzyme production	[108]
18.	Fruit peels	*Aspergillus cervinus*	Pectinase	Plackett–Burman	Optimization of enzyme production	[91]

The choice of the design of experiments.

- **Full factorial design:** A full factorial approach is required to capture interactions between *N* design variables in an approximation model. A factorial experiment is a type of experiment where multiple design variables are changed at once rather than one at a time. A portion of a full factorial design may be utilized if the number of design variables increases; however, this will only allow for the estimation of a small number of possible combinations. This method, known as fractional factorial design, is typically employed for screening crucial design factors [102].
- **Central composite design:** With CCD, a model can be built effectively. A second-order model's tuning parameters can be estimated using CCD designs that have extra center and axial points.
- **D-optimal designs:** The quadratic model construction process is made more effective by the D-optimality criterion. From a broader pool of candidate points, P design points must be chosen. The advantage of this approach is that it allows for the use of nontraditional shapes and the integration of additional design components [91, 107]. D-optimality is often one of the most common criteria used in computer-generated trial design.

5.8 Purification of Microbial Pectinases

The complicated series of steps involved in purification processes improves the pectinases activity. For their possible applications, purified pectinases are effective and preferable to utilize [49, 109]. A straightforward centrifugation process, sedimentation, or precipitation can be applied to remove cell-soluble particles. Ammonium sulfate salts can be used to salt out contaminants to remove both inorganic and organic pollutants. A more stable protein with improved activity is produced by purification or partial purification process [38, 110]. Despite the preference for salt-based precipitation's stability an economical approach for removing organic and inorganic contaminants is solvent precipitation employing solvents like acetone, ethanol, methanol, etc., based on protein solubility. Salt-free proteins can be produced by dialysis, which are then dissolved in buffers for the best possible activity. It is simple to produce aqueous protein through purification utilizing counter solvents like butanol or octanol or by ultrafiltration. As a result, salt-based methods of dialysis can be used without the need for precipitation [56, 111, 112].

With the use of ion exchange, gel filtration, and affinity-based chromatographic methods, a higher level of purity is frequently attained. Microbial pectinases are purified using chromatographic procedures based on their size, shape, charge, hydrophobicity, or ability to bind to stationary phase [25, 113, 114]. These processes refer to the exchange of ions, surface adsorption, partitioning, and size exclusion of atoms based on the molecular properties and interactions of molecules. For column, thin layer, and paper chromatography, a stationary bed is utilized. Column chromatography is typically used to purify proteins. Proteins can be purified to the highest level of purity by using inhibitors as ligands in the stationary phase of affinity chromatography [64].

Chromatographic techniques like ion exchange or gel filtration have been most commonly applied which result in enzyme fractions that are significantly purer and have a higher specific activity [2, 115]. By comparing the enzyme's molecular mass to a mixture of proteins with known molecular masses, such purification techniques can also be used to determine the enzyme's molecular weight. When an inhibitor is employed as the ligand in the stationary phase of the purification process, affinity chromatography may be used as the last step. Reports on the purification of microbial pectinases are included in Table 5.4.

5.9 Immobilization of Microbial Pectinases

Immobilized enzymes are those that are physically localized or contained inside a specified area of space while maintaining their catalytic activity and are able to be used repeatedly and continuously [126, 127]. Associating the biocatalysts with an insoluble matrix enables immobilization, allowing for the retention of the biocatalysts in the appropriate reactor geometry for their sustainable reuse. By essentially separating the enzyme from the flow of the liquid containing the reagents and products, immobilization is therefore possible [126]. The ability to eliminate the enzyme is a big advantage because it is better in the food sector to prevent having extraneous substances in the finished products. The three methods of immobilization are entrapment, encapsulation, and binding to solid carriers. Microbial pectinases have been immobilized using calcium alginate beads-based entrapments, cross-linking with glutaraldehyde, using nano polymers, etc. [35]. Considering that carrier-bound enzymes introduce a significant amount of noncatalytic material, the latter offers an option. Most biocatalysts contain these components in a large proportion, resulting in low yields, productivity, and in some cases, loss of more than 50% native activity, especially at high enzyme loadings [128].

Since an immobilized enzyme cannot easily cross biological membranes, it has minimal to no allergenicity [129, 130]. A more stable biocatalyst that may be used in a wider range of reaction conditions, including those involving organic solvents that are insoluble in water, is produced as a result of immobilization, which also stops the enzyme's tertiary structure from unfolding. Table 5.5 collects reports on different modes of immobilizations used for microbial pectinases.

The use of immobilized enzymes in continuous flow processes, such as packed bed or plug flow reactors, has the extra advantage of being suited [141]. One of its disadvantages is that immobilization frequently causes some activity loss. This occurs frequently because the carrier interacts with the incorrect conformation, and of course, the carrier's additional cost must be considered.

5.10 Future Prospects and Conclusion

Future pectinase demands may be further addressed by genetically modified organisms, altered strains, and laboratory-chosen mutants with improved capabilities generated through strain improvement procedures. Producers can choose

Table 5.4 Purification studies of microbial pectinases.

S. no.	Source	Microbe	Enzyme and fermentation substrate	Purification	Characteristics	References
1.	Soil	*Bacillus* sp.	PNL Culture medium	Gel filtration and ion exchange chromatography	67.2-fold, specific activity = 730.3 U/mg	[11]
2.	Enriched from soil	*Bacillus halodurans*	Pectinase Cell culture	DEAE-Sepharose fast flow	Specific activity = 142 U mg, fold = 10.9	[116]
3.	Sediment soil from beach	*Bacillus subtilis*	Pectinase SmF	Ammonium sulfate, DEAE-ion exchange column	18.12 fold and specific activity of 10.6 units = mg	[110]
4.	Soil contaminated by agricultural crop wastes	*Bacillus subtilis*	Pectinase	Ethanol and ammonium sulfate	Specific activity of 217.44 U/mg	[117]
5.	Soil	*Bacillus subtilis*	Alkaline pectinases	Ammonium sulfate, PEG-2000, ion-exchange	specific activity of 52,372.52 U/mg	[118]
6.	Cut aged flue-cured tobacco leaves	*Bacillus subtilis*	Pectinase	Ammonium sulfate, ion exchange	18.67-fold with a specific activity of 1252.82 U/mg	[111]
7.	Orange peel	*Bacillus* sp.	Pectate lyase	Ni-affinity chromatography	K_m and V_{max} of PelB-B2 were 1.64 g/l and 232.56 mol/(l min)	[109]
8.	Soil	*Bacillus amyloliquefaciens*	Pectinase SSF Banana peels	Ammonium sulfate and macro prep high Q column	0.51 U/mg specific activity	[25]
9.	Avocado peel waste	*Serratia marcescens*	Pectinase SmF	Ammonium sulfate	47.32 specific activity	[13]
10.	Soil	*Bacillus subtilis*	Pectinase SmF	Ammonium sulfate and affinity chromatography	99.6 U/mg specific activity and 11.6-fold purity	[49]

(Continued)

Table 5.4 (Continued)

S. no.	Source	Microbe	Enzyme and fermentation substrate	Purification	Characteristics	References
11.	Egyptian orange fruit	*Aspergillus niger*	PG SSF Fruit peel	By acetone	Specific activity −18,523, fold-632	[5]
12.	Soil, decayed fruits, and other vegetables	*Rhizomucor pusilis*	PG SSF Sugarcane Bagasse	Ammonium sulfate, Sephadex G-200 and Sephacryl S-100	Specific activity 61.35 U/mg, fold purification and yield were 12.34 and 27.06	[119]
13.	Contaminated tissue culture media	*Aspergillus flavus*	PNL SmF	DEAE-anion exchange and Sephadex G-100	100-Fold purification, specific activity 8 U/mg protein, 2.5% yield	[120]
14.	Soil	*Aspergillus niger*	PNL SmF Wheat bran and citrus pectin	Anion exchange and gel chromatography	Specific activity −26.85, yield −4.1	[121]
15.	Soil	*Aspergillus niger*	Pectinase SSF	Sephadex G-75	Specific activity of 60 U/mg Specific fold 8.5	[54]
16.	Soil	*Aspergillus bingensis*	PG SmF Cheeku Extract	Ammonium sulfate precipitation	Specific activity −9.7, Fold −1.7, Yield −88.51	[36]
17.	Soil sample	*Zygoascus hellenicus*	PG SmF Seaweed waste	Ammonium sulfate precipitation, DEAE cellulose chromatography, SephadexG-100 gel filtration	Specific activity-2469.77 U/mg, fold −16.8 g	[122]
18.	Soil sample	*Trichoderma viride*	PG SSF Agro-waste	Ammonium sulfate precipitation, ethyl alcohol, acetone	Specific activity −2.8, fold −1.39	[123]
19.	Soil of fruit processing sites	*Aspergillus niger*	PG SSF Dried papaya peel	Ion exchange chromatography, gel filtration chromatography	24.8-Fold with a 52.6% yield	[124]

20.	Decomposing plant material soil	*Aspergillus fumigatus*	Pectinase SSF Banana, plantain, and orange peels	80% ammonium sulfate saturation, CM-Sephadex C-50 and Sephacryl S-200	Fold of 4.45-specific activity 38.88 U/mg	[56]
21.	Rotten fruit sample	*Aspergillus tamarii*	PG SmF Wheat bran and Eucalyptus	Ammonium sulfate fractionation, ion exchange chromatography	Specific activity −57.57, fold −2.27, yield −61.25%	[112]
22.	Soil sample	*Aspergillus parvisclerotigenus*	Pectinase SmF Apple pomace	Salt precipitation and gel chromatography.	Fold of 2.10, yield 2.91%, specific activity = 1081.66 U/mg	[37]
23.	Phyanthus emblica fruit juice	*Meyerozyma*	Pectinase SSF Agro-waste	Ammonium sulfate. Acetone, ethanol precipitation	Specific activity −382.71, fold −7.80, Yield −9.75	[115]
24.	Soil	*Aspergillus japonicus*	PNL SSF Citrus peel	Gel chromatography	Specific activity −7.9, fold −2.9, yield −81%	[62]
25.	Agro-industrial wastes	*Aspergillus pullulans*	PG SmF Citrus pectin	Gel filtration using Sephadex G50	17-fold and 9.53 U/mg specific activity	[125]
26.	Soil sample	*Aspergillus aculeatus*	Pectinase SSF Banana peel	Ammonium sulfate precipitation, gel filtration	Specific activity −725.0, Fold −3.6	[64]

Table 5.5 Immobilization studies of microbial pectinase over different polymers.

S. no.	Microbe	Enzyme	Immobilization method	Characteristics of study	Application	References
1.	*Streptomyces* sp.	Pectinase	Whole-cell immobilization	Enhanced by 32%		[131]
2.	*Aspergillus niger*	Pectinase	Activated polyethylene	50% activity retained	Apple juice clarification	[132]
3.	*Bacillus licheniformis*	Pectinase	Calcium alginate beads via entrapment	Retained more than 80% of its initial activity		[133]
4.	*Penicillium oxalicum*	Pectinase	Magnetic cornstarch microspheres	Retained 60%	Apple juice clarification	[134]
5.	*Bacillus licheniformis*	Pectinase	Agar–agar matrix	Retained 82% activity	—	[135, 136]
6.	*Bacillus licheniformis*	Pectinase	Chitosan beads entrapment	Retained 90% activity	—	[135, 136]
7.	*Aspergillus niger*	Pectinase	Rigid polyurethane foam	35% activity retained		[137]
8.	*Aspergillus aculeatus*	Pectinase	Alginate beads cross-linking	59.71% of yield		[129]
9.	*Bacillus paralicheniformis*	*Endo*-PG	Calcium alginate beads	63.3% activity retained	Bioscouring of cotton fibers	[138]
10.	*Aspergillus aculeatus*	Pectinases	Sodium alginate bead entrapment	Yield of 56.71%	Umbu juice clarification	[129]
11.	*Aspergillus awamori*	Pectinase	Entrapment on alginate and agar beads.	60% of pectinase's original activity was retained		[127]
12.	*Aspergillus ibericus*	Pectinase	Nano porous activated carbon	Residual activity stored for up to 6 cycles	Treatment of wastewater	[127]
13.	*Aspergillus aculeatus*	Pectinases	Entrapment on alginate-montmorillonite beads	53% activity retained	Pineapple juice clarification	[139]
14.	*Aspergillus terreus*	Pectinase	Monoamino-*N*-aminoethyl (MANAE)-agarose	66% and 98% yield	Decreased viscosity of guava juice	[140]
15.	*Geotrichum candidum*	Pectinase	Calcium alginate beads	60% activity retained		[4]
16.	*Bacillus* sp.	Pectinase	Cross-linking enzyme aggregate	Retained 80% activity		[24]
17.	*Halomonas halodurans* and *Bacillus halodurans*	Pectinase	Alginate beads cross-linking	Retained 40% activity	Removal of phenolic impurities from wastewater	[141]
18.	*Bacillus* sp.	Pectinase	Graphene oxide/chitosan composite	Retained about 92%	Guava juice clarification	[35]
19.	*Aspergillus niger*	Pectinase	Iron oxide nanoparticles	Retained more than 74%		[6]
20.	*Bacillus subtilis*	Pectinase	Iron oxide nanocarrier	90% activity retained		[128]

from a variety of strain modification techniques (such as metabolic, genetic, or protein engineering) to boost their output on a wider scale. Wild-type (WT) strains of naturally occurring organisms are typically used in industrial processes. To create persistent pectinolytic mutants, these organisms undergo a variety of physical (X-rays, UV radiation, and gamma rays), chemical (ethidium bromide, colchicine, hydrogen peroxide), and both purposeful and inadvertent alterations. Immobilization of enzymes over inexpensive matrices might be a preferable option because it increases productivity by allowing for long-term storage stability and effective pectinase utilization. This increases stability and lowers storage costs. For downstream processing, automated sampling apparatus may be useful for collecting more information during bioreactor sampling. By automating and integrating downstream processes in industrial settings, GMP (Good manufacturing practice) standards can be maintained, and the synthesis of pectinase can be done faster and in a more efficient manner. An ongoing downstream process may benefit from the selection of a multicolumn chromatography system, and cutting-edge AI (Artificial Intelligence) tools can be used for process control and device integration. The most significant topic for pectinase production research is the design of reactors with various upgrades and alterations.

This chapter provides a thorough overview of pectinase, including information on its origin, production process, and industrial use. Extremophiles are very useful for industrial applications because they can be used for a wide range of purposes. The use of agro-industrial by-products would be a superior choice because they are more environmentally friendly among the numerous substrates that have been documented so far. Large-scale enterprises should choose fermentation methods such as SSF because they are the most dependable for fungal strains. Exact discussions are also given about the many types of bioreactors that are currently in use. Future studies should concentrate on methods for strain improvement, enhancing enzyme stability, and enhancing downstream processing methods to produce strains with high enzyme activity that may be useful in the industry. In light of this, pectinases continue to be a godsend in the field of industrial biotechnology and serve as vital biocatalysts in many industrial processes.

References

1 Amin, F., Bhatti, H.N., and Bilal, M. (2019). Recent advances in the production strategies of microbial pectinases—a review. *Int. J. Biol. Macromol.* 122: 1017–1026.

2 Anand, G., Yadav, S., and Yadav, D. (2016). Purification and characterization of polygalacturonase from *Aspergillus fumigatus* MTCC 2584 and elucidating its application in retting of *Crotalaria juncea* fiber. *3 Biotech* 6: 201.

3 Hidayah, A.A., Azizah, A., Winarsa, R., and Muzakhar, K. (2020). Utilization of coffee pulp as a substrate for pectinase production by *Aspergillus* sp. VTMS through solid state fermentation. *AIP Conf. Proc.* 2296 (1): 020012-1–020012-5.

4 Ejaz, U., Hanif, H., and Sohail, M. (2020). Two layered strategy for cost effective production of pectinase: immobilization of yeast and utilization of crude substrate. *Heliyon* 6 (11): e05456.

5 Esawy, M.A., Gamal, A.A., and Kamel, Z. (2022). Optimization of *Aspergillus niger* NRC1ami pectinase using citrus peel pectin, purification, and thermodynamic characterization of the free and modified enzyme. *Waste Biomass Valorization* 13 (12): 4823–4837.

6 Kharazmi, S. and Taheri-Kafrani, A. (2023). Bi-enzymatic nanobiocatalyst based on immobilization of xylanase and pectinase onto functionalized magnetic nanoparticles for efficient fruit juice clarification. *LWT* 183: 114914.

7 Junior, A.N., Mansoldo, F.R.P., Godoy, M.G. et al. (2021). Production of an endo-polygalacturonase from *Fusarium proliferatum* isolated from agro-industrial waste. *Biocatal. Agric. Biotechnol.* 38: 102199.

8 Yang, Y. and Anderson, C.T. (2020). Biosynthesis, localisation, and function of pectins in plants. In: *Pectin: Technological and Physiological Properties* (ed. V. Kontogiorgos), 1–15. Cham: Springer.

9 Jayani, R.S., Saxena, S., and Gupta, R. (2005). Microbial pectinolytic enzymes: a review. *Process Biochem.* 40 (9): 2931–2944.

10 Kashyap, D., Chandra, S., and Kaul, A. (2000). Production, purification and characterization of pectinase from a *Bacillus* sp. DT7. *World J. Microbiol. Biotechnol.* 16: 277–282.

11 Kashyap, D.R., Vohra, P.K., Chopra, S., and Tewari, R. (2001). Applications of pectinases in the commercial sector: a review. *Bioresour. Technol.* 77 (3): 215–227.

12 Shin, Y., Chane, A., Jung, M., and Lee, Y. (2021). Recent advances in understanding the roles of pectin as an active participant in plant signaling networks. *Plants* 10 (8): 1712.

13 Haile, S., Masi, C., and Tafesse, M. (2022). Isolation and characterization of pectinase-producing bacteria (*Serratia marcescens*) from avocado peel waste for juice clarification. *BMC Microbiol.* 22: 145.

14 Shrestha, S., Janak, R.K., Xiaodong, Z. et al. (2021). Screening and molecular identification of novel pectinolytic bacteria from forest soil. *Fermentation* 7 (1): 40.

15 Haile, S. and Ayele, A. (2022). Pectinase from microorganisms and its industrial applications. *Sci. World J.* 2022: 1881305.

16 Anderson, C.T. (2019). Pectic polysaccharides in plants: structure, biosynthesis, functions, and applications. In: *Extracellular Sugar-Based Biopolymers Matrices* (ed. E. Cohen and H. Merzendorfer), 487–514. Cham: Springer.

17 Patidar, M.K., Nighojkar, S., Kumar, A., and Nighojkar, A. (2018). Pectinolytic enzymes-solid state fermentation, assay methods and applications in fruit juice industries: a review. *3 Biotech* 8 (4): 199.

18 Satapathy, S., Rout, J.R., Kerry, R.G. et al. (2020). Biochemical prospects of various microbial pectinase and pectin: an approachable concept in pharmaceutical bioprocessing. *Front. Nutr.* 7: 117.

19 Yadav, S., Maurya, S.K., Anand, G. et al. (2017a). Purification, characterization and retting of *Crotolaria juncea* fibres by an alkaline pectin lyase from *Fusarium oxysporum* MTCC 1755. *3 Biotech* 7: 1–9. http://doi.org/10.1007/s13205-017-0750-5.

20 Shet, A.R., Desai, S.V., and Achappa, S. (2018). Pectinolytic enzymes: classification, production, purification and applications. *Res. J. Life Sci. Bioinf. Pharm. Chem. Sci.* 4: 337–348.

21 de Souza, T.S. and Kawaguti, H.Y. (2021). Cellulases, hemicellulases, and pectinases: applications in the food and beverage industry. *Food Bioprocess Technol.* 14 (8): 1446–1477.

22 Vanitha, T. and Khan, M. (2019). Role of pectin in food processing and food packaging, 10. In: *Pectins-Extraction, Purification, Characterization and Applications* (ed. M. Masuelli), 1–20. IntechOpen https://doi.org/10.5772/intechopen.83677.

23 Yadav, S., Maurya, S.K., Anand, G. et al. (2017b). Purification and characterization of a highly alkaline pectin lyase from *Fusarium lateritum* MTCC 8794. *Biol. Theory* 72 (3): 245–251.

24 Amadi, O.C., Awodiran, I.P., Moneke, A.N. et al. (2022). Concurrent production of cellulase, xylanase, pectinase and immobilization by combined cross-linked enzyme aggregate strategy-advancing tri-enzyme biocatalysis. *Bioresour. Technol. Rep.* 18: 101019.

25 Doan, C.T., Chen, C.L., Nguyen, V.B. et al. (2021). Conversion of pectin-containing by-products to pectinases by *Bacillus amyloliquefaciens* and its applications on hydrolyzing banana peels for prebiotics production. *Polymers* 13 (9): 148.

26 Pedrolli, D.B., Monteiro, A.C., Gomes, E., and Carmona, E.C. (2009). Pectin and pectinases: production, characterization and industrial application of microbial pectinolytic enzymes. *Open Biotechnol. J.* 3: 9–18.

27 Yadav, S., Anand, G., Singh, V.K., and Yadav, D. (2020). Molecular cloning and structural insights into pectin lyase proteins from different strains of fusarium. *Curr. Proteomics* 18: 326–337. http://doi.org/10.2174/1570164617999200720170153.

28 Tapre, A.R. and Jain, R.K. (2014). Pectinases: enzymes for fruit processing industry. *Int. Food Res. J.* 21 (2): 447.

29 Yadav, S., Yadav, P.K., Dubey, A.K. et al. (2017c). Molecular biology, genomics and bioinformatics insights into fungal pectin lyase: an overview. In: *Applications of Biotechnology for Sustainable Development* (ed. K. Mukhopadhyay, A. Sachan, and M. Kumar), 51–64. Singapore: Springer Singapore.

30 Anand, G., Yadav, S., Tanveer, A. et al. (2018). Genome-wide assessment of polygalacturonases-like (PGL) genes of *Medicago truncatula*, *Sorghum bicolor*, *Vitis vinifera* and *Oryza sativa* using comparative genomics approach. *Interdiscip. Sci.: Comput. Life Sci.* 10: 704–721.

31 Batool, S., Asad, M.J., Naqvi, S.S. et al. (2013). Production and partial purification of pectin lyase by *Aspergillus niger* grown on orange peels. *Afr. J. Microbiol. Res.* 7 (13): 1144–1149. https://doi.org/10.5897/AJMR12.2330.

32 Labrath, Y.P. and Gaikar, V.G. (2020). Solid state fermentation of orange peels for production of cellulase, pectinase and recovery of orange oil using *Aspergillus* species NCIM 1432.

33 Favela-Torres, E., Aguilar, C., Contreras-Esquivel, J.C., and Viniegra-González, G. (2006). Pectinases. In: *Enzyme Technology* (ed. A. Pandey, C. Webb, C.R. Soccol, and C. Larroche), 273–296. New York, NY: Springer.

34 Dubey, A.K., Yadav, S., Kumar, M. et al. (2016). Molecular biology of microbial pectate lyase: a review. *Br. Biotechnol. J.* 13 (1): 1–26.

35 Kamal, S., Rehman, S., Bibi, I. et al. (2022). Graphene oxide/chitosan composites as novel support to provide high yield and stable formulations of pectinase for industrial applications. *Int. J. Biol. Macromol.* 220: 683–691.

36 Patidar, M., Nighojkar, A., Nighojkar, S., and Kumar, A. (2016). Purification and characterization of pectin methylesterase produced in solid state fermentation by *Aspergillus tubingensis*. *Br. Biotechnol. J.* 12 (1): 1–10.

37 Satapathy, S., Soren, J.P., Mondal, K.C. et al. (2021). Industrially relevant pectinase production from *Aspergillus parvisclerotigenus* KX928754 using apple pomace as the promising substrate. *J. Taibah Univ. Sci.* 15 (1): 347–356.

38 Koshy, M. and De, S. (2019). Effect of *Bacillus tequilensis* SALBT crude extract with pectinase activity on demucilation of coffee beans and juice clarification. *J. Basic Microbiol.* 59 (12): 1185–1194.

39 Murugan, T., Deepika, P., Kowsalya, A. et al. (2021). Production and characterization of extracellular pectinase from a newly isolated *Bacillus* species from fruit waste soil. *Mater. Today Proc.* 45: 2087–2090.

40 Roy, K., Dey, S., Uddin, M.K. et al. (2018). Extracellular pectinase from a novel bacterium *Chryseobacterium indologenes* strain SD and its application in fruit juice clarification. *Enzyme Res.* 2018.

41 Ibrahim, N.A., Eid, B.M., Abdel Aziz, M.S. et al. (2019). Environmentally benign scouring of cotton knits using locally produced acid pectinase enzyme. *Fibers Polym.* 20: 787–793.

42 Bhattacharyya, R., Mukhopadhyay, D., Nagarakshita, V.K. et al. (2021). Thermostable and organic solvent-tolerant acid pectinase from *Aspergillus terreus* FP6: purification, characterization and evaluation of its phytopigment extraction potential. *3 Biotech* 11: 1–11.

43 Wong, L.Y., Saad, W.Z., Mohamad, R., and Tahir, P.M. (2017). Optimization of cultural conditions for polygalacturonase production by a newly isolated *Aspergillus fumigatus* R6 capable of retting kenaf. *Ind. Crops Prod.* 97: 175–183.

44 Ruiz, H.A., Rodríguez-Jasso, R.M., Rodríguez, R. et al. (2012). Pectinase production from lemon peel pomace as support and carbon source in solid-state fermentation column-tray bioreactor. *Biochem. Eng. J.* 65: 90–95.

45 Thakur, A., Pahwa, R., Singh, S., and Gupta, R. (2010). Production, purification, and characterization of polygalacturonase from *Mucor circinelloides* ITCC 6025. *Enzyme Res.* 2010: 1–7.

46 Kavuthodi, B. and Sebastian, D. (2018). Biotechnological valorization of pineapple stem for pectinase production by *Bacillus subtilis* BKDS1: media formulation and statistical optimization for submerged fermentation. *Biocatal. Agric. Biotechnol.* 16: 715–722.

47 Oumer, O.J. and Abate, D. (2018). Screening and molecular identification of pectinase producing microbes from coffee pulp. *BioMed Res. Int.* 2018: 2961767. https://doi.org/10.1155/2018/2961767.

48 Neelkant, K.S., Shankar, K., Jayalakshmi, S.K., and Sreeramulu, K. (2019). Optimization of conditions for the production of lignocellulolytic enzymes by *Sphingobacterium* sp. ksn-11 utilizing agro-wastes under submerged condition. *Prep. Biochem. Biotechnol.* 49 (9): 927–934.

49 Alqahtani, Y.S., More, S.S., Shaikh, I.A. et al. (2022). Production and purification of pectinase from *Bacillus subtilis* 15a-b92 and its biotechnological applications. *Molecules* 27 (13): 4195.

50 Serrat, M., Bermúdez, R.C., and Villa, T.G. (2002). Production, purification, and characterization of a polygalacturonase from a new strain of *Kluyveromyces marxianus* isolated from coffee wet-processing wastewater. *Appl. Biochem. Biotechnol.* 97 (3): 193–208.

51 Patil, S.R. and Dayanand, A. (2006). Exploration of regional agrowastes for the production of pectinase by *Aspergillus niger*. *Food Technology & Biotechnology* 44 (2): 289–292.

52 Damasio, A., Maller, A., Da Silva, T.S. et al. (2011). Biotechnological potential of alternative carbon sources for production of pectinases by *Rhizopus microsporus* var. *rhizopodiformis*. *Braz. Arch. Biol. Technol.* 54 (1): 141–148.

53 Tu, T., Meng, K., Bai, Y. et al. (2013). High-yield production of a low-temperature-active polygalacturonase for papaya juice clarification. *Food Chem.* 141 (3): 2974–2981.

54 Khatri, B.P., Bhattarai, T., Shrestha, S., and Maharjan, J. (2015). Alkaline thermostable pectinase enzyme from *Aspergillus niger* strain MCAS2 isolated from Manaslu Conservation Area, Gorkha, Nepal. *SpringerPlus* 4 (1): 1–8.

55 Mao, K., Chen, H., Qi, H. et al. (2019). Visual degumming process of ramie fiber using a microbial consortium RAMCD407. *Cellulose* 26: 3513–3528.

56 Okonji, R.E., Itakorode, B.O., Ovumedia, J.O., and Adedeji, O.S. (2019). Purification and biochemical characterization of pectinase produced by *Aspergillus fumigatus* isolated from soil of decomposing plant materials. *J. Appl. Biol. Biotechnol.* 7 (3): 1–8.

57 Ketipally, R., Kumar, G.K., and Ram, M.R. (2019). Polygalacturonase production by *Aspergillus nomius* MR103 in solid state fermentation using agro-industrial wastes. *J. Appl. Nat. Sci.* 11 (2): 305–310.

58 Marzo, C., Díaz, A.B., Caro, I., and Blandino, A. (2019). Valorization of agro-industrial wastes to produce hydrolytic enzymes by fungal solid-state fermentation. *Waste Manage. Res.* 37 (2): 149–156.

59 Mondal, S., Soren, J.P., Mondal, J. et al. (2020). Contemporaneous synthesis of multiple carbohydrate debranching enzymes from newly isolated *Aspergillus fumigatus* SKF-2 under solid state fermentation: a unique enzyme mixture for proficient saccharification of plant bioresources. *Ind. Crops Prod.* 150: 112409.

60 Begum, G. and Munjam, S. (2021). Carbon and nitrogen sources effect on pectinase synthesis by *Aspergillus niger* under submerged fermentation. *Biosci. Biotechnol. Res. Asia* 18 (1): 185–195.

61 Meini, M.R., Cabezudo, I., Galetto, C.S., and Romanini, D. (2021). Production of grape pomace extracts with enhanced antioxidant and prebiotic activities through solid-state fermentation by *Aspergillus niger* and *Aspergillus oryzae*. *Food Biosci.* 42: 101168.

62 de Alencar Guimarães, N.C., Glienke, N.N., Galeano, R.M.S. et al. (2022). Polygalacturonase from *Aspergillus japonicus* (PGAj): enzyme production using low-cost carbon source, biochemical properties and application in clarification of fruit juices. *Biocatal. Agric. Biotechnol.* 39: 102233. https://doi.org/10.1016/j.bcab.2021.102233.

63 Takeyama, M.M., de Carvalho, M.C., Carvalho, H.S. et al. (2022). Pectinases secretion by *Saccharomyces cerevisiae*: optimization in solid-state fermentation and identification by a shotgun proteomics approach. *Molecules* 27 (15): 4981.

64 Omeje, K.O., Nnolim, N.E., Ezema, B.O. et al. (2023). Valorization of agro-industrial residues for pectinase production by *Aspergillus aculeatus*: application in cashew fruit juice clarification. *Cleaner Circ. Bioecon.* 4: 100038.

65 Lopes, F.C. and Ligabue-Braun, R. (2021). Agro-industrial residues: eco-friendly and inexpensive substrates for microbial pigments production. *Front. Sustainable Food Syst.* 5: 589414.

66 Adejumo, I.O. and Adebiyi, O.A. (2020). Agricultural solid wastes: causes, effects, and effective management. In: *Strategies of Sustainable Solid Waste Management, Intechopen*, 8, 1–19. http://doi.org/10.5772/intechopen.93601.

67 Arora, N.K., Mishra, J., and Mishra, V. (ed.) (2020). *Microbial Enzymes: Roles and Applications in Industries*. Springer.

68 Ravindran, R., Hassan, S.S., Williams, G.A., and Jaiswal, A.K. (2018). A review on bioconversion of agro-industrial wastes to industrially important enzymes. *Bioengineering* 5 (4): 93.

69 Dahiya, D. and Nigam, P.S. (2020). Waste management by biological approach employing natural substrates and microbial agents for the remediation of dyes' wastewater. *Appl. Sci.* 10 (8): 29.

70 Selvarajan, R., Sibanda, T., and Venkatachalam, S. (2018). Industrial wastewaters harbor a unique diversity of bacterial communities revealed by high-throughput amplicon analysis. *Ann. Microbiol.* 68: 445–458.

71 Saeed, M.U., Hussain, N., Sumrin, A. et al. (2022). Microbial bioremediation strategies with wastewater treatment potentialities–a review. *Sci. Total Environ.* 818: 151754.

72 Maloney, A.J., Dong, C., Campbell, A.S., and Dinu, C.Z. (2015). Emerging enzyme-based technologies for wastewater treatment. *ACS Symp. Ser.* 1192: 69–85.

73 Liu, L., You, Y., Deng, H. et al. (2019). Promoting hydrolysis of apple pomace by pectinase and cellulase to produce microbial oils using engineered *Yarrowia lipolytica*. *Biomass Bioenergy* 126: 62–69.

74 Biz, A., Finkler, A.T.J., Pitol, L.O. et al. (2016). Production of pectinases by solid-state fermentation of a mixture of citrus waste and sugarcane bagasse in a pilot-scale packed-bed bioreactor. *Biochem. Eng. J.* 111: 54–62. http://doi.org/10.1016/j.bej.2016.03.007.

75 El Enshasy, H.A., Elsayed, E.A., Suhaimi, N. et al. (2018). Bioprocess optimization for pectinase production using *Aspergillus niger* in a submerged cultivation system. *BMC Biotech.* 18: 1–13.

76 Ortiz, G.E., Ponce-Mora, M.C., Noseda, D.G. et al. (2017). Pectinase production by *Aspergillus giganteus* in solid-state fermentation: optimization, scale-up, biochemical characterization and its application in olive-oil extraction. *J. Ind. Microbiol. Biotechnol.* 44 (2): 197–211.

77 Hill, W.J. and Hunter, W.G. (1966). A review of response surface methodology: a literature survey. *Technometrics* 8 (4): 571–590.

78 Abbasi, H. and Fazaelipoor, M.H. (2010, 2010). Continuous production of polygalacturonases (PGases) using *Aspergillus niger* in a surface culture bioreactor and modelling the process. *Biotechnol. Bioprocess Eng.* 15: 308–313.

79 Zeni, J., Ambrozini, E., Pili, J. et al. (2015). Production and characterization of *Penicillium brasilianum* pectinases with regard to industrial application. *Biocatal. Biotransform.* 33 (5–6): 270–278.

80 Buyukkileci, A.O., Lahore, M.F., and Tari, C. (2015). Utilization of orange peel, a food industrial waste, in the production of exo-polygalacturonase by pellet forming *Aspergillus sojae. Bioprocess. Biosyst. Eng.* 38: 749–760.

81 Bennamoun, L., Hiligsmann, S., Dakhmouche, S. et al. (2016). Production and properties of a thermostable, pH—stable exo-polygalacturonase using *Aureobasidium pullulans* isolated from Saharan soil of Algeria grown on tomato pomace. *Foods* 5 (4): 72.

82 Finkler, A.T.J., Biz, A., Pitol, L.O. et al. (2017). Intermittent agitation contributes to uniformity across the bed during pectinase production by *Aspergillus niger* grown in solid-state fermentation in a pilot-scale packed-bed bioreactor. *Biochem. Eng. J.* 121: 1–12.

83 Wolf-Márquez, V.E., Martínez-Trujillo, M.A., Osorio, G.A. et al. (2017). Scaling-up and ionic liquid-based extraction of pectinases from *Aspergillus flavipes* cultures. *Bioresour. Technol.* 225: 326–335.

84 Mahmoodi, M., Najafpour, G.D., and Mohammadi, M. (2019a). Bioconversion of agro-industrial wastes to pectinases enzyme via solid state fermentation in trays and rotating drum bioreactors. *Biocatal. Agric. Biotechnol.* 21: 101280.

85 Lamidi, S., Olaleye, N., Bankole, Y. et al. (2022). Applications of response surface methodology (RSM) in product design, development, and process optimization. In: *Response Surface Methodology - Research Advances and Applications* (ed. P. Kayarogannam). IntechOpen https://doi.org/10.5772/intechopen.106763.

86 Hassan, S.S., Williams, G.A., and Jaiswal, A.K. (2021). Lignocellulosic biorefineries in Europe: current state and prospects. *Trends Biotechnol.* 37 (3): 231–234.

87 Spier, M.R., Vandenberghe, L.P.D.S., Medeiros, A.B.P., and Soccol, C.R. (2011). Application of different types of bioreactors in bioprocesses. In: *Bioreactors: Design, Properties and Applications* (ed. P.G. Antolli and Z. Liu), 55–90. Nova Science Publishers, Inc.

88 Pitol, L.O., Biz, A., Mallmann, E. et al. (2016). Production of pectinases by solid-state fermentation in a pilot-scale packed-bed bioreactor. *Chem. Eng. J.* 283: 1009–1018.

89 Šelo, G., Planinić, M., Tišma, M. et al. (2021). A comprehensive review on valorization of agro-food industrial residues by solid-state fermentation. *Foods* 10 (5): 927.

90 Myers, R.H. (1999). Response surface methodology—current status and future directions. *J. Qual. Technol.* 31 (1): 30–44.

91 Shet, A.R., Muhsinah, A.B., Alsayari, A. et al. (2022). Media optimization by response surface methodology for the enhanced production of acidic extracellular pectinase by the indigenously isolated novel strain *Aspergillus cervinus* ARS2 using solid-state fermentation. *Fermentation* 8 (10): 485.

92 Palaniyappan, M., Vijayagopal, V., Viswanathan, R., and Viruthagiri, T. (2009). Statistical optimization of substrate, carbon and nitrogen source by response surface methodology for pectinase production using *Aspergillus fumigatus* MTCC 870 in submerged fermentation. *Afr. J. Biotechnol.* 8 (22): 6355–6363.

93 Pradhan, D., Abdullah, S., and Pradhan, R.C. (2020). Optimization of pectinase assisted extraction of Chironji (*Buchanania lanzan*) fruit juice using response surface methodology and artificial neural network. *Int. J. Fruit Sci.* 20 (sup2): S318–S336.

94 Rai, P., Majumdar, G.C., Dasgupta, S.D.E.S., and De, S. (2004). Optimizing pectinase usage in pretreatment of mosambi juice for clarification by response surface methodology. *J. Food Eng.* 64 (3): 397–403.

95 Abdullah, A.L., Sulaiman, N.M., Aroua, M.K., and Noor, M.M.M. (2006). Response surface optimization of conditions for clarification of carambola fruit juice using a commercial enzyme. *J. Food Eng.* 81 (1): 65–71. http://doi.org/10.1016/j.jfoodeng.2006.10.013.

96 Tari, C., Gögus, N., and Tokatli, F. (2007). Optimization of biomass, pellet size and polygalacturonase production by *Aspergillus sojae* ATCC 20235 using response surface methodology. *Enzyme Microb. Technol.* 40 (5): 1108–1116. http://doi.org/10.1016/j.enzmictec.2006.08.016.

97 Sharma, D.C. and Satyanarayana, T. (2006). A marked enhancement in the production of a highly alkaline and thermostable pectinase by *Bacillus pumilus* dcsr1 in submerged fermentation by using statistical methods. *Bioresour. Technol.* 97 (5): 727–733.

98 Sin, H.N., Yusof, S., Hamid, N.S.A., and Rahman, R.A. (2006). Optimization of enzymatic clarification of sapodilla juice using response surface methodology. *J. Food Eng.* 73 (4): 313–319.

99 Wang, Q., Fan, X.R., Hua, Z.Z., and Chen, J. (2007). Optimizing bioscouring condition of cotton knitted fabrics with an alkaline pectinase from *Bacillus* *subtilis* WSHB04-02 by using response surface methodology. *Biochem. Eng. J.* 34 (2): 107–113.

100 Baladhandayutham, S., Thangavelu, V., and Ezhumalai, S. (2009). Optimization of process variables using response surface methodology (RSM) in the solid-state fermentative production of pectinase by *Aspergillus awamori*. *Asian J. Food Agro-Ind.* 2 (3): 302–314.

101 Kaur, S., Sarkar, B.C., and Sharma, H.K. (2009, 2009). Optimization of enzymatic hydrolysis pretreatment conditions for enhanced juice recovery from guava fruit using response surface methodology. *Food Bioprocess Technol.* 2: 96–100.

102 Bari, M.R., Alizadeh, M., and Farbeh, F. (2010). Optimizing endopectinase production from date pomace by *Aspergillus niger* PC5 using response surface methodology. *Food Bioprod. Process.* 88 (1): 67–72. http://doi.org/10.1016/j.fbp.2009.03.004.

103 Yin, X., You, Q., and Jiang, Z. (2011). Optimization of enzyme assisted extraction of polysaccharides from *Tricholoma matsutake* by response surface methodology. *Carbohydr. Polym.* 86 (3): 1358–1364.

104 Gonçalves, D.B., Teixeira, J.A., Bazzolli, D.M.S. et al. (2012). Use of response surface methodology to optimize production of pectinases by recombinant *Penicillium griseoroseum* T20. *Biocatal. Agric. Biotechnol.* 1 (2): 140–146.

105 Tepe, O. and Dursun, A.Y. (2014). Exo-pectinase production by *Bacillus pumilus* using different agricultural wastes and optimizing of medium components using response surface methodology. *Environ. Sci. Pollut. Res.* 21: 9911–9920.

106 Li, P.J., Xia, J.L., and Shan, Y. (2015). Optimizing production of pectinase from orange peel by *Penicillium oxalicum* PJ02 using response surface methodology. *Waste Biomass Valorization* 6: 13–22.

107 Uzuner, S. and Cekmecelioglu, D. (2015). Enhanced pectinase production by optimizing fermentation conditions of *Bacillus subtilis* growing on hazelnut shell hydrolyzate. *J. Mol. Catal. B: Enzym.* 113: 62–67.

108 Ahmed, N.E.E. and Rahman, H.M. (2021). Optimizing the production of pectinase of orange peel waste by *Penicillium chrysogenum* MF318506 using response surface methodology in submerged fermentation. *J. Microbiol. Biotechnol. Food Sci.* 11 (1): e3931.

109 Guan, Y., Wang, D., and Lv, C. (2020). Screening of pectinase-producing bacteria from citrus peel and characterization of a recombinant pectate lyase with applied potential. *Arch. Microbiol.* 202: 1005–1013.

110 Joshi, M., Nerurkar, M., and Adivarekar, R. (2015). Characterization, kinetic, and thermodynamic studies of marine pectinase from *Bacillus subtilis*. *Prep. Biochem. Biotechnol.* 45 (3): 205–220.

111 Zhou, M., Wu, J., and Wang, T. (2017). The purification and characterization of a novel alkali-stable pectate lyase produced by *Bacillus subtilis* PB1. *World J. Microbiol. Biotechnol.* 33: 190.

112 Munir, M., Abdullah, R., Haq, I.U. et al. (2020). Purification, characterization, kinetics and thermodynamic analysis of polygalacturonase from *Aspergillus* *tamarii* for industrial applications. *Revista Mexicana de Ingeniería Química.* 19 (Sup. 1): 293–304.

113 Anand, G., Yadav, S., and Yadav, D. (2017a). Production, purification and biochemical characterization of an exo-polygalacturonase from *Aspergillus niger* MTCC 478 suitable for clarification of orange juice. *3 Biotech* 7: 1–8.

114 Anand, G., Yadav, S., and Yadav, D. (2017b). Purification and biochemical characterization of an exo-polygalacturonase from *Aspergillus flavus* MTCC 7589. *Biocatal. Agric. Biotechnol.* 10: 264–269.

115 Meena, B., Sowmeya, V.G., Praveen, A.B. et al. (2021). Pectin degradation in fruit juices by pectinase from Meyerozyma sp. VITPCT75 isolated from *Phyllanthus emblica. J. Pure Appl. Microbiol.* 15 (2): 926–935. https://doi.org/10.22207/JPAM.15.2.51.

116 Mei, Y., Chen, Y., Zhai, R., and Liu, Y. (2013). Cloning, purification and biochemical properties of a thermostable pectinase from *Bacillus halodurans* M29. *J. Mol. Catal. B: Enzym.* 94: 77–81.

117 Mercimek Takcı, H.A. and Turkmen, F.U. (2016). Extracellular pectinase production and purification from a newly isolated *Bacillus subtilis* strain. *Int. J. Food Prop.* 19 (11): 2443–2450.

118 Yu, P., Zhang, Y., and Gu, D. (2017). Production optimization of a heat-tolerant alkaline pectinase from *Bacillus subtilis* ZGL14 and its purification and characterization. *Bioengineered* 8 (5): 613–623.

119 Siddiqui, M., Pande, V., and Arif, M. (2012). Production, purification, and characterization of polygalacturonase from *Rhizomucor pusillus* isolated from decomposting orange peels. *Enzyme Res.* 2012: 138634.

120 Yadav, S., Dubey, A.K., Anand, G., and Yadav, D. (2013). Purification and characterization of pectin lyase secreted by *Aspergillus flavus* MTCC 10938. *Appl. Biochem. Microbiol.* 49: 400–405.

121 Xu, S.X., Qin, X., Liu, B. et al. (2014). An acidic pectin lyase from Aspergillus niger with favourable efficiency in fruit juice clarification. *Lett. Appl. Microbiol.* 60 (2): 181–187.

122 Lu, X., Lin, J., Wang, C. et al. (2016). Purification and characterization of exo-polygalacturonase from *Zygoascus hellenicus* V25 and its potential application in fruit juice clarification. *Food Sci. Biotechnol.* 25: 1379–1385. https://doi.org/10.1007/s10068-016-0215-3.

123 Ismail, A.S., Abo-Elmagd, H.I., and Housseiny, M.M. (2016). A safe potential juice clarifying pectinase from *Trichoderma viride* EF-8 utilizing Egyptian onion skins. *J. Genet. Eng. Biotechnol.* 14 (1): 153–159. https://doi.org/10.1016/j.jgeb.2016.05.001.

124 Patidar, M.K., Nighojkar, A., Nighojkar, S., and Kumar, A. (2017). Purification and characterization of polygalacturonase produced by *Aspergillus niger* AN07 in solid state fermentation. *Can. J. Biotechnol.* 1 (1): 11.

125 Oskay, M. (2022). Production, partial purification, and characterization of polygalacturonase from *Aureobasidium pullulans* P56 under submerged fermentation using agro-industrial wastes. *Curr. Microbiol.* 79 (10): 296.

126 Rehman, H., Baloch, A.H., and Nawaz, M.A. (2021). Pectinase: immobilization and applications. A review. *Trends Pept. Protein Sci.* 6: 1–16.

127 Wahab, W.A.A., Karam, E.A., Hassan, M.E. et al. (2018). Optimization of pectinase immobilization on grafted alginate-agar gel beads by 24 full factorial CCD and thermodynamic profiling for evaluating of operational covalent immobilization. *Int. J. Biol. Macromol.* 113: 159–170.

128 Behram, T., Pervez, S., Nawaz, M.A. et al. (2023). Development of pectinase based nanocatalyst by immobilization of pectinase on magnetic iron oxide nanoparticles using glutaraldehyde as crosslinking agent. *Molecules* 28 (1): 404.

129 de Oliveira, R.L., da Silva, O.S., Converti, A., and Porto, T.S. (2018a). Thermodynamic and kinetic studies on pectinase extracted from *Aspergillus aculeatus*: free and immobilized enzyme entrapped in alginate beads. *Int. J. Biol. Macromol.* 115: 1088–1093.

130 de Oliveira, R.L., Dias, J.L., da Silva, O.S., and Porto, T.S. (2018b). Immobilization of pectinase from *Aspergillus aculeatus* in alginate beads and clarification of apple and umbu juices in a packed bed reactor. *Food Bioprod. Process.* 109: 9–18.

131 Kuhad, R.C., Kapoor, M., and Rustagi, R. (2004). Enhanced production of an alkaline pectinase from *Streptomyces* sp. RCK-SC by whole-cell immobilization and solid-state cultivation. *World J. Microbiol. Biotechnol.* 20: 257–263.

132 Saxena, S., Shukla, S., Thakur, A., and Gupta, R. (2008). Immobilization of polygalacturonase from *Aspergillus niger* onto activated polyethylene and its application in apple juice clarification. *Acta Microbiol. Immunol. Hung.* 55 (1): 33–51.

133 Rehman, H.U., Aman, A., Silipo, A. et al. (2013). Degradation of complex carbohydrate: immobilization of pectinase from *Bacillus licheniformis* KIBGE-IB21 using calcium alginate as a support. *Food Chem.* 139 (1–4): 1081–1086.

134 Wang, B., Cheng, F., Lu, Y. et al. (2013). Immobilization of pectinase from *Penicillium oxalicum* F67 onto magnetic cornstarch microspheres: characterization and application in juice production. *J. Mol. Catal. B: Enzym.* 97: 137–143.

135 Rehman, H.U., Aman, A., Zohra, R.R., and Qader, S.A.U. (2014a). Immobilization of pectin degrading enzyme from *Bacillus licheniformis* KIBGE IB-21 using agar-agar as a support. *Carbohydr. Polym.* 102: 622–626.

136 Rehman, H.U., Nawaz, M.A., Aman, A. et al. (2014b). Immobilization of pectinase from *Bacillus licheniformis* KIBGE-IB21 on chitosan beads for continuous degradation of pectin polymers. *Biocatal. Agric. Biotechnol.* 3 (4): 282–287.

137 Bustamante-Vargas, C.E., de Oliveira, D., Nyari, N.L. et al. (2015). In situ immobilization of commercial pectinase in rigid polyurethane foam and application in the hydrolysis of pectic oligosaccharides. *J. Mol. Catal. B: Enzym.* 122: 35–43. http://doi.org/10.1016/j.molcatb.2015.08.009.

138 Khan, M.M., Choi, Y.S., and Kim, Y.K. (2018). Immobilization of an alkaline endopolygalacturonase purified from *Bacillus paralicheniformis* exhibits bioscouring of cotton fabrics. *Bioprocess. Biosyst. Eng.* 41: 1425–1436.

139 Mohammadi, M., Heshmati, M.K., Sarabandi, K. et al. (2019b). Activated alginate-montmorillonite beads as an efficient carrier for pectinase immobilization. *Int. J. Biol. Macromol.* 137: 253–260.

140 Vaz, R.P., Vici, A.C., de Moraes, T. et al. (2021). Immobilization studies of a pectinase produced by *Aspergillus terreus*. *Biotechnol. Appl. Biochem.* 68 (1): 197–208.

141 Benit, N., Lourthuraj, A.A., Barathikannan, K. et al. (2022). Immobilization of *Halomonas halodurans* and *Bacillus halodurans* in packed bed bioreactor for continuous removal of phenolic impurities in waste water. *Environ. Res.* 209: 112822. http://doi.org/10.1016/j.envres.2022.112822.

6

Hydrocarbon-degrading Enzymes from Mangrove-associated Fungi and Their Applications

Mark Gabriel M. Galinato and Adeline Su Yien Ting

Monash University Malaysia, School of Science, Jalan Lagoon Selatan, Bandar Sunway, Selangor, Darul Ehsan 47500, Malaysia

6.1 Introduction

Hydrocarbon pollution continues to become a challenge in environmental protection. Despite the dangers of hydrocarbons, environmental contamination is common due to anthropogenic activities. This includes the extensive use of crude oil as an energy source for productivity, as well as its consequent dumping and chronic oil spills. It has been estimated that the yearly seepage of natural crude oil is as high as 600,000–800,000 metric tonnes [1]. Once hydrocarbons reach pristine environments, these contaminants alter the nature of those environments by negatively impacting microbial communities [2]. One of the ecosystems greatly vulnerable to hydrocarbon pollution is mangroves as they are located in coastal regions where oil spills converge. In the last decades, more than 200 notable oil spills linked to mangrove pollution have been documented. Duke [3] reported that ~5.5 million tonnes of oil have contaminated mangroves in coastal areas since 1958, collectively destroying over 126,000 ha of mangrove vegetation. Mangrove plants affected by hydrocarbon pollution display yellowing of leaves, defoliation, germination failure, decreased canopy cover, increased sensitivity to other stresses, and tree death [4].

To mitigate hydrocarbon pollution, various remediation strategies have been employed, such as chemical and physical remediation as well as phytoremediation [5]. These technologies are, however, costly and often result in incomplete degradation of contaminants. In addition, phytoremediation, which uses plants to absorb or fixate pollutants, has many logistical limitations (e.g. ability to degrade various types of hydrocarbons, long process, mobilization or translocation, handling of contaminated plants) [6]. On the other hand, microbial remediation is known for its cost-effectiveness and eco-friendliness. It utilizes microorganisms (e.g. bacteria, fungi) to bioremediate hydrocarbon contaminated environments. It was noted that unlike other methods, microbial remediation has no negative effects toward the environment [7]. The concept of microbial remediation of hydrocarbons is based on ability of microorganisms to metabolize and utilize hydrocarbons as carbon and

Microbial Enzymes: Production, Purification, and Industrial Applications, First Edition.
Edited by Dinesh Yadav, Pankaj Chowdhary, Gautam Anand, and Rajarshi Kumar Gaur.

energy source [8]. Upon metabolism, hydrocarbons are oxidized to simpler and nontoxic compounds. Hence, microbial remediation can be performed to treat soil, water, and wastewater *in situ*, eliminating the risks in translocating contaminants (e.g., bioaccumulation during phytoremediation) [9].

Microbial degradation of hydrocarbons is mostly owed to bacteria and fungi. Some bacteria are obligate hydrocarbonoclastic or they feed exclusively on hydrocarbons. Examples of hydrocarbonoclastic bacteria are *Alcanivorax*, *Cycloclasticus*, and *Thalassolitus* [10]. Generally, bacteria carry out specific metabolic pathways to degrade hydrocarbons using the enzymes alkane monooxygenase and dioxygenase, while the utilization of different hydrocarbons by fungi includes the use of nonspecific enzyme complexes (e.g., laccase, manganese peroxidase, and lignin peroxidase) [11]. The latter types of enzymes are called ligninolytic enzymes, which are primarily found in white-rot fungi. *Bjerkandera*, *Irpex*, *Pleurotus*, and *Trametes* are some of the known white-rot fungi that have been previously linked to hydrocarbon degradation [12–16]. Interestingly, fungal hydrocarbon degraders are also found in mangrove ecosystems.

Mangroves act as sinks for various pollutants including hydrocarbons [17]. This makes the ecosystem a good site to study microbial hydrocarbon degradation [18–22]. This is further supported by the fact that mangroves are ecological hotspots for biodiversity and they are geographically positioned in such a way that they are perpetually exposed to fluctuating environmental conditions (e.g. water submersion, salinity). This includes mangrove environments that have been or are chronically exposed to hydrocarbon pollution. Leahy and Colwell [23] stated that microbial communities with prior exposure to hydrocarbon pollutants have increased rates of hydrocarbon degradation as part of their mechanism to adapt. In environments contaminated with oil, the survival of hydrocarbon-utilizing microorganisms is favorably enriched by the condition and the hydrocarbon-catabolizing genes are amplified [23]. For these reasons, mangroves can be catapulted as one of the top sources of hydrocarbon-degrading bacteria and fungi.

The chapter describes the present status and various threats linked to hydrocarbon pollution in mangrove environments. Moreover, it presents mangrove-associated fungi as promising sources of hydrocarbon-degrading enzymes. Currently, little attention is given to this ecological group of fungi despite their potential in bioremediation. Hence, this chapter highlights the potential of their ligninolytic enzymes and the mechanisms that may eventually address a global challenge, that is, hydrocarbon pollution. The chapter also provides a summary of the current applications of mangrove fungal-derived ligninolytic enzymes in degrading hydrocarbons, as well as their potential applications in bioremediating hydrocarbon-polluted environments.

6.2 Hydrocarbon Pollution

6.2.1 Hydrocarbons

Hydrocarbons are composed of carbon and hydrogen molecules. They are simple organic compounds that can be formed as straight chains, branched chains, or

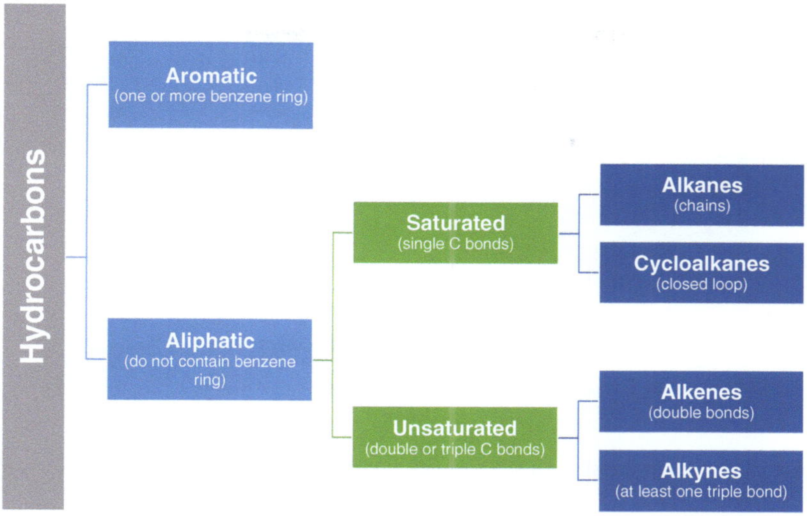

Figure 6.1 Classification of hydrocarbons.

cyclic molecules [24]. Hydrocarbons predominantly make up crude oil, petroleum (e.g. gasoline, kerosene, fuel oil), coal tar, and dyestuff, to name a few [25]. These molecules can be classified as either aromatic or aliphatic hydrocarbons (Figure 6.1). Aromatic hydrocarbons contain one or more benzene rings in their chemical structure to which hydrogen atoms are attached. On the other hand, aliphatic hydrocarbons do not contain a benzene ring and are categorized into four main groups: (i) alkanes, which are saturated hydrocarbons containing only single bonds (C—C), (ii) cycloalkanes (alicyclic), which are saturated hydrocarbons in a closed loop, forming a ring-shaped structure, (iii) alkenes, which are unsaturated hydrocarbons that contain double carbon bonds (C=C), and (iv) alkynes, which are unsaturated hydrocarbons that contain triple carbon bonds (C≡C) [26].

Aromatic hydrocarbons can contain a single benzene ring or more [27]. When two or more rings are present in their structure, these hydrocarbons are called polycyclic aromatic hydrocarbons (PAHs). The simplest PAH is naphthalene, which has two aromatic rings. PAHs are mostly insoluble in water but are highly lipophilic [28]. They are generated through incomplete combustion of organic compounds during anthropogenic activities. Aromatic hydrocarbons also persist in the environment as fractions of natural products such as lignin, coal, and crude oil [27, 29–32]. On the other hand, aliphatic hydrocarbons consist of chains of C atoms. The simplest aliphatic hydrocarbon is methane (CH_4) which is the main constituent of natural gas. Similar to aromatics, aliphatic hydrocarbons are found in natural oil and gas deposits and are released into the environment via spills and emissions [32].

6.2.2 Hydrocarbon Pollution and Management

The threats of hydrocarbon pollution have been well documented for more than half a century. In marine ecosystems, hydrocarbon pollution often originates from

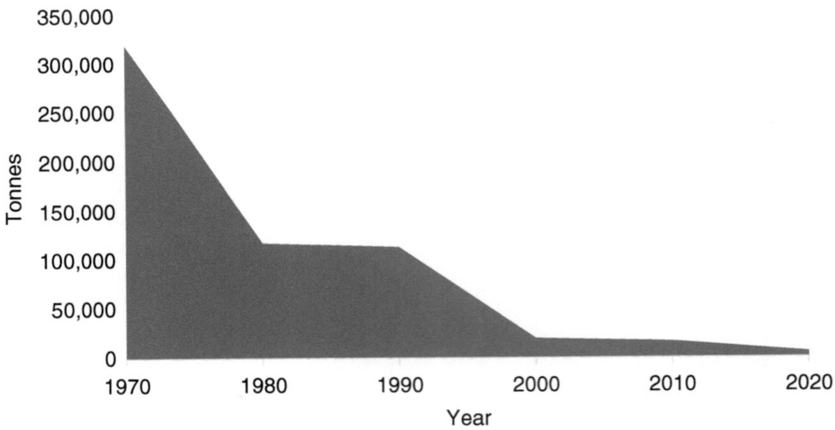

Figure 6.2 Quantity (tonnes) of oil spilled globally from 1970 to 2020s. Source: Data from Roser and Ritchie [34].

industrial and anthropogenic activities [33]. For instance, oil spills occur in marine regions, which subsequently result in decrease in ecosystem productivity (i.e. lesser production of organic matter by different organisms, lower biodiversity). Roser and Ritchie [34] reported that oil spillage has resulted in over 590,000 tonnes of oil spilled globally in the last 60 years (Figure 6.2). Although the quantity of oil spilled has gradually decreased over time, hydrocarbon pollution remains to be a global challenge. In fact, the effects of oil spills persist for long periods of time especially if left untreated. Kingston [35] noted that "signatures" of oil spill incidents may remain measurable for decades in salt marshes and mangrove swamps.

The extent and impacts of hydrocarbon pollution on the environment presents a need for effective strategies to manage and rehabilitate the affected areas. Over the past years, several remediation approaches have been practiced to decontaminate soil and water, most of which are by means of physical and chemical remediation. Ossai et al. [36] summarized various remediation options that may be applicable in treating soil and water. This included containment methods (e.g. stabilization, immobilization, hydraulics, solidification, ventrification), separation methods (e.g. solvent extraction, microwave heating, flushing, dosing, air floatation, electrocoagulation), and deactivation methods (e.g. dehalogenation, emulsification, UV oxidation, nanoremediation, incineration, pyrolysis). Application of these techniques is limited due to the cost, and subsequent impact to the environment and the atmosphere. Plants have also been utilized to remove hydrocarbon contaminants from soil and water. This approach is called phytoremediation. For example, the black needle rush plant (*Juncus roemerianus*; Order Poales) was discovered to have hydrocarbon removal efficiencies toward PAHs and *n*-alkanes [37]. Other plants that have been studied for remediating hydrocarbons are described by Abdullah et al. [38]. Although the cost of phytoremediation is low, its disadvantages include the relatively longer time it takes for plants to bioremediate, the suitability of plants to grow on selected environments, and the health and environmental impacts of bioaccumulation of hydrocarbons in plant compartments (which is the main mechanism of phytoremediation) [6]. For these reasons, a more efficient remediation system is needed.

The use of microorganisms is one of the most feasible options to remove or degrade hydrocarbons from the environment (microbial remediation). Microbial remediation is known to be effective toward aliphatic hydrocarbons [39, 40], aromatic hydrocarbons [7, 13, 15, 16, 41], and even mixed hydrocarbons such as petroleum [20, 42]. Microorganisms are also known to have efficient enzyme systems that break down and utilize different types of hydrocarbons as sources of carbon and energy [1]. Bacterial and fungal species are indigenous in contaminated environments; hence, their bioremediation process is a natural breakdown process, thereby having less negative impact as compared to chemical and physical remediation [7]. In many aspects, microorganisms are also easier and faster to grow compared to plants (e.g. bacteria and fungi can survive in wider range of environments, from aquatic to terrestrial). In this way, microorganisms can be controlled more systematically during treatments. However, there is also a factor that limit the efficacy of microbial remediation. In some cases, hydrocarbons are only partially degraded by microorganisms. For example, the white-rot fungus *Phanerochaete chrysosporium* in the study of Bumpus et al. [43] only partially degraded PAHs. Consequently, another microbial group (e.g. soil bacteria) is required to further metabolize the partially degraded products [44]. It is therefore imperative to explore microbial systems for more effective hydrocarbon remediation.

6.3 Mangrove Environments

Mangroves are the epitome of functionally complex habitats. The term "mangrove" can either refer to the entire habitat (e.g. tidal forest, swamp, wetland) or to a specific species belonging to this plant group [45–47]. Mangroves are primarily found along coastal areas, and they provide shelter and energy resources to a remarkably rich assemblage of organisms. As such, the varying physicochemical properties of mangrove habitats influence microbial biodiversity [48]. Moreover, mangroves are important blue carbon sinks [49] as their carbon sequestration capabilities significantly impacted their relevance in mitigating climate change [50]. Mangroves also enhance the water quality in coastal areas through fine sediment stabilization and through absorption of pollutants (e.g. hydrocarbons, heavy metals) [51, 52]. The U.S. Environmental Protection Agency (USEPA) characterizes mangrove environments as comprising of halophytic plants growing in brackish to saline environments wherein they form "impenetrable maze of woody vegetation" [53]. The different tropical and subtropical plants growing at the interface of land and sea will therefore make up a mangrove forest [54]. Mangrove plants are generally characterized as having extensive root systems, often with exposed breathing roots (e.g. pneumatophores), salt-excreting leaves, and viviparous water-dispersed propagules [55]. Some of these plants can grow in environments with harsh conditions such as fluctuating salinity and anoxia [56]. For instance, mangrove plants in estuaries perpetually experience an extreme range of salinity as the increase and decrease in salinity are dependent on the rise and fall of tides throughout the day (Figure 6.3). Such phenomenon renders mangrove soils saturated and anoxic at most times. However, mangroves are able to survive in these conditions mainly due to their complex root systems with abilities to filter salt efficiently, as well as their exposed roots called pneumatophores for additional respiration (Figure 6.4) [56]. Pneumatophores are the specialized breathing roots of mangroves that are developed upwards to function as site of oxygen intake (e.g. root respiration in hydrophytic trees).

(a) (b)

Figure 6.3 A mangrove forest in Malaysia during high tide (a) and low tide (b).

Figure 6.4 Pneumatophores (exposed breathing roots) of the mangrove *Avicennia*.

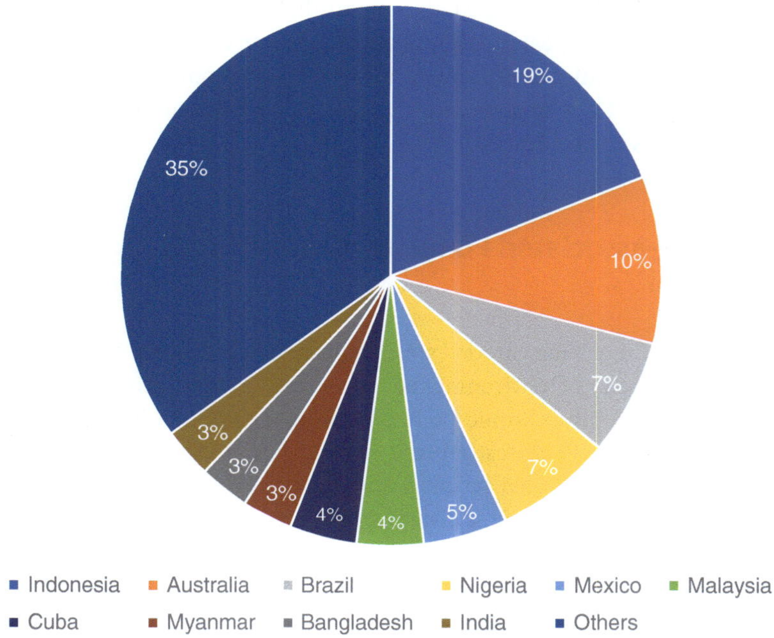

Figure 6.5 Percentage of mangrove coverage per country. Source: Data from [61, 62].

Mangroves are found in over 123 countries worldwide in which they cover more than 150,000 km^2 of the Earth's surface [57, 58]. Over 20 families and 70 species of mangroves have been described to date [59]. Majority of the species can be found in Asia, wherein 55 are endemic [60]. Globally, Indonesia has the largest mangrove coverage (19%), followed by Australia (10%), and Brazil and Nigeria (7% each) (Figure 6.5) [61, 62]. Majority of the planet's mangrove areas are also in Asia [63, 64]. Gevaña et al. [65] reported that Indonesia harbors 50% of SEA's mangrove area, followed by Malaysia and the Philippines which account for 11% and 8%, respectively.

Mangroves are no less susceptible to hydrocarbon toxicity. Hydrocarbons travel their way to mangrove ecosystems through oil spills and other anthropogenic means such as land runoff and sewage. Nansingh and Jurawan [66] recognized mangroves as highly sensitive to environmental stress relative to oil spills. Duke et al. [67] also stated that crude oil has adverse effects on mangrove swamps due to the high persistence of oil in muddy environments. The clay fractions in mangrove sediments have also been positively correlated with PAHs concentrations. PAHs can be absorbed in the organic matter of clay, resulting to prolonged contamination [66]. PAHs have also been documented in various mangrove systems across the world. In the study by Billah et al. [68], 18 countries have reported the occurrence of PAHs in mangroves, four of which are in SEA (i.e. Indonesia, Malaysia, Singapore, Vietnam). To put things into perspective, about 39% of mangrove forests in the world are found in SEA [63, 64, 69]. A good example of a case of mangrove decline caused by hydrocarbon pollution (due to accidental oil spill) is the mangrove forest in

Guimaras Islands, Philippines (SEA). Studies report that hydrocarbons in the form of PAHs (e.g. benzo[*a*]pyrene) caused significant decrease in canopy cover of about 48–58%, as well as deformities and necrosis in various plant compartments a year after the incident [70, 71]. It is cases like this that call for improved or updated management strategies and solutions.

6.4 Mangrove-associated Fungi as Hydrocarbon Degraders

Mangroves are part of the "blue carbon" sink that connects terrestrial and marine ecosystems. The gradient of environmental conditions in this ecosystem (e.g. sea level, fluctuating salinity, chronic pollution to some) leads to high diversity of microorganisms (e.g. both terrestrial and marine fungi). Mangroves may be the only plant group with adapted mechanisms to extreme conditions [72]. This makes them a niche for different fungi, varying from endophytes to mycorrhizas. Mangrove-associated fungi virtually exist within the plant tissues of mangroves (e.g. roots, trunk, leaves, fruits), as well as externally to the plants (sediment, rhizosphere) (Figure 6.6).

Metagenomic studies reveal that mangrove-associated fungal communities differ across locations and host plant structures [73, 74]. The fungal diversity in mangroves is high and the ecosystem is one of the few habitats to constitute majority of the marine fungi [75]. Schmit and Shearer [76] determined that 625 fungal taxa are associated with mangroves at a global scale (Figure 6.7). From this number, only true fungi have been considered ($n = 600$) wherein the majority are ascomycetes ($n = 278$) while a few are basidiomycetes ($n = 30$), and the rest are anamorphic

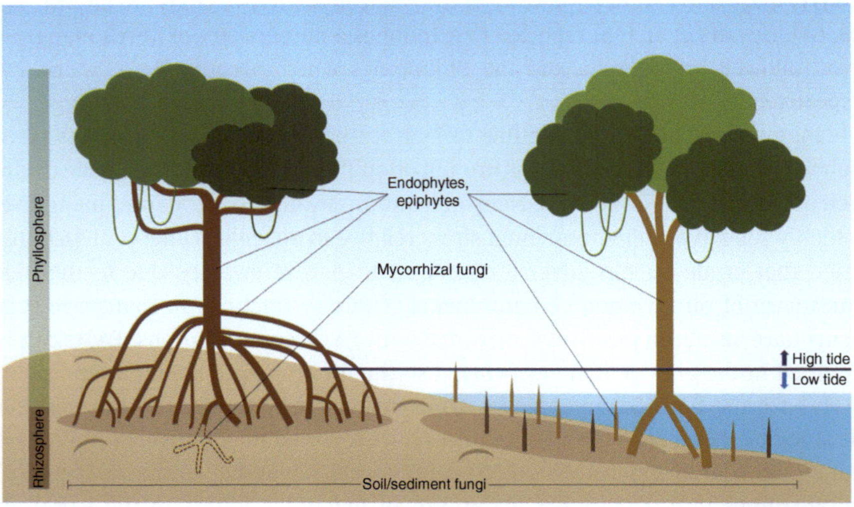

Figure 6.6 Illustrative distribution of associated fungal communities in a mangrove ecosystem.

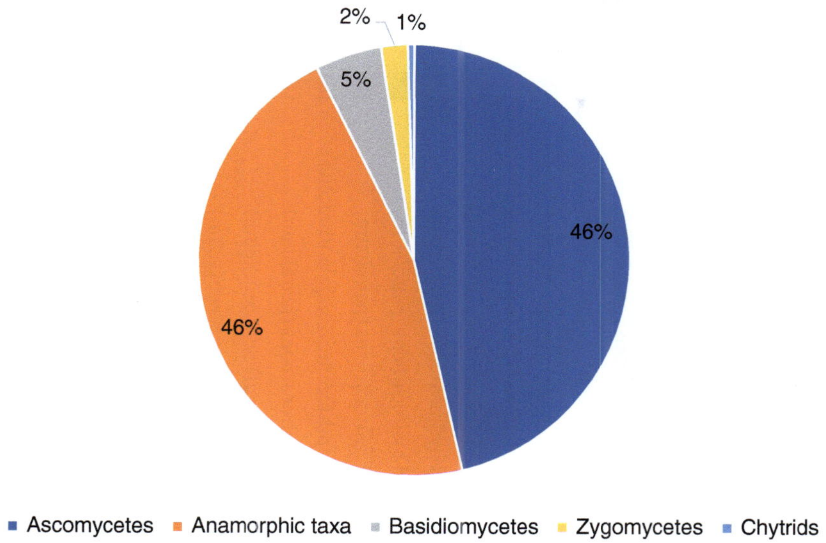

Figure 6.7 Percentage of reported mangrove-associated fungi per fungal group. Source: Data from Schmit and Shearer [76].

taxa ($n = 277$), zygomycetes ($n = 12$), and chytrids ($n = 3$). The Phylum Ascomycota has been consistently reported to be the predominant group of fungi in mangrove environments, whereas Basidiomycota is underrepresented in literature [74, 77]. A few reasons have been raised to explain this pattern of occurrence. Firstly, basidiomycetes generally use macroscopic basidiomata (fruiting bodies) for reproduction which is not suitable in intertidal environments, as wave action can hinder their formation [77]. Secondly, most basidiomycetes cannot tolerate tidal fluctuations and immersion in seawater, resulting in lesser basidiospores being dispersed in mangrove environments [78]. Lastly, ascomycetes are better adapted in marine and intertidal habitats since their fruiting bodies (i.e. ascomata) are microscopic, allowing both passive release of ascospores during immersion in water (high tide) and active ascospore discharge during low tide [77].

Mangrove-associated fungi have also been linked to hydrocarbon degradation, although only a few studies reported this (Table 6.1). These studies revealed that hydrocarbon degradation can be performed by fungi discovered from all mangrove parts, in which degradation of PAHs or mixed hydrocarbons is the most commonly reported. The most studied group of mangrove-associated fungi is isolated from soil sediments compared to other mangrove samples. Moreover, majority of the hydrocarbon-degrading fungi in mangroves are ascomycetes, while there are no reports yet on hydrocarbon-degrading mangrove basidiomycetes. Interestingly, in a recent study, spores of two fungal species from the Phylum Glomeromycota (i.e. *Diversispora aurantium*, *Glomus claroideum*) have been detected from soil of the rhizospheric region of the mangrove *Avicennia germinans* [82]. Fungi from this phylum are known to form arbuscular mycorrhiza. This occurrence will be further discussed in the following subsections, as well as the hydrocarbon-degrading potential of

Table 6.1 Fungi associated with mangrove ecosystems and their reported hydrocarbon degradation activities.

Fungi	Role	Mangrove host/source	Type of hydrocarbon degraded	References
Ascomycota				
Alternaria alternata	Sediment fungi	Sediment	Mixed hydrocarbons (petroleum)	[20, 42]
Aspergillus sp.	Endophyte	Stem, leaves, and roots	Mixed hydrocarbons (petroleum)	[79]
Aspergillus niger	Endophyte	Stem, leaves, and roots	Mixed hydrocarbons (petroleum)	
Aspergillus nomius	Sediment fungi	Sediment	Mixed hydrocarbons (petroleum)	[20]
Aspergillus sydowii	Sediment fungi	Sediment	PAH (anthracene)	[80]
Aspergillus terreus	Sediment fungi	Sediment	Mixed hydrocarbons (petroleum)	[20, 42]
Cladosporium sp.	Endophyte	Stem, leaves, and roots	Mixed hydrocarbons (petroleum)	[79]
Cladosporium sphaerospermum	Sediment fungi	Sediment	Mixed hydrocarbons (petroleum)	[20, 42]
Curvularia sp.	Endophyte	Stem, leaves, and roots	Mixed hydrocarbons (petroleum)	[79]
Eupenicillium hirayamae	Sediment fungi	Sediment	Mixed hydrocarbons (petroleum)	[20, 42]
Fusarium sp.	Endophyte	Stem, leaves, and roots	Mixed hydrocarbons (petroleum)	[79]
Fusarium solani	Sediment fungi	Sediment	PAHs (anthracene, benz[a]anthracene)	[81]
Geosmithia pallida	Sediment fungi	Sediment	Mixed hydrocarbons (petroleum)	[20]
Nigrospora sp.	Endophyte	Stem, leaves, and roots	Mixed hydrocarbons (petroleum)	[79]
Paecilomyces variotii	Sediment fungi	Sediment	Mixed hydrocarbons (petroleum)	[20, 42]
Penicillium vinaceum	Sediment fungi	Sediment	Mixed hydrocarbons (petroleum)	[20]
Pestalotiopsis adusta	Endophyte	Stem, leaves, and roots	Mixed hydrocarbons (petroleum)	[79]
Phialophora alba	Sediment fungi	Sediment	Mixed hydrocarbons (petroleum)	[20]
Glomeromycota				
Diversispora aurantium	Mycorrhiza	Rhizosphere of *Avicennia germinans*	—	[82]
Glomus claroideum				

endophytic, epiphytic, and other mangrove-associated fungal communities (i.e. mycorrhizas, mangrove sediment fungi).

6.4.1 Endophytes of the Mangrove Ecosystems

Endophytic fungi live asymptomatically within healthy plant tissues and are known to have beneficial associations with their host plants [83]. Over 200 fungal taxa of endophytes have been successfully isolated from mangroves, representing one of the largest communities of marine fungi [84]. In a study by Yao et al. [73], the diversity and richness of endophytic mangrove fungi are reported to be dependent on the host plant while other non-endophytic fungi are influenced by external factors. Mangrove endophytes form part of the fungal community in mangroves, and may have functional roles that benefit their host plant (e.g. alleviating stress). According to Chaterjee and Abraham [85], some of the commonly reported endophytes of mangroves are species of the genera *Aspergillus*, *Cladosporium*, *Fusarium*, *Penicillium*, and *Trichoderma*, all of which are ascomycetes. Mangrove-associated endophytes are also considered rich sources of bioactive secondary metabolites with various properties (e.g. antimicrobial, antioxidants, immunosuppresants, anticytotoxics) [85]. Apart from their symbiotic roles and bioactive metabolites, endophytes isolated from mangroves are capable of degrading hydrocarbons (Table 6.1). To date, the first and only study that confirms the hydrocarbon degradation potential of mangrove endophytic fungi is by Sawant and Rodrigues [79]. Seven species exhibited hydrocarbon degradation abilities, particularly *Aspergillus* sp., *Aspergillus niger*, *Cladosporium* sp., *Curvularia* sp., *Fusarium* sp., *Nigrospora* sp., and *Pestalotiopsis adusta*. These fungi, all of which are ascomycetes, degraded residual petroleum oil collected from actual transport vehicles which showed their application in biodegrading mixed hydrocarbons that are usually found in the environment.

6.4.2 Epiphytes of the Mangrove Ecosystems

Mangroves also harbor epiphytic fungi (or epiphytes) that are found on plant surfaces (e.g. leaves, stems). Unlike endophytes, epiphytes are exposed to external environment. Epiphytes can be further categorized as resident or casual epiphytes. Resident epiphytes are able to grow and multiply on plant surfaces, while casual epiphytes exist as spores or mycelia with limited growth [86]. There is high variability of one epiphytic group to another in a single plant due to external factors in the environment (e.g. temperature, wind speed, relative humidity) which dictate the incidental occurrence of epiphytes on plant surfaces [73]. Mangrove fungal epiphytes have been studied for their secondary metabolites which have antibacterial and anticancer properties [87, 88]. Furthermore, epiphytes contribute to leaf litter decomposition and in carbon and nutrient cycling in the environment [89]. In general, fungi use ligninolytic enzymes to decompose organic matter [90]. Although hydrocarbon degradation activities have not yet been reported in epiphytic fungi isolated from mangroves, the presence of ligninolytic enzymes (which can degrade hydrocarbons) in this fungal group make them good prospects for hydrocarbon degradation studies. *Cladosporium* and *Nigrospora* are among the genera reported as mangrove epiphytes [73] which have been discovered to produce ligninolytic enzymes [91, 92], and exist as mangrove endophytes with hydrocarbon degradation potential [79]. Hence, tapping mangrove epiphytic fungi for hydrocarbon degradation can lead to important discoveries.

6.4.3 Mycorrhizas

Mycorrhizas are fungi of the Phylum Glomeromycota, and they are known to form symbiotic relationship with plant roots. Mangrove mycorrhizal associations are primarily established by arbuscular mycorrhizal fungi (AMF) which aid in the supply of water and nutrients from the soil to the host plant by forming arbuscules within the cortical layer of roots [93]. They are symbiotic with more than 80% of terrestrial plants and 70% of all vascular plants [94, 95]. However, AMF arbuscular formation in mangroves is uncommon due to the nature of mangrove environments being saline and nutrient-poor [96, 97]. Such environments may limit the spore density and germination of these fungi, as well as the growth of hyphae [98]. The AMF discovered from mangrove ecosystems are therefore rare, especially those from hydrocarbon polluted environments. Martínez-Hernández et al. [82] reported that *G. claroideum* and *D. aurantium* spores were detected from the rhizosphere of the mangrove *A. germinans* wherein traces of hydrocarbons were present due to past exposure to chronic oil spills. Although their presence is noted, the roles of these fungi in degrading hydrocarbons were not investigated as direct degradation test was not conducted. Instead, their relative abundance have been positively correlated to tolerance to weathered crude oil [82]. Nevertheless, the study introduced the possibility of AMF to contribute to hydrocarbon remediation.

6.4.4 Mangrove Sediment Fungi

Fungi associated with mangroves can also be found in the soils and sediments of mangrove environments. These groups of fungi are highly diverse as shown in several metagenomic studies [99–103]. Mangrove sediment fungi also include several marine fungi which are occasionally carried onto the soil region during tidal fluctuations. They produce many bioactive metabolites with wide range of applications such as antimicrobials, anticancer agents, antineoplastic agents, antioxidants, and antiparasitics [104]. They are also the major decomposers of fallen mangrove vegetation [105, 106]. Due to the high rates of decomposition in this region, ligninolytic metabolism is also increased, making them promising for hydrocarbon degradation studies. To date, there are only three studies on the hydrocarbon degradation potential of mangrove sediment fungi (Table 6.1). As such, only eleven (11) fungal species have so far been documented, all of which are from Ascomycota. In the studies of Ameen et al. [20, 42], mangrove sediment isolates of *Alternaria alternata*, *Aspergillus nomius*, *Aspergillus terreus*, *Cladosporium sphaerospermum*, *Eupenicillium hirayamae*, *Fusarium solani*, *Geosmithia pallida*, *Paecilomyces variotii*, *Penicillium vinaceum*, and *Phialophora alba*, all demonstrated capacities to grow in the presence of crude oil. These fungi exhibited greater accumulation of biomass in culture media supplemented with crude oil (i.e. diesel oil, engine oil) compared to controls (without crude oil). Three isolates (i.e. *C. sphaerospermum*, *E. hirayamae*, *P. variotii*) were even observed to develop close association with engine oil by growing around oil droplets in the broth [42]. Furthermore, Bankole et al. [80] studied the optimal conditions in which a mangrove sediment-derived strain *Aspergillus sydowii* degraded the polycyclic aromatic hydrocarbon, anthracene (ANT). The fungus optimally degraded anthracene (98.7%) within three days under neutral pH, at 30 °C, and under 0.2% w/v salinity, among other factors which will be elaborated in the continuing section.

6.5 Ligninolytic Enzymes from Mangrove-associated Fungi

The degradation of hydrocarbons in mangrove ecosystems is linked to ligninolytic fungi. Ligninolytic fungi produce enzymes that degrade broad range of organopollutants (e.g. chlorophenols, pesticides, PAHs). These enzymes can be categorized into two types: oxidases (i.e. laccases) and peroxidases (i.e. manganese peroxidase, lignin peroxidase, versatile peroxidases) [107]. Saprophytic fungi are generally the main producers of ligninolytic enzymes. Among them, white-rot fungi are regarded as the most important producers of ligninolytic enzymes, after brown rot and soft rot fungi [108]. However, it is important to clarify that non-rot fungi such as *A. terreus* [109] *F. solani* [110], and *Trichoderma harzianum* [111] can also produce ligninolytic enzymes. For mangrove-associated fungi, laccase, manganese peroxidase, and lignin peroxidase are the primary ligninolytic enzymes reported in literature. Unfortunately, only a few studies relate their hydrocarbon degradation to the presence of ligninolytic enzymes (Table 6.2). To date, all reported mangrove-associated fungi with one or more ligninolytic enzymes used in hydrocarbon degradation are ascomycetes. The concept behind this is that lignin-degrading fungi can also use their ligninolytic enzymes to degrade hydrocarbons due to their structural similarities as lignin is made up of both aliphatic and aromatic hydrocarbons [112]. Therefore, they possess ligninolytic enzymes and are expected to degrade hydrocarbons due to the structural similarities of lignin and hydrocarbon polymers [75].

6.5.1 Laccase

Laccase (Lac) (EC 1.10.3.2) is a multicopper oxidase with molecular weight of about 60–80 kDa [113]. Laccases are mainly monomeric, dimeric, and tetrameric glycoproteins. The structure of monomeric Lac molecules contain four copper atoms which have three classifications depending on absorbance under UV/visible and electronic paramagnetic resonance (EPR) spectroscopy [114]. Type 1 copper (T1) gives the enzyme an intense blue color at 600 nm (UV/visible). Type 2 copper (T2), although colorless, can be detected using EP. Lastly, type 3 copper

Table 6.2 Mangrove-associated fungi with ligninolytic enzymes used for hydrocarbon degradation.

Fungi	Ligninolytic enzyme	Type of hydrocarbon degraded	References
Alternaria alternata	Lac MnP	Mixed hydrocarbons (petroleum)	[20, 42]
Aspergillus nomius	Lac MnP LiP	Mixed hydrocarbons (petroleum)	[20]
Aspergillus sydowii	Lac MnP LiP	PAH (anthracene)	[80]
Aspergillus terreus	Lac MnP LiP	Mixed hydrocarbons (petroleum)	[20, 42]
Cladosporium sphaerospermum	Lac LiP	Mixed hydrocarbons (petroleum)	
Eupenicillium hirayamae	MnP LiP	Mixed hydrocarbons (petroleum)	
Fusarium solani	Lac	PAHs (anthracene, benz[a]anthracene)	[81]
Geosmithia pallida	MnP LiP	Mixed hydrocarbons (petroleum)	[20]
Paecilomyces variotii	Lac MnP	Mixed hydrocarbons (petroleum)	[20, 42]
Penicillium vinaceum	Lac	Mixed hydrocarbons (petroleum)	[20]
Phialophora alba	Lac MnP LiP	Mixed hydrocarbons (petroleum)	

laccase (Lac), manganese peroxidase (MnP), lignin peroxidase (LiP).

(T3) consists of copper atoms in pair which have weak absorbance near the UV spectrum [114]. T1 is the binding site for the reducing substrate while T2 and T3 form a trinuclear cluster which is the reduction site of molecular oxygen (O_2) to water [115].

During its catalytic mechanism, Lac stores electrons from each individual oxidation reaction with four reducing substrate molecules. During oxidation of the substrate, free radicals are being generated. During lignin degradation, Lac reacts with the phenolic subunits of lignin, allowing for the cleavage of α-carbon and β-carbon bonds [114]. Free radicals result from this reaction which can then can be converted to quinone (a stable aromatic derivative) via a second enzyme-catalyzed reaction [114, 115]. Both the free radicals and quinones can subsequently be polymerized [116]. Furthermore, Lac also reacts with non-phenolic substrates by inserting mediators (organic compounds with low molecular weight) [115]. These mediators (oxidized by laccase) oxidize non-phenolic compounds which Lac alone cannot do so. Some of the most common mediators of Lac are 2,2′-azinobis-(3-ethylbenzthiazoline-6-sulfonate) (ABTS), 1-hydroxy benzotriazole (HOBT), *N*-hydroxyphthalimide (NHPI), and 3 hydroxyanthranilic acid [117]. Laccase oxidizes different substrates, specifically aromatic compounds with hydroxyl and amine groups (e.g. phenols, aromatic amines) [118, 119]. This specificity makes laccase effective in degrading lignin [120].

Lac is an extracellular enzyme produced mainly by fungi and plants, but was recently found in some bacteria and insects. Fungal laccases generally originates from ascomycetes and basidiomycetes [115, 121]. In fact, the first fungal laccase was characterized from the ascomycete, *Monocillium indicum* [122]. Since then, many ascomycetes were studied for laccase production and, to date, one of the most documented ascomycete genus is *Trichoderma* [115]. Interestingly, as studies on fungal laccase production increased, it also revealed that basidiomycetes have higher expression levels of laccase compared to ascomycetes [123]. More specifically, white-rot fungi (Basidiomycota) such as *Phlebia radiata*, *Pleurotus ostreatus*, and *Trametes versicolor* have been extensively studied for their high laccase production and efficient lignin degradation [115]. In mangrove-associated fungi, Lac has been detected in several species, both from Ascomycota and Basidiomycota. However, there are only nine (9) mangrove-associated fungi reported in which their Lac production was linked to hydrocarbon degradation. These fungi are *A. alternata, A. nomius, A. sydowii, A. terreus, C. sphaerospermum*, *P. variotii*, *P. vinaceum*, and *P. alba*, all of which are ascomycetes [20, 42]. They degraded petroleum oils which composed of mixed hydrocarbons. Likewise, a mangrove sediment-derived strain of *F. solani* was determined to produce Lac that degraded PAHs (i.e. anthracene, benz[*a*]anthracene [BAA]) [81]. Compared to laccases that are of bacterial and plant origin, laccases produce by fungi have higher redox potential (up to +800 mV) and are therefore more relevant for bioremediation [124].

6.5.2 Manganese Peroxidase

Manganese peroxidase (MnP) (EC 1.11.1.13) is a Class II heme-peroxidase which uses hydrogen peroxide (H_2O_2) as an electron acceptor during substrate oxidation [125]. MnP has a molecular weight of about 38–62.5 kDa [126]. In a crystallographic analysis [127], it was revealed that the active site of MnP comprises one heme molecule and side chain residues of Glu-35, Glu-39, and Asp-179. It also contains two calcium ions and five disulfide bridges for stability [126]. The heme molecule of MnP, acts as a cofactor that allows Mn^{2+} to bind to the center of the active site [126]. In its native state, the enzyme contains a penta-coordinated Fe^{3+} structure that is integrated with the porphyrin ring of the heme cofactor, as well as a proximal histidine [128]. Finally, the distal end of the enzyme is a peroxide-bonding pocket composed of histidine and an arginine residue [127].

MnP oxidizes Mn^{2+} in a multi-step process and converts it to Mn^{3+}, which subsequently mediates the oxidation of numerous phenolic and non-phenolic compounds, as well as lignin and its derivatives [90]. The catalytic reactions of MnP can be summarized as follows [125]:

$$MnP + H_2O_2 \rightarrow MnP\text{-}I + H_2O,$$

$$MnP\text{-}I + Mn^{2+} \rightarrow MnP\text{-}II + Mn^{3+},$$

$$MnP\text{-}II + Mn^{2+} \rightarrow MnP + Mn^{3+} + H_2O.$$

MnP catalytic cycle is initiated by the transfer of two electrons from the heme group to H_2O_2, resulting in the production of water and compound I (MnP-I). Subsequently, compound I oxidizes Mn^{2+} to produce compound II (MnP-II), Mn^{3+}, and a free radical [126]. Compound II then catalyzes Mn^{2+} oxidation, forming Mn^{3+} and allowing MnP to return to its native state. Mn^{3+} is stabilized by organic acids (e.g. oxalate) and becomes the mediator that oxidizes organic compounds such as lignin [129].

MnP can be found in many wood-rot fungi (basidiomycetes) and ascomycetes that are involved in decomposing soil litter. MnP was first characterized from the white-rot fungus *P. chrysosporium* (Basidiomycota) in 1985 [130]. It was initially thought to be strictly of fungal origin and specifically limited to a few families under Basidiomycota but this enzyme is now reported to be present in Ascomycota [131, 132]. Fungal MnP from mangrove ecosystems is also known to effectively degrade different types of hydrocarbons although literature on this is scarce (Table 6.2). Specifically, eight mangrove-associated fungi have been reported to produce hydrocarbon-degrading MnP. These fungi are *A. alternata*, *A. nomius*, *A. sydowii*, *A. terreus*, *E. hirayamae*, *G. pallida*, *P. variotii*, and *P. alba* which are all ascomycetes. These isolates were obtained from sediment samples in the mangrove ecosystem situated along the Red Sea coastline of Saudi Arabia, and were able to degrade petroleum composed of mixed hydrocarbons [20, 42].

6.5.3 Lignin Peroxidase

Lignin peroxidase (LiP) (EC 1.11.1.14) is also a Class II heme-peroxidase that uses H_2O_2 as co-substrate to degrade lignin and its derivatives. Its molecular weight is about 38–68 kDa [131, 132]. Crystallographic studies of LiP show it possesses four disulfide bonds and contains ~343 amino acid residues [133, 134]. LiP is composed of three tryptophans and eight methionines, as well as phenylalanines located between the enzyme's distal and proximal heme surfaces. Asp-183 is also hydrogen-bonded to the heme propionate of LiP. Moreover, the heme iron of LiP is associated with histidine in which the bond between each other is known to increase the enzyme's redox potential, thereby creating a deficiency of electrons in the porphyrin iron ring [132]. The catalytic cycle of lignin peroxidase, which involves three steps, can be summarized as follows [132]:

$$LiP + H_2O_2 \rightarrow LiP\text{-}I + H_2O,$$

$$\text{LiP-I} + \text{VA} \rightarrow \text{LiP-II} + \text{VA}^{0+},$$

$$\text{LiP-II} + \text{S} \rightarrow \text{LiP} + \text{VA}^{0+}.$$

The LiP catalytic cycle is initiated by the oxidation of the enzyme in native state by H_2O_2 (as an electron acceptor), forming compound I. Subsequently, compound I (deficient of $2e^-$) is reduced by one electron ($1e^-$) by a substrate molecule (e.g. veratryl alcohol) (VA), forming compound II (deficient of $1e^-$) and veratraldehyde (VA^{0+}). Compound II can be further reduced ($1e^-$) by another substrate molecule (S) thereby returning LiP to its native state. This indicates a complete oxidation cycle [131]. To degrade lignin, VA^{0+} works as an oxidant of the lignin matrix that initiates a cascade of radical reactions on lignin polymers (e.g. depolymerization) [135]. Of the three described ligninolytic enzymes, LiP uniquely catalyzes cleavage of both ether (C—O—C) bonds and C—C bonds in lignin and lignin models [131]. The enzyme is also relatively non-specific as it is able to oxidize phenolic aromatic substrates and other organic compounds with up to 1.4 V of redox potential [136].

LiP was first detected in the extracellular medium of the white-rot fungus *P. chrysosporium* (Basidiomycota) [137, 138]. Since then, the enzyme has been increasingly discovered in different basidiomycetes such as *T. versicolor* [139], *P. radiata* [140], and *Phanerochaete sordida* [141]. Various LiP-producing ascomycetes have also been isolated from the guts of the termite *Macrotermes nigeriense*. These fungi were identified as *A. niger*, *Microsporum distortum*, *Trichophyton megininii*, and *Trichophyton mentagrophytes* [142]. In mangrove-associated fungi, LiP was detected in the brown-rot fungus *Laetiporus sulphuerus* (Basidiomycota) found along the bases of decomposing mangrove shrubs in Tanzania [143]. Likewise, LiP production is also present in ascomycetes such as *Colletotrichum* sp., *Fusarium sambucinum*, and *Penicillium citrinum*, all of which have been isolated as mangrove endophytes [118, 119]. The mechanism of lignin degradation of LiP can also be applied for hydrocarbon degradation. To date, seven mangrove-associated fungi have been determined to produce LiP linked to hydrocarbon degradation (Table 6.2). These fungi are *A. nomius*, *A. sydowii*, *A. terreus*, *C. sphaerospermum*, *E. hirayamae*, *G. pallida*, and *P. alba* which are all capable of degrading petroleum (mixed hydrocarbons) and PAH (i.e. anthracene) [20, 42, 80].

6.6 Applications and Future Prospects

6.6.1 Current Applications of Ligninolytic Enzymes from Mangrove-associated Fungi

Hydrocarbon degradation by mangrove-associated fungi is still a growing research area compared to other applied research such as the use of fungal secondary metabolites for pharmaceutical use (e.g. antimicrobial, anticancer, antioxidant). The current evidences of hydrocarbon degradation of ligninolytic enzymes of fungi isolated from mangrove ecosystems have only been demonstrated in the laboratory by inducing their production under different conditions. At present, these hydrocarbon-degrading enzymes have yet to be isolated for large-scale clean-ups. Nevertheless, the present works (all *in vitro*) discovered valuable findings and insights that may assist in establishing mangrove-associated fungi as prominent sources of hydrocarbon-degrading enzymes.

In the study of Ameen et al. [20], profuse fungal growth was observed in nine (9) mangrove-associated ascomycetes cultured in a medium with engine oil (mixed hydrocarbons) as the sole carbon source (Table 6.2). The highest biomass accumulation recorded (vs. the control) was 45% and 41.2% by *E. hirayamae* and *C. sphaerospermum*, respectively. These two fungi, alongside *P. variotii*, were also visually observed to develop affinity toward engine oil as they grew around the oil droplets. Furthermore, significant levels of ligninolytic enzymes such as laccase (Lac), manganese peroxidase (MnP), and lignin peroxidase (LiP) were detected from the culture media, indicating their role in degrading hydrocarbons. Of the nine fungal isolates, eight produced Lac in the presence of engine oil, while eight produced MnP as well, and five produced LiP. Their claim on hydrocarbon utility by the fungal isolates was strengthened through chromatographic analysis which revealed the notable disappearance of oil peaks (indicating degradation of these molecules) and the simultaneous appearance of several peaks of low mass ions (indicating the breakdown of hydrocarbons into residues by ligninolytic enzymes). In a separate study, Ameen et al. [42] used diesel oil (mixed hydrocarbons) as the sole carbon source of mangrove-associated ascomycetes to study their biodegradation rate of mixed hydrocarbons. Similar to the results of the previous study [20], *E. hirayamae* and *C. sphaerospermum* accumulated the greatest biomass (at 43.3% and 40%, respectively) in Ameen et al. [42]. A significant increase in the production of ligninolytic enzymes were also detected. All five isolates produced both Lac and MnP, while only three produced LiP (Table 6.2). The study highlighted the link between hydrocarbon degradation and enzymatic production, suggesting that the degradation of hydrocarbons must be facilitated by extracellular enzymes. Therefore, the elevated enzyme levels in the media supplemented with diesel oil were direct demonstration of ligninolytic enzyme activities. Moreover, a synergistic effect of a fungal consortium in degrading hydrocarbons was noted in the study. When co-cultured in one treatment setup, all five isolates exhibited the highest degradation potential of diesel fuel as indicated by dry weight accumulation and the highest level of enzymatic activities. These results led to the discovery that a consortium of mangrove-associated fungi is generally more effective in degrading hydrocarbons as they provide a wider spectrum of enzyme activities since various fungal taxa (capable of different metabolic expressions) are involved [42].

There are also mangrove-associated fungi that can utilize PAHs. In the study by Wu et al. [81], ANT and BAA were effectively degraded by two strains of *F. solani* isolated from mangrove sediments. The removal of ANT and BAA were up to 60% and 40%, respectively. Through solid-phase microextraction combined with gas chromatography–mass spectrometry (GC/MS), metabolites were identified, with one product being 1,2-benzenedicarboxylic acid. This indicates that the two *F. solani* strains produced Lac which is responsible for degrading ANT and BAA. The enzyme can transform ANT and BAA to quinones, which are subsequently transformed into 1,2-benzenedicarboxylic acid through a number of processes [81]. The presence of Lac was further confirmed spectrophotometrically, whereas MnP and LiP were not detected. ANT degradation was also reported for *A. sydowii* isolated from mangrove soil [80]. The study investigated different conditions in which *A. sydowii* could optimally degrade ANT in terms of efficiency and enzyme production. The fungal strain recorded 99.8% ANT degradation efficiency within 72 hours under optimal culture conditions of neutral pH, 0.2% w/v salinity, 30 °C temperature, 2 g biomass, ANT concentration of 200 mg/l, and the addition of citric acid as an inducer for enzyme production. Due to the inducer, high levels of Lac, MnP, and LiP were detected at 131%, 107%, and 89%, respectively. The presence of these enzymes were also linked to the various metabolites detected using GC/MS as these products were produced from their respective catalytic mechanisms. Hence, detecting transformed hydrocarbon products may lead to valuable insights on the type of enzymes being produced by a certain fungus, as well as their mechanisms in degrading hydrocarbons.

The use of mixed hydrocarbons (i.e. engine oil, diesel oil) and PAHs (i.e. anthracene, benz[*a*]anthracene) in these studies provides a realistic scenario that reflects the different types of hydrocarbons observed in polluted mangrove environments. This allows for a more accurate estimation on the application of ligninolytic enzymes in bioremediation. These pioneering works are therefore important for further studies such as the use of other mangrove-associated fungi from different taxonomic classes for enzyme production toward large scale bioremediation.

6.6.2 Future Prospects in Bioremediation and Commercialization of Enzymes

The study of mangrove-associated fungi and their enzymes for hydrocarbon degradation is still in its early stages. The ligninolytic enzymes of this ecological group of fungi have not yet been isolated for in-depth studies. Nevertheless, they potentially offer various applications which stem from the nature of fungi as decomposers of lignocellulosic compounds. The broad substrate range of their enzymes allow them to expand their environmental role (i.e. lignin degradation) to other applications such as fungal-mediated bioremediation or "mycoremediation." In mycoremediation, fungi and their enzymes are utilized as primary tools in removing different types of pollutants from the environment [144]. One good example of mycoremediation is using *Phlebia brevispora* in degrading high-molecular-weight PAHs [145]. A previous study has isolated *P. brevispora* strains from mangroves which produced all three ligninolytic enzymes (i.e. Lac, MnP, LiP). LiP isolated from a non-mangrove strain of *P. brevispora* exhibited high redox potential which attracted relevant interest in treating wastewater and catalyzing various chemical transformations [146]. A mangrove-derived strain of this fungus may be targeted for studies that include enzyme isolation since mangrove-associated fungal strains are potentially better sources of hydrocarbon-degrading enzymes due to their chronic exposure to hydrocarbons. Likewise, mangrove fungal-derived Lac, MnP, and LiP can be considered to form part of a biological treatment technology for soils and groundwater contaminated with various organopollutants (including hydrocarbons) since there is a currently a need to integrate enzymes in remediation technologies [147]. It is also imperative to apply such mechanisms in actual contaminated environments to test the translatability of *in vitro* models on-site [148].

Furthermore, the industrial potential of ligninolytic enzymes has long been recognized. These enzymes are commercialized but are limited to Lac and MnP only. Presently, there are no commercialized enzymes that had been produced by mangrove-associated fungi, although most commercially available Lac and MnP are of fungal origin [149]. For instance, Lac isolated from *Trametes villosa* and *Trametes pubescens* ("Novozym 51003") has been commercialized by Novozymes (Bagsværd, Denmark) [80]. Novozym 51,003 is reported to be highly efficient in lignin modification processes. Other commercialized laccases include those derived from ascomycetes, e.g. *Aspergillus* sp. (Sigma-Aldrich), as well as other basidiomycetes, e.g. *Cerrena unicolor* (Jena Biosciences) and *T. versicolor* (Sigma-Aldrich) [149]. MnP from the white rot fungus *P. chrysosporium* is also commercially distributed by Sigma-Aldrich. Strains of these fungal species have been previously isolated from mangrove ecosystems [79, 150, 151]. Hence, ligninolytic enzymes produced by mangrove-associated fungi can be potentially marketed due to their lignocellulosic degradation capabilities which support their potential in bioremediation.

6.7 Conclusion

Hydrocarbon pollution remains an environmental threat that must be addressed. Mycoremediation appears to be the most promising strategy to remove hydrocarbons particularly in terms of cost-effectiveness, as well as eliminating secondary contamination and harmful by-products (resulting from chemical treatments). Due to chronic exposures of mangrove ecosystems to hydrocarbon contaminants, mangrove-associated fungi have increased rates of degradation as a form of adaptation to these pollutants. Ligninolytic enzymes, which degrade hydrocarbons, have also been found in mangrove-associated fungi. Therefore, fungi from mangroves have the potential to be tapped as primary removers of hydrocarbons from the environment, and this can be realized with the use of greater biotechnological tools.

References

1 Das, N. and Chandran, P. (2011). Microbial degradation of petroleum hydrocarbon contaminants: an overview. *Biotechnol. Res. Int.* 2011: 1–13. http://doi.org/10.4061/2011/941810.

2 Truskewycz, A., Gundry, T.D., Khudur, L.S. et al. (2019). Petroleum hydrocarbon contamination in terrestrial ecosystems-fate and microbial responses. *Molecules* 24 (18): 3400. http://doi.org/10.3390/molecules24183400.

3 Duke, N.C. (2016). Oil spill impacts on mangroves: recommendations for operational planning and action based on a global review. *Mar. Pollut. Bull.* 109 (2): 700–715. http://doi.org/10.1016/j.marpolbul.2016.06.082.

4 Hoff, R.Z. and Michel, J. (2014). *Oil Spills in Mangroves: Planning & Response Considerations*, 1–96. National Oceanic and Atmospheric Administration.

5 Lv, Y., Bao, J., and Zhu, L. (2022). A comprehensive review of recent and perspective technologies and challenges for the remediation of oil-contaminated sites. *Energy Rep.* 8: 7976–7988. http://doi.org/10.1016/j.egyr.2022.06.034.

6 Farraji, H., Zaman, N., Tajuddin, R., and Faraji, H. (2016). Advantages and disadvantages of phytoremediation: a concise review. *Int. J. Environ. Technol. Sci.* 2: 69–75.

7 Davie-Martin, C.L., Stratton, K.G., Teeguarden, J.G. et al. (2017). Implications of bioremediation of polycyclic aromatic hydrocarbon-contaminated soils for human health and cancer risk. *Environ. Sci. Technol.* 51: 9458–9468.

8 Zhang, H., Yuan, X., Xiong, T. et al. (2020). Bioremediation of co-contaminated soil with heavy metals and pesticides: influence factors, mechanisms and evaluation methods. *Chem. Eng. J.* 398: 125657.

9 Wang, M., Chen, S., Jia, X., and Chen, L. (2021). Concept and types of bioremediation. In: *Handbook of Bioremediation* (ed. M. Hasanuzzaman and M.N.V. Prasad), 3–8. Beijing: Academic Press http://doi.org/10.1016/b978-0-12-819382-2.00001-6.

10 Yakimov, M.M., Timmis, K.N., and Golyshin, P.N. (2007). Obligate oil-degrading marine bacteria. *Curr. Opin. Biotechnol.* 18 (3): 257–266.

11 Galitskaya, P., Biktasheva, L., Blagodatsky, S. et al. (2021). Response of bacterial and fungal communities to high petroleum pollution in different soils. *Sci. Rep.* 11: http://doi.org/10.1038/s41598-020-80631-4.

12 Pozdnyakova, N.N. (2012). Involvement of the Ligninolytic system of white-rot and litter-decomposing fungi in the degradation of polycyclic aromatic hydrocarbons. *Biotechnol. Res. Int.* 1–20. http://doi.org/10.1155/2012/243217.

13 Collins, P.J. and Dobson, A.D.W. (1996). Oxidation of fluorene and phenanthrene by Mn^{2+}-dependent peroxidase activity in whole cultures of *Trametes (Coriolus) versicolor*. *Biotechnol. Lett* 18 (7): 801–804.

14 Pointing, S.B. (2001). Feasibility of bioremediation by white-rot fungi. *Appl. Microbiol. Biotechnol.* 57 (1–2): 20–33.

15 Baborová, P., Möder, M., Baldrian, P. et al. (2006). Purification of a new manganese peroxidase of the white-rot fungus *Irpex lacteus*, and degradation of polycyclic aromatic hydrocarbons by the enzyme. *Res. Microbiol.* 157 (3): 248–253. http://doi.org/10.1016/j.resmic.2005.09.001.

16 Bezalel, L., Hadar, Y., and Cerniglia, C.E. (1996). Mineralization of polycyclic aromatic hydrocarbons by the white rot fungus *Pleurotus ostreatus*. *Appl. Environ. Microbiol.* 62 (1): 292–295.

17 Maiti, S.K. and Chowdhury, A. (2013). Effects of anthropogenic pollution on mangrove biodiversity: a review. *J. Environ. Prot.* 4 (12): 1428–1434.

18 Brito, E.M., Guyoneaud, R., Goñi-Urriza, M. et al. (2006). Characterization of hydrocarbonoclastic bacterial communities from mangrove sediments in Guanabara Bay, Brazil. *Res. Microbiol.* 157 (8): 752–762.

19 Andrade, L.L., Leite, D.C., Ferreira, E.M. et al. (2012). Microbial diversity and anaerobic hydrocarbon degradation potential in an oil-contaminated mangrove sediment. *BMC Microbiol.* 12: 186. http://doi.org/10.1186/1471-2180-12-186.

20 Ameen, F., Hadi, S., Moslem, M. et al. (2015). Biodegradation of engine oil by fungi from mangrove habitat. *J. Gen. Appl. Microbiol.* 61 (5): 185–192.

21 Barnes, N.M., Khodse, V.B., Lotlikar, N.P. et al. (2018). Bioremediation potential of hydrocarbon-utilizing fungi from select marine niches of India. *3 Biotech* 8 (1): 21. http://doi.org/10.1007/s13205-017-1043-8.

22 Fakhrzadegan, I., Hassanshahian, M., Askari Hesni, M., and Saadatfar, A. (2019). A study of crude oil-degrading bacteria from mangrove forests in the Persian Gulf. *Mar. Ecol.* 40 (2): e12544. http://doi.org/10.1111/maec.12544.

23 Leahy, J.G. and Colwell, R.R. (1990). Microbial degradation of hydrocarbons in the environment. *Microbiol. Rev.* 54 (3): 305–315.

24 Speight, J.G. (2011). Chemistry and chemical technology. In: *Handbook of Industrial Hydrocarbon Processes* (ed. J.G. Speight), 1–41. Elsevier http://doi.org/10.1016/B978-0-7506-8632-7.10001-5.

25 Abrajano, T.A., Yan, B., Song, J. et al. (2007). High-molecular-weight petrogenic and pyrogenic hydrocarbons in aquatic environments. In: *Treatise on Geochemistry* (ed. H.D. Holland and K.K. Turekian), 1–50. Elsevier.

26 Speight, J.G. (2017). Organic chemistry. In: *Environmental Organic Chemistry for Engineers* (ed. J.G. Speight), 43–86. Elsevier http://doi.org/10.1016/C2013-0-16021-7.

27 World Health Organization - Regional office for Europe Copenhagen *Air Quality Guidelines for Europe*, European Series, 2e, 91. WHO Regional Publications.

28 Weiss, V. and Edwards, J.M. (1980). *The Biosynthesis of Aromatic Compounds.* New York: Wiley.

29 Olah, G.A. (2005). Beyond oil and gas: the methanol economy. *Angew. Chem. Int. Ed.* 2636–2639.

30 Speight, J.G. (2012). *The Chemistry and Technology of Coal*, 3e. USA: CRC Press http://doi.org/10.1201/b12497.

31 Speight, J.G. (2014). *The Chemistry and Technology of Petroleum*, 5e. USA: CRC Press.

32 Moore, J.W. and Ramamoorthy, S. (1984). Aliphatic hydrocarbons. In: *Organic Chemicals in Natural Waters*, Springer Series on Environmental Management. New York: Springer http://doi.org/10.1007/978-1-4613-9538-6_3.

33 Mironov, O.G. (1968). Hydrocarbon pollution of the sea and its influence on marine organisms. *Helgol. Wiss. Meeresunters.* 17: 335–339.

34 Roser, M. and Ritchie, H. (2022). Oil spills. http://www.ourworldindata.org/oil-spills (accessed 15 January 2023).

35 Kingston, P.F. (2002). Long-term environmental impact of oil spills. *Spill Sci. Technol. Bull.* 7: 53–61. http://doi.org/10.1016/S1353-2561(02)00051-8.

36 Ossai, I.C., Ahmed, A., Hassan, A., and Hamid, F.S. (2020). Remediation of soil and water contaminated with petroleum hydrocarbon: a review. *Environ. Technol. Innovation* 17: 100526. http://doi.org/10.1016/j.eti.2019.100526.

37 Lin, Q. and Mendelssohn, I.A. (2009). Potential of restoration and phytoremediation with *Juncus roemerianus* for diesel-contaminated coastal wetlands. *Ecol. Eng.* 35: 85–91.

38 Abdullah, S.R.S., Al-Baldawi, I.A., Almansoory, A.F. et al. (2020). Plant-assisted remediation of hydrocarbons in water and soil: application, mechanisms, challenges and opportunities. *Chemosphere* 125932. http://doi.org/10.1016/j.chemosphere.2020.125932.

39 Stroud, J.L., Paton, G.I., and Semple, K.T. (2007). Microbe-aliphatic hydrocarbon interactions in soil: implications for biodegradation and bioremediation. *J. Appl. Microbiol.* 102 (5): 1239–1253. http://doi.org/10.1111/j.1365-2672.2007.03401.x.

40 Hussein, A.H., Lisowska, B.K., and Leak, D.J. (2015). Chapter One—the genus *Geobacillus* and their biotechnological potential. In: *Advances in Applied Microbiology* (ed. S. Sariaslani and G.M. Gadd). Cambridge, MA: Academic Press.

41 Daugulis, J. and McCracken, C.M. (2003). Microbial degradation of high and low molecular weight polyaromatic hydrocarbons in a two-phase partitioning bioreactor by two strains of *Sphingomonas* sp. *Biotechnol. Lett* 25 (17): 1441–1444.

42 Ameen, F., Moslem, M., Hadi, S., and Al-Sabri, A.E. (2016). Biodegradation of diesel fuel hydrocarbons by mangrove fungi from Red Sea Coast of Saudi Arabia. *Saudi J. Biol. Sci.* 23 (2): 211–218.

43 Bumpus, J.A., Tien, M., Wright, D. et al. (1985). Oxidation of persistent environmental pollutants by a white rot fungus. *Science* 228 (4706): 1434–1436.

44 Brodkorb, T.S. and Legge, R.L. (1992). Enhanced biodegradation of phenanthrene in oil tar-contaminated soils supplemented with *Phanerochaete chrysosporium*. *Appl. Environ. Microbiol.* 58 (9): 3117–3121.

45 Tomlinson, P.B. (1986). *The Botany of Mangroves*. New York: Cambridge University Press.

46 Duke, N.C., Meynecke, J., Dittmann, S. et al. (2007). A world without mangroves. *Science* 317: 41–42.

47 Webber, M., Calumpong, H., Ferreira, F. et al. (2016). Mangroves. In: *The First Global Integrated Marine Assessment: World Ocean Assessment I* (ed. L. Inniss, A. Simcock, A.Y. Ajawin, et al.), 877–886. Cambridge University Press.

48 Kelaher, B.P. (2003). Changes in habitat complexity negatively affect diverse gastropod assemblages in coralline algal turf. *Oecologia* 135: 431–441.

49 Chatting, M., Al-Maslamani, I., Walton, M. et al. (2022). Future mangrove carbon storage under climate change and deforestation. *Front. Mar. Sci.* 9: http://doi.org/10.3389/fmars.2022.781876.

50 Donato, D.C., Kauffman, J.B., Murdiyarso, D. et al. (2011). Mangroves among the most carbon-rich forests in the tropics. *Nat. Geosci.* 4: 293.

51 Nyanga, C. (2020). The role of mangroves forests in decarbonizing the atmosphere. In: *Carbon-Based Material for Environmental Protection and*

Remediation (ed. M. Bartoli, M. Frediani, and L. Rosi). IntechOpen http://doi.org/10.5772/intechopen.92249.

52 Analuddin, K., Sharma, S., Septiana, A. et al. (2017). Heavy metal bioaccumulation in mangrove ecosystem at the coral triangle ecoregion, Southeast Sulawesi, Indonesia. *Mar. Pollut. Bull.* 125: 472–480.

53 Office of Water (OW), United States Environmental Protection Agency (USEPA). (2018). Mangrove Swamps. Retrieved from: https://www.epa.gov/wetlands/mangrove-swamps (Accessed 14 January 2023).

54 Kathiresan, K. and Bingham, B.L. (2001). Biology of mangroves and mangrove ecosystems. *Adv. Mar. Biol.* 40: 81–251.

55 Kannappan, T., Shanmugavelu, M., and Karthikeya, M.M. (2012). Concentration on heavy metals in sediments and Magngroves from Manakudy Estuary (South West Coast of India). *Eur. J. Biol. Sci.* 4 (4): 109–113.

56 Sharma, S. (2018). Introductory chapter: mangrove ecosystem research trends - where has the focus been so far. In: *Mangrove Ecosystem Ecology and Function* (ed. S. Sharma). IntechOpen http://doi.org/10.5772/intechopen.80962.

57 Bunt, J.S. (1992). Introduction. In: *Tropical Mangrove Ecosystem*, 1–6. Washington, DC: American Geophysical Union.

58 Spalding, M. (1997). The global distribution and status of mangrove ecosystems. *Proceedings of the International News Letter of Coastal Management-Inter-Coastal Network*, Special Edition 1, pp. 20–21.

59 Kathiresan, K. (2011). Eco-biology of mangroves. In: *Mangroves: Ecology, Biology and Taxonomy* (ed. J.N. Metras), 1–50. New York, USA: Nova Science Publishers.

60 Quadros, A.F. and Zimmer, M. (2017). Dataset of “true mangroves” plant species traits. *Biodivers. Data J.* 5: 1–21.

61 Food and Agriculture Organization of the United Nations (FAO) (2007). The World’s mangroves 1980-2005. *FAO Forestry Paper* 153: 5.

62 Priyashantha, A.K.H. and Taufikurahman, T. (2020). Mangroves of Sri Lanka: distribution, status and conservation requirements. *Trop. Plant Res.* 7 (3): 654–668.

63 Spalding, M., Kainuma, M., and Collins, L. (2010). *World Atlas of Mangroves*, 1e. London: Earthscan Publishers Ltd.

64 Giri, C., Ochieng, E., Tieszen, L. et al. (2011). Status and distribution of mangrove forests of the world using earth observation satellite data. *Global Ecol. Biogeogr.* 20: 154–159.

65 Gevaña, D.T., Camacho, L.D., and Pulhin, J.M. (2018). Conserving mangroves for their blue carbon: insights and prospects for community-based mangrove management in Southeast Asia. In: *Threats to Mangrove Forests. Coastal Research Library* (ed. C. Makowski and C. Finkl). Cham: Springer http://doi.org/10.1007/978-3-319-73016-5_26.

66 Nansingh, P. and Jurawan, S. (1999). Environmental sensitivity of a tropical coastline (Trinidad, West Indies) to oil spills. *Spill Sci. Technol. Bull.* 5 (2): 161–172.

67 Duke, N.C., Burns, K.A., Swannell, R.P.J. et al. (2000). Dispersant use and a bioremediation strategy as alternate means of reducing the impacts of large oil spills on mangroves: the Gladstone field trials. *Mar. Pollut. Bull.* 41: 403–412.

68 Billah, M.M., Bhuiyan, M.K.A., Amran, M.I.U.A. et al. (2022). Polycyclic aromatic hydrocarbons (PAHs) pollution in mangrove ecosystems: global synthesis and future research directions. *Rev. Environ. Sci. Biotechnol.* 21: 747–770.

69 Valiela, I., Bowen, J.L., and York, J.K. (2001). Mangrove forests: one of the World's threatened major tropical environments: at least 35% of the area of mangrove forests has been lost in the past two decades, losses that exceed those for tropical rain forests and coral reefs, two other well-known threatened environments. *Theory Biosci.* 51 (10): 807–815.

70 Sadaba, R.B., Barnuevo, A.B., Madas, C.S. et al. (2009). Assessment of the short-term damage in the Guimaras mangrove forests by the M/T solar I oil spill. *Philipp. J. Nat. Sci.* Oil Spill Issue 55: 71–82.

71 Sadaba, R.B. and Barnuevo, A.B. (2010). Status of mangroves within Taklong Island National Marine Reserve, Nueva Valencia, Guimaras, Philippines: a one-year post spill monitoring study. *Mem. Fac. Fish.*Kagoshima University Special Issue 9–17.

72 Worthington, T. and Spalding, M. (2018). *Mangrove Restoration Potential: A Global Map Highlighting a Critical Opportunity*. University of Cambridge http://doi.org/10.17863/CAM.39153.

73 Yao, H., Sun, X., He, C. et al. (2019). Phyllosphere epiphytic and endophytic fungal community and network structures differ in a tropical mangrove ecosystem. *Microbiome* 7: 57.

74 Lee, N.L.Y., Huang, D., Quek, Z.B.R. et al. (2019). Mangrove-associated fungal communities are differentiated by geographic location and host structure. *Front. Microbiol.* 10: 2456.

75 Sridhar, K.R. (2004). Mangrove fungi in India. *Curr. Sci.* 86: 1586–1587.

76 Schmit, J.P. and Shearer, C.A. (2003). A checklist of mangrove–associated fungi, their geography and known host plants. *Mycotaxon* 80: 423–477.

77 Bandarupalli, D., Jones, E.B.G., Ghate, S.D. et al. (2021). Biodiversity of marine fungi in mangroves with reference to Muthupet mangroves, Tamil Nadu, east coast of India. *Mar. Biodivers.* 51: 88. http://doi.org/10.1007/s12526-021-01214-8.

78 Jones, E.B.G., Pang, K.-L., Abdel-Wahab, M.A. et al. (2019). An online resource for marine fungi. *Fungal Diversity* 96: 347–433.

79 Sawant, A. and Rodrigues, B.F. (2020). Biodegradation of residual petroleum hydrocarbons by using fungal endophytes from the mangrove ecosystem. *J. Adv. Sci. Res.* 11 (4): 257–264.

80 Bankole, P.O., Semple, K.T., Jeon, B.H. et al. (2020). Enhanced enzymatic removal of anthracene by the mangrove soil-derived fungus, *Aspergillus sydowii* BPOI. *Front. Environ. Sci. Eng.* 14: 113.

81 Wu, Y.R., Luo, Z.H., and Vrijmoed, L.L. (2010). Biodegradation of anthracene and benz[*a*]anthracene by two *Fusarium solani* strains isolated from mangrove sediments. *Bioresour. Technol.* 101 (24): 9666–9672.

82 Martínez-Hernández, I.A., Rivera-Cruz, M.d.C., Carballar-Hernández, S. et al. (2021). Arbuscular mycorrhizal colonization in a mangrove forest exposed to weathering oil for half a century. *Water Air Soil Pollut* 232: 34.

83 Aamir, M., Rai, K.K., Zehra, A. et al. (2020). Fungal endophytes: classification, diversity, ecological role, and their relevance in sustainable agriculture. In: *Microbial Endophytes* (ed. A. Kumar and V.K. Singh), 291–323. Cambridge: Woodhead Publishing.

84 Liu, A.R., Wu, X.P., and Xu, T. (2007). Research advances in endophytic fungi of mangrove. *J. Appl. Ecol.* 18 (4): 912–918.

85 Chatterjee, A. and Abraham, J. (2020). Chapter 2 - Mangrove endophytes: a rich source of bioactive substances. In: *Biotechnological Utilization of Mangrove Resources* (ed. J.K. Patra, R.R. Mishra, and H. Thatoi), 27–47. ScienceDirect; Academic Press.

86 Sital, V.D., Da Silva, P.N.B., and Pestano, F. (2020). Investigating the diversity of endophytic fungi colonizing leaves of three species of mangroves in Corentyne, Berbice, Guyana. *GSC Biol. Pharm. Sci.* 13 (3): 244–250.

87 Zhu, F., Chen, G., Chen, X. et al. (2011). Aspergicin, a new antibacterial alkaloid produced by mixed fermentation of two marine-derived mangrove epiphytic fungi. *Chem. Nat. Compd.* 47: 767–769.

88 Deshmukh, S.K., Gupta, M.K., Prakash, V., and Reddy, M.S. (2018). Mangrove-associated fungi: a novel source of potential anticancer compounds. *J. Fungi* 4 (3): 101.

89 Voříšková, J. and Baldrian, P. (2013). Fungal community on decomposing leaf litter undergoes rapid successional changes. *ISME J.* 7: 477–486.

90 Kumar, A. and Chandra, R. (2020). Ligninolytic enzymes and its mechanisms for degradation of lignocellulosic waste in environment. *Heliyon* 6 (2): e03170. http://doi.org/10.1016/j.heliyon.2020.e03170.

91 Bonugli-Santos, R.C., Durrant, L.R., Da Silva, M., and Sette, L.D. (2010). Production of laccase, manganese peroxidase and lignin peroxidase by Brazilian marine-derived fungi. *Enzym. Microbiol. Technol.* 46: 32–37.

92 Potin, O., Veignie, E., and Rafin, C. (2004). Biodegradation of polycyclic aromatic hydrocarbons (PAHs) by *Cladosporium sphaerospermum* isolated from an aged PAH contaminated soil. *FEMS Microbiol. Ecol.* 51 (1): 71–78.

93 Akaji, Y., Inoue, T., Taniguchi, T. et al. (2022). Arbuscular mycorrhizal fungal communities of a mangrove forest along a salinity gradient on Iriomote Island. *Plant Soil* 472: 145–159.

94 Smith, S.E. and Read, D.J. (2008). *Mycorrhizal Symbiosis*, 3e. New York: Academic Press.

95 Brundrett, M.C. (2009). Mycorrhizal associations and other means of nutrition of vascular plants: understanding the global diversity of host plants by resolving conflicting information and developing reliable means of diagnosis. *Plant Soil* 320: 33–77.

96 D'Souza, J. and Rodrigues, B.F. (2013). Biodiversity of arbuscular mycorrhizal (AM) fungi in mangroves of Goa in West India. *J. For. Res.* 24: 515–523.

97 Gupta, N., Bihari, K.M., and Sengupta, I. (2016). Diversity of arbuscular mycorrhizal fungi in different salinity of mangrove ecosystem of Odisha, India. *Adv. Plants Agric. Res.* 3: 19–23.

98 Evelin, H., Kapoor, R., and Giri, B. (2009). Arbuscular mycorrhizal fungi in alleviation of salt stress: a review. *Ann. Bot.* 104: 1263–1280.

99 Arfi, Y., Marchand, C., Wartel, M., and Record, E. (2012). Fungal diversity in anoxic-sulfidic sediments in a mangrove soil. *Fungal Ecol.* 5 (2): 282–285.

100 Ghizelini, A.M., Mendonça-Hagler, L.C.S., and Macrae, A. (2012). Microbial diversity in Brazilian mangrove sediments: a mini review. *Braz. J. Microbiol.* 43 (4): 1242–1254.

101 Haldar, S. and Nazareth, S.W. (2019). Diversity of fungi from mangrove sediments of Goa, India, obtained by metagenomic analysis using Illumina sequencing. *3 Biotech* 9 (5): 164.

102 Devadatha, B., Jones, E.B.G., Pang, K.L. et al. (2021). Occurrence and geographical distribution of mangrove fungi. *Fungal Diversity* 106: 137–227.

103 Zhang, Z.-F., Pan, Y.-P., Liu, Y., and Li, M. (2021). High-level diversity of basal fungal lineages and the control of fungal community assembly by stochastic processes in mangrove sediments. *Appl. Environ. Microbiol.* 87 (17): http://doi.org/10.1128/aem.00928-21.

104 Li, K., Chen, S., Pang, X. et al. (2022). Natural products from mangrove sediments-derived microbes: structural diversity, bioactivities, biosynthesis, and total synthesis. *Eur. J. Med. Chem.* 230: 114117.

105 Findlay, R.H., Fell, J.W., Coleman, N.K., and Vestal, J.R. (1986). Biochemical indicators of the role of fungi and thraustochytrids in mangrove detrital systems. In: *The Biology of Marine Fungi* (ed. S.T. Moss), 91–104. Cambridge: Cambridge University Press.

106 Holguin, G., Vazquez, P., and Bashan, Y. (2001). The role of sediment microorganisms in the productivity, conservation, and rehabilitation of mangrove ecosystems: an overview. *Biol. Fertil. Soils* 33: 265–278.

107 Zainith, S., Chowdhary, P., Mani, S., and Mishra, S. (2020). Microbial ligninolytic enzymes and their role in bioremediation. In: *Microorganisms for Sustainable Environment and Health* (ed. P. Chowdhary, D. Verma, A. Raj, and Y. Akhter), 179–203. Elsevier.

108 Niladevi, K. (2009). Ligninolytic enzymes. In: *Biotechnology for Agro-Industrial Residues Utilisation* (ed. P. Singh nee' Nigam and A. Pandey). Dordrecht: Springer http://doi.org/10.1007/978-1-4020-9942-7_22.

109 Kanayama, N., Tohru, S., and Keiichi, K. (2002). Purification and characterization of an alkaline manganese peroxidase from *Aspergillus terreus* LD-1. *J. Biosci. Bioeng.* 93 (4): 405–410.

110 Saparrat, M.C.N., Martínez, M.J., Tournier, H.A. et al. (2000). Production of ligninolytic enzymes by *Fusarium solani* strains isolated from different substrata. *World J. Microbiol. Biotechnol.* 16: 799–803.

111 Bagewadi, Z.K., Mulla, S.I., and Ninnekar, H.Z. (2017). Purification and immobilization of laccase from *Trichoderma harzianum* strain HZN10 and its application in dye decolorization. *J. Genet. Eng. Biotechnol.* 15 (1): 139–150.

112 Abu Ghalia, M. and Dahman, Y. (2017). Synthesis and utilization of natural fiber-reinforced poly (lactic acid) bionanocomposites. In: *Lignocellulosic Fibre and Biomass-Based Composite Materials* (ed. M. Jawaid, M.T. Paridah, and N. Saba), 313–345. Woodhead Publishing.

113 Heinzkill, M., Bech, L., Halkier, T. et al. (1998). Characterization of laccases and peroxidases from wood-rotting fungi (family Coprinaceae). *Appl. Environ. Microbiol.* 64 (5): 1601–1606.

114 Viswanath, B., Rajesh, B., Janardhan, A. et al. (2014). Fungal laccases and their applications in bioremediation. *Enzyme Res.* 2014: 163242. http://doi.org/10.1155/2014/163242.

115 Shraddha, Shekher, R., Sehgal, S. et al. (2011). Laccase: microbial sources, production, purification, and potential biotechnological applications. *Enzyme Res.* 2011: 1–11. http://doi.org/10.4061/2011/217861.

116 Thurston, C.F. (1994). The structure and function of fungal laccases. *Microbiology* 140 (1): 19–26.

117 Bourbonnais, R. and Paice, M.G. (1996). Enzymatic delignification of Kraft pulp using laccase and a mediator. *Tappi J.* 79 (6): 199–204.

118 Martinho, V., Dos Santos Lima, L.M., Barros, C.A. et al. (2019). Enzymatic potential and biosurfactant production by endophytic fungi from mangrove forest in southeastern Brazil. *AMB Express* 9 (1): 130.

119 Arregui, L., Ayala, M., Gómez-Gil, X. et al. (2019). Laccases: structure, function, and potential application in water bioremediation. *Microb. Cell Fact.* 18: 200.

120 Youn, H.-D., Hah, Y.C., and Kang, S.-O. (1995). Role of laccase in lignin degradation by white-rot fungi. *FEMS Microbiol. Lett.* 132 (3): 183–188.

121 Gianfreda, L., Xu, F., and Bollag, J.M. (1999). Laccases: a useful group of oxidoreductive enzymes. *Biorem. J.* 3 (1): 1–25.

122 Thakker, G.D., Evans, C.S., and Koteswara Rao, K. (1992). Purification and characterization of laccase from *Monocillium indicum* Saxena. *Appl. Microbiol. Biotechnol.* 37 (3): 321–323.

123 Bentil, J.A. (2021). Biocatalytic potential of basidiomycetes: relevance, challenges and research interventions in industrial processes. *Sci. Afr.* 11: e00717. http://doi.org/10.1016/j.sciaf.2021.e00717.

124 Kunamneni, A., Ballesteros, A., Plou, F.J., and Alcalde, M. (2007). Fungal laccase – a versatile enzyme for biotechnological applications. In: *Communicating Current Research and Educational Topics and Trends in Applied Microbiology* (ed. A. Méndez-Vilas), 233–245. Badajoz: FORMATEX.

125 Kumar, A. and Arora, P.K. (2022). Biotechnological applications of manganese peroxidases for sustainable management. *Front. Environ. Sci.* 10: http://doi.org/10.3389/fenvs.2022.875157.

126 Saikia, S., Yadav, M., Hoque, R.A., and Yadav, H.S. (2022). Bioremediation mediated by manganese peroxidase – an overview. *Biocatal. Biotransform.* 1–13. http://doi.org/10.1080/10242422.2022.2113517.

127 Sundaramoorthy, M., Gold, M.H., and Poulos, T.L. (2010). Ultrahigh (0.93 Å) resolution structure of manganese peroxidase from *Phanerochaete* *chrysosporium*: implications for the catalytic mechanism. *J. Inorg. Biochem.* 104 (6): 683–690.

128 Chang, Y., Yang, D., Li, R. et al. (2021). Textile dye biodecolorization by manganese peroxidase: a review. *Molecules* 26: 4403.

129 Hofrichter, M. (2002). Review: lignin conversion by manganese peroxidase (MnP). *Enzyme Microb. Technol.* 30 (4): 454–466.

130 Paszczynski, A., Huynh, V.B., and Crawford, R. (1985). Enzymatic activities of an extracellular, manganese-dependent peroxidase from *Phanerochaete chrysosporium*. *FEMS Microbiol. Lett.* 29: 37–41.

131 Wong, W.S.D. (2009). Structure and action mechanism of ligninolytic enzymes. *Appl. Biochem. Biotechnol.* 157: 174–209.

132 Falade, A.O., Nwodo, U.U., Iweriebor, B.C. et al. (2016). Lignin peroxidase functionalities and prospective applications. *MicrobiologyOpen* 6 (1): e00394.

133 Choinowski, T., Blodig, W., Winterhalter, K.H., and Piontek, K. (1992). The crystal structure of lignin peroxidase at 1.70 Å resolution reveals a hydroxy group on the Cβ of tryptophan 171: a novel radical site formed during the redox cycle. *J. Mol. Biol.* 286: 809–827.

134 Edwards, S.L., Raag, R., Wariishi, H. et al. (1993). Crystal structure of lignin peroxidase. *Proc. Natl. Acad. Sci.* 90: 750–754.

135 Baciocchi, E., Bietti, M., Gerini, M.F., and Lanzalunga, O. (2002). The mediation of veratryl alcohol in oxidations promoted by lignin peroxidase: the lifetime of veratryl alcohol radical cation. *Biochem. Biophys. Res. Commun.* 293: 832–835.

136 Valli, K., Wariishi, H., and Gold, M.H. (1990). Oxidation of monomethoxylated aromatic compounds by lignin peroxidase: role of veratryl alcohol in lignin biodegradation. *Biochemistry* 29: 8535–8539. http://doi.org/10.1021/bi00489a005.

137 Glenn, J.K., Morgan, M.A., Mayfield, M.B. et al. (1983). An extracellular H_2O_2-requiring enzyme preparation involved in lignin biodegradation by the white rot basidiomycete, *Phanerochaete chrysosporium*. *Biochem. Biophys. Res. Commun.* 114: 1077–1083.

138 Tien, M. and Kirk, K. (1983). Lignin-degrading enzyme from the hymenomycete *Phanerochaete chrysosporium*. *Science* 221: 661–663.

139 Johansson, T., Welinder, K.G., and Nyman, P.O. (1993). Isozymes of lignin peroxidase and manganese (II) peroxidase from the white-rot basidiomycete *Trametes versicolor*. II. Partial sequences, peptide maps, and amino acid and carbohydrate compositions. *Arch. Biochem. Biophys.* 300: 57–62.

140 Moilanen, A.M., Lundell, T., Vares, T., and Hatakka, A. (1996). Manganese and malonate are individual regulators for the production of lignin and manganese peroxidase isozymes and in the degradation of lignin by *Phlebia radiata*. *Appl. Microbiol. Biotechnol.* 45: 792–799.

141 Sugiura, T., Yamagishi, K., Kimura, T. et al. (2009). Cloning and homologous expression of novel lignin peroxidase genes in the white-rot fungus *Phanerochaete sordida* YK-624. *Biosci., Biotechnol., Biochem.* 73: 17931798.

142 Egwim, E.C., Kabiru, A.Y., and Tola, A. (2015). Partial characterization of lignin peroxidase expressed by bacterial and fungal isolates from termite gut. *Biokemistri* 27 (1): 33–38.

143 Mtui, G. and Masalu, R. (2016). Extracellular enzymes from brown-rot fungus *Laetiporus sulphureus* isolated from mangrove forests of coastal Tanzania. *Int. J. Histol. Cytol.* 4 (4): 310–317.

144 Kulshreshtha, S., Mathur, N., and Bhatnagar, P. (2014). Mushroom as a product and their role in mycoremediation. *AMB Express* 4: 29.

145 Harry-Asobara, J.L. and Kamei, I. (2019). Growth management of white-rot fungus *Phlebia brevispora* improved degradation of high-molecular-weight polycyclic aromatic hydrocarbons. *3 Biotech* 9 (11): 403.

146 Yadav, M. and Yadav, H.S. (2015). Applications of ligninolytic enzymes to pollutants, wastewater, dyes, soil, coal, paper and polymers. *Environ. Chem. Lett.* 13: 309–318. http://doi.org/10.1007/s10311-015-0516-4.

147 Duran, N. and Esposito, E. (2000). Potential applications of oxidative enzymes and phenoloxidase like compounds in waste water and soil treatment. *Appl. Catal., B* 28: 83–89.

148 Sasek, V. (2003). Why mycoremediations have not yet come into practice. In: *The Utilization of Bioremediation to Reduce Soil Contamination: Problems and Solutions* (ed. V. Sasek, J.A. Glaser, and P. Baveye), 247–260. Amsterdam: Kluwer Academic Publishers.

149 Mate, D.M. and Alcalde, M. (2017). Laccase: a multi-purpose biocatalyst at the forefront of biotechnology. *Microb. Biotechnol.* 10 (6): 1457–1467.

150 D'Souza-Ticlo, D., Sharma, D., and Raghukumar, C.A. (2009). Thermostable metal-tolerant laccase with bioremediation potential from a marine-derived fungus. *Mar. Biotechnol.* 11: 725–737. http://doi.org/10.1007/s10126-009-9187-0.

151 De Paula, N.M., da Silva, K., Brugnari, T. et al. (2022). Biotechnological potential of fungi from a mangrove ecosystem: enzymes, salt tolerance and decolorization of a real textile effluent. *Microbiol. Res.* 254: 126899. http://doi.org/10.1016/j.micres.2021.126899.

7

Industrially Important Microbial Enzymes Production and Their Applications

Gebiru Sinshaw[1,2,3], *Abate Ayele*[1,2], *Gamachis Korsa*[1,2], *Gessesse K. Bekele*[1,2], *and Mesfin T. Gemeda*[1,2]

[1] *Addis Ababa Science and Technology University, College of Natural and Applied Science, Department of Biotechnology, P.O. Box 16417, Addis Ababa 1000, Ethiopia*

[2] *Addis Ababa Science and Technology University, Biotechnology and Bioprocess Center of Excellence, Addis Ababa 1000, Ethiopia*

[3] *Debre Berhan University, College of Natural and Computational Sciences, Department of Biotechnology, P.O. Box 445, Debre Berhan 1000, Ethiopia*

7.1 Introduction

Enzymes are molecules that are found in small amounts in the cells of living things and can speed up chemical reactions without changing themselves in the process [1]. They work in a wide range of industries, including those that produce food, fermented products, animal nutrition, detergents, cosmetics, brewing, paper, and pulp, pharmaceuticals (medicine), textiles, laundry, and biofuels, as well as research and development [2–4].

With their many useful applications in industry, enzymes are the potential catalysts in biological processes that have attracted attention from researchers throughout the world. Microorganisms have been discovered to be a very useful source for enzyme production due to their wide range of diversity in biochemical structure, ease of manipulating their genetic structure, and potential in a huge range of culture conditions. Even though there are many sources from which enzymes can be extracted and purified, such as microbial, plant, and animal sources, microorganisms have been discovered to be very useful sources for enzyme production [5].

Industrial enzymes come from bacteria, animals, and plants. But because of the significant yield they provide and the cost and labor savings, microorganisms are used to make these enzymes. According to a source called *Global Industrial Enzymes Markets*, 7th edition, Marketresearch.com, the market for industrial enzymes was estimated to reach US$6 billion in 2017, $12.16 billion in 2022, and $16.9 billion by 2027 at a compound annual growth rate (CAGR) of 6.8% [6].

Production of microbial enzymes is a crucial process in the industrial sectors because of the high and superior performances of enzymes from various microorganisms, which work successfully under a wide range of varied physical and

Microbial Enzymes: Production, Purification, and Industrial Applications, First Edition.
Edited by Dinesh Yadav, Pankaj Chowdhary, Gautam Anand, and Rajarshi Kumar Gaur.

chemical conditions. Additionally, medical diseases associated with a genetically caused deficiency in human enzymes are treated by microbial enzymes. Microbial enzymes are utilized in industrial applications in addition to rising consumer goods demand, the need to minimize costs, the depletion of natural resources, and environmental safety [7–9].

Microbial enzymes have gained attention for their wide range of applications in industries and medicine because they are more stable, catalytically active, and easy to generate than plant and animal enzymes. Enzymes are being utilized more and more frequently in a wide range of industries, including food, agriculture, chemicals, and medicine, because of their short processing times, low energy requirements, affordability, nontoxic nature, and environmental friendliness. Enzyme progress in industrial fields is hampered, nonetheless, by their stability and high cost [10].

The enzymes isolated and extracted from microbial sources are more significant than those generated from animals or plants due to their stability. The ability to easily produce microbial enzymes in huge quantities utilizing incredibly cost-effective fermentation procedures is a fundamental component of exploiting them for applications in the food sector [11]. Because of industrial applications, the usage of a combination of these different pectinase classes, together with cellulase and hemicelluloses, should be advised. To break down all components of a polymer at optimal levels of degradation, several pectinases, cellulases, and hemicelluloses are required. This technique is often employed by the industry that makes fruit juice [12].

By applying directed evolution to the entire pathway, engineered proteins can be found that synergistically improve the phenotype either through a balanced flux of the pathway or through an improvement in overall protein activity [13]. The enhancement of protein functions is also produced through directed evolution guided by machine learning. Since it has been used in microorganisms to diversify the target sequence, transform the resulting library of mutant sequences into cells (the platform), and screen or select the required character [3, 14].

This chapter is focused on an overview of industrially important microbial enzymes, their sources and applications, the technologies currently used for the modification of enzymes to increase their productivity and characterization, and challenges and future perspectives.

7.2 Sources of Industrially Important Microbial Enzymes

Industries that generate microbial enzymes choose from a variety of microorganisms, including bacteria, fungi, yeasts, and archaea. Figure 7.1. Although many enzymes are produced in industries, protease, amylase, glucose isomerase, and glucoamylase are the most common enzymes that are produced on a large scale in industries [15].

The majority of the readily available enzyme manufacturers are microorganisms. Due to their clean, economical, and environmentally friendly applications, as well as their importance in many biotechnological processes, rapid growth rate,

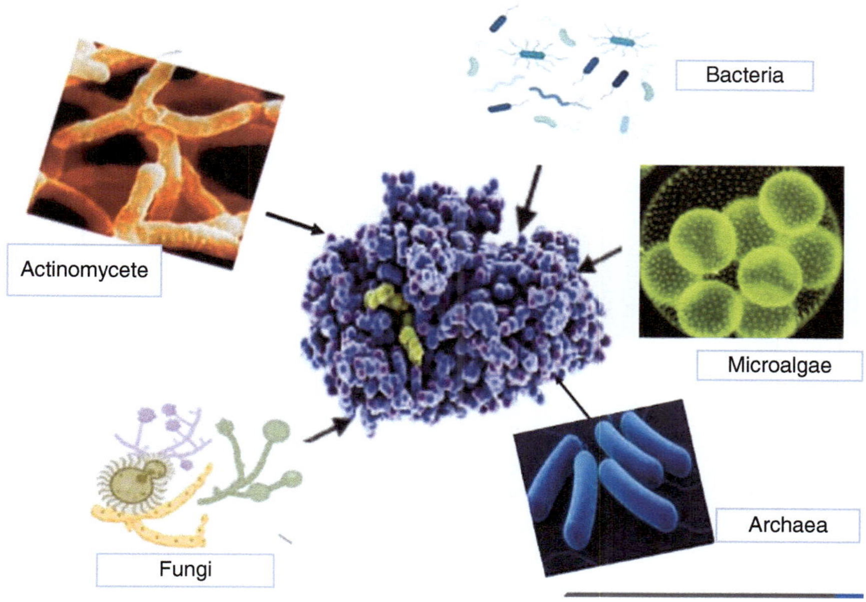

Figure 7.1 Different sources of microbial enzymes.

and ease of nutritional requirement, microbial enzymes are becoming more and more necessary every day [14, 16–18]. Enzymes' distinctive qualities, such as their thermophilic nature, tolerance to a wide range of pH, and stability of enzyme activity under other difficult reaction circumstances, pique our interest in using them for commercial and industrial purposes [19].

7.2.1 Microbial Enzyme Production

The study of chemicals and knowledge of the physiology of microorganisms are both required to scale up a fermentation process properly. Submerged fermentation (SmF) and solid-state fermentation (SSF) are the two most important fermentation technologies. Although SSF has lately had a rebirth in significance for a limited few applications and specific industries, the majority of industries still employ SmF to make enzymes [20].

The development of a low-cost medium for the manufacture of microbial enzymes is crucial to meeting industrial demand. Both SmF and SSF can be used to produce it [21]. Research has been done on under-submerged (SmF) microbial enzyme production as well as SSF [22]. Physical factors like pH, temperature, agitation/aeration, inoculum sizes, incubation times, nutrients like carbon, nitrogen, trace elements, and vitamins in SmF and SSF (Table 7.1), as well as moisture content, water activity, and substrate particle size, are essential for growth and the production of microbial enzymes. Microbial enzyme generation and growth at high temperatures and pH levels are of the greatest significance due to their use in various industries [39].

Table 7.1 Production of microbial enzymes, sources, and their applications in various industries.

Enzyme	Substrate	Microbial sources	Temp (°C)	Ferm.	Industries	Main function	References
Amylolytic enzymes (bacteria), amylolytic enzymes (fungi)	Banana, mango, orange, mixed fruit pomace waste	*Fusariumsolani, Rhizopusstolonifer, Aspergillus oryzae, Lactobacillus*	90–100 50–60	SSF	Brewing, fruit	Starch-degrading	[23–25]
Lignocellulolytic enzymes and laccases	Orange bagasse, banana waste, palm oil fiber	*Pseudomonas putida, Pseudomonas fluorescence*	45–55	SSF	Texturizing and flavoring of products	Hydrolyze complex polysaccharides into fermentable sugars	[23, 26]
Pectinolytic enzymes (pectinase)	Pineapple, orange, lemon, mixed fruit	*Aspergillus niger, Penicillium chrysogenum, Aspergillus foetidus, Lactobacillus*	—	SSF	Food and wine industries	Catalyze the breakdown of substrates containing pectin	[24, 27, 28]
Tannase	Grape peel	*Trichoderma viride*	—	SSF	Brewing tea	Degradation of gallotannins and ellagicitannins	[23, 29, 30]
Protease	Mango, potato peel, orange, and papaya	*Bacillus subtilis, Aspergillus niger*	65–85	SSF	Wine, dairy, meat, baking, and detergent industry	Enzymes that break down protein and meat tenderization	[23, 31, 32]
Lipase	Lemon peel, watermelon, orange bagasse	*Chaloropsisthielarioides, Colletotrichum,* and *gloesporioides, Aspergillus oryzae*	30–70	SSF Slurry state	Fats and oils, milk, cheese, and detergent industry	Hydrolyze fats into fatty acids	[33, 34]

Invertase	Orange peel, pineapple peel, pomegranate peel, carrot peels, red carrot jam processing residue	*Aspergillus niger*, *Aspergillus flavus*	—	SSF	Sweetener, sugar, and confectionery	By hydrolysis of production of high disucrose	[23, 35]
Catalase	Orange, watermelon, mixed fruit pomace waste	*Vibrio rumoiensis*, *Lactobacillus*	—	SSF	—	Decomposition of hydrogen peroxide to water and oxygen	[24, 36–38]
Xylanase	Mango, guyabano, passion fruit, passion fruit	*Trichoderma reesei* All *Aspergillus niger* species	45–65	SSF	Pulp and paper, bioleaching, and food	Breakdown of xylan at the β-1,3D-xylanosidic bond	[39, 40]
Polygalactouranase	Tomato and orange peel	*Aspergillus niger*	—	SSF	Fruit juice extraction, tea fermentation, and wastewater treatment	Hydrolyzes the alpha-1,4 glycosidic bonds between galacturonic acid	[11]
Glucoamylase	banana peel, pineapple pee	*Aspergillus* sp., *Aspergillus awamori*, and *Rhizopus oryzae*	—	SMF	Production beer and ethanol	Produce high-glucose syrup	[41]

Ferm, fermentation; Func, function; SMF, submerged fermentation; SSF, solid-state fermentation; Temp, temperature

7.2.1.1 Solid-state Fermentation

According to Costa et al. [42], SSF is a three-phase heterogeneous process that includes solid, liquid, and gaseous phases. High volumetric productivity, much higher product concentration, a decrease in effluent generation, and the requirement for basic fermentation equipment are three of the main advantages of SSF. The biosynthesis of microbial enzymes in the SmF process is also commercially important due to the enormous impact that catabolic and end-product repressions have on it. It is known that the SSF method can use up to 20–30% substrate, in contrast to the SmF method's maximum of 5% [43].

The choice of the type of appropriate substrate and the pretreatment of the substrate are the main variables that influence the microbial production of enzymes in an SSF system. Other key factors are the kind and amount of the inoculum, the length of cultivation, the gaseous atmosphere, the temperature control of fermenting matter, and the elimination of metabolic heat [39].

7.2.1.2 Submerged Fermentation

The growth of microorganisms in a liquid nutrient broth is known as SmF. This method can be used to create industrial enzymes. Specifically, chosen bacteria and fungi are grown in confined vessels with a rich nutrient broth (the fermentation medium) and a lot of oxygen in this process. The desired enzymes are released into the solution by the microorganisms as they break down the nutrients [44].

To maintain uniform conditions throughout the experiment and to scale up the process easily, SmF is preferred [39]. During SmF, microorganisms are grown in a liquid medium with a high oxygen content. The viscosity of the broth is the fundamental difficulty with fungal SmFs. Because of restrictions in mass and oxygen transfer, the formation of mycelium and the proliferation of fungal cells obstruct impeller performance. It is suitable for the manufacture of enzymes utilizing natural substrates like agricultural waste by SmF and SSF of microbial enzymes because SmF mimics the conditions in which fungi normally thrive [43, 45].

7.3 Application of Microbial Enzymes in Industries

The speed and selectivity of many biotechnological reactions and metabolic processes are greatly accelerated by enzymes. This includes both DNA synthesis and food digestion. In addition, the majority of enzymes are used in a variety of industrial processes, including those related to animal feed, food processing, polymer synthesis, paper and pulp production, detergent production, pharmaceutical production, textile production, and biofuel production. In a variety of industrial processes, protease, cellulase, xylanase, amylase, and lipases are a few of the enzymes that are commercially used in Figure 7.2 [43, 47, 48].

7.3.1 Food Industry

The United Nations Department of Economics projects that by 2050, the global population will rise from 6.9 billion to 9.1 billion, and food demand will have increased

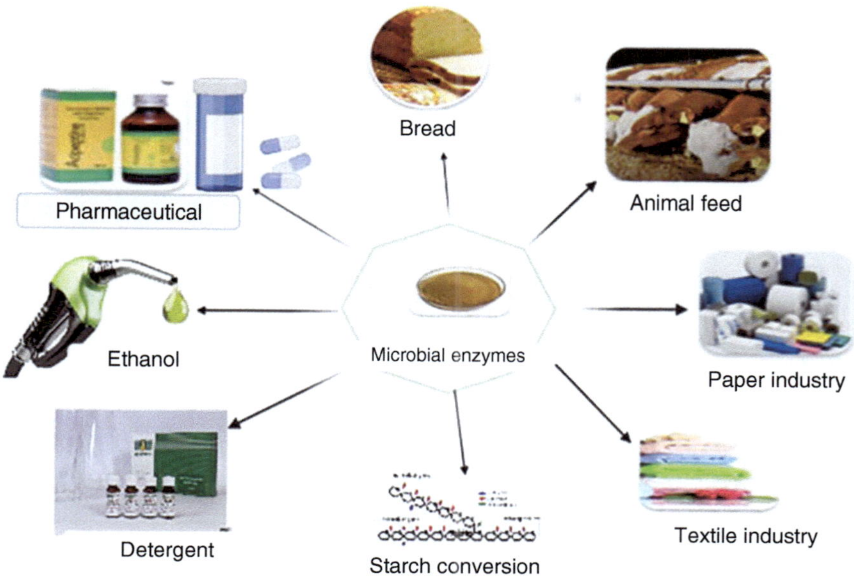

Figure 7.2 Microbial enzymes in different industrial applications [14, 46]. Source: Singh et al. [3]/Springer Nature/CC BY 4.0.

by 70%. The use of enzymes in the food business can help address the problem of a high-quality food supply, and reducing food waste is one of the main objectives of the current study as well as a target established by the UN to create a more sustainable world by 2030 [49]. Additionally, microbial enzymes effectively contribute to the synthesis of food and its other qualities, including nutritional value, flavor, texture, color, and appearance [50].

Several natural functional foods and products are seen as a difficult undertaking for scientists to reduce risks to global health. Functional elements obtained from food are not only consumed for taste but also because they provide nutrients for human health and well-being. As a result, creating foods and food-based products with bioactive components is difficult. Due to several advantages, enzymatic use in the manufacturing of functional foods is one of the green technologies attracting the greatest amount of study [51].

7.3.1.1 Baking Industry

The baking industry currently heavily relies on enzymes, with an estimated 6–8% yearly growth rate. Exogenous enzymes can be added to major baked goods, such as bread, pastries, cakes, and cookies, to achieve particular quality characteristics. Three of the six enzyme types can be added to dough formulations to enhance them for bread. Amylases have a variety of functions that help a loaf of bread's quality [15].

Glucoamylase, known as amyloglucosidase (EC 3.2.1.3), is a biocatalyst that inverts the anomeric structure of a-1, 4 glycosidic linkages in raw (sparsely soluble) or soluble starches and related oligosaccharides to produce β-glucose. It is one of the most significant and widely used enzymes in the baking industry [52, 53].

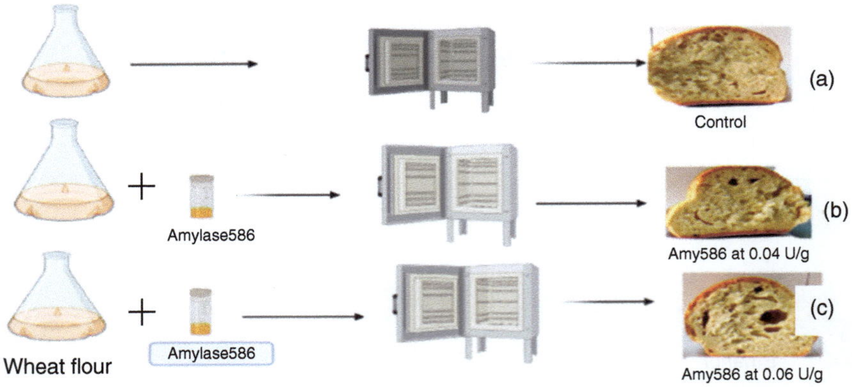

Figure 7.3 Performance evaluation of the purified amylases Amy586 on bread properties. (a) The control, (b) addition of Amy586 at 0.04 U/g of flour, and (c) addition of Amy586 at 0.06 U/g of wheat flour. Source: Trabelsi et al. [57]/with permission of John Wiley & Sons.

Along with a-1, 4 links, the enzyme also slowly hydrolyzes a-1, 6 bonds of glycosidic starch. According to Norouzian et al. [54], the production of glucoamylases involves submerged, solid-state, and semisolid-state fermentation in stirred tank vessels, airlift reactors, or stacked trays. The output of glucoamylase is influenced by the bioreactor's design and method of operation. Additionally, it produces bioreactors that are flask-, tray-, rotary-, and column-based (horizontal and vertical) [55].

Nowadays, filamentous fungi like *Aspergillus niger, Rhizopus niveus*, and *Rhizopus delemar* are the main sources of commercial glucoamylases. These biocatalysts, which have slow catalytic activity and intermediate thermostability, are used to produce glucose in large quantities from raw starch or soluble oligonucleotides [56]. Glucoamylase may catalyze the hydrolysis of −1, 4 and −1, 6 glycosidic linkages from nonreducing ends of starch and related oligosaccharides to produce -D-glucose. The bread's quality in the control and experimental parts differs substantially even if the amylase content fluctuates, as (Figure 7.3) demonstrates [58].

7.3.1.2 Beverage Industry

Enzymes are cutting-edge alternatives to chemical or mechanical techniques for enhancing yield and quality in the beverage industry. The most often utilized enzymes in the beverage sector are pectinase, amylase, cellulase, and xylanase [59].

Enzymes are triggered throughout the malting and fermentation processes. They have also been necessary for the brewing process and the production of low-calorie beer [60]. Early in the brewing process, fermentable sugar breaks down from starch. Amylase and glucoamylase enzymes are added to starch to aid in digestion [61]. Additionally, it is crucial to use unmalted cereal grains such as adjuncts, rice, and maize. To boost yeast fermentation yield, the wort's maltose and tiny dextrin levels are raised. Generally speaking, introducing a microbial enzyme (amylase) encourages the gelatinization of starch and improves yield from nutrients for the fermentation process, speeds up the process, and changes the flavor, color, and clarity of the finished product [59].

7.3.1.3 Animal Feed

Production of natural enzyme-supplemented feed is anticipated to increase in the future because the animal feed industry is one of the most rapidly expanding industries in the world [62]. With a 6.4% CAGR from 2022 to 2031, the market for dairy enzymes is projected to increase from 574.2 million dollars in 2021 to 1.1 billion dollars by 2031. Production of feed enzymes has continuously expanded to keep up with the rising global demand for milk and meat [63].

Feed enzymes are gaining importance as they can increase the digestibility of nutrients and feed utilization by animals. Phytase, proteases, glucanase, xylanase, amylase, and polygalacturonase are the most common enzymes found in poultry feed. These hydrolytic enzymes remove antinutritional factors from feed ingredients and improve feed digestibility in the animal gut [64]. Monogastric animals are unable to digest plant-based meals containing significant levels of cellulose and hemicellulose. Proteases are also used to overcome antinutritional factors by degrading proteins into their constituent amino acids [65].

7.3.1.4 Fruit Juice Industry

In addition to harnessing microbial enzymes (such as pectinase and amylase), fruit juice is also produced. Pectinase, xylanase, and cellulase are enzymes that improve the separation of juice from pulp [26]. Pectinases and amylases are used in the cleaning of juices. In a process similar to this, enzymes are widely used in the production of wine to increase yield and enhance the extraction of vital components [66]. To process and clarify fruit juice, enzymes including catalase, amylase, and pectinases are utilized [19]. This increases yield and improves efficiency and cost-effectiveness in the beverage industry.

According to Patel et al. [20], enzymes can be used to hydrolyze proteins (neutral proteinase), hydrolyze starch (typically alpha-amylases), reduce filtering issues brought on by malt's beta-glucan content, and manage haze during maturation, filtration, and storage shown (Figure 7.4) below.

7.3.2 Pharmaceutical (Medicine) Industries

For example, group protection and deprotection, selective acylation and deacylation, selective hydrolysis, deracemization, kinetic resolution of racemic mixtures, esterification, transesterification, and many other chemical transformation reactions are highly applicable due to the unique properties of enzymes in the pharmaceutical industry [67]. Enzymes have a variety of vital roles in the pharmaceutical and diagnostic industries. Microbial enzymes are used for a variety of medical purposes, with the removal of dead skin and the treatment of burns being two of the most common. The potent fibrinolytic enzyme nattokinase is a potential thrombosis treatment technique [65].

In the pharmaceutical industry, microbial enzymes have a significant role in the treatment of infectious diseases, cancer, and other disorders, as well as in the repair of damaged tissue and other treatments [68]. The treatment of wounds, cancer, infectious diseases, and digestive disorders all make use of proteases, which comprise a

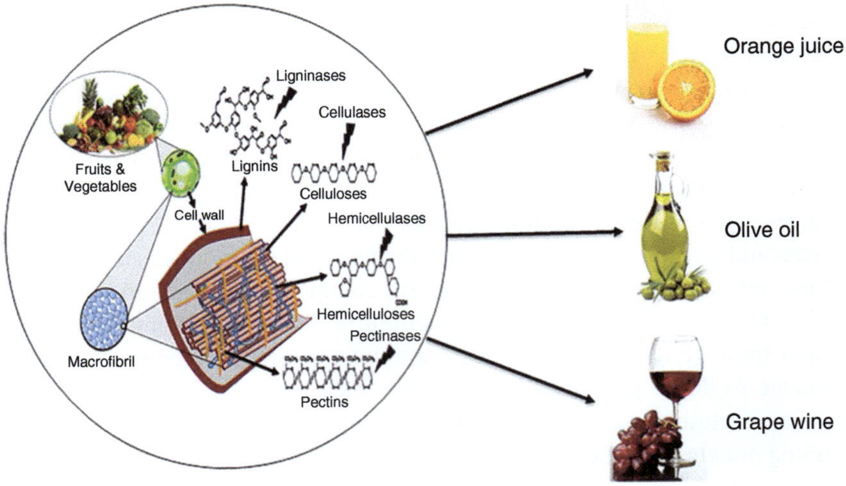

Figure 7.4 Schematic illustration of lignocellulosic substrates in related food industries. Source: Toushik et al. [26]/with permission of John Wiley & Sons.

sizable category of industrial enzymes today [69]. Microbial enzymes have received a lot of attention for their diverse range of uses in the pharmaceutical sector due to their higher catalytic activity, stability, ease of synthesis, and optimization than animal and plant enzymes [65]. Serine proteases make up the majority of therapeutic proteases available today. By controlling the concentration and synthesis of cytokines, growth factors, chemokines, and cellular receptors, proteases serve the body to maintain its physiological function [70].

In addition to other infectious disorders and different treatments, dextranase, rhodanese, and acid protease are used to treat tooth decay, cyanide poisoning, and alimentary dyspepsia, respectively [71]. HIV is inhibited by the lysozyme that Staphylococcus bacteria produce. Chondroitin sulfate, which supports the repair of damage, is one of many enzymes with proteolytic activity that are derived from various bacteria and have been shown to remove burned and dead skin [70].

Microbial enzymes are preferred among various exo-enzymes due to their high productivity, stability, and simplicity of use [72].

7.3.3 Detergent Industries

With around 25–30% of all enzyme sales, the detergent industry is one of the greatest industrial users of enzymes. Enzymes (including amylase, lipase, protease, cellulase, and cutinase) are most useful when added to detergents, which are mostly used for dishwashing, laundry, and institutional and industrial cleaning [47].

The most common type of detergent enzymes are hydrolases, which eliminate stains from fat, protein, and polysaccharide-based filth. Food, grass, blood, animal and vegetable fat, and dirt are a few examples of stains [73]. Proteases, amylases, lipases, and mannanases are among the common hydrolases found in detergents [74]. In the production of detergents, other types of enzymes, such as cellulases and pectinases, also have particular uses [75].

The principal end uses for enzymes are in the detergent industry. Therefore, as enzymatic detergents, liquid detergents use more than 90% amylases in their formulation. In starch polymers, which are typically present in foods like pasta, fruit, and chocolate, these enzymes catalyze the hydrolysis of glucosidic connections [76]. The hydrolase classes of enzymes, of which amylase and proteases are the most common, are useful for detergents. To maintain fabric, brighten colors, create soft materials, and remove fine threads, other enzymes such as pectinase, cellulase, and lipase are also required [70].

The detergent industry typically uses 30% of the market for industrial enzymes. Detergents are made more powerful in removing stubborn stains and are environmentally friendly by adding enzymes. The "classic" detergent enzymes, proteases, and amylases are continually underway in new and improved engineered forms [43].

7.3.4 Textile and Leather Industries

One of the most substantial contributors to environmental pollution is the textile sector, which is in charge of producing a sizable amount of waste from the desizing of fabrics, bleaching chemicals, and dye [77, 78]. Enzymes are employed in these sectors to enable the development of ecologically friendly fiber processing technology. Amylase, cellulase, cutinase, protease, pectinase, and lipase are hydrolases, and catalase, laccase, peroxidase, and ligninase are oxidoreductases used in the pretreatment and finishing processes of cotton in the textile industry [10].

The two distinct types of enzymes most frequently utilized in the textile industry are hydrolase and oxidoreductase. The hydrolase enzymes (amylase, cellulase, pectinase, cutinase, protease, and lipase/esterase) are used to treat wool, remove starch size, and bio-polish and bio-scour fabric. They are also used to soften cotton, finish denim, enhance color and surface vividness, and finish cotton fabrics. For the textile industry, the employment of cellulases, pectinases, lipases, esterases, and lipases is extremely advantageous for biopolishing and bioscouring fabric, cotton softening, denim finishing, desizing, wool finishing, and altering synthetic fibers [19].

Enzymatic dehairing procedures reduce or completely do away with the need for hazardous chemicals including sulfide, lime, and amines. An effective substitute to enhance leather quality and save waste is biodegradable enzymes [79]. Serious environmental and health issues are being brought on by waste discharges from various stages of the leather processing process. However, microbial enzymes (such as neutral proteases, lipases, and proteases) can be used to address environmental issues [10].

Biodegradable enzymes have shown to be an effective replacement in the leather industry. Microbial enzymes have been used to improve the quality of leather since the dawn of time at numerous steps of the manufacturing process, including tanning, curing, plucking, degreasing, liming, soaking, dehairing, and bating [80]. Dehairing is the most important and labor-intensive stage in the tannery's production to dissolve grease and enable leather, and it requires a variety of environmentally friendly enzymes like lipases, amylases, and proteases [81].

In the paper pulp industry, xylanases, cellulases, and ligninases are used to enhance deinking procedures, softness, drainage, and waste reduction. Microbial lipases and proteases are used in the leather industry for curing, soaking, liming, dehairing, bating, plucking, degreasing, and tanning [19]. Aspergillus flavus, Bacillus sp., and Streptomyces sp. are the usual sources of proteases used in enzymatic dehairing procedures on skin and hides. Proteolytic enzymes from bacteria are used in the tanning process to produce soft, flexible leather, which is used to build many types of hands. Numerous microbial lipases have been successfully employed in dyeing and finishing processes [70].

7.3.5 Paper and Pulp Industries

One of the global industries with the quickest growth is the paper and pulp sector. The pulp and paper industry releases enormous amounts of wastewater containing hazardous organochlorine compounds that are produced throughout numerous processing steps during the production of paper and pulp [82]. Various simple, nonpolluting methods can be used to potentially mitigate effluents that are released into the environment. Several xylanolytic enzymes, such as xylanases, laccases, cellulases, and hemicellulases, are used to hydrolyze raw materials while making paper. These enzymes are very selective, renewable, and dynamic in their ability to enhance paper quality [83].

Numerous industrial processes, including bio-pulping, biobleaching, deink removal, pitch removal, fiber grafting, paper coloring, and bioremediation of effluents, can benefit from the employment of microbial enzymes [10]. Starch serves well as a coating for paper as well as a sizing agent, which enhances the final product's quality and erasability. The paper sector benefits from cold active amylase as well since it makes starch less viscous, enabling adequate coating [84].

7.3.6 Starch Liquefaction and Saccharification

One of the most important applications for a-amylase is the liquefaction of starch to produce glucose and fructose syrups [85]. Starch is converted into high-fructose corn syrup, which is widely used in the beverage industry as a sweetener for soft drinks due to its potent sweetening capabilities. The extremely thermostable enzyme a-amylase is required to liquefy the starch [16, 17]. Under the correct conditions, alpha-amylase degrades starch, starts the liquefaction process, and transforms starch into liquid sugar. An enzyme starts the hydrolysis and breakdown of starch molecules to create short chains of starch (Figure 7.5). Gelatinization, which entails the dissolution of starch granules and production of a viscous suspension; liquefaction, which entails partial hydrolysis and loss of viscosity; and saccharification, which entails the production of glucose and maltose through additional hydrolysis; are all examples of the enzymatic conversion of all starch [87].

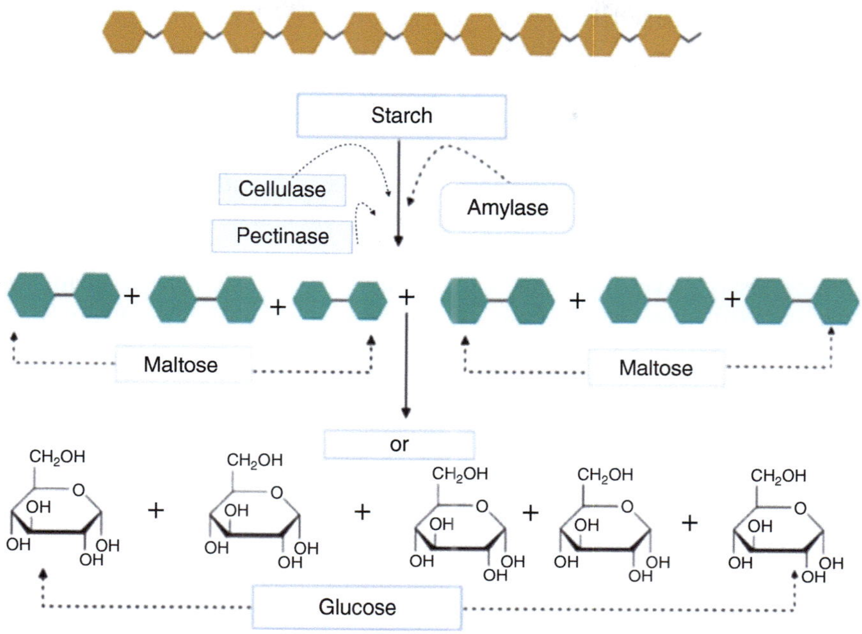

Figure 7.5 Starch hydrolysis process in the presence of amylase. Source: Modified from [86].

The enzymatic conversion process consists of three steps: saccharification, liquefaction, and gelatinization. Liquefaction is the process by which viscosity is decreased through partial hydrolysis, saccharification is the process by which maltose and fructose are created, and gelatinization is the process by which starch granules dissolve into a viscous solution. Enzymes from *Bacillus licheniformis* and *Bacillus stearothermophilus* are commonly used because of their high thermostability [88, 89].

7.3.7 Bioenergy Production

Plant waste and microbial biomass are two examples of biological sources from which biofuels can be produced. Bioethanol and biogas are the two most often used biological fuels nowadays. These fuels are among the potential future energy alternatives to fossil fuels. Microorganisms that may utilize organic waste include bacteria, fungi, and microalgae. Algal biomass, agricultural waste, and plant residues are required as raw materials for the fermentation process as well as an adequate microbial system [47, 90].

Advanced biofuels include cellulosic ethanol, biomass-based diesel, biobutanol, bio-oil, green petrol, and bio-based jet fuel. This day is quickly approaching. According to the International Energy Agency, biofuels may meet more than 25% of the global demand for transportation fuels by 2050 [91].

Soon, biofuels will be assessed as potential alternatives to current energy sources. Biofuel is believed to be essential for the production of bioenergy, which can support the 2030 UN Sustainable Development Goals Agenda [92].

Lignocellulosic materials can be pretreated in several ways to convert them into fermentable sugars, including with acidic and enzymatic processes (ethanol production is higher with the enzymatic pretreatment) [93]. Most microbial lignocellulolytic enzymes aid in the production of biofuels from pretreated lignocellulosic biomass. These biomass-degrading enzymes have been screened using just a small number of cultivated microorganisms. These problems with biomass-degrading enzymes can be remedied by using metagenomic techniques to test novel microbial enzymes [94].

It is necessary to switch to biofuels due to the increasing emissions of greenhouse gases and particulate matter from the combustion of fossil fuels. Biofuels are preferable to fossil-based fuels since there are affordable and numerous renewable feedstocks available. Biofuel production can be increased by applying metabolic engineering approaches to a range of microorganisms [95].

Additionally, several techniques (such as mutagenesis, adaptive laboratory evolution, particular gene knockout, and metabolic engineering) have been considerably encouraged for improving the metabolic engineering of *Zymomonas mobilis* for enhancing bio-ethanol production from biomass resources [96].

Many different types of complex carbohydrates can be broken down by microbial enzymes into more useful energy sources. The simple carbohydrates can then be converted into ethanol or other biofuels by a large number of fermentative microorganisms. The potential of biofuel is highlighted by the United States energy independence and the renewable fuel standard, which calls for the production of 36 billion gallons of biofuel yearly by 2022 [91] shown in Figure 7.6.

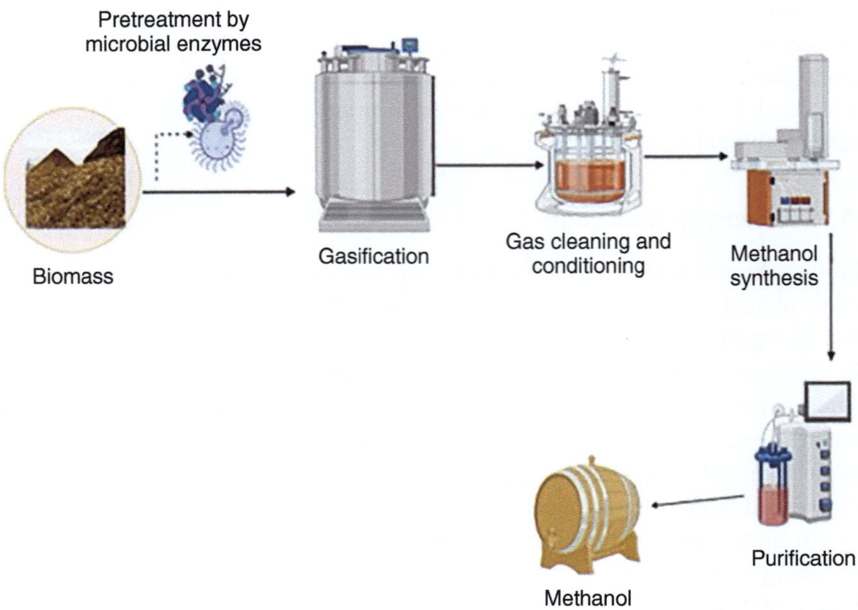

Figure 7.6 Systematic illustration of the production of methanol from biomass with pretreatment microbial enzymes. Source: Okoro et al. [95]/Elsevier/CC BY 4.0.

7.4 Challenges and Future Trends of Microbial Enzymes

Almost every industrial sector – including food, feed, pharmaceuticals, paper, detergents, textiles, leather, drinks, bioenergy, and others – is significantly impacted by enzymes, and the market for industrial enzymes is increasing quickly to keep up with consumer demand [11, 65].

Microbial enzymes can be utilized in many industrial processes to raise the quality and output of finished goods. However, the stability of microbial enzymes and the price of enzymes prevent their usage in industrial industries right once. For commercialization, the enzyme must be resistant to high temperatures, conditions with an acidic pH, and organic solvents. The employment of enzymes in industrial processes is constrained by their inability to endure the harsh conditions present there. There are several ways to maximize microbial enzyme production; however, the enzymes are unstable, and doing so comes at a higher cost. Thermophilic enzymes are receiving more attention in research because it is difficult and expensive to control temperature during large-scale fermentation processes [97].

To further save expenses, an investigation on the immobilization of microbial enzymes for re-use is needed. Protein engineering is a far more effective solution because the alterations are entirely under control [98]. A specific gene from a microorganism that naturally generates the desired enzyme (donor) is transferred to a microbe that will make the enzyme more effective (host) [99].

Finding strains that generate the enzyme in conjunction with other enzymes will take further investigation, and each application will require a specific mixture of these enzymes [100]. According to Patel et al. [20], future studies on microbial enzymes should concentrate on high-throughput screening mechanisms that control enzyme secretion as well as the mechanisms by which different microbial enzymes act against one another and their substrates. In order to increase the structure-function link and modify crucial enzyme features like activity, substrate selectivity, and stability to broaden their uses, computational methods, and modeling are being used more and more [101, 102].

Thus, well-designed research can offer strong tools for controlling microorganisms to generate vast amounts of effective and affordable enzymes. The development of new enzyme-based technologies has been made possible by the numerous enzyme engineering design strategies that have emerged in recent years to produce enzymatic diversity and abundance for the demands of enzyme kinetics and molecular biology (clustered regularly interspaced short palindromic repeats [CRISPR] technology) [103, 104].

Furthermore, improvements in high-throughput screening techniques, genetic engineering tools, and "omics" technologies will lead to the creation of more efficient protein engineering techniques, which will subsequently help in the development of improved enzymes for additional specific applications [105]. For effective enzyme remodeling and the creation of metabolically stable enzymes, more development and research are needed in critical areas of protein engineering, such as peptidomimetics, flow cytometry, and designing divergent evolution [106]. Metabolic engineering has significantly improved enzyme properties with numerous industrial uses in recent years [107].

Future advancement and design of novel enzymes with desirable properties drawn from natural resources, as well as altering the current repertoire of enzymes for desired uses, will be supported by more sophisticated techniques and technologies. Metagenomics will help identify novel genes encoding enzymes on a wide scale for enzyme engineering by combining with next-generation DNA sequencing technology (NGS) and high-throughput screening technologies [106, 108].

Microbial enzymes have become more attention in industrial applications because of their simplicity (control), adaptability, quick growth, large-scale production, and availability as the least expensive and most accessible substrates [20, 109].

7.5 Conclusion

The biological catalyst that has the greatest prevalence in nature and the environment is an enzyme, which speeds up all biochemical reactions. Instead, these biomolecules might be continuously exploited to supply the world's rising food needs. However, microbial enzymes are preferred due to their high yields, activity, repeatability, cost-effectiveness, exponential growth, use of inexpensive media, ease of optimization, and strain improvement.

Based on extensive research, it has been understood that microbial enzymes are essential for the significant development or improvement of enzymes for industrial applications. It holds great potential for the control of waste and, implicitly, for the development of a green environment. Enzymes are successfully employed in many industries to manufacture things of higher quality at a faster rate of response with little pollution. The results are promising because it also has an oddly discernible role in several industrial operations. SSF and SmF are the most efficient processes for producing the particular enzymes needed for commercial usage, according to several studies.

To successfully implement this approach for the use of microbial enzymes, research should focus on protein engineering, metagenomic techniques, omics, and CRISPR technology to obtain more robust and versatile enzymes. It should also optimize manufacturing processes using new strains.

List of Abbreviations

NGS	next-generation DNA sequencing technology
SMF	submerged fermentation
SSF	solid-state fermentation
UNDESA	United Nations Department of Economic and Social Affairs

Authors' Contributions

All authors Gebiru Sinshaw, Abate Ayele, Gamachis Korsa, Gessesse K. Bekele, and Mesfin T. Gemeda equally contributed to this chapter. Also, the authors have approved the latest version of the manuscript and agree to be held accountable for the content therein.

Acknowledgments

We would like to express our gratitude to Addis Ababa Science and Technology University in particular. This institution was instrumental in creating this chapter and conducting various workshops on the scientific art of writing for various journals and articles.

References

1 Haile, S. and Ayele, A. (2022). Pectinase from microorganisms and its industrial applications. *Sci. World J.* 2022: 1881305.

2 Enez, B. (2021). Purification and characterization of thermostable α-amylase from soil bacterium *Bacillus* sp. *Protein Pept. Lett.* 28 (12): 1372–1378.

3 Singh, A., Bajar, S., Devi, A., and Bishnoi, N.R. (2021). Adding value to agro-industrial waste for cellulase and xylanase production via solid-state bioconversion. *Biomass Convers. Biorefin.* 13: 1–10.

4 Yassin, S.N., Jiru, T.M., and Indracanti, M. (2021). Screening and characterization of thermostable amylase-producing bacteria isolated from soil samples of afdera, Afar region, and molecular detection of amylase-coding gene. *Int. J. Microbiol.* 2021: 1–14.

5 Anbu, P., Gopinath, S.C., Chaulagain, B.P., and Lakshmipriya, T. (2017). Microbial enzymes and their applications in industries and medicine 2016. *Biomed Res. Int.* 2017: 2195808.

6 Arnau, J., Yaver, D., and Hjort, C.M. (2020). Strategies and challenges for the development of industrial enzymes using fungal cell factories. In: *Grand Challenges in Fungal Biotechnology* (ed. H. Nevalainen), 179–210. Springer.

7 Anbu, P., Gopinath, S.C., Chaulagain, B.P. et al. (2015). Microbial enzymes and their applications in industries and medicine 2014. *Biomed Res. Int.* 2015: 1–3.

8 Choi, J.M., Han, S.S., and Kim, H.S. (2015). Industrial applications of enzyme biocatalysis: current status and future aspects. *Biotechnol. Adv.* 33 (7): 1443–1454.

9 Korsa, G., Konwarh, R., Masi, C. et al. (2023). Microbial cellulase production and its potential application for textile industries. *Ann. Microbiol.* 73 (1): 13.

10 Singh, R., Kumar, M., Mittal, A., and Mehta, P.K. (2016b). Microbial enzymes: industrial progress in 21st century. *3 Biotech* 6: 1–15.

11 Raveendran, S., Parameswaran, B., Ummalyma, S.B. et al. (2018). Applications of microbial enzymes in food industry. *Food Technol. Biotechnol.* 56 (1): 16.

12 Sudeep, K.C., Upadhyaya, J., Joshi, D.R. et al. (2020). Production, characterization, and industrial application of pectinase enzyme isolated from fungal strains. *Fermentation* 6 (2): 59.

13 Eriksen, D.T., Hsieh, P.C.H., Lynn, P., and Zhao, H. (2013). Directed evolution of a cellobiose utilization pathway in *Saccharomyces cerevisiae* by simultaneously engineering multiple proteins. *Microb. Cell Fact.* 12: 1–11.

14 Okpara, M.O. (2022). Microbial enzymes and their applications in food industry: a mini-review. *Adv. Enzyme Res.* 10 (1): 23–47.

15 Al-Maqtari, Q.A., Waleed, A.A., and Mahdi, A.A. (2019). Microbial enzymes produced by fermentation and their applications in the food industry – a review. *Int. J. Agric. Innovations Res.* 8 (1): 2319–1473.

16 Singh, R., Singh, A., and Sachan, S. (2019a). Enzymes used in the food industry: friends or foes? In: *Enzymes in Food Biotechnology* (ed. K. Mohammed), 827–843. Academic Press.

17 Singh, R.S., Singh, T., and Pandey, A. (2019b). Microbial enzymes—an overview. In: *Advances in Enzyme Technology* (ed. S.S. Ram, R.S. Reeta, P. Ashok, and L. Christian), 1–40. Elsevier.

18 Temsaah, H.R., Azmy, A.F., Raslan, M. et al. (2018). Isolation and characterization of thermophilic enzymes producing microorganisms for potential therapeutic and industrial use. *J. Pure Appl. Microbiol.* 12 (4): 1687–1702.

19 Sikdar, D., Kanungo, I., and Das, D. (2022). Microbial enzymes: a summary focusing on biotechnology prospective for combating industrial pollutants. *Conference BioSangam 2022: Emerging trends in Biotechnology (BIOSANGAM 2022),* pp. 70–76). Atlantis Press, Available Online 14 December 2022.

20 Patel, A.K., Singhania, R.R., and Pandey, A. (2017). Production, purification, and application of microbial enzymes. In: *Biotechnology of Microbial Enzymes* (ed. B. Goutam), 13–41. Elsevier.

21 Martău, G.A., Unger, P., Schneider, R. et al. (2021). Integration of solid state and submerged fermentations for the valorization of organic municipal solid waste. *J. Fungi* 7 (9): 766.

22 Ire, F.S. and Nwanguma, A.C. (2020). Comparative evaluation on tannase production by *Lasiodiplodia plurivora* ACN-10 under submerged fermentation (SmF) and solid state fermentation (SSF). *Asian J. Biotechnol. Bioresour. Technol.* 6 (1): 39–49.

23 Panda, S.K., Mishra, S.S., Kayitesi, E., and Ray, R.C. (2016). Microbial-processing of fruit and vegetable wastes for production of vital enzymes and organic acids: biotechnology and scopes. *Environ. Res.* 146: 161–172.

24 Garg, N., Singh, B., Vaish, S., and Kumar, S. (2021). Enzyme production from different fruit and vegetable waste using lactic acid fermentation. *J. Nat. Fibers* 16: 74–76.

25 Batista, B.N., Matias, R.R., Oliveira, R.L.E., and Albuquerque, P.M. (2022). Hydrolytic enzyme production from açai palm (*Euterpe precatoria*) endophytic fungi and characterization of the amylolytic and cellulolytic extracts. *World J. Microbiol. Biotechnol.* 38 (2): 30.

26 Toushik, S.H., Lee, K.T., Lee, J.S., and Kim, K.S. (2017). Functional applications of lignocellulolytic enzymes in the fruit and vegetable processing industries. *J. Food Sci.* 82 (3): 585–593.

27 Patidar, M.K., Nighojkar, S., Kumar, A., and Nighojkar, A. (2018). Pectinolytic enzymes-solid state fermentation, assay methods and applications in fruit juice industries: a review. *3 Biotech* 8 (4): 199.

28 Abdollahzadeh, R., Pazhang, M., Najavand, S. et al. (2020). Screening of pectinase-producing bacteria from farmlands and optimization of enzyme production from selected strain by RSM. *Folia Microbiol.* 65: 705–719.

29 Zhang, S., Gao, X., He, L. et al. (2015). Novel trends for use of microbial tannases. *Prep. Biochem. Biotechnol.* 45 (3): 221–232.

30 Shao, Y., Zhang, Y.H., Zhang, F. et al. (2020). Thermostable tannase from *Aspergillus niger* and its application in the enzymatic extraction of green tea. *Molecules* 25 (4): 952.

31 Fatima, S., Faryad, A., Ataa, A. et al. (2021). Microbial lipase production: a deep insight into the recent advances of lipase production and purification techniques. *Biotechnol. Appl. Biochem.* 68 (3): 445–458.

32 Bhandari, S., Poudel, D.K., Marahatha, R. et al. (2021). Microbial enzymes used in bioremediation. *J. Chem.* 2021: 1–17.

33 Panesar, P.S., Kaur, R., Singla, G., and Sangwan, R.S. (2016). Bio-processing of agro-industrial wastes for production of food-grade enzymes: progress and prospects. *Appl. Food Biotechnol.* 3 (4): 208–227.

34 Patel, A.K., Dong, C.D., Chen, C.W. et al. (2023). Production, purification, and application of microbial enzymes. In: *Biotechnology of Microbial Enzymes* (ed. B. Goutam), 25–57. Academic Press.

35 Sainz-Polo, M.A., Ramírez-Escudero, M., Lafraya, A. et al. (2013). Three-dimensional structure of Saccharomyces invertase: role of a non-catalytic domain in oligomerization and substrate specificity. *J. Biol. Chem.* 288 (14): 9755–9766.

36 Mhamdi, A.G., Chaouch, S., Vanderauwera, S. et al. (2010). Catalase function in plants: a focus on *Arabidopsis* mutants as stress-mimic models. *J. Exp. Bot.* 61: 4197–4220.

37 Glorieux, C. and Calderon, P.B. (2017). Catalase, a remarkable enzyme: targeting the oldest antioxidant enzyme to find a new cancer treatment approach. *Biol. Chem.* 398 (10): 1095–1108.

38 Goyal, M.M. and Basak, A. (2010). Human catalase: looking for complete identity. *Protein Cell* 1 (10): 888–897.

39 Walia, A., Guleria, S., Mehta, P. et al. (2017). Microbial xylanases and their industrial application in pulp and paper biobleaching: a review. *3 Biotech* 7: 1–12.

40 Bhardwaj, N., Kumar, B., and Verma, P. (2019). A detailed overview of xylanases: an emerging biomolecule for current and future prospective. *Bioresour. Bioprocess.* 6 (1): 1–36.

41 Pavezzi, F.C., Gomes, E., and da Silva, R. (2008). Production and characterization of glucoamylase from fungus *Aspergillus awamori* expressed in yeast *Saccharomyces cerevisiae* using different carbon sources. *Braz. J. Microbiol.* 39 (1): 108–114.

42 Costa, J.A., Treichel, H., Kumar, V., and Pandey, A. (2018). Advances in solid-state fermentation. In: *Current Developments in Biotechnology and Bioengineering* (ed. P. Ashok, L. Christian, and R.S. Carlos), 1–17. Elsevier.

43 Liu, X. and Kokare, C. (2017). Microbial enzymes of use in industry. In: *Biotechnology of Microbial Enzymes: Production, Biocatalysis and Industrial Applications*, vol. 2017, 267–298. Elsevier.

44 Naureen, I., Bashir, M.J., Ahmed, W. et al. (2021). A review on microbial enzymes, synthesis, biological role, current applications and future perspectives. *Scholars Bull.* 7 (3): 44–48.

45 Doriya, K., Jose, N., Gowda, M., and Kumar, D.S. (2016). Solid-state fermentation vs submerged fermentation for the production of l-asparaginase. *Adv. Food Nutr. Res.* 78: 115–135.

46 Arora, N.K., Mishra, J., and Mishra, V. (ed.) (2020). *Microbial Enzymes: Roles and Applications in Industries*, 1–110. Berlin Heidelberg: Springer.

47 Thapa, S., Li, H., OHair, J. et al. (2019). Biochemical characteristics of microbial enzymes and their significance from industrial perspectives. *Mol. Biotechnol.* 61: 579–601.

48 dos Santos Ferreira, J., de Oliveira, D., Maldonado, R.R. et al. (2020). Enzymatic pretreatment and anaerobic co-digestion as a new technology to high-methane production. *Appl. Microbiol. Biotechnol.* 104: 4235–4246.

49 Raak, N., Symmank, C., Zahn, S. et al. (2017). Processing-and product-related causes for food waste and implications for the food supply chain. *Waste Manage. (Oxford)* 61: 461–472.

50 Kaur, H. and Gill, P.K. (2019). Microbial enzymes in food and beverages processing. In: *Engineering Tools in the Beverage Industry* (ed. M.G. Alexandru and M.H. Alina), 255–282. Woodhead Publishing.

51 Singhal, G., Bhagyawant, S.S., and Srivastava, N. (2020). Microbial enzymes in food industry: types and applications. In: *Microbial Fermentation and Enzyme Technology* (ed. T. Hrudayanath, K.D.M. Pradeep, M. Sonali, and C.M. Keshab), 61–71. CRC Press.

52 Farias, T.C., Kawaguti, H.Y., and Koblitz, M.G.B. (2021). Microbial amylolytic enzymes in foods: technological importance of the Bacillus genus. *Biocatal. Agric. Biotechnol.* 35: 102054.

53 Hashim, S.O. (2020). Starch-modifying enzymes. *Alkaliphiles Biotechnol.* 172: 221–244.

54 Norouzian, D., Akbarzadeh, A., Scharer, J.M., and Young, M.M. (2006). Fungal glucoamylases. *Biotechnol. Adv.* 24 (1): 80–85.

55 Li, L.X., Yu, L.Y., Wang, B., and Pan, L. (2022). Impact of overexpressing NADH kinase on glucoamylase production in *Aspergillus niger*. *J. Ind. Microbiol. Biotech.* 49 (4): kuac015.

56 Del Moral, S., Barradas-Dermitz, D.M., and Aguilar-Uscanga, M.G. (2018). Production and biochemical characterization of α-glucosidase from *Aspergillus niger* ITV-01 isolated from sugar cane bagasse. *3 Biotech* 8: 1–9.

57 Trabelsi, S., Ben Mabrouk, S., Kriaa, M. et al. (2019). The optimized production, purification, characterization, and application in the bread making industry of three acid-stable alpha-amylases isoforms from a new isolated *Bacillus subtilis* strain US586. *J. Food Biochem.* 43 (5): e12826.

58 Tong, J., Wang, S., He, Z., and Zhang, Y. (2021). Effects of reduced nitrogen fertilization and irrigation on structure and physicochemical properties of starch in two bread wheat cultivars. *Agriculture* 11 (1): 26.

59 Uzuner, S. and Cekmecelioglu, D. (2019). Enzymes in the beverage industry. In: *Enzymes in Food Biotechnology* (ed. K. Mohammed), 29–43. Academic Press.

60 Spier, M.R., Nogueira, A., Alberti, A. et al. (2016). Potential applications of enzymes in brewery and winery. In: *Agro-industrial Wastes as Feedstock for Enzyme Production* (ed. S.D. Gurpreet and K. Surinder), 261–278. Academic Press.

61 Xu, Q.S., Yan, Y.S., and Feng, J.X. (2016). Efficient hydrolysis of raw starch and ethanol fermentation: a novel raw starch-digesting glucoamylase from *Penicillium oxalicum*. *Biotechnol. Biofuels* 9 (1): 1–18.

62 Kocabaş, D.S., Akçelik, M.E., Bahçegül, E., and Özbek, H.N. (2021). Bulgur bran as a biopolymer source: production and characterization of nanocellulose-reinforced hemicellulose-based biodegradable films with decreased water solubility. *Ind. Crops Prod.* 171: 113847.

63 Salter, A.M. (2017). Improving the sustainability of global meat and milk production. *Proc. Nutr. Soc.* 76 (1): 22–27.

64 Singh, P. and Yadav, S.K. (2018). Feed enzymes: source and applications. In: *Enzymes in Food Technology: Improvements and Innovations*, 347–358.

65 Singh, G., Capalash, N., Kaur, K. et al. (2016a). Enzymes: applications in pulp and paper industry. In: *Agro-Industrial Wastes as Feedstock for Enzyme Production* (ed. S.D. Gurpreet and K. Surinder), 157–172. Academic Press.

66 García, C.Á. (2018). Application of enzymes for fruit juice processing. In: *Fruit Juices* (ed. R. Gaurav and K.T. Brijesh), 201–216. Academic Press.

67 Meghwanshi, G.K., Kaur, N., Verma, S. et al. (2020). Enzymes for pharmaceutical and therapeutic applications. *Biotechnol. Appl. Biochem.* 67 (4): 586–601.

68 Bhatt, A.P., Redinbo, M.R., and Bultman, S.J. (2017). The role of the microbiome in cancer development and therapy. *CA: Cancer J. Clin.* 67 (4): 326–344.

69 Silva-López, R.E. and Gonçalves, R.N. (2019). Therapeutic proteases from plants: biopharmaceuticals with multiple applications. *J. Appl. Biotechnol. Bioeng.* 6 (2): 101–109.

70 Bhatt, P. (ed.) (2022). *Industrial Applications of Microbial Enzymes*. CRC Press.

71 Kumari, A., Divya Kapoor, K.R., Sharma, P. et al. (2020). Microbial diversity. *Interventions and Scope* 25: 259.

72 Dhankhar, R., Kawatra, A., Mohanty, A., and Gulati, P. (2021). Microbial enzymes used in prodrug activation for cancer therapy: insights and future perspectives. *Curr. Protein Pept. Sci.* 22 (7): 514–525.

73 Jayasekara, S. and Ratnayake, R. (2019). Microbial cellulases: an overview and applications. *Cellulose* 22: 92.

74 de Souza Vandenberghe, L.P., De Carvalho, J.C., Libardi, N. et al. (2016). Microbial enzyme factories: current trends in production processes and commercial aspects. In: *Agro-industrial Wastes as Feedstock for Enzyme Production* (ed. S.D. Gurpreet and K. Surinder), 1–22. Academic Press.

75 Gürkök, S. (2019). Microbial enzymes in detergents: a review. *Int. J. Sci. Eng. Res.* 10 (9): 75–81.

76 Al-Ghanayem, A.A. and Joseph, B. (2020). Current prospective in using cold-active enzymes as eco-friendly detergent additive. *Appl. Microbiol. Biotechnol.* 104 (7): 2871–2882.

77 Choudhury, A.K.R. (2017). Sustainable chemical technologies for textile production. In: *Sustainable Fibres and textiles* (ed. S.M. Subramanian), 267–322. Woodhead Publishing.

78 Subramanian, B.T., Alla, J.P., Essomba, J.S., and Nishter, N.F. (2020). Non-fluorinated superhydrophobic spray coatings for oil-water separation applications: an eco-friendly approach. *J. Cleaner Prod.* 256: 120693.

79 Wanyonyi, W.C. and Mulaa, F.J. (2020). Alkaliphilic enzymes and their application in novel leather processing technology for next-generation tanneries. In: *Alkaliphiles in Biotechnology* (ed. G. Mamo and B. Mattiasson), 195–220. Springer.

80 Khambhaty, Y. (2020). Applications of enzymes in leather processing. *Environ. Chem. Lett.* 18 (3): 747–769.

81 Mesbah, N.M. (2022). Industrial biotechnology based on enzymes from extreme environments. *Front. Bioeng. Biotechnol.* 10: 1–16.

82 Adamu, M.T., Dahiru, M., and Garba, L. (2020). Microorganisms involved in the bioremediation of pentachlorophenol and lignin discharged by the pulp and paper industry. *J. Environ. Biorem. Toxicol.* 3 (2): 21–25.

83 Gupta, G.K., Dixit, M., Kapoor, R.K., and Shukla, P. (2022). Xylanolytic enzymes in pulp and paper industry: new technologies and perspectives. *Mol. Biotechnol.* 64: 1–14.

84 Li, H., Qi, Y., Zhao, Y. et al. (2019). Starch and its derivatives for paper coatings: a review. *Prog. Org. Coat.* 135: 213–227.

85 Samanta, S. (2020). Enhancement of characteristics and potential applications of amylases: a brief review. *Am. J. Pure Appl. Sci.* 2 (2): 24–35.

86 Srishti, K., Rohit, R., and Rashmi, K. (2022). Microbial production of amylase using lignocellulosic biomass: recent developments and prospects. *Res. J. Biotechnol.* 17: 5.

87 Souza, P.M.D. (2010). Application of microbial α-amylase in industry - a review. *Braz. J. Microbiol.* 41: 850–861.

88 Sindhu, R., Binod, P., and Pandey, A. (2017). α-Amylases. In: *Current Developments in Biotechnology and Bioengineering* (ed. P. Ashok, N. Sangeeta, and R.S. Carlos), 3–24. Elsevier.

89 Sumardiono, S. and Budiarti, G. (2018). Conversion of cassava starch to produce glucose and fructose by enzymatic process using microwave heating. *MATEC Web of Conferences*, Vol. 156, p. 01024). EDP Sciences, The 24th Regional Symposium on Chemical Engineering (RSCE 2017).

90 Singh, V., Singh, N., Tabassum, N., and Mishra, V. (2020). Microbial system: an emerging application in the bioenergy production. In: *Microbial Strategies* *for Techno-economic Biofuel Production* (ed. N. Srivastava, M. Srivastava, P.K. Mishra, and V.K. Gupta), 249–264. Singapore: Springer.

91 Tuohy, K. (2016). *Microbial Enzymes in Bioconversions of Biomass* (ed. V.K. Gupta). New York: Springer International Publishing.

92 Nazari, M.T., Mazutti, J., Basso, L.G. et al. (2021). Biofuels and their connections with the sustainable development goals: a bibliometric and systematic review. *Environ. Dev. Sustainability* 23 (8): 11139–11156.

93 El-Zawawy, W.K., Ibrahim, M.M., Abdel-Fattah, Y.R. et al. (2011). Acid and enzyme hydrolysis to convert pretreated lignocellulosic materials into glucose for ethanol production. *Carbohydr. Polym.* 84 (3): 865–871.

94 Singh, N., Singh, V., and Singh, M.P. (2022). Microbial degradation of lignocellulosic biomass for bioenergy production: a metagenomic-based approach. *Biocatal. Biotransform.* 41: 1–11.

95 Okoro, V., Azimov, U., and Munoz, J. (2022). Recent advances in production of bioenergy carrying molecules, microbial fuels, and fuel design – a review. *Fuel* 316: 123330.

96 Banta, A.B., Enright, A.L., Siletti, C., and Peters, J.M. (2020). A high-efficacy CRISPR interference system for gene function discovery in *Zymomonas mobilis*. *Appl. Environ. Microbiol.* 86 (23): e01621-20.

97 Niyonzima, F.N., Veena, S.M., and More, S.S. (2020). Industrial production and optimization of microbial enzymes. In: *Microbial Enzymes: Roles and Applications in Industries* (ed. N. Arora, J. Mishra, and V. Mishra), 115–135. Springer.

98 Woo, W.X., Koh, H.S., Tan, J.P. et al. (2022). An overview on cell and enzyme immobilization for enhanced biohydrogen production from lignocellulosic biomass. *Int. J. Hydrogen Energy* 47: 40714–40730.

99 Virolle, C., Goldlust, K., Djermoun, S. et al. (2020). Plasmid transfer by conjugation in Gram-negative bacteria: from the cellular to the community level. *Genes* 11 (11): 1239.

100 Karim, A.S., Dudley, Q.M., Juminaga, A. et al. (2020). In vitro prototyping and rapid optimization of biosynthetic enzymes for cell design. *Nat. Chem. Biol.* 16 (8): 912–919.

101 Ali, M., Ishqi, H.M., and Husain, Q. (2020). Enzyme engineering: reshaping the biocatalytic functions. *Biotechnol. Bioeng.* 117 (6): 1877–1894.

102 Madhavan, A., Arun, K.B., Binod, P. et al. (2021). Design of novel enzyme biocatalysts for industrial bioprocess: harnessing the power of protein engineering, high throughput screening and synthetic biology. *Bioresour. Technol.* 325: 124617.

103 Mitra, R., Xu, T., Xiang, H., and Han, J. (2020). Current developments on polyhydroxyalkanoates synthesis by using halophiles as a promising cell factory. *Microb. Cell Fact.* 19: 1–30.

104 Wohlgemuth, R. (2021). Biocatalysis–key enabling tools from biocatalytic one-step and multi-step reactions to biocatalytic total synthesis. *New Biotechnol.* 60: 113–123.

105 Zhu, B., Wang, D., and Wei, N. (2022). Enzyme discovery and engineering for sustainable plastic recycling. *Trends Biotechnol.* 40 (1): 22–37.

106 Sharma, A., Gupta, G., Ahmad, T. et al. (2021). Enzyme engineering: current trends and future perspectives. *Food Rev. Int.* 37 (2): 121–154.

107 Calero, P. and Nikel, P.I. (2019). Chasing bacterial chassis for metabolic engineering: a perspective review from classical to non-traditional microorganisms. *Microb. Biotechnol.* 12 (1): 98–124.

108 Glanville, D.G., Mullineaux-Sanders, C., Corcoran, C.J. et al. (2021). A high-throughput method for identifying novel genes that influence metabolic pathways reveals new iron and heme regulation in *Pseudomonas aeruginosa*. *Msystems* 6 (1): e00933-20.

109 Bhardwaj, N., Kumar, B., Agrawal, K., and Verma, P. (2021). Current perspective on production and applications of microbial cellulases: a review. *Bioresour. Bioprocess.* 8: 1–34.

8

Peroxidases: Role in Bioremediation

Huda Afreen[1], Ravi Kant Singh[2], and Pradeep Kumar[3]

[1] *Dr. D. Y. Patil Vidhyapeeth, Dr. D. Y. Patil Biotechnology and Bioinformatics Institute, Department of Biotechnology, Pune, Maharashtra 411033, India*
[2] *Amity University Uttar Pradesh, Amity Institute of Biotechnology, Noida, Uttar Pradesh 201313, India*
[3] *University of Lucknow, Department of Botany, Lucknow, Uttar Pradesh 226007, India*

8.1 Introduction

In today's world, because of the rapidly growing industry-oriented world, health issues in people have increased at an alarming rate because of environmental pollution and lifestyle, especially in fast-growing countries. The origin and source of this pollution are several industrial processes running, including excavation of land and metal extraction process, oil and gas, refineries and industrial complexes, industry effluents, the manufacturing of chemical-based weapons, the pulp and paper industry, the dye industry, and industrial manufacturing, as well as manmade activities, including more petrol- and diesel-based vehicles, use of agricultural pesticides and other inorganic compounds. Forest fires, dust in deserts, and malpractices in waste management (pesticides and different inorganic fertilizers and agricultural wastes in agriculture), and the alarming development of cities are some of the reasons for pollution. There are several components in the environment that have a significant potential to form pollution. These pollutants have an impact on different biotic components, including plants, animals, and human beings. These pollutants could be dispersed throughout one or every earth compartment. Polluting substances are frequently found in mixtures of both organic and inorganic components, in addition to various combinations of distinct organic compounds. Hence, there is a greater need for complete removal of such pollutants.

In the natural environment, peroxidases are present in abundance. Green plants, animals, and certain microbes are just a few of the sources that create these enzymes. *Candida krusei, Coprinopsis cinerea, Phanerochaete chrysosporium, actinomycetes* (*Streptomyces* sp. and *Thermobifida fusca*), and yeast are among the microbes that actually produce peroxidases that are used in the deterioration of some textile dyes. They also help in the building up of animal feedstock, in the production of basic materials for different organic and inorganic chemicals, in agricultural

Microbial Enzymes: Production, Purification, and Industrial Applications, First Edition.
Edited by Dinesh Yadav, Pankaj Chowdhary, Gautam Anand, and Rajarshi Kumar Gaur.

industry, paper manufacture industry. Numerous plant sources, including banana (*Musa paradisiacal*), horseradish, and papaya (*Carica papaya*) naked skin, have been identified as sources of peroxidases sweet flag (*Acorus calamus*) [1].

8.1.1 Bioremediation Through Enzymes

Numerous approaches have been used to clean up polluted systems, and many of them have produced good outcomes when put into practice at the intended locations. In recent days, an emerging technology called bioremediation has been the most commonly used technique in which microorganisms and enzymes are used for the removal of hazardous pollutants.

This method proved to be not only very beneficial but also energy-efficient, simple to use, wide specific range, and adaptable to a wide range of ionic strengths, pH, and temperature [2].

Following standard treatment, these pollutants are typically discharged into waterways or poured into the soil. Such pollutants have great potential to negatively impact important biotransformation reactions for other pollutants, like denitrification, nitrogen fixation, organic compound degradation, etc. As a result, an effective method of completely destroying them is imperative. One such method is a bioprocess that uses microorganisms and their enzymes as biocatalysts. This method is attractive due to its less energy needs, simple process, wide specificity working band, ability to operate above a very elaborate range of temperature and pH, and wide concentration of different charges. As a result, there is increasing interest in finding efficient remedial solutions for the partial or complete rehabilitation of polluted places [3, 4].

Either *in situ* or *ex situ* remediation through these enzymes can be done. The least disruptive in situ methods are used to provide the free or leftover enzyme (remaining enzymes on the mineral substrate, which lessen the enzymatic activity) to the soil. This method is less expensive because there is no requirement for dirt transportation or digging it off. *Ex situ* techniques can be used in situations where quick action is required or the soil is significantly contaminated with harmful contaminants. This process involved digging up the soil and treating it in various bioreactors to get it ready for enzyme action.

Involvement of living things, including certain microbes, plants, and the presence of their enzymatic suite makes bioremediation and plant-based remediation a need of today as an enticing technological tool. Peroxidases have the potential to decrease environmental pollution by bio-remediating wastewater from which phenols, cresols, and phenols are chlorinated. The majority of drawbacks associated with the employment of microbes may be overcome by the use of enzymatic proteins. There are various advantageous traits of enzymes.

All the biota's alterations are primarily mediated by them. They can be used to combine a wide variety of different chemicals since they are catalysts with either very short or wide specific range. The structural and toxicological characteristics of pollutants may undergo significant changes, and they may even be completely transformed into safe, inorganic, less-toxic products. They can carry out several works in fact for which already known effective chemicals cannot do.

Enzymes may also be superior to both microbial remediation and conventional treatments. Some of the enzymes working as catalysts accelerate the entire biological reactions and create a favorable environment to promote the change of such types of substrates to the products and lower the first step of taking that much of energy to start up the reactions [5]. In fact, in particular, they accelerate chemical processes that cell's needs; they are not permanently altered or depleted by these processes. They can thus be applied in a cyclic way.

The cellular process required for living beings would not be possible quickly enough in the absence of these enzymes.

8.1.2 Peroxidases

Breakdown of several xenobiotic substances through chemical method is crucial. To overcome this problem, functions based on numerous enzymes helping in bioremediation are listed below.

Through their oxireduction ability, microbial oxidoreductases can reduce heavy metals, reverse toxicity induced by xenobiotics, and degrade both natural and synthetic contaminants.

In fact, inhibitors of microbial catabolism and anabolism do not inhibit enzymes. The activity of these enzymes is suitable in harsh environments so we can stop certain microbial activity. The enzyme shows maximum activity in the presence of microbial antagonists or predators; they are effective even at low pollutant concentrations. They react with specific classes of substrate, and due to their smaller size, they can move more freely in comparison to different microorganisms. These qualities make these enzymes ecologically friendly catalysts and environmentally friendly processes.

Detoxification of aromatic chemicals through hydroxylation and ring breakage can be possible through monooxygenases and dioxygenases enzyme.

Due to their thermostability and ability to oxidize different substrates, peroxidases play a role in bioremediation processes. Through oxidative processes, decarboxylation, and demethylation, laccase type of enzymes can affect a wide range of pollutants, such as polyhydroxy acid (PHAs), different types of coloring agents, polyethylene and dyes. They can also affect the degeneration of cellulosic compounds and different dyes.

Peroxidase is an enzyme that is present in several types of species, including microorganisms, plants, and animals, with MW of 30–150 kDa. They degrade hydrogen peroxide (H_2O_2), one of the poisons created as a consequence of breathing in oxygen.

The reactions catalyzed are shown in equations

$$AH_2 + H_2O_2 \rightarrow A + 2H_2O$$

$$2AH + H_2O_2 \rightarrow AA + 2H_2O$$

These enzymes are present in almost all creatures, and they shield cells from free radical damage and cell stress caused by the presence of H_2O_2. They are crucial as reasonably priced and ecologically friendly alternatives to chemical reactions in sectors like cloth manufacture, pharmaceuticals, soap processing industries, and pulp and paper industry. By releasing oxygen (O_2) from H_2O_2, enzymes often interact with H_2O_2 or other peroxides as oxidizing agent and interact with a variety of substrates (xenobiotics, lignin, and other phenolic compounds) also. Numerous oxygen transfer processes are catalyzed by it [1, 6]. Peroxidase enzymes are valuable in many biotechnological practices because they reduce peroxides at the expense of substrates that donate electrons. Many processes in numerous sectors have already used a number of these enzymes of particular importance as organocatalysts.

8.2 Classification of Peroxidases

Peroxidases are omnipresent and belong to the class of oxidoreductases. There are different types of peroxides (PRXs) in which heme peroxidases and nonheme peroxidases are two main categories. Peroxidase cyclogenase superfamily and peroxidase catalase superfamily are further divided into animal peroxidases and nonanimal peroxidases, the two other subgroups. The nonanimal peroxidases are further divided into three classes: Class I, Class II, and Class III (Figure 8.1).

Plants, bacteria, and yeasts all include intracellular enzymes known as Class I PRXs. Examples include bacterial catalase: peroxidase, ascorbate peroxidase, and microbial cytochrome c peroxidase.

Class II peroxidases are secreted oxidoreductive enzymes that originate from fungi.

Plant-specific secreted enzymes known as Class III peroxidases originate from plants.

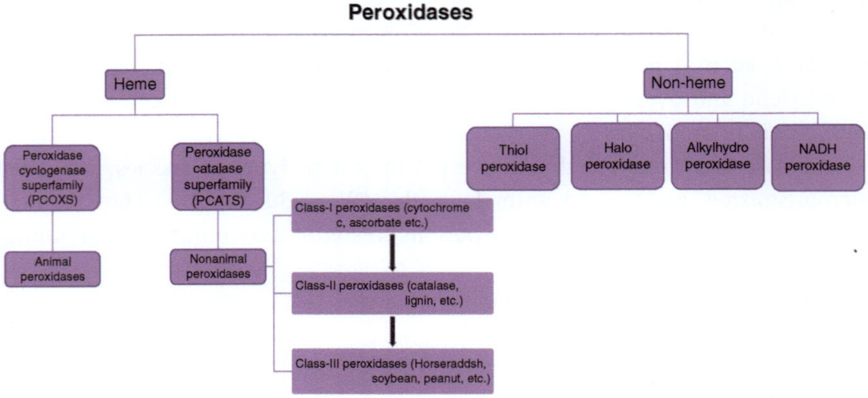

Figure 8.1 Peroxidases and their types.

8.3 Applications of Different Peroxidases for Environmental Pollution Management

8.3.1 Non-animal Peroxidases

Non-animal peroxidases are categorized into the following classes – class I, class II, and class III – depending on their sequence homologies [7]. Ascorbate peroxidases (APXs), yeast mitochondrial protein (Cyt-c), and bacterial mobilizing peroxidases were found as main components of class-1. Recent studies have compared the ability of LiPs to have a high redox potential to that of different peroxidases (1.2 V at pH 3) and discovered as oxidize lignin without the use of a mediator [8]. Similar to how LiP uses the same reaction mechanism throughout the peroxidative cycle, MnP does the same. However, by oxidizing Mn^{2+} to Mn^{3+}, MnPs have a distinct effect on cellulose and phenolic cellulose compounds. The phenol-based chemicals in cellulose/lignin are finally oxidized to phenoxy radicals by $Manganese^{3+}$ ions to form a complex with organic acids secreted by the fungal cells [9]. Versatile PXs come under the family of class-2 peroxidase, which has the properties of LiP and MnP. Peroxidase, which is versatile in nature, showed deterioration capabilities for perfumed alcohol dimers of phenolic and nonphenolic compounds [10]. Almost 70% of peroxidases generated from plants are peroxidases of class-3, which are actually evenly dispersed throughout the plant kingdom [11]. Numerous studies in the field of peroxidases focused on different sources that belong to this group. HRP (horseradish peroxide) [12], SBP (soybean peroxide), and other environmental bioremediation compounds are examples [13]. Plant-based peroxides nevertheless engaged in a significant number of reactions in which several chemical compounds have come from the peroxidative response and share a common arrangement with class-2 peroxidases [14]. Once H_2O_2 combines with the peroxidase heme in its natural state, a transitional compound forms from which oxoferryl ferryl ion (IV) and a nonionic porphyrin are formed.

8.3.2 Enzyme-based Peroxidases

Among microorganisms, bacterial and fungal cells mostly used organisms for the formation of industry-based enzyme. This is because microbial sources are cheaper and their enzyme production and secretion systems are well known and better controlled. Therefore, it is preferred over other enzyme sources and functions over a wide pH range at high temperature and pressure. In most cases, it depends on the origin (manufacturer) of the enzyme. Bacillus is one of the most commonly used enzyme-producing bacteria for several reasons. Bacillus produces more than ten biologically active molecules and various enzymes, offering great usefulness for biotechnology and biopharmaceutical applications [15]. Difficult to remove from Bacillus material, often causing contamination, but maintaining such persistence requires biotechnological techniques, especially microorganisms that can withstand harsh conditions such as extreme temperatures. Peroxidases (EC number 1.11.1.x) represent a large family of redox enzymes known to catalyze the oxidation of various inorganic and organic substrates using H_2O_2. They share a similar catalytic mechanism to the decomposition of H_2O_2. This is a two-electron redox consisting of three distinct steps. These enzymes are ubiquitous in nature and present in both eukaryotes and prokaryotes [16]. They are involved in biological processes such as toxin breakdown, heavy metal detoxification, and hormone regulation. Furthermore, it is used as a catalyst in several industries like clinical biochemistry, enzyme immunoassay, degradation of peroxides using industry wastes, and production of certain aromatic chemicals. It also plays a role in remediating air pollution damage, biobleaching processes, and soil and water detoxification.

8.3.3 Plant-based Peroxidases

As we have discussed in classification that class III peroxidases are plant-based and have a catalytic process similar with already present peroxidases. Plant-based peroxidases used for different biotechnological processes. Plant peroxidases have received considerable interest due to their ability to remove phenolic contaminants from manufactured and refined wastewaters. Examples of plant peroxide come from soybean, horseradish, and beet. HRP was once thought to be the most promising plant peroxidase option for wastewater contaminated with phenolic chemicals [17]. However, other peroxidases (including laccase produced by microorganisms) appear to outperform this. Enzyme immobilization was thoroughly investigated as a method to increase the efficiency of enzymes and the robustness of biocatalysts.

Akhtar and Husain used various immobilized plant peroxidases to remove phenolic impurities. Plant peroxidases often obstructed by ill heterologous expression of compounds and limited stability, but the optimal neutral pH and broad substrate specificity of plant peroxidases make them attractive biocatalysts for a variety of syntheses. It is a chromophore that can be used as an electron-giver ion [18]. A number of plant peroxidase sources were studied in the past due to their broad selectivity for H_2 donors, stability, broad substrate specificity, good catalytic efficiency, and tolerance over a wide pH and temperature range, horseradish peroxidase (HRP) isozymes are the most extensively investigated enzymes [18–21]. These enzymes are also commonly utilized in the production of ELISAs, diagnostic kits, and different sweet-smelling compounds.

Immobilized plant peroxide used to demonstrate the enzyme-catalyzed breakdown and transformation of many polycyclic aromatic hydrocarbons (PAHs), polychlorinated biphenyls (PCBs), organochlorines, phenol-based compounds and dyes. Researchers discovered a similar investigation that peroxidase made from potato pulp was particularly effective at eliminating phenol from synthetic and industrial effluent (95% phenol removal effectiveness). Several plant peroxidases have recently been shown to remove phenolic compounds effectively; however, the usage of plant enzymes favors microorganism-derived enzymes since they can be made more quickly and affordably by utilizing recombinant methods. It appears to have been replaced.

8.3.4 Microbial Peroxidases

Microbial chemicals produced peroxidases using bacteria, actinomycetes, cyanobacteria, fungi, yeast, and other microorganisms were thoroughly investigated in numerous studies. These microorganisms include bacteria (*Bacillus subtilis, Bacillus sphaericus, Escherichia coli*, and *Citrobacter* spp.). They are extensively utilized in the manufacture of animal fodder, the breakdown of contaminants, the treatment of sewage, the decomposition of dyes, and the decomposition of lignin in the paper and pulp industries [1, 22]. Microorganisms are a great source of enzymes due to their dispersed biochemical presence and openness to genetic modification. Peroxidases accelerate using oxidative reactions of lignin, lignocellulosic materials, other phenolic mixtures, and coal to low molecular mass fractions and hydrogen-free compounds. Similar types of peroxidases present as heme or nonheme proteins are linked to easy organic processes with a wide range of hosts.

Due to short-chain water-soluble particles, which come from the cleavage of polymeric materials, these compounds (enzymes) are produced as metabolically active and nonspecific free radicals, which are initially derived from peroxides. As a result, they are allowed to pass through microbial layers which causes the intracellular destruction of the cell. These relate to the breakdown of auxin, the organization of lignin and suberin in plants, the cross-connecting of cell division segments, a defense mechanism against pathogens, or cell expansion. Additionally, microbes help in the formation of bio-paste, bio-coloring, and also the formation of long polymers. Some fungal species are very specific because of the presence of numerous LiP and MnP isoenzymes Table 8.1.

8.3.5 Peroxidases of Microbial Lignin

In terrestrial ecosystems, the breakdown of lignocellulose is a critical step in the carbon recycling process. During the delignification process, basidiomycetes are surprisingly stable. The white-rot and brown-rot basidiomycetes mainly release heme proteins known as lignin peroxidases through the optional digestion of lignocellulose as a component of their metabolic activities. They are very successful in destroying the woodlands. In comparison, the brown rot fungus is more picky. The degradation of lignin and other phenolic compounds occurs in the presence of cosubstrate H_2O_2 and veratrole liquid LiP. In this process, LiP is oxidized, which allows H_2O_2 to be reduced to water and nascent oxygen by receiving an electron from LiP. To return to its starting state, LiP receives one electron from veratrole liquor. Veratraldehyde is produced as a result, and after receiving electrons from the substrate, it transforms back into veratrole liquor [36].

8.3.6 Microorganismal Manganese Peroxidases

The lignin-degrading basidiomycetes organism contains the extracellular heme chemical known as MnP (Manganese peroxidase). It takes several steps for manganate to oxidize into manganite.

Table 8.1 Examples of oxidoreductases being used for the remediation of real-life polluted samples.

S. no.	Source of polluted sample	Enzyme used	Site	References
1	Industrial (Kraft) effluent from paper industry	Immobilized lignin peroxidase	Brazil	[23]
2	Pulp, paper, and textile industries (Kraft E1)	Effluent immobilized horseradish peroxidase	Brazil	[24]
3	Industrial effluent (coal–gas conversion plant)	Immobilized polyphenol oxidase	South Africa	[25]
4	2,4-Dichorophenol contaminated soil	Shepherd's purse peroxidase	South Korea	[26]
5	Olive oil mill waste	*Trametes versicolor* laccase	Morocco	[27]
6	Liquefied petroleum gas station	Laccase	China	[28]
7	Refinery wastewater	Soybean peroxidase	Canada	[29]
8	PAH-contaminated shoal soil	Immobilized (nanofiber) laccase	China	[30]
9	Alkyd resin wastewater (paint industrial waste)	Soybean peroxidase	Canada	[31]
10	Municipal wastewater	*Trametes pubescens* laccase	Italy	[32]
11	Coffee processing wastewater	Immobilized null soybean peroxidase	Brazil	[33]
12	Textile factory wastewater	Free and immobilized manganese peroxidase	Pakistan	[12]
13	Chemical plant wastewater	Trametes versicolor laccase	South Korea	[34]
14	Municipal wastewater	Horseradish peroxidase	South Korea	[35]

Source: Neyadi et al. [17]/Taylor & Francis.

Table 8.2 Decolorization and detoxification of synthetic, textile dyes, and other industry effluent by microbial peroxidase(s).

S. no.	Type of peroxidase	Type of microorganism	Microorganism	Application	References
(1)	Peroxidase	Bacteria	*Escherichia coli*	Dye degradation	[37]
(2)	Peroxidase	Bacteria	*Bacillus* sp.	Dye degradation	[38]
(3)	Manganese-dependent peroxidase (MnP), lignin peroxidase (LiP),	Fungi	Fourbasidiomycetous fungi (*Pleurotus ostreatus*) sensu Cooke, *Coriolus versicolor* (L.) Quel., *Tyromyces albidus* (Schaeff.) Donk, and *Trametes gallica*	Biodelignification	[39]
(4)	Lignin peroxidase	Bacteria	*Citrobacter freundii* and *Citrobacter* sp.	Black liquor (pulping by product cause serious environmental problem)	[40]
(5)	Lignin peroxidase	Yeasts	*Candida krusei*	Basic Violet 3 (BV) extensively used in human and veterinary medicine as a biological stain and in various commercial textile processes	[41]
(6)	Lignin peroxidase	Bacteria	*Pseudomonas desmolyticum*	Diazo dye Direct Blue-6	[42]
(7)	Mn-peroxidase	Bacteria	*Pseudomonas* sp.	Malachite green, a widely used recalcitrant dye, has been confirmed to be carcinogenic and mutagenic against many organisms	[43]
(8)	Lignin peroxidase	White-rot fungi	*Pleurotus ostreatus*	Remazol Brilliant Blue R (artificial dye)	[44]
(9)	Peroxidase	Bacteria	*Pseudomonas* sp.	Congo red decolorization	[45]

(Continued)

Table 8.2 (Continued)

S. no.	Type of peroxidase	Type of microorganism	Microorganism	Application	References
(10)	Lignin peroxidase isoenzymes (LiP 4.65, LiP 4.15, and LiP 3.85)	Fungi	*Phanerochaete chrysosporium*	Azo, triphenyl methane, heterocyclic, and polymeric dyes	[46]
(11)	Peroxidase	Bacteria	*Clostridium bifermentans*	Reactive azo dyes	[47]
(12)	Versatile peroxidase	Fungi	*Thanatephorus cucumeris*	Anthraquinone dye, reactive blue 5	[48]
(13)	DyP-type peroxidases	Fungi	*Auricularia auricula-judae*	High-redox potential dyes	[49]
(14)	Extracellular LiP	Bacteria	*Bacillus* sp.	Navy blue 2GL-azo dye	[50]
(15)	Dye-decolorizing peroxidases (DyP)	Fungi	*Pleurotus ostreatus*	Azo dyes	[9]

Source: Bansal and Kanwar [1]/Hindawi/CC BY 3.0 DEED.

The reaction is started by MnP using Mn^{2+} as a substrate. As a result, Mn^{3+} is produced, which oxidizes various phenolic mixtures. The ensuing Mn^{3+} chelate oxalate readily disperses in areas that are not accessible to certain catalyst, such as lignin/cellulose or structures that are similar to them but are deeply buried in the ground, such as xenobiotic toxins, which are not accessible to proteins.

8.3.7 Microbial Adaptable Peroxidases

Methoxybenzenes, Mn(II), and pleasant odor phenol like substrates, e.g. those of MiP, LiP, and HRP are all instantly oxidized by versatile peroxidase (VP) chemicals, which have an incredibly broad substrate specificity. In contrast to other peroxidases, VP can oxidize substrates without the slightest trace of manganese. The excellent working capability of VP with both phenolic and nonphenolic lignin creates dimers, which is an additional characteristic. It is mostly requested for biotechnology work, including bioremediation due to its high productivity Table 8.2.

8.4 Conclusion

Peroxidases are a veritably protean set of enzymes with the capability to degrade organic pollutants and clean-up of wastewater. The significance of peroxidase is in the curing of toxified surroundings; it is grounded on their capability to catalyze the decay of peroxides, similar to H_2O_2, and also the decay of different organic and inorganic composites as well as the aggregation of poisonous composites by cross-reaction, with other phenolics or with co-substrates and generates complex products (dimmers, trimmers, hybrid oligomers). Textile dyes can be discolored by peroxidases, and they can also degrade pesticides, PBPs, chlorine-contained soil alkanes and alkenes, phenoxy herbicides, triazine herbicides, dioxins, and certain insecticides. They might also be able to bioremediate sewage.

Acknowledgment

The authors are thankful to their departments and respective universities for their support in doing this research.

References

1 Bansal, N. and Kanwar, S.S. (2013). Peroxidase(s) in environment protection. *Sci. World J.* 2013: 714639.

2 Torres, E., Bustos-Jaimes, I., and Le Borgne, S. (2003). Potential use of oxidative enzymes for the detoxification of organic pollutants. *Appl. Catal., B* 46 (1): 1–15. https://doi.org/10.1016/S0926-3373(03)00228-5.

3 Heberer, T. (2002). Occurrence, fate and removal of pharmaceutical residues in the aquatic environment. A review of recent research data. *Toxicol. Lett.* 131 (1–2): 5–17. https://doi.org/10.1016/S0378-4274(02)000441. PMID: 11988354.
4 Rooklidge, S.J. (2004). Environmental antimicrobial contamination from terraccumulation and diffuse pollution pathways. *Sci. Total Environ.* 325 (1–3): 1–13. https://doi.org/10.1016/j.scitotenv.2003.11.007. PMID: 15144773.
5 Karigar, C.S. and Rao, S.S. (2011). Role of microbial enzymes in the bioremediation of pollutants: a review. *Enzyme Res.* 2011: 805187.
6 Zhang, Z., Lai, J., Wu, K. et al. (2018). Peroxidase-catalyzed chemiluminescence system and its application in immunoassay. *Talanta* 180: 260–270.
7 Passardi, F., Bakalovic, N., Teixeira, F.K. et al. (2007). Prokaryotic origins of the non-animal peroxidase superfamily and organelle-mediated transmission to eukaryotes. *Genomics* 89 (5): 567–579. https://doi.org/10.1016/j.ygeno.2007.01.006.
8 Ertan, H., Siddiqui, K.S., Muenchhoff, J. et al. (2012). Kinetic and thermodynamic characterization of the functional properties of a hybrid versatile peroxidase using isothermal titration calorimetry: insight into manganese peroxidase activation and lignin peroxidase inhibition. *Biochimie* 94 (5): 1221–1231. https://doi.org/10.1016/j.biochi.2012.02.012.
9 Passardi, F., Theiler, G., Zamocky, M. et al. (2007). PeroxiBase: the peroxidase database. *Phytochemistry* 68: 1605–1611.
10 Camarero, S., Sarkar, S., Ruiz-Dueñas, F.J. et al. (1999). Description of a versatile peroxidase involved in the natural degradation of lignin that has both manganese peroxidase and lignin peroxidase substrate interaction sites. *J. Biol. Chem.* 274 (15): 10324–10330. https://doi.org/10.1074/jbc.274.15.10324.
11 Bakalovic, N., Passardi, F., Ioannidis, V. et al. (2006). PeroxiBase: a class III plant peroxidase database. *Phytochemistry* 67 (6): 534–539. https://doi.org/10.1016/j.phytochem.2005.12.020.
12 Bilal, M., Asgher, M., Iqbal, M. et al. (2016). Chitosan beads immobilized manganese peroxidase catalytic potential for detoxification and decolorization of textile effluent. *Int. J. Biol. Macromol.* 89: 181–189.
13 Mashhadi, N., Taylor, K.E., Biswas, N. et al. (2019). Oligomerization of 3-substituted quinolines by catalytic activity of soybean peroxidase as a wastewater treatment. Product formation and computational studies. *Chem. Eng. J.* 364: 340–348. https://doi.org/10.1016/j.cej.2019.01.184.
14 Liszkay, A., Kenk, B., and Schopfer, P. (2003). Evidence for the involvement of cell wall peroxidase in the generation of hydroxyl radicals mediating extension growth. *Planta* 217 (4): 658–667. https://doi.org/10.1007/s00425-003-1028-1.
15 Baysal, O. and Yildiz, A. (2017). *Bacillus subtilis*: an industrially important microbe for enzyme production. *EC Microbiol.* 5: 148–156.
16 Adewale, I.O. and Adekunle, A.T. (2018). Biochemical properties of peroxidase from white and red cultivars of Kola nut (*Cola nitida*). *Biocatal. Agric. Biotechnol.* 14: 1–9.

17 Al Neyadi, A., Rauf, M.A., and Ashraf, S.S. (2018). Oxidoreductases for the remediation of organic pollutants in water – a critical review. *Crit. Rev. Biotechnol.* 38 (7): 1–18. https://doi.org/10.1080/07388551.2017.1423275.

18 Racz, A., Hideg, E., and Czegeny, G. (2018). Selective responses of class III plant peroxidase isoforms to environmentally relevant UV-B doses. *J. Plant Physiol.* 221: 101–106.

19 Kanwar, S.S. and Bansal, N. (2014). Decolorization of industrial dyes by an extracellular peroxidase from *Bacillus* sp. F31. *JAM* 1: 252–265.

20 Shigeto, J. and Tsutsumi, Y. (2016). Diverse functions and reactions of class III peroxidases. *New Phytol.* 209: 1395–1402.

21 Gholami-Borujeni, F., Mahvi, A.H., Naseri, S. et al. (2011). Application of immobilized horseradish peroxidase for removal and detoxification of azo dye from aqueous solution. *Res. J. Chem. Environ* 15: 217–221.

22 Rajkumar, R., Yaakob, Z., Takriff, M.S. et al. (2013). Optimization of medium composition for the production of peroxidase by *Bacillus* sp. *Pharma Chem.* 5: 167–174.

23 Dezott, M., Innocentini-Mei, L.H., and Durán, N. (1995). Silica immobilized enzyme catalyzed removal of chlorolignins from eucalyptus kraft effluent. *J. Biotechnol.* 43: 161–167.

24 Peralta-Zamora, P., Esposito, E., Pelegrini, R. et al. (1998). Effluent treatment of pulp and paper, and textile industries using immobilized horseradish peroxidase. *Environ. Technol.* 19: 55–63.

25 Edwards, W., Bownes, R., and Leukes, W.D. (1999). A capillary membrane bioreactor using immobilized polyphenoloxidase for the removal of phenols from industrial effluents. *Enzyme Microb. Technol.* 24: 209–217.

26 Park, J.W., Park, B.K., and Kim, J.E. (2006). Remediation of soil contaminated with 2,4-dichlorophenol by treatment of minced shepherd's purse roots. *Arch. Environ. Contam. Toxicol.* 50: 191–195.

27 Canfora, L., Iamarino, G., Rao, M.A. et al. (2008). Oxidative transformation of natural and synthetic phenolic mixtures by *Trametes versicolor* laccase. *J. Agric. Food. Chem.* 56: 1398–1407.

28 Wu, Y., Teng, Y., Li, Z. et al. (2008). Potential role of polycyclic aromatic hydrocarbons (PAHs) oxidation by fungal laccase in the remediation of an aged contaminated soil. *Soil Biol. Biochem.* 40: 789–796.

29 Steevensz, A., Al-Ansari, M.M., Taylor, K.E. et al. (2009). Comparison of soybean peroxidase with laccase in the removal of phenol from synthetic and refinery wastewater samples. *J. Chem. Technol. Biotechnol.* 84: 761–769.

30 Dai, Y., Yin, L., and Niu, J. (2011). Laccase-carrying electro spun fibrous membranes for adsorption and degradation of PAHs in shoal soils. *Environ. Sci. Technol.* 45: 10611–10618.

31 Steevensz, A., Madur, S., Feng, W. et al. (2014). Crude soybean hull peroxidase treatment of phenol in synthetic and real wastewater: enzyme economy enhanced by Triton X-100. *Enzyme Microb. Technol.* 55: 65–71.

32 Spina, F., Cordero, C., and Schilir, T. (2015). Removal of micropollutants by fungal laccases in model solution and municipal wastewater: evaluation of estrogenic activity and ecotoxicity. *J. Cleaner Prod.* 100: 185–194.
33 Chagas, P.M.B., Torres, J.A., Silva, M.C. et al. (2015). Immobilized soybean hull peroxidase for the oxidation of phenolic compounds in coffee processing wastewater. *Int. J. Biol. Macromol.* 81: 568–575.
34 Le, T.T., Murugesan, K., Lee, C.S. et al. (2016). Degradation of synthetic pollutants in real wastewater using laccase encapsulated in core–shell magnetic copper alginate beads. *Bioresour. Technol.* 216: 203–210.
35 Na, S.-Y. and Lee, Y. (2017). Elimination of trace organic contaminants during enhanced wastewater treatment with horseradish peroxidase/hydrogen peroxide (HRP/H_2O_2) catalytic process. *Catal. Today* 282: 86–94.
36 Deivasigamani, C. and Das, N. (2011). Biodegradation of basic violet 3 by *Candida krusei* isolated from textile wastewater. *Biodegradation* 22 (6): 1169–1180.
37 Gennaro, P.D., Bargna, A., Bruno, F., and Sello, G. (2013). Purification of recombinant catalase-peroxidase HPI from *E. coli* and its application in enzymatic polymerization reactions. *J. Appl. Microbiol. Biotechnol.* 98: 1119–1126.
38 Bansal, N. and Kanwar, S.S. (2013). Purification and characterization of an extracellular peroxidase of a bacterial isolate *Bacillus* sp. F31. *Curr. Biotechnol.* 2 (2): 155–161.
39 Hong, Y., Dashtban, M., Chen, S. et al. (2012). Enzyme production and lignin degradation by four basidiomycetous fungi in submerged fermentation of peat. *Int. J. Biol. Medium* 4: 172–180.
40 Kalme, S.D., Parshetti, G.K., Jadhav, S.U., and Govindwar, S.P. (2007). Biodegradation of benzidine based dye Direct Blue-6 by *Pseudomonas* desmolyticum NCIM 2112. *Bioresour. Technol.* 98 (7): 1405–1410.
41 Du, L.N., Wang, S., Li, G. et al. (2011). Biodegradation of malachite green by *Pseudomonas* sp. strain DY1 under aerobic condition: characteristics, degradation products, enzyme analysis and phytotoxicity. *Ecotoxicology* 20 (2): 438–446.
42 Shin, K.S., Young, H.K., and Lim, J.S. (2005). Purification and characterization of manganese peroxidase of the white-rot fungus *Irpex lacteus*. *J. Microbiol.* 43 (6): 503–509.
43 Telke, A.A., Joshi, S.M., Jadhav, S.U. et al. (2010). Decolorization and detoxification of Congo red and textile industry effluent by an isolated bacterium *Pseudomonas* sp. SU-EBT. *Biodegradation* 21 (2): 283–296.
44 Ollikka, P., Alhonmaki, K., Leppanen, V.-M. et al. (1993). Decolorization of azo, triphenyl methane, heterocyclic, and polymeric dyes by lignin peroxidase isoenzymes from *Phanerochaete chrysosporium*. *Appl. Environ. Microbiol.* 59 (12): 4010–4016.
45 Joe, M.H., Lim, S.Y., Kim, D.H., and Lee, I.N. (2008). Decolorization of reactive dyes by *Clostridium bifermentans* SL186 isolated from contaminated soil. *World J. Microbiol. Biotechnol.* 24 (10): 2221–2226.

46 Sugano, Y., Matsushima, Y., and Shoda, M. (2006). Complete decolorization of the anthraquinone dye Reactive blue 5 by the concerted action of two peroxidases from *Thanatephorus cucumeris*. *Appl. Microbiol. Biotechnol.* 73 (4): 862–871.

47 Liers, C., Bobeth, C., Pecyna, M. et al. (2010). DyP-like peroxidases of the jelly fungus *Auricularia auricula*-judae oxidize nonphenolic lignin model compounds and high-redox potential dyes. *Appl. Microbiol. Biotechnol.* 85 (6): 1869–1879.

48 Faraco, V., Piscitelli, A., Sannia, G., and Giardina, P. (2007). Identification of a new member of the dye-decolorizing peroxidase family from *Pleurotus ostreatus*. *World J. Microbiol. Biotechnol.* 23 (6): 889–893.

49 Chandra, R., Abhishek, A., and Sankhwar, M. (2011). Bacterial decolorization and detoxification of black liquor from rayon grade pulp manufacturing paper industry and detection of their metabolic products. *Bioresour. Technol.* 102 (11): 6429–6436.

50 Dawkar, V.V., Jadhav, U.U., Jadhav, S.U., and Govindwar, S.P. (2008). Biodegradation of disperse textile dye Brown 3REL by newly isolated *Bacillus* sp. VUS. *J. Appl. Microbiol.* 105 (1): 14–24.

9

Microbial α-L-Rhamnosidase and Its Significance in Therapeutics

Vinita Yadav

University of Michigan, Division of Cardiovascular Medicine, Department of Internal Medicine, Ann Arbor, MI 48109, USA

9.1 Introduction

Enzymes are the largest group of proteins that are indispensable in metabolic processes, gene expression, cell division, and crucial immune system reactions. Since their discovery, they have explored and exploited for potential use in several fields in the pharmaceutical and biotechnological industries. They accelerate chemical reactions, promoting coordinated metabolic pathways within cells. The enzymes are broadly grouped into six categories according to the types of reaction they catalyze. They have been classified into six major groups: oxidoreductases, transferases, hydrolases, lyases, isomerases, and ligases (https://iubmb.qmul.ac.uk/enzyme/rules.html). Although all living beings synthesize enzymes to drive cellular pathways for their sustainability, in the last few decades, the exploration of microbial enzymes has increased exponentially.

The α-L-rhamnosidases (E.C. 3.2.1.40) enzyme belongs to glycosidases. Glycosidases are also known as glycoside hydrolase or glycosyl hydrolase, which comes from the word carbohydrate (*Glycoside*) and hydrolysis (*enzyme catalyzing hydrolysis reaction*). Glycosidases (3 : 2 : 1…) subgroup is under the group hydrolases (3 : 2…) (https://iubmb.qmul.ac.uk/enzyme/rules.html). These enzymes catalyze the hydrolysis of O- and S-glycosidic bonds. On BRENDA, the enzyme database 214 types of enzymes have been reported from more than four thousand organism sources (https://www.brenda-enzymes.org/). One of the noble enzymes under the group is α-L-rhamnosidases, classified as 3.2.1.40. The enzyme has been reported in 59 different microorganisms, and as the study grows in the field, more sources will be reported (Brenda: https://www.brenda-enzymes.org/). The enzyme hydrolyzes terminal L-rhamnose from steroidal, peptidal, terpenoidal glycosides, or rhamnose attached to lipid molecules or other carbohydrates. L-rhamnose is a deoxy sugar that exists in nature as a bound form and not in free form. After hydrolysis of rhamnosides with α-L-rhamnosidase, the products formed play vital roles in the

Microbial Enzymes: Production, Purification, and Industrial Applications, First Edition.
Edited by Dinesh Yadav, Pankaj Chowdhary, Gautam Anand, and Rajarshi Kumar Gaur.

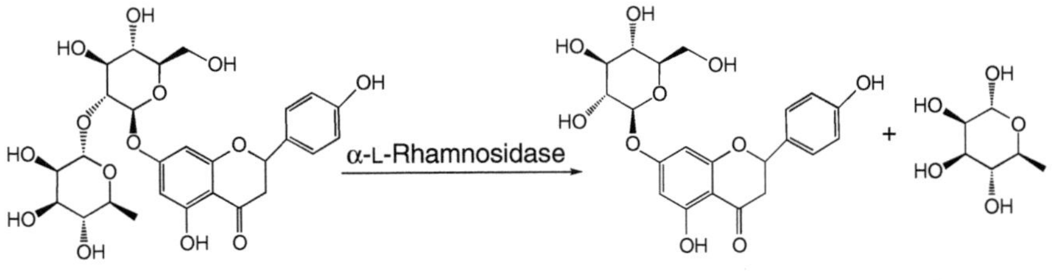

Figure 9.1 Hydrolysis of naringin into prunin and L-rhamnose.

beverages industry and pharmaceutical industry, e.g. terpenoids and flavonoids are important in the wine and beverage, peptidal and steroidal rhamnosides are helpful in the therapeutic industry [1]. Figure 9.1 describes the specific hydrolytic reaction of the enzyme, in which it cleaves terminal L-rhamnose from naringin. A recently emerged subarea of rhamnosidase is its presence in the human microbiome system. The applicability of the enzyme in various areas and its ubiquitous presence in nature make it a unique subject for exploration.

This chapter focuses on source organisms, the estimation of activity or assay methods, commonly used purification methods, properties, and exploration of therapeutic applicability of α-L-rhamnosidase.

9.2 Sources

The enzyme, α-L-rhamnosidase, has been reported from various organisms; however, fungal and bacterial strains are the most studied source organisms. The list of organisms that have been reported to produce a-L-rhamnosidase is given in Table 9.1. The two early sources reported for α-L-rhamnosidase were animals and plants [2, 4, 27]. Also, it is evident from Table 9.1 that microorganisms like yeast, fungi, and bacteria are the most explored sources for rhamnosidases. Currently, commercial rhamnosidases are available, which have been cloned and overexpressed in *Escherichia coli* [33]. Also, scientists have discovered bacterial rhamnosidases in the last few decades from human microbiomes [8, 34, 35]. It is the area of rhamnosidases study that got more attention recently; however, the study spiked shortly as it has significance in human health [36].

9.3 Substrate Specificity and Optimality

The rhamnosidases are active on several substrates from a range of natural sources. These compounds fall into the bioactive compound category. Figure 9.2 is a concise representation of rhamnoside compounds discovered from different sources. There is an abundance of natural sources that contain flavonoids [38].

Table 9.1 Source organisms of α-L-rhamnosidase enzyme among different class.

S. no.	Source type	Species	References
1	Plants	*Fagopyrum esculentum*	[2]
2	Animals	*Pig liver*	[3]
		Turbo cornutus	[4]
3	Yeast	*Clavispora lusitaniae*-84, *Clavispora lusitaniae*-B82, *Candida* sp.-86, and *Candida hyderabadensis*-S82	[5]
		Pichia pastoris	[6]
		Cryptococcus albidus	[7]
		Pichia guilliermondii	[8]
		Pichia angusta	[9]
4	Fungi	*Alternaria alternata* SK37.001	[10]
		Aspergillus niger JMU-TS528, *Aspergillus terreus* CCF3059, *Aspergillus kawachii*	[11]
		Aspergillus aculeatus	[12]
		Aspergillus clavato-nanicus MTCC-9611	[13]
		Aspergillus oryzae	[14]
		Aspergillus nidulans	[15]
		Aspergillus brasiliensis	[16]
		Aspergillus flavus	[17]
		Penicillium griseoroseum	[18]
		Penicillium tardum	[7]
		Penicillium decumbens	[19]
		Penicillium commune	[20]
		Penicillium chrysogenum	[21]
		Fusarium moniliforme MTCC-2088	[22]
	Bacteria	*Bacteroides thetaiotaomicron* VPI-5482	[23]
		Parabacteroides distasonis	[24]
		Bacteroides JY-6	[25]
		Bacillus GL1	[26]
		Bacteroides thetaiotaomicron	[23]
		Klebsiella oxytoca	[27]
		Lactobacillus plantarum	[28]
		Novosphingobium sp.	[29]
		Pseudoalteromonas sp.	[30]
		Sphingomonas paucimobilis FP2001	[31]
		Clostridium stercorarium	[32]

Figure 9.2 Citrus fruits and grapes are great sources of naringin and hesperidin. *Myrica esculenta* (Indian name-kafal) leaves and barks are rich in flavonoids like myricitrin, *Fagopyrum tataricum* (buckwheat), a rich source of rutin, and other flavonoids. Lotus seeds contain numerous L-rhamnose-containing flavonoids. Source: Zhu et al. [37]/Frontiers Media S.A./CC BY 4.0.

As mentioned in the Introduction, terminal L-rhamnose is present in a variety of compounds. A few examples of flavonoids and other bioactive compounds are shown in Figure 9.3.

As described in the introduction, the enzyme is active toward several substrates that contain terminal L-rhamnose, and its optimal condition, like pH and temperature, also range. Table 9.2 describes rhamnosidases from sources with optimal pH and temperature conditions along with substrate specificity. The pH optima for rhamnosidases range from very acidic to basic solution, which opens the window wide to explore the applicability of the enzyme. It is known the alkaline solution naringin is converted into prunin; however, further transformation of prunin to naringenin is prohibited. Another example of pH-dependent transformations, proscillaridin A, a steroid that needs acidic to neutral pH for its activity; the rhamnosidase from *Sphingomonas paucimobilis* with pH 7.8 shows high affinity toward substrate [13, 48].

Likewise, it can be suggested that the enzyme shows high affinity toward the substrate if pH optima and activity for the substrate fall in a similar range.

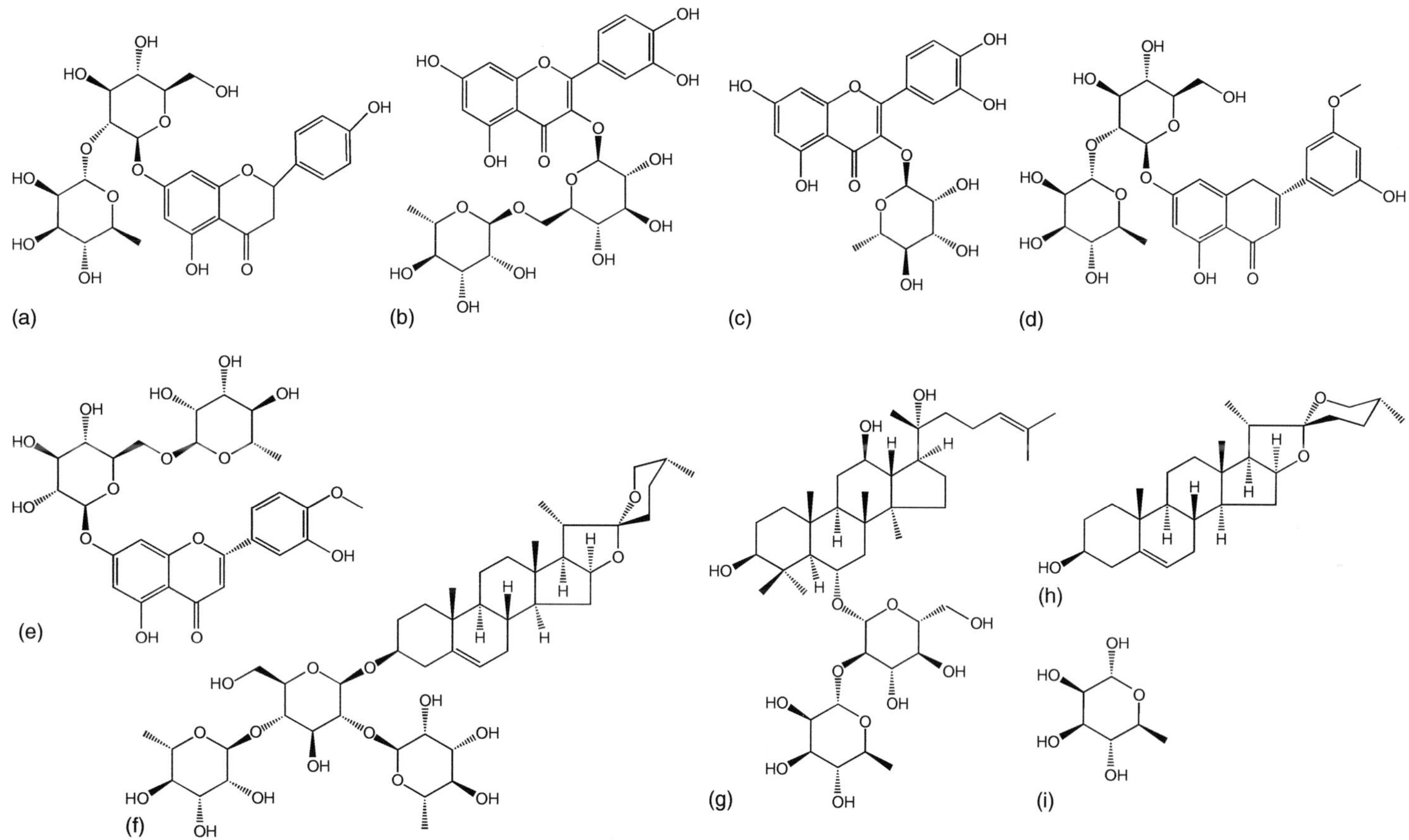

Figure 9.3 (a) Naringin, (b) rutin, (c) quercitrin, (d) hesperidin, (e) neohesperidin, (f) dioscin, (g) ginsenoside Rg2, (h) diosgenin, and (i) L-rhamnose.

Table 9.2 Biochemical and kinetic properties of α-L-rhamnosidase from different sources.

S. no.	Species	pH optima	Temperature optima	Substrate, K_m (mM)	References
1	*Absidia* sp. (in: Fungi)	5.0	50	—	[39]
2	*Acrostalagmus luteo albus*	8.0	55	*pnpr* (3.38)	[40]
3	*Alternaria alternata*	5.5	60	*pnpr* (4.16)	[10]
4	*Alternaria* sp. L1	—		*pnpr* (1.47)	[41]
5	*Aspergillus aculeatus*	5.5–6	30	*pnpr* (0.3)	[42]
6	*Aspergillus flavus*	11	50	*pnpr* (1.89 and naringin (1.60)	[17]
7	*Aspergillus niger*	5–6	60	*pnpr* (12.90)	[23]
8	*Aspergillus oryzae*	4.5	65	*pnpr* (1.4); hesperidin (1.71); naringin (0.53); rutin (0.39)	[14]
9	*Aspergillus terreus*	6–8	44	*pnpr* (0.48)	[43]
10	*Aspergillus tubingensis*	4	50–60	Naringin (0.47)	[44]
11	*Bacillus* sp. (in: Bacteria)	6.5–7	30	*pnpr* (0.28)	[45]
12	*Bacteroides thetaiotaomicron*	6.5	55	*pnpr* (2.87)	[33]
13	*Fusarium sambucinum*	5.5–6.5	55–60	—	[46]
14	*Fusarium solani*	6.5			[46]
15	*Fusarium verticillioides*	10.5	50	*pnpr* (0.5)	[22]
16	*Lactiplantibacillus plantarum*	5	50	*pnpr* (0.57 for RhaB1; 0.51 for RhaB2), hesperidin (3.39 for RhaB1; 0.78 for RhaB2), rutin (1.77 for RhaB1; 1.06 for RhaB2)	[28]
17	*Mucor racemosus*	5.5–6.5	55–60	—	[46]

18	*Novosphingobium* sp. PP1Y	6–7.5	35–45	Quercitrin (0.15), naringin (0.59), hesperidin (0.067), *pnpr* (0.16)	[29]
19	*Ogataea angusta*	6	40	—	[9]
20	*Penicillium decumbens*	6.7	30	*pnpr* (6.1)	[47]
21	*Sphingomonas paucimobilis*	7.8	45	Proscillaridin A (0.07), saikosaponin C (0.88), rutin (0.13), quercitrin (0.89), *pnpr* (1.18), naringin (0.17), hesperidin(0.06)	[48]
22	*Thermoclostridium stercorarium*	7.5	60	—	[32]
23	*Trichoderma longibrachiatum*	4.5–5.5	60–65	—	[46]
24	*Turbo cornutus*	2.8	—	*pnpr* (2.0)	[4]

9.4 Isolation of Microbial Strains for Producing α-L-Rhamnosidase Enzyme

For isolating fungal strains that produce α-L-rhamnosidase, the soil where fruit wastes are dumped or decaying fruit portions is brought into the laboratory and isolated by screening the pure population of the strains. The pure population of the strains is confirmed by the scientist who has expertise in fungal science. The fungi were isolated using the following steps: (i) the soil or decayed fruit samples were streaked on potato dextrose agar plates under sterile conditions. (ii) incubated at 37 °C for two to three days, (iii) the colonies that appeared on plates were picked conscientiously and streaked on four to five agar plates, and (iv) the process was repeated until we got the pure colonies. Once the experts have identified the pure colony, they are ready to grow in a liquid culture medium for production and determination of enzyme activity.

Briefly, under aseptic conditions, about half a million fungal spores from the agar plate/slant are added per 1000 ml of the media that contains $CaCl_2$ – 10.0 g, $MgSO_4 \cdot 7H_2O$ – 30.0 g, KH_2PO_4 – 200.0 g, $N(CH_2COONa)_3$ – 15.0 g, $MnSO_4$ – 10.0 g, $ZnSO_4 \cdot 7H_2O$ – 1.0 g, $CuSO_4 \cdot 5H_2O$ – 1.0 g, $FeSO_4 \cdot 7H_2O$ – 1.0 g, sucrose – 400.0 g, ammonium tartrate – 80.0 g, and H_3BO_3 – 0.1 g in one liter of double-distilled water with inducers naringin or rutin from 0.5% to 1.5%. Other L-rhamnose containing bioactive compounds like hesperidin, myricitrin, and quercitrin, or rhamnoside-rich agro/food wastes (fruit peels and fibers) can be used to induce the α-L-rhamnosidase expression. The fungal cultures were incubated at 25 °C under static conditions. One milliliter from the culture was withdrawn every 24 hours. To measure the optimum expression of α-L-rhamnosidase, one ml culture filtrate was withdrawn every 24 hours, filtered, and used to check the activity.

9.5 Assay Method

The most commonly used assays are performed spectroscopically using two substrates: (i) naringin and (ii) p-nitrophenyl α-L-rhamnopyranoside. The high-performance liquid chromatography (HPLC) method is also used for assaying the enzyme. In this chapter, we will discuss all the three methods.

9.5.1 Naringin as Substrate (Davis Method)

This approach makes use of naringin to measure the activity of the enzyme. The reaction mixture contains 2.5 ml of 860 μM naringin in a buffer solution of 200 mM Na-acetate-acetic acid of pH 4.5 kept at 60 °C. 250 μl of the enzyme or culture extract was added to the mixture, and 100 μl of the reaction solution was quickly taken out and mixed in 2.5 ml of 90% diethylene glycol. At five-minute intervals, 100 μl aliquots were drawn and processed in the same way as previously mentioned. The reaction solutions were kept at room temperature for at least 10 minutes before OD (420 nm) was spectrophotometrically measured.

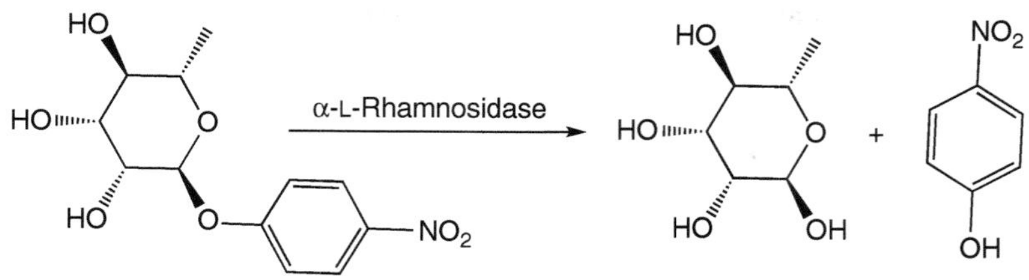

Figure 9.4 Hydrolysis of *p*-nitrophenyl-α-L-rhamnopyranoside by α-L-rhamnosidase.

The absorbance values were transformed into the concentrations of naringin by utilizing a calibration curve. The plot of naringin concentration versus time was used to calculate the rate of naringin hydrolysis. The amount of enzyme needed to hydrolyze one micromole of naringin per minute under the assay mentioned above conditions was considered one unit of enzyme activity (IU) [49].

9.5.2 *p*-Nitrophenyl α-L-Rhamnopyranoside (*pnpr*) as Substrate

This method was initially developed by Romero et al. 1985 [50]. The reaction mixture consists of 0.5 ml of 3.5 mM *pnpr* in 0.1 M potassium hydrogen phthalate/HCl buffer of pH 3.5, which is added to 0.5 ml of the same buffer. The reaction solution was incubated at 57 °C, further 100 μl of an enzyme extract was added. Afterward, 50 μl of the reaction solution was withdrawn at two-minute intervals and mixed in 0.5 M NaOH of volume 3 ml. The absorbance of the solution thus obtained was read at 400 nm. Under the conditions specified above, one unit of α-L-rhamnosidase activity liberates one micromole of *p*-nitrophenolate ion per minute. The molar extinction coefficient value of *p*-nitrophenol released by enzymatic activity, 21.44 m/M/cm, was used to calculate the enzyme unit. UV-visible spectrophotometer (model U-2000, Hitachi, Japan) fitted with an electronic temperature control unit was used for spectroscopic measurements (Figure 9.4).

9.5.3 HPLC Method for Rhamnosidases Assay

Recently, the HPLC-based method used for rhamnosidases assay was developed by Ni et al. in 2013 [51]. In this method, the scientists qualitatively and quantitatively analyzed naringin, prunin, and naringenin on Waters HPLC equipped with a reverse phase C18 column. First, the reaction mixture was prepared using naringin substrate (1.9 ml) in citric acid buffer of pH 5.0 and 0.1 ml of enzyme solution maintained at 50 °C for five minutes and then 100 °C for another five minutes, later cooled at room temperature. Thus, the obtained reaction mixture was filtered and subjected to HPLC having elution mobile phase composition methanol (11.4%), acetonitrile (26.6%), and purified deionized water (62%). Signals for the reaction compounds were detected at 280 nm by a UV detector.

The calibration curves for naringin and prunin were prepared at 10, 50, 100, 150, 200, 300, 400, and 500 μg/ml in 10 mM citric acid buffer (pH 5.0) followed by heating at 100 °C for five minutes to imitate inactivation of the enzyme. The naringenin standard was made in methanol because of its poor solubility in water. The enzyme unit was calculated as the amount of α-L-rhamnosidase that is required to hydrolyze 1 μM naringin to prunin.

9.6 Purification Method

There are several reports available on the purification of the native enzyme and recombinant enzyme from different sources. This section describes the purification of α-L-rhamnosidases from bacterial and fungal sources, which is fundamental. The methods in other reports of the literature will have slight variations in the method depending on which trial worked best for them.

9.6.1 α-L-Rhamnosidase Purification from Bacterial Source

Briefly, the bacterial cell culture was grown aerobically at 28 °C in shaking incubator at 100 rpm for 48 hours. The liquid culture medium contains of 0.1% $(NH_4)_2SO_4$, 0.1% KH_2PO_4, 0.1% Na_2HPO_4, 0.01% $MgSO_4$. $7H_2O$, 0.01% yeast extract, and 0.5% gellan (pH 7.2). After 48 hours, the cells were harvested by centrifugation at 13,000 g, 4 °C for 10 minutes. Subsequently, the cells were washed in 20 mM potassium phosphate buffer (pH 7.0), which consists of 20% (w/v) glycerol, 1 mM ethylenediaminetetraacetic acid, 1 mM dithiothreitol, 0.2 mM, pepstatin A, and 1 mM phenyl-methane-sulfonyl fluoride (buffer A). After resuspending the cells in the same buffer, they were opened using ultrasonication (Insonator, Kubota Model 201M, Tokyo, Japan) at 0 °C, 9 kHz for five minutes. The solution was centrifuged at 15,000 g, 4 °C for 20 minutes, separating the clear intracellular protein solution and cell debris. Thus, obtained clear protein solution was dialyzed in buffer A for >12 hours. The dialysate was used in further purification steps. All purification steps were done at 0–4 °C.

The cell lysate was subjected to ammonium sulfate fractionation at 30–50% saturation; the precipitate was collected by centrifugation (15,000 g, 4 °C) for 20 minutes. So obtained residue was solubilized in 50 ml of buffer A and passed through a diethylaminoethyl (DEAE)-Sepharose CL-6B column (2.6 by 30 cm) pre-equilibrated in buffer A. The linear gradient of sodium chloride (0–1 M) in buffer A (1 l) was utilized to elute the enzyme solution, and fractions of about 8 ml were collected per eight minutes. The enzyme activity was found in fractions eluted at 0.6 M NaCl concentration, and the ammonium sulfate saturation of the active fractions eluted was 30%. Afterward, the protein solution was passed through a pre-equilibrated butyl-toyopearl 650 M column (2.6 by 15 cm) in buffer A with 30% ammonium sulfate saturation. Active enzyme fractions were eluted using a linear ammonium sulfate gradient ranging from 30% to 0% in buffer A and volumes of 2 ml were collected every two minutes. The active fractions eluted are saturated with 8% ammonium sulfate. The active protein solution fractions were pooled and concentrated by ultrafiltration to about 3 ml. The concentrator applied in this method was Amicon Model 8200 from Amicon Co., Lexington, MA. The concentrated enzyme solution was applied to column Sephacryl S-200HR of dimensions 2.7 by 64 cm, which was pre-equilibrated with 20 mM potassium phosphate buffer of pH 7.0, with 0.15 M NaCl. Further, 3-ml fractions of the enzyme were eluted and collected every six minutes. The active enzyme fractions were bunched together and subjected to overnight dialysis against buffer A. The enzyme passed over QAE Sephadex A-25 column, which was pre-equilibrated with buffer A. The NaCl linear gradient from 0–0.5 M concentration in buffer A was used for the last elution, and fractions of 0.8 ml were collected every one minutes. Further, the active fractions were pooled and dialyzed against buffer A overnight, which was used as the purified enzyme [26].

9.6.2 Purification of α-L-Rhamnosidase from Fungal Source

In brief, about five million spores of the fungal strain were added aseptically in liquid culture medium with 0.5% rutin in 100-ml flasks with a volume of 20 ml. The enzyme activity was tested each day for 14 days to find out the maximum activity and the maximum activity observed on the seventh day of incubation. So, for purification purposes, the fungal cultures of the strain in the aforementioned media were grown for seven days and harvested. The procedure took place as follows – the culture was sieved utilizing four to five layers of cheesecloth in order to remove the mycelia and debris – the fungal culture filtrate was centrifuged at 4000 g for 20 minutes at 4 °C to remove any particulate matter from the solution and to obtain clear extracellular protein solution. Subsequently, the protein solution was subjected to ultrafiltration to make it concentrated, and the concentrated solution was dialyzed in buffer (0.01 M sodium-acetate/acetic acid of pH 5.0). The dialyzed enzyme solution was passed through a pre-equilibrated DEAE-cellulose column of dimensions 10 mm × 170 mm. The buffer applied for column pre-equilibration was the same buffer. For protein elution from the column, the linear gradient of sodium chloride from 0 to 1 M concentration in the same buffer was applied. The fractions of volume 4.5 ml were collected, and α-L-rhamnosidase activity and total protein concentration were measured in all the fractions to get the elution profile of the enzyme. The fractions with the enzyme activity were pooled together and concentrated by ultrafiltration using an Amicon concentrator with a cutoff of 10 kDa. The purified enzyme was aliquoted in small portions and was stored in the refrigerator at −20 °C for further application studies [18].

9.7 Biochemical Properties and Application of α-L-Rhamnosidase

The vitality of the enzyme hinges on either the product made by the enzyme or its interaction with other biomolecules that can affect particular metabolic pathways. Since the research area of α-L-rhamnosidase is in its emerging state, the biophysical and biochemical properties like pH optima, temperature optima, temperature and pH stability, K_m, V_{max} with substrates (naringin, *pnpr*, hesperidin, etc.) have been studied, that has been tabularized in Table 9.2.

To the best of our knowledge, the importance of α-L-rhamnosidase is in the products we obtain from its hydrolysis reaction on rhamnoside-containing natural substrates. Here, we discuss the application of potential hydrolysis products of the enzyme.

9.7.1 L-Rhamnose

L-rhamnose is one main product of hydrolysis reaction performed by α-L-rhamnosidase. L-rhamnose is a naturally found L-form of deoxy carbohydrate. It typically exists as a bound form in nature. However, the plants of *Rhamnus* genus have free rhamnose. Since there is no metabolic pathway for the synthesis of L-rhamnose in humans, and its presence is significant in several ways, its isolation or synthesis under sustainable conditions becomes crucial. Here, the enzyme α-L-rhamnosidase will be an essential game player.

Here, we discuss a few examples that present the vitality of L-rhamnose in human lives. The study on humans showed that the propionate formed from L-rhamnose in the colon by bacterial fermentation inhibits the formation of cholesterol and fatty acids [52]. It has also been discovered that L-rhamnose lowers the rate of gastric emptying, which means it resists the hunger feeling [53].

Recent studies have shown that L-rhamnose has an antiaging effect and positively affects skin reconstruction. The study used human papillary dermal fibroblasts for *in vitro* experiments and old and young human skin samples. In both experimental setups, L-rhamnose enhances the reconstruction of the samples and increases the collagen-IV [54].

The other study found in recent literature has suggested that L-rhamnose increases the gene expression Cd137, Cited1, Tbx1, Prdm16, Tmem26, and Ucp1, in 3T3-L1 adipocytes, and protein levels of *p*-hormone sensitive lipase (HSL), *p*-AMP-activated protein kinase (AMPK), acyl-CoA oxidase (ACOX), and carnitine palmitoyl transferase 1 (CPT1), which are markers for brown adipocytes, hence upregulating lipolysis and lipid catabolism. At the same time, it downregulates the expression of acetyl CoA carboxylase (ACC), fatty acid synthase (FAS), CCAAT/enhancer binding protein α (C/EBPα), and peroxisome proliferator-activated receptor gamma (PPARγ), thus reducing adipogenesis and lipogenesis [55].

9.7.2 Prunin

The administration of prunin (= naringenin 7-*O*-β-D-glucoside) into rats with streptozotocin-induced diabetes dissipates the glycemic content and total lipid content in their blood [56].

9.7.3 Hesperetin

Hesperetin, commonly found in citrus fruits, exhibits anti-inflammatory, antioxidative, antitumor activities. A very recent study has shown that hesperetin significantly lowers the colitis symptom by blocking intestinal epithelial necrosis. Its administration in disuccinimidyl suberate-induced colitis helps in downregulating the expression of tumor necrosis factor-α (TNF-α), interleukin (IL)-1β, IL-18, high mobility group box 1 (HMGB1), and IL-6 and upregulation of zonula occludens-1 (ZO-1), occludin, and mucin2 (MUC-2) [57]. Cisplatin is an anticancer drug; however, its clinical application is limited because of its nephrotoxic nature. Hesperetin reduces the reactive oxygen species (ROS) level in cisplatin-treated HK-2 cells and clarifies the oxidative stress by reducing malondialdehyde (MDA)/myeloperoxidase (MPO) levels and increasing superoxide dismutase (SOD)/glutathione (GSH) levels hence protecting against kidney damage caused by cisplatin [58]. Neuroinflammation is critical in cognitive development, memory loss, neurodegenerative disorders like Alzheimer's and Parkinson's diseases. Lipopolysaccharide (LPS) treatment elevated the microglial cell activation and expression of inflammation markers like TNF-α, phosphorylated-nuclear factor-κB (*p*-NF-κB), and IL-1β. However, when these cells were cotreated with hesperetin, a significant reduction in inflammatory cytokines was observed. It also inhibits reactive oxygen species (ROS) generation [59].

9.7.4 Quercetin

Another flavonoid of pharmacological importance, quercetin, possesses antioxidant, anti-inflammatory, and antiproliferative properties. It can be used to treat numerous diseases, for instance, cancers, diabetes, hypertension, and obesity. When quercetin is combined with other small-molecule drugs, it improves the overall efficacy of that drug [60].

9.7.5 Myricetin

The flavonoid myricetin is one of the oldest flavanol discovered as a yellow dye from the bark of *Myrica nagi* [61]. It is ubiquitously present in various fruits, vegetables, and beverages [62]. The most recent review reports on myricetin discuss its biological activity and therapeutic impacts on cancer, cardiovascular diseases, and fatty liver diseases. Also, its antiviral and anti-obesity impact on humans [36, 63, 64].

Ischemia/reperfusion injury is caused by inflammation, oxidative stress, and endothelial cell injury, which further progresses into tissue injury. Phosphorylation of Jun N-terminal kinase (JNK), TNF-α, IL-1β, and IL-6 are upregulated when inflammation is high; myricetin inhibits the expression of these marker proteins [65]. A recent study on myricetin has shown that it modulates gut microbiota that attenuates the biogenesis of hepatic lipids and inflammation in non-fatty liver diseases [66].

The most studied therapeutic application of myricetin is its antiviral role. Scientists have shown its potential in hepatitis B, herpes simplex virus, African swine fever (ASF), bourbon virus, and SARS-CoV-2 [67–70].

9.8 Summary

Nature is an intriguing model of co-existence. The presence of L-rhamnose is present as a bound form in humans, and the abundance of rhamnosylated substrates drives us to perceive the presence of molecule/s that can utilize these substrates and generate L-rhamnose and de-rhamnosylated products of great therapeutic potential. The enzyme α-L-rhamnosidase is omnipresent; hence, identifying more sources can manifest the immense potential of the enzyme and its products. The regressive study of biochemical and biophysical properties of the enzyme can integrate with pertinence and emerge into unexplored areas of natural compounds and their vital role in human welfare. The presence of substantial sources of microorganisms that produce α-L-rhamnosidase with varying properties, suited to various substrate hydrolysis, to some extent unravels the coexistence and the interdependency of life on earth.

References

1 Yadav, V., Yadav, P.K., Yadav, S., and Yadav, K.D.S. (2010). α-L-Rhamnosidase: a review. *Process Biochem.* 45 (8): 1226–1235.

2 Bourbouze, R.P.-S. and Percheron, F. (1975). Rhamnodiastese et alpha-L-rhamnosidase de Fagopyrum esculentum. *Phytochemistry* 14: 1279–1282.

3 Qian, S., Yu, H., Zhang, C. et al. (2005). Purification and characterization of dioscin-alpha-L-rhamnosidase from pig liver. *Chem. Pharm. Bull. (Tokyo)* 53 (8): 911–914.

4 Kurosawa, Y., Ikeda, K., and Egami, F. (1973). L-Rhamnosidases of the liver of *Turbo cornutus* and *Aspergillus niger*. *J. Biochem.* 73 (1): 31–37.

5 Singh, P., Sahota, P.P., and Singh, R.K. (2015). Evaluation and characterization of new α-L-rhamnosidase-producing yeast strains. *J. Gen. Appl. Microbiol.* 61 (5): 149–156.

6 Markošová, K., Weignerová, L., Rosenberg, M. et al. (2015). Upscale of recombinant α-L-rhamnosidase production by *Pichia pastoris* Mut(S) strain. *Front. Microbiol.* 6: 1140.

7 Gudzenko, O.V., Borzova, N.V., and Varbanets, L.D. (2015). Thermal stability of *Cryptococcus albidus* α-L-rhamnosidase. *Ukr. Biochem. J.* 87 (3): 23–30.

8 Rodríguez, M.E., Lopes, C.A., Valles, S., and Caballero, A.C. (2010). Characterization of α-rhamnosidase activity from a patagonian *Pichia guilliermondii* wine strain. *J. Appl. Microbiol.* 109 (6): 2206–2213.

9 Yanai, T. and Sato, M. (2000). Purification and characterization of an alpha-L-rhamnosidase from *Pichia angusta* X349. *Biosci., Biotechnol., Biochem.* 64 (10): 2179–2185.

10 Zhang, T., Yuan, W., Li, M. et al. (2018). Purification and characterization of an intracellular α-L-rhamnosidase from a newly isolated strain, *Alternaria alternata* SK37.001. *Food Chem.* 269: 63–69.

11 Koseki, T., Mese, Y., Nishibori, N. et al. (2008). Characterization of an alpha-L-rhamnosidase from *Aspergillus kawachii* and its gene. *Appl. Microbiol. Biotechnol.* 80 (6): 1007–1013.

12 Manzanares, P., Orejas, M., Gil, J.V. et al. (2003). Construction of a genetically modified wine yeast strain expressing the *Aspergillus aculeatus* rhaA gene,

encoding an alpha-L-rhamnosidase of enological interest. *Appl. Environ. Microbiol.* 69 (12): 7558–7562.

13 Yadav, V., Yadav, S., Yadav, S., and Yadav, K.D. (2012). Alpha-L-rhamnosidase from *Aspergillus clavato*-nanicus MTCC-9611 active at alkaline pH. *Prikl. Biokhim. Mikrobiol.* 48 (3): 328–333.

14 Ishikawa, M., Shiono, Y., and Koseki, T. (2017). Biochemical characterization of *Aspergillus oryzae* recombinant α-L-rhamnosidase expressed in *Pichia pastoris*. *J. Biosci. Bioeng.* 124 (6): 630–634.

15 Tamayo-Ramos, J.A., Flipphi, M., Pardo, E. et al. (2012). L-Rhamnose induction of *Aspergillus nidulans* α-L-rhamnosidase genes is glucose repressed via a CreA-independent mechanism acting at the level of inducer uptake. *Microb. Cell Fact.* 11: 26.

16 Shanmugaprakash, M., Vinothkumar, V., Ragupathy, J., and Reddy, D.A. (2015). Biochemical characterization of three phase partitioned naringinase from *Aspergillus brasiliensis* MTCC 1344. *Int. J. Biol. Macromol.* 80: 418–423.

17 Yadav, V., Yadav, S., Yadava, S., and Yadav, K.D.S. (2011). α-L-Rhamnosidase from *Aspergillus flavus* MTCC-9606 isolated from lemon fruit peel. *Int. J. Food Sci. Technol.* 46 (2): 350–357.

18 Yadav, S., Yadava, S., and Yadav, K.D. (2017). α-L-Rhamnosidase selective for rutin to isoquercitrin transformation from *Penicillium griseoroseum* MTCC-9224. *Bioorg. Chem.* 70: 222–228.

19 Provencher, L., Steensma, D.H., and Wong, C.H. (1994). Five-membered ring azasugars as potent inhibitors of alpha-L-rhamnosidase (naringinase) from *Penicillium decumbens*. *Bioorg. Med. Chem.* 2 (11): 1179–1188.

20 Rzaieva, O.M., Borzova, N.V., and Varbanets, L.D. (2008). Investigations of functional groups of *Penicillium commune* 266 alpha-L-rhamnosidases. *Ukr. Biokhim. Zh. (1999)* 80 (6): 42–51.

21 Matsumoto, S., Yamada, H., Kunishige, Y. et al. (2017). Identification of a novel *Penicillium chrysogenum* rhamnogalacturonan rhamnohydrolase and the first report of a rhamnogalacturonan rhamnohydrolase gene. *Enzyme Microb. Technol.* 98: 76–85.

22 Kumar, D., Yadav, S., Yadava, S., and Yadav, K.D.S. (2019). An alkali tolerant α-L-rhamnosidase from *Fusarium moniliforme* MTCC-2088 used in de-rhamnosylation of natural glycosides. *Bioorg. Chem.* 84: 24–31.

23 Li, L.J., Wu, Z.Y., Yu, Y. et al. (2018). Development and characterization of an α-L-rhamnosidase mutant with improved thermostability and a higher efficiency for debittering orange juice. *Food Chem.* 245: 1070–1078.

24 Bokkenheuser, V.D., Shackleton, C.H., and Winter, J. (1987). Hydrolysis of dietary flavonoid glycosides by strains of intestinal Bacteroides from humans. *Biochem. J.* 248 (3): 953–956.

25 Jang, I.S. and Kim, D.H. (1996). Purification and characterization of alpha-L-rhamnosidase from Bacteroides JY-6, a human intestinal bacterium. *Biol. Pharm. Bull.* 19 (12): 1546–1549.

26 Hashimoto, W., Miyake, O., Nankai, H., and Murata, K. (2003). Molecular identification of an alpha-L-rhamnosidase from *Bacillus* sp. strain GL1 as an enzyme involved in complete metabolism of gellan. *Arch. Biochem. Biophys.* 415 (2): 235–244.

27 O'Neill, E.C., Stevenson, C.E., Paterson, M.J. et al. (2015). Crystal structure of a novel two domain GH78 family α-rhamnosidase from *Klebsiella oxytoca* with rhamnose bound. *Proteins* 83 (9): 1742–1749.

28 Ávila, M., Jaquet, M., Moine, D. et al. (2009). Physiological and biochemical characterization of the two alpha-L-rhamnosidases of *Lactobacillus plantarum* NCC245. *Microbiology (Reading)* 155 (Pt 8): 2739–2749.

29 Mensitieri, F., De Lise, F., Strazzulli, A. et al. (2018). Structural and functional insights into RHA-P, a bacterial GH106 α-L-rhamnosidase from *Novosphingobium* sp. PP1Y. *Arch. Biochem. Biophys.* 648: 1–11.

30 Mazzaferro, L.S., Orrillo, G.A., Ledesma, P., and Breccia, J.D. (2008). Dose-dependent significance of monosaccharides on intracellular alpha-L-rhamnosidase activity from *Pseudoalteromonas* sp. *Biotechnol. Lett* 30 (12): 2147–2150.

31 Miyata, T., Kashige, N., Satho, T. et al. (2005). Cloning, sequence analysis, and expression of the gene encoding *Sphingomonas paucimobilis* FP2001 alpha-L-rhamnosidase. *Curr. Microbiol.* 51 (2): 105–109.

32 Zverlov, V.V., Hertel, C., Bronnenmeier, K. et al. (2000). The thermostable alpha-L-rhamnosidase RamA of *Clostridium stercorarium*: biochemical characterization and primary structure of a bacterial alpha-L-rhamnoside hydrolase, a new type of inverting glycoside hydrolase. *Mol. Microbiol.* 35 (1): 173–179.

33 Wu, T., Pei, J., Ge, L. et al. (2018). Characterization of a α-L-rhamnosidase from *Bacteroides thetaiotaomicron* with high catalytic efficiency of epimedin C. *Bioorg. Chem.* 81: 461–467.

34 Amaretti, A., Raimondi, S., Leonardi, A. et al. (2015). Hydrolysis of the rutinose-conjugates flavonoids rutin and hesperidin by the gut microbiota and bifidobacteria. *Nutrients* 7 (4): 2788–2800.

35 Bang, S.H., Hyun, Y.J., Shim, J. et al. (2015). Metabolism of rutin and poncirin by human intestinal microbiota and cloning of their metabolizing α-L-rhamnosidase from *Bifidobacterium dentium*. *J. Microbiol. Biotechnol.* 25 (1): 18–25.

36 Wang, L., Wu, H., Yang, F., and Dong, W. (2019). The protective effects of myricetin against cardiovascular disease. *J. Nutr. Sci. Vitaminol.* 65 (6): 470–476.

37 Zhu, M., Liu, T., and Guo, M. (2016). Current advances in the metabolomics study on lotus seeds. *Front. Plant Sci.* 7: 891.

38 Kumar, S. and Pandey, A.K. (2013). Chemistry and biological activities of flavonoids: an overview. *Sci. World J.* 2013: 162750.

39 Yu, H., Liu, H., Zhang, C. et al. (2004). Purification and characterization of gypenoside-alpha-L-rhamnosidase hydrolyzing gypenoside-5 into ginsenoside Rd. *Process Biochem.* 39: 861–867.

40 Rojas, N.L., Voget, C.E., Hours, R.A., and Cavalitto, S.F. (2011). Purification and characterization of a novel alkaline α-L-rhamnosidase produced by *Acrostalagmus luteo albus*. *J. Ind. Microbiol. Biotechnol.* 38 (9): 1515–1522.

41 Xu, L., Liu, X., Yin, Z. et al. (2016). Site-directed mutagenesis of α-L-rhamnosidase from *Alternaria* sp. L1 to enhance synthesis yield of reverse hydrolysis based on rational design. *Appl. Microbiol. Biotechnol.* 100 (24): 10385–10394.

42 Manzanares, P., van den Broeck, H.C., de Graaff, L.H., and Visser, J. (2001). Purification and characterization of two different alpha-L-rhamnosidases, RhaA and RhaB, from *Aspergillus aculeatus*. *Appl. Environ. Microbiol.* 67 (5): 2230–2234.

43 Ge, L., Li, D., Wu, T. et al. (2018). B-factor-saturation mutagenesis as a strategy to increase the thermostability of α-L-rhamnosidase from *Aspergillus terreus*. *J. Biotechnol.* 275: 17–23.

44 Li, L., Gong, J., Wang, S. et al. (2019). Heterologous expression and characterization of a new clade of *Aspergillus* α-L-rhamnosidase suitable for citrus juice processing. *J. Agric. Food. Chem.* 67 (10): 2926–2935.

45 Cui, Z., Maruyama, Y., Mikami, B. et al. (2007). Crystal structure of glycoside hydrolase family 78 alpha-L-Rhamnosidase from *Bacillus* sp. GL1. *J. Mol. Biol.* 374 (2): 384–398.

46 Scaroni, E., Cuevas, C., Carrillo, L., and Ellenrieder, G. (2002). Hydrolytic properties of crude alpha-L-rhamnosidases produced by several wild strains of mesophilic fungi. *Lett. Appl. Microbiol.* 34 (6): 461–465.

47 Kim, J.H., Curtis-Long, M.J., Seo, W.D. et al. (2005). Alpha-rhamnosidase inhibitory activities of polyhydroxylated pyrrolidine. *Bioorg. Med. Chem. Lett.* 15 (19): 4282–4285.

48 Miake, F., Satho, T., Takesue, H. et al. (2000). Purification and characterization of intracellular alpha-L-rhamnosidase from *Pseudomonas paucimobilis* FP2001. *Arch. Microbiol.* 173 (1): 65–70.

49 Davis, W.B. (1947). Determination of flavanones in citrus juice. *Anal. Chem.* 19: 46–48.

50 Romero, C., Manjón, A., Bastida, J., and Iborra, J. (1985). A method for assaying the rhamnosidase activity of naringinase. *Anal. Biochem.* 149 (2): 566–571.

51 Ni, H., Xiao, A.-F., Wang, Y.Q. et al. (2013). Development and evaluation of an HPLC method for accurate determinations of enzyme activities of naringinase complex. *J. Agric. Food. Chem.* 61 (42): 10026–10032.

52 Vogt, J.A., Pencharz, P.B., and Wolever, T.M. (2004). L-Rhamnose increases serum propionate in humans. *Am. J. Clin. Nutr.* 80 (1): 89–94.

53 Byrne, C.S., Preston, T., Brignardello, J. et al. (2018). The effect of L-rhamnose on intestinal transit time, short chain fatty acids and appetite regulation: a pilot human study using combined (13)CO(2)/H(2) breath tests. *J. Breath Res.* 12 (4): 046006.

54 Pageon, H., Azouaoui, A., Zucchi, H. et al. (2019). Potentially beneficial effects of rhamnose on skin ageing: an in vitro and in vivo study. *Int. J. Cosmet. Sci.* 41 (3): 213–220.

55 Choi, M., Mukherjee, S., Kang, N.H. et al. (2018). L-Rhamnose induces browning in 3T3-L1 white adipocytes and activates HIB1B brown adipocytes. *IUBMB Life* 70 (6): 563–573.

56 Choi, J.S., Yokozawa, T., and Oura, H. (1991). Improvement of hyperglycemia and hyperlipemia in streptozotocin-diabetic rats by a methanolic extract of *Prunus davidiana* stems and its main component, prunin. *Planta Med.* 57 (3): 208–211.

57 Zhang, J., Lei, H., Hu, X., and Dong, W. (2020). Hesperetin ameliorates DSS-induced colitis by maintaining the epithelial barrier via blocking RIPK3/MLKL necroptosis signaling. *Eur. J. Pharmacol.* 873: 172992.

58 Chen, X., Wei, W., Li, Y. et al. (2019). Hesperetin relieves cisplatin-induced acute kidney injury by mitigating oxidative stress, inflammation and apoptosis. *Chem. Biol. Interact.* 308: 269–278.

59 Muhammad, T., Ikram, M., Ullah, R. et al. (2019). Hesperetin, a citrus flavonoid, attenuates LPS-induced neuroinflammation, apoptosis and memory impairments by modulating TLR4/NF-κB signaling. *Nutrients* 11 (3).

60 Zou, H., Ye, H., Kamaraj, R. et al. (2021). A review on pharmacological activities and synergistic effect of quercetin with small molecule agents. *Phytomedicine* 92: 153736.

61 Perkin, A.G. and Hummel, J.J. (1896). LXXVI—the colouring principle contained in the bark of *Myrica nagi*. Part I. *J. Chem. Soc. Trans.* 69 (0): 1287–1294.

62 Semwal, D.K., Semwal, R.B., Combrinck, S., and Viljoen, A. (2016). Myricetin: a dietary molecule with diverse biological activities. *Nutrients* 8 (2): 90.

63 Song, X., Tan, L., Wang, M. et al. (2021). Myricetin: a review of the most recent research. *Biomed. Pharmacother.* 134: 111017.

64 Jiang, M., Zhu, M., Wang, L., and Yu, S. (2019). Anti-tumor effects and associated molecular mechanisms of myricetin. *Biomed. Pharmacother.* 120: 109506.

65 Sun, Y., Lian, M., Lin, Y. et al. (2018). Role of p-MKK7 in myricetin-induced protection against intestinal ischemia/reperfusion injury. *Pharmacol. Res.* 129: 432–442.

66 Sun, W.L., Li, X.Y., Dou, H.Y. et al. (2021). Myricetin supplementation decreases hepatic lipid synthesis and inflammation by modulating gut microbiota. *Cell Rep.* 36 (9): 109641.

67 Xiao, T., Cui, M., Zheng, C. et al. (2021). Myricetin inhibits SARS-CoV-2 viral replication by targeting M(pro) and ameliorates pulmonary inflammation. *Front. Pharmacol.* 12: 669642.

68 Parvez, M.K., Al-Dosari, M.S., Arbab, A.H. et al. (2020). Bioassay-guided isolation of anti-hepatitis B virus flavonoid myricetin-3-*O*-rhamnoside along with quercetin from *Guiera senegalensis* leaves. *Saudi Pharm. J.* 28 (5): 550–559.

69 Li, W., Xu, C., Hao, C. et al. (2020). Inhibition of herpes simplex virus by myricetin through targeting viral gD protein and cellular EGFR/PI3K/Akt pathway. *Antiviral Res.* 177: 104714.

70 Hao, S., Ning, K., Wang, X. et al. (2020). Establishment of a replicon reporter of the emerging tick-borne bourbon virus and use it for evaluation of antivirals. *Front. Microbiol.* 11: 572631.

10

The Use of Microbial Enzymes in the Food Industries: A Global Perspective

Hina Radadiya[1], Rajesh Patel[2], and Ramesh Kothari[1]

[1] *Saurashtra University, Department of Biosciences, Saurashtra University Road, Rajkot, Gujarat 360005, India*
[2] *Veer Narmad South Gujarat University, Department of Biosciences, Udhana - Magdalla Road, Surat, Gujarat 395007, India*

10.1 Introduction

Microbial enzymes are immeasurable and significant for the evolution of industrial bioprocesses, and they play a vital role in various industrial applications. Approximately 150 industrial process enzymes come from microbial cell cultures used as catalysts. However, prior expansion is still needed for more novel, unique, and workable with low economic cost and high-yield production with the help of new, improved, or additional multipurpose enzymes [1, 2].

After acquiring advanced rDNA technology in bacteria and fungi, they are highly in demand for industrial enzyme production. So far, the highest consumers of industrial enzymes are in North America and Europe, and in the Asia Pacific section, mainly Japan, India, and China, which is now experiencing a rapid rise in enzyme demand [3, 4].

The production of commercial enzymes comes from various sources, but enzymes from microbes hold more market share than other sources because microbes are the most significant and suitable source of commercial enzymes (Table 10.1). Sixty percent are from fungi, 24% are from bacteria, 2% are from Yeast, 6% are from animals, and 4% are from plants. The benefit of microbial enzymes is that they can produce bulk amounts of enzymes under ideal growth environments for the cultivation of microbes by using low raw substrates as well, and they have a short production period. By using advanced genetic engineering techniques, the production of the chosen product is possible. From the isolation to the recovery of enzymes, processes are elementary compared to plants and animals [6].

Most enzymes are proteins and are catalysts for different chemical reactions, converting raw materials into the final food product. Enzymes are used in flavor development, texture processing, or as preservatives, and they mainly cover the dairy, backing, beverages, meat, and fish industries. Food processing is the world's prime and uppermost predominant sector in production, consumption, and trade. Microbial enzymes are used extensively to maintain the nutritive value of food and

Microbial Enzymes: Production, Purification, and Industrial Applications, First Edition.
Edited by Dinesh Yadav, Pankaj Chowdhary, Gautam Anand, and Rajarshi Kumar Gaur.

Table 10.1 List of companies manufacturing industrial enzymes.

Company	Location
AB enzymes	Germany
Advance enzymes	India
Amano	Japan
Amway	Michigan
Aum enzymes	India
B.A.S.F.	Germany
Biocatalyst	UK
Chr Hansen	Denmark
D.S.M.	Netherland
DU Pont	US
Novozymes	Denmark
Nutritech	New Zealand
Roche	Switzerland
Sunson	China

Source: Adapted from Li et al. [5].

other properties such as antioxidant capacity, fruit ripening, flavor development, aroma, appearance, texture strengthening, and meat tenderization. Processing food can ensure some important criteria, such as food being safe to consume and also preventing food spoilage so it causes less food waste and maintains all the nutritional value. Carbohydrase, protease, and lipase are dominating the enzyme market [7–10].

10.2 Global Perspective and Demand for Microbial Enzymes in the Food Industry

During ancient times, knowingly or unknowingly, enzymes have performed a leading role in food making, from pickles, curd, wine, beer, and many more. Currently, enzymes from microbes play a vital part in food industries for producing and processing food. In combination with advanced technology, it gives a new direction for the food industry and increases the demand worldwide [11].

The growing public interest and realization regarding health care lead to safe and healthy foods that will increase the whole global food enzyme market in the forecast period. Concurrently, increased urging for nutraceutical products and enlarged demand for alcoholic and nonalcoholic beverages in several industries are noteworthy for the growth of the food enzymes market [12].

Many companies are participating in enzyme manufacturing globally, and producers from North America, Europe, Latin America, and the Asia Pacific play a major role in the production. Europe and Asia are leading the race regarding Enzymes from microorganisms. They cover almost 90% of the global market. US-based company Novozyme is the largest enzyme company globally and holds a dominant share of 48% of the enzyme market [13].

The realization of health and the nutritional benefits of food enzymes also increases the global demand for new enzymes. As per a recent report worldwide, the value of the food and beverage enzyme market in 2011 was US$ 1200 million, and in 2012, it increased by US$ 1355.8 million, and in 2018, it reached around US$ 2306.4 million. By 2021, expect to touch around US$ 2940 million.

List of prominent players in the food enzymes market

- DuPont, Enzyme Development Corporation, Novozymes, Creative Enzymes (US)
- Associated British Foods plc, Biocatalysts Ltd. (UK)
- Amano Enzyme Inc. (Japan)
- D.S.M. (Netherlands)
- C.H.R. Hansen (Denmark)
- Kerry Group (Ireland)
- Puratos Group (Belgium)
- Advanced Enzyme Technologies Ltd, AUM Enzymes, Enzyme Bioscience Private Limited, Antozyme Biotech Pvt Ltd (India)
- E.N.M.E.X.
- Xike Biotechnology Co. Ltd., S.U.N.S.O.N. Industry Group Co., Jiangsu Boli Bioproducts Co. (China)

The pandemic due to COVID-19 has called attention to the predominant safety and health of humans. Food plays a crucial role, and the main factor is the nutrition of food. It leads the market of food enzymes to the next level because of the use of enzymes in various products, especially nutritional immune-busting products. Due to the majority of people eating meat and animal products, it is high in North America, which is the prime aspect for enzyme use in food in the industry.

Biocatalysts Ltd announced the release of their new Enzyme PromodTM 517MDP (P517MDP) in 2021. Enzyme is precisely aimed at the dairy protein industry, and it hydrolyzed casein protein at a rate of more than 40%.

10.3 Production of Industrial Enzymes

All microorganisms or every single organism strain can produce different types of enzymes. Each has different properties, such as hydrolyzing, oxidizing or reducing, and metabolic.

For the production of industrial enzymes, there are two main parts: (i) the screening and (ii) the fermentation process. One of the essential parts of production media is nutrition. Media contains all the micro- and macronutrients required for microbes' growth and suitable carbon and nitrogen sources. Three methods of production: (i) batch fermentation, (ii) continuous fermentation, and (iii) feed batch fermentation [5, 14] Figure 10.1.

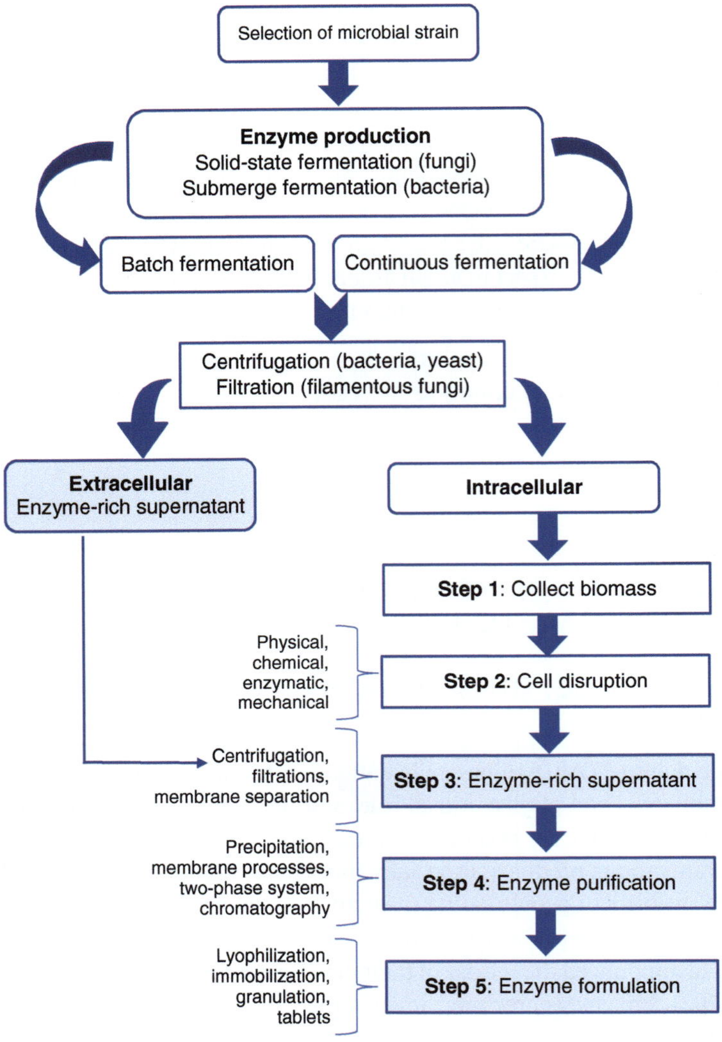

Figure 10.1 A schematic diagram of microbial enzyme production. Source: Adapted from Fernandes and Carvalho [15].

Fermentation is done in solid-state fermentation (SSF) or submerged fermentation (SMF). Bacterial enzyme production is accomplished by submerged fermentation (SMF) because bacterial cell growth, as well as enzyme secretion, are more appropriate in submerged conditions compared to SSF, but in the case of fungi, most possibly use SSF for enzyme production. In SMF, before inoculation of bacterial culture, media sterilization is most necessary. Various parameters are important for production, pH and temperature of media play a key role in the production, as well as dissolved oxygen, aeration, agitation, and rotation [16–18].

After the fermentation process ends, the next step is a downstream process, which includes the recovery of the enzyme, purification, and formulation of the product. Generally, the downstream processing is more complex in intracellular than extracellular enzymes. The most overpriced part downstream is enzyme purification; at the commercial level, chromatography primarily purifies enzymes [19, 20].

Food enzymes can be distributed in liquid or solid form, so the formulation of enzyme concentration is important. The solid formulation includes tablets or granulation, lyophilization, and immobilization. Immobilization of enzymes gives more opportunities in industries, such as stability and reusability, which highly enhance the yield of production. Immobilization techniques include different methods for enzyme entrapment and different matrix materials [21].

10.4 Approach to Boost Properties of Microbial Enzymes

The constantly increasing requirement for enzymes from microorganisms in food processing industries has directed the search for new and upgraded biocatalysts compared to earlier times. Nowadays, there has been a significant increase in enzymes due to advanced techniques like molecular biology and protein engineering. Several methods and techniques are available to modify the enzyme and achieve the target product [22]. Various factors matter when it comes to industrial enzymes, such as enzyme–substrate binding, enzymes' stability in various conditions, narrow substrate specificity, and substrate/product. Overcoming these problems in microbial enzymes can be possible with the help of advanced techniques by improving their characteristics to survive in particular environments and make them suitable for particular applications. Many commercial enzymes for food production are currently resulting from largely selected or genetically modified microorganisms [23].

New enzymes can come from nature and can be accomplished in three ways: metagenomic screening, genome mining, and taking advantage of the diversity of extremophiles [24] (Figure 10.2).

The most commonly applied strategies in protein engineering are (i) direct evaluation, (ii) rational designing, (iii) semirational designing, and (iv) structure-based designing (Table 10.2). The rational design approach includes site-directed mutagenesis to target amino acid substitutions; it demands detailed facts about the chemical mechanism, 3D structure, and enzymatic reaction. For desired changes by using site-directed mutagenesis in microbial enzymes, three important things are the protein's structure, function, and catalytic mechanism, which must be well understood to reach the aim with the least number of variants. It improves kinetic properties, enhances substrate and reactant specificity, increases thermostability, alters pH optima, increases catalytic capacity, and increases substrate specificity and yield. In some cases, this has boosted activity by 10×-fold [25, 26].

The directed evolution method involves only the data of the protein sequence. This method comprises repeated cycles of gene recombination, random, and mutagenesis, followed by screening or selection for positive mutants, which agrees for high throughput and has been broadly applied, targeting more efficient enzymes.

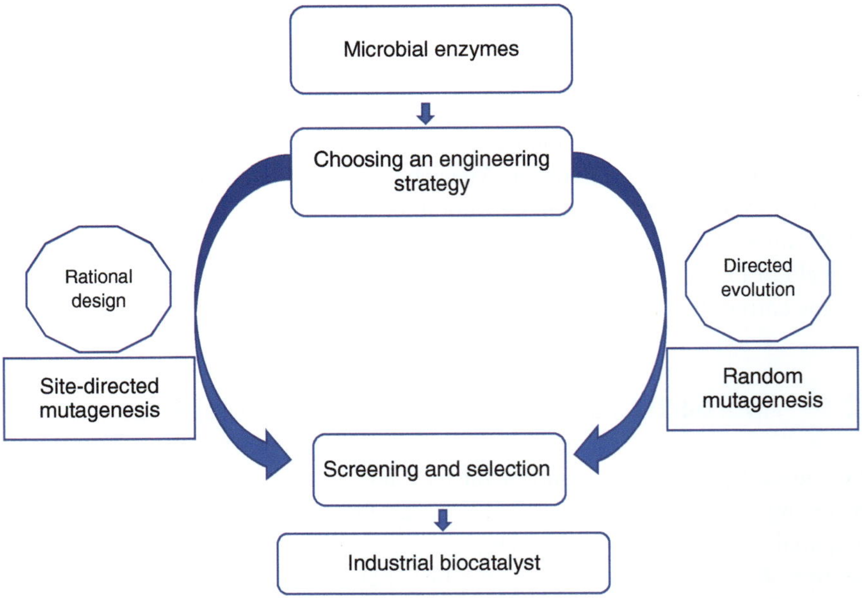

Figure 10.2 A schematic diagram illustrating the protein engineering process. Source: Mehta and Sehgal [17]/Springer Nature.

rDNA technology and genetic engineering have empowered: (i) industrial important enzymes microbe production by industrial microbes of enzymes obtained formerly from pathogenic microbes. Those enzymes are obtained from extremophiles (ii) enhanced enzyme productivity using good promotors, signal sequences, and multiple gene copies [22, 27–29].

10.5 Microbial Enzymes in Food Industries

Enzymes are produced by almost all living cells for their metabolic process, which helps in their biochemical reactions. Enzymes are vital in food processing to upgrade the nutritional value and enhance particular flavors. Specially enzymes from microorganisms play a required role in food industries because of their access to production and genetic modification in both microorganisms' enzymes. The food-processing industry successfully uses microbial enzymes to produce various beverages, breads, cheese, and other products at the commercial level [30].

Globally, various enzymes are used in food industries, including α-amylase, glucoamylase, lipase, pectinase, chymosin, and protease, and different enzymes play diverse roles in various food processes. Lipases can be used for both purposes of hydrolyzing or synthesis, depending on the presence of water. Lipase helps enhance flavor and reduces the time for cheese ripening. The role of the α-amylase enzyme is to convert starch into dextrin and produce corn syrup, which is helpful for different purposes like enhancing sweetness in food products.

Table 10.2 Industrial microbial enzyme, enzyme classes, types of reaction, and their role.

S. no.	Class	Reaction	Industrial enzymes	Role
1	Hydrolases	Hydrolytic cleavage of bonds	Amylases, protease, lipase, cellulase, phytase, peptidase, pullulanase, xylanase, glucoamylase, glucanase, galactosidase, pectinase, invertase, phospholipase, lactase	Bread making, cultured milk products, modification of milk fat, fermented sausage, meat tenderizing, hydrolysis of lipids, cheese ripening, saccharification, starch hydrolysis, extraction and clarification of fruit juices, flavor enhancement of food, debittering, color stability and prevention of off flavors, starch liquefaction and saccharification, bread softness and volume, flour adjustment, low-calorie beer, production of inverted sugar syrup, synthesis of aromatic molecules, milk clotting, low-allergenic infant-food formulation, enhanced digestibility and utilization, prevention of chill haze formation in brewing
2	Transferase	Catalyze the transfer of groups of atoms among the molecule	Glucosyltransferase, fructosyltransferase, transglutaminase, acyltransferase, transaminase	Meat processing, synthesis of fructose oligomers, laminated dough strength, production of prebiotics
3	Isomerases	Transfer of group from one position to another within the same molecule	Glucose isomerase, arabinose isomerase	High-fructose corn syrup production
4	Oxidoreductase	Oxidation reactions involve the transfer of electrons or hydrogen or oxygen atoms from one molecule to another	Catalase, dehydrogenase, glucose oxidase, laccases, peroxidase, oxygenases, lipoxygenase	Glucose removal, flavor enhancement of food, cheese processing, dough strengthening, clarification of fruit juices
5	Lyase	Nonhydrolytic cleavage by addition or elimination reaction	Fumarase, arginosuccinase, pactate lyases, hydratases, acetolactate, decarboxylase	Maturation of beer and clarification of fruit

Source: Adapted from Mehta and Sehgal [17].

Pectinase is a hydrolytic enzyme used in fruit juice extraction, clarification, and filtration. Bacterial and fungal protease enzymes produce fish meals, meat extracts, texturized proteins, and meat extenders. The key role of microbial enzymes is to enhance the process and other properties such as aroma, color, flavor, consistency, composition, structure, and appearance [31, 32].

10.5.1 Dairy Industry

Enzymes mainly used in the dairy industry are rennet, lactase, lipase, protease, catalase, and esterase. According to Fonterra analysis, in 2011, dairy companies worldwide processed about 378 billion liter of milk annually. Based on data on the production and use of cheese, nearly 9 million tons of cheese are produced yearly. Fresh milk processing is primarily derived from caw and other sources such as goats, buffalo camels, and other mammals [33–35].

Animal rennet is used in milk clotting in the dairy industry to manufacture first-class cheeses with food flavor, texture, and aroma.

The rise in cheese production worldwide is because demand leads to a search for rennet substitutes, such as microbial rennet instead of calf rennet. There has been a 4% increase per year for the past 30 years. Rennet from microorganisms is used for one-third of all the cheese produced worldwide [36]. In the substitute of a calf, rennet uses rennet-like proteinases from microorganisms. Rennet comes from *Aspergillus oryzae*, *Rhizomucor pusillus*, *Rhizomucor miehei*, *Endothia parasitica*, and *Lactococcus lactis* for large cheese production. Microbial rennets come from several microbes under trade names such as Formase, Rennilase, Marzyme, Henilase, etc.

The only downside of rennet from microorganisms in cheese manufacturing is the change of flavors and unpleasant taste. To overcome this problematic property, with the help of advanced techniques, industries use recombinant rennet in diverse microbial hosts. Various standard cheeses have been magnificently made using recombinant rennet on a trial or small pilot scale [37, 38].

Lipase is a water-soluble enzyme that helps catalyze the hydrolysis of the ester bond in triacylglycerol and releases free fatty acids and glycerol. Lipolysis contributes to Swiss cheese flavors mainly due to the lipolytic enzymes of starter cultures. Lipase also plays a vital role in cheese production by enhancing flavors, speeding the process of cheese making, creating modified milk products, and cutting the milk fat. The characteristic peppery flavor of blue cheese is due to methyl ketones and short-chain fatty acids. Fat hydrolysis in blue cheese is catalyzed by *Penicillium roqueforti* lipase, with a lesser contribution from indigenous lipase. Sometimes, a combination of enzymes can also be used in the cheese ripening process [39, 40].

Lactase enzyme is used in the production of a wide range of properties such as frozen desserts, ice cream, and yoghurt, and to improve scoop and soupiness, syrupiness, juiciness, and digestibility and to reduce sandiness due to the crystallization of lactose in concentrated preparations. Lactase is most commonly used for the hydrolysis of the most common sugar of milk lactose. Lactase is obtained from *Streptococcus lactis* and *Kluyveromyces* sp. At present, the manufacturing of a lactose-free product is a significant concentration of the dairy industry because the LII (lactose intolerance index) is globally high in the United States, Africa, and Asia at 50%, and after that comes Britain, and North Europeans, Australasian, and North Americans [41, 42].

Therefore, a lower amount of lactose present or lactose-free product allows the lactose-intolerant community to fascinating less lactose-fermented milk products. In dairy processing, some enzymes have restrictive applications, such as glucose oxidase, sulfhydryl oxidase, and lysozymes. In preservation, glucose oxidase and catalase are used together often. The glucose oxidase has countless marketable applications to stop decomposition and enhance the boost in the time of dried egg products by removing glucose from a dried egg. Cow milk is used as infant milk by adding shielding features like lysozyme, and it also acts as a preservative by plummeting bacterial count. Transglutaminase (Tgase) is a catalyst in the polymerization of milk protein and boosts the properties of milk foodstuffs [43, 44].

10.5.2 Bakery Industry

Bread manufacture is one of the most standard food dispensation methods worldwide. Varieties of bread types are available in different zones; some common baked foods products are a wide range of breads, pastries, cakes, pies, pastries, pizza, biscuits, and many more. The United States bread market recorded US$ 20.5 billion in 2008. These include fresh bread, frozen bread, rolls, bun biscuits, and pastries; fresh bread sales are higher than frozen.

The top characteristics of bakery products comprise elongated faintness, freshness, and crunchiness. Liable for the physical and chemical properties of the closing product, these products are different in their formulae. Starch is the core component of bakery products; a formulation for any bakery product mainly contains starch, gluten, fat, carbohydrates, sugar, eggs, emulsifiers, milk, enzymes, and water [45, 46].

Any baking process is divided into two segments: (i) dough making and (ii) baking process. During the dough-making process, mix all the components, such as suitable flour, Yeast, sugar, salt, water, and some flour enzymes to help ingredients undergo complex bio-physiochemical reactions. Thus, yeast affects dough's rheological properties like gas holding capacity, dough extensibility and viscoelasticity, and water absorption capacity. During this process, the flour is hydrated with water and forms a transient network of gluten proteins.

Even throughout the postbacking chilling procedure, the biological, physical, and chemical connections between the starch, protein, and lipid biopolymers are continued, subsequent in the formation of an amylose polar-lipid complex, and it is in control for the softness of fresh bread. An opportunity to improve the process, like shortening the baking process and postponing the staling process. Several exogenous enzymes such as α-amylase, protease, lipase microbial glucose-oxidase, and endo xylanases used to produce a sourdough result in improved and fast-tracked lactic acidification as the textural properties of sourdoughs [46, 47].

To maintain and improve a few properties of dough like strength, elasticity, enhancement, and even composition, α-amylase, protease, lipase, xylanase, and laccase are involved, although lipoxygenases give viscoelastic properties in the dough. Amylase and additional enzymes are added to the bread flour to retain moistness more capably, resulting in amplified freshness, gentleness, and lifespan [48].

Lipoxygenase and glucose oxidase are added supplementary to enhance dough whitening and strengthening properties, as well as some additional enzymes such as laccase and α-amylase. Meanwhile, lipase and xylanase are used for dough stability and firmness. Phytase acts on phytin and enhances the bioavailability of minerals like Ca^{2+}, Fe^{2+}, and Mg^{2+}. Throughout the second segment, the collective effects of temperature, moisture, and baking period lead to starch gelatinization, heat-setting of gluten proteins, and formation of the gluten network into a continual network and development of the baked bread [49, 50].

For the production of gluten-free bread, transglutaminase is used along with laccase. Transglutaminase also boosts the quality of the texture of bread and flour. The use of enzymes suggestively cuts bread staling and boosts bread's shelf life. Enzymatic glucose oxidase treatment brings out free sulfhydryl groups and amplified glutenin contents [51].

10.5.3 Beverages

The most incredibly significant ground of enzyme application in the beverage industry is vegetable and fruit juice extraction. Pectinase plays an essential role in the beverage process, such as reducing the waste from fruit and enhancing the quality of the juice extracted. The beverage industry covers various fields like distillation, wine, juice, and brewing [52].

Diverse enzymes play a vital part in the distilling procedure: cellulases, hemicellulases, xylanases, and β-glucanases, which increase yield and pointedly lower the viscosity of wheat mashes, barley, and rye. The α-amylases play a crucial part in starch liquefaction and lower mash viscosity. Proteases boosted fermentation by enhancing yeast nutrition, resulting in alcohol quality and production yield. Glucoamylases and fungal amylases lead to dextrin conversion into fermentable sugars in saccharification.

In winemaking, process enzymes play an essential role: proteases, pectinases, xylanases, and glucanases, which boost wine clarification and transformation. Glycosidase plays a vital role in fragrances, while ureases continue with a decrease in the formation of ethyl carbamate. Significant factors in winemaking are the aging of wine, flavor enhancement, and color stability [53, 54].

In producing some malt liquors and beer, enzymes play a chief role and provide some significant functions during fermentation, such as controlling viscosity and sugar formation. The problem faced in the beverage industry is the formation of haze, turbidity, and browning during the production process or storage of fruit juices, beer, and wine.

Some of the characteristics are important in the production of juice and alcoholic beverages, including aroma, clarity, taste, flavor, color, laccases, and other oxidase enzymes that help by modifying the phenolic saccharides. After the laccase action, filtration or other techniques can remove the oxidized and polymerized undesirable phenolic substances [55].

The pectin enzymes play a key role in cleaving saccharide bonds and breaking down the grape pulp and cell wall. The initial marketable enzyme development of pectinase was used in the wine industry. The primarily fungal source is highly used in the marketable production of wine. Anthocyanins and tannins are the fundamental phenolic classes in the case of red wine. For the formation of pigment polymers with the anthocyanins, stable pigments to red wine long-standing color stability and tannins add a mouth feel to wines [56, 57].

In the beverage industry, naringinase (a heterodimeric enzymatic complex made up of two subunits, which is commonly obtained from fungi α-L-mannosidase and β-D-glucosidase, denotes an appreciated substitute for the removal of the spare bitter taste of fruit juices of grapefruit. This enzyme hydrolyses flavonoid glycoside to naringenin, glucose, and rhamnose. However, it has boundaries to use at the industrial level because of high production costs.

Nestlé is the world's largest food and beverage company, and Pepsi Co. is the most prominent US-based food and beverage company. Dole Food Company is the world's largest fruit company. The capacity of enzymes to transform the raw material into a product is just like converting carbohydrates from grains into simple sugars. So, the desired alcohol content can be accomplished by adding a slighter grain volume, leading to magnificent results in a beer with some carbohydrate calories plus great taste [49–51, 58, 59].

10.5.4 Meat Industry

Quality and tenderness result from a mixture of a breakdown inside muscle fibers, mainly from the activity of enzymes. From the beginning of the meat industry, protein-degrading enzymes have been used extensively to improve a few properties of meat, such as texture, elasticity, firmness, homogenization, and emulsification of other meat products such as sausage. Enzymes help bind the small pieces of meat and shape them into larger pieces. Transglutaminase compensates over other enzymes in cases of high nutritional value and low cost. Protease is highly used with thermolysin for the enhanced ripening of dry sausage and other food proteins.

Producers use starter cultures of lactic acid bacteria or a mixture of coagulase-negative *Staphylococci* and yeasts. Microbial enzymes are incredible and involved in changing carbohydrates, proteins, and lipids through their biochemical changes, and they help improve color, flavor, and texture [60].

The latent process in the meat industry is meat tenderizing, achieved with enzymes such as bromelain and papain. In 2012, nearly 304 million tons of meat were produced globally, and meat is an available rich source of proteins, minerals, and vitamins. A massive challenge to the meat industry is to develop organoleptic characteristics. Based on the reports of Global Industry Analysts in 2015, the world's fresh meat market is probable to touch around 300 million tons [61].

Worldwide meat production will increase to 455 million tons by 2050, as the Food and Agriculture Organization estimates. Much beef production occurs in Australia, Brazil, and the United States. Beef, poultry, and pork comprise 24%, 34%, and 40% of meat consumption. For the production of prime quality meat, meat tenderization is highly important, like the flavor development of the meat [62].

The protein-degrading enzymes benefit the process of meat tenderization by removing the use of various chemicals. Correspondingly, protease enzyme is also discovered for marination and tenderization. Significant ancient and present meat-packers in the United States include Armour and Company, Cargill Meat Solutions, Hormel Foods, and many others [63].

Feed enzymes include proteases, α-amylases, xylanases, phytases, α-galactosidases, glucanases, and polygalacturonases. Phytase helps hydrolyze the phosphorus bond from phytate and increase digestibility. Feed enzymes increase nutritional value and meat quality for improved animal feed conversion [64].

10.5.5 Fish and Seafood

People are becoming increasingly aware of the importance of protein as nutrition for good health, and in that case, the seafood industry plays an influential role in providing protein-rich food to many of the globe's inhabitants. Fishing and processing activities employ oodles of publics around the globe. The main Enzymes involved in fish and seafood are protease and transglutaminase, which are used in fish sauce and other seafood flavorings, collagen extraction, deskinning, and protein hydrolysis. Some of the enzymes are used to prevent spoilage of fish and seafood.

According to a survey, the demand for seafood increases by 3% yearly. Globally, the seafood market covers nearly US$ 100 billion per year. Japan is leading the race in the case of the highest consumption of seafood, and Tokyo's Tsukiji market is the largest wholesale seafood market, selling more than 400 different varieties of seafood [65].

(i) Protease: The exclusion of fish skin without causing damage to flesh, a process presently achieved by rough mechanical actions, imparting a risk of damaging the flesh and producing excess waste. Enzymatic skin removal can enhance the eatable profit. Protease enzymes take part in the ripening of salted fish such as salmon, anchovy, and cod, and a complex biochemical process categorized by the degradation of muscle proteins with endogenous enzymes, increased peptides, and free amino acids.
(ii) Trans glutaminase: MTGases (microbial TGA; MTGase) are used to boost fish and seafood products, both functional and mechanical and used as hold together ingredients for reconstructing raw meats and production of surimi.
(iii) Lipase: Triacylglycerol acyl hydrolases encourage the hydrolysis of triacylglycerides to glycerol and fatty acids in the presence of water, while in less water or absent of water conditions, they encourage ester synthesis. Lipases are also used for isolating oil and fats from seafood by-products and in preparing ω-3-polyunsaturated fatty acids (ω-PUFAs) and enriched marine oils, given the high nutritional value of these compounds.

Around 30% of seafood is produced for human consumption, and the remaining is processed and marketed for feeding. In this division, frozen fish fillets and fish are ready-to-eat meals [66].

10.5.6 Vegetables and Fruits

Enzymes play multitask properties in the food industry, especially in fruit juice. They offer numerous benefits, including a high reaction rate, broad substrate specificity, easy-to-control reaction rate, and generally less operational costs and investment. Microbial enzymes in the juice-making process help confirm that the supreme volume of juice is extracted from the fruit, dropping waste and monitoring costs.

The addition of pectinases to improve the breakdown of the pectin material in the cell wall, which leads to the originality of compounds such as color, viscosity, and turbidity of the end product, as well as removes the bitterness of citrus juice and extract pigments [67].

The core motives for using biocatalysts are to improve and expand juice production, soften the complete fruit, and minimize waste. Maintain the nutritional value of fruit juice and break down insoluble components such as starch, pectin, and hemicellulose. The life span of any citrus fruit can be extended with the help of various enzymes such as oxidase and catalase. Further catalase applications are in removing O_2 from preserved bottled drinks [68, 69].

10.5.7 Starch Processing Industry

In plants, energy is stored mainly in the form of starch, which is a renewable resource. Starch comprises two common polysaccharides, amylose, and amylopectin, which are molecules of glucose units. Enzyme action on starch helps with two crucial phases: saccharification and liquefaction [70].

For the production of various syrups, starch is used as a basic component, as is syrup, such as high fructose, fructose, dextrin, and maltose. For syrup production, the most common enzymes involved are amylases and glucoamylases. During syrup production, important factors for enzymes are high reaction rate, high temperature with acid, and pH stability. Pullulanase also plays a key role in syrup production.

Hydrolyze α-1,6-linkages liberating glucose residues linked by α-1,4-bonds from linear oligosaccharides. In beverages, the isomerization of starch-derived glucose is preferred due to the higher sweetness of the syrup [15].

10.6 Conclusion and Future Perspectives

Snowballing world population-evolving enzymes from microorganisms are used to improve health status and meet better-quality food requirements. Enzymes from microorganisms generate quite good interest in the food industry all over the world because of their multifunction properties, such as high accuracy, wild action on a substrate, and biodegradability, which allow enzyme-sponsored processes in the industry to change slow-going reactions to fast-moving ones, with multifunctionality, organic, and eco-friendly nature, as well as enhanced yields, low toxicity, and low waste generation.

Advanced technologies help increase enzyme production and recovery in downstream process problems like enzyme stability, which can be maintained with the help of these new technologies. Some other disadvantages, such as thermos stability and pH profiling, require changes for many food processes, which are recovered by recent advances in technology, including rDNA technology, metagenomics, protein engineering, and productive expression systems, and have smoothed the encounter of novel extremozymes. Much future research will use the merger of engineered and *de novo-designed* enzymes coupled with chemistry to generate additional chemicals and materials from economic and viable resources This subsequently comes up with a new bio-based economy, green growth, and green chemistry.

References

1 Singh, R., Kumar, M., Mittal, A., and Mehta, P.K. (2016). Microbial enzymes: industrial progress in 21st century. *3 Biotech* 6 (2): 1–5.

2 Adrio, J.L. and Demain, A.L. (2014). Microbial enzymes: tools for biotechnological processes. *Biomolecules* 4 (1): 117–139.

3 Boopathy, R. (1994). Enzyme technology in food and health industries. *Indian Food Ind.* 13: 22.

4 Raveendran, S., Parameswaran, B., Ummalyma, S.B. et al. (2018). Applications of microbial enzymes in the food industry. *Food Technol. Biotechnol.* 56 (1): 16.

5 Li, S., Yang, X., Yang, S. et al. (2012). Technology prospecting on enzymes: application, marketing, and engineering. *Comput. Struct. Biotechnol. J.* 2 (3): e201209017.

6 Nigam, P.S. (2013). Microbial enzymes with special characteristics for biotechnological applications. *Biomolecules* 3 (3): 597–611.

7 Fasim, A., More, V.S., and More, S.S. (2021). Large-scale production of enzymes for biotechnology uses. *Curr. Opin. Biotechnol.* 69: 68–76.

8 Collados, A., Conversa, V., Fombellida, M. et al. (2020). Applying food enzymes in the kitchen. *Int. J. Gastron. Food Sci.* 21: 100212.

9 Chaudhary, S., Sagar, S., Kumar, M. et al. (2015). The use of enzymes in food processing: a review. *South Asian J. Food Technol. Environ.* 1 (3&4): 190–210.

10 Shahidi, F. and Kamil, Y.J. (2001). Enzymes from fish and aquatic invertebrates and their application in the food industry. *Trends Food Sci. Technol.* 12 (12): 435–464.

11 DiCosimo, R., McAuliffe, J., Poulose, A.J., and Bohlmann, G. (2013). Industrial use of immobilized enzymes. *Chem. Soc. Rev.* 42 (15): 6437–6474.

12 Campbell-Platt, G. (1994). Fermented foods—a world perspective. *Food Res. Int.* 27 (3): 253–257.

13 Bhatia, S. (2018). History, scope, and development of biotechnology. In: *Introduction to Pharmaceutical Biotechnology, Volume 1: Basic Techniques and Concepts* (ed. S. Roche), 1–67. IOP Publishing.

14 El-Mansi, E.M., Bryce, C.F., Hartley, B.S., and Demain, A.L. (2019). Fermentation microbiology and biotechnology: a historical perspective. *Ferment. Microbiol.* 23: 1.

15 Fernandes, P. and Carvalho, F. (2017). Microbial enzymes for the food industry. In: *Biotechnology of Microbial Enzymes* (ed. G. Brahmachari), 513–544. Academic Press.

16 Søndergaard, H.A., Grunert, K.G., and Scholderer, J. (2005). Consumer attitudes to enzymes in food production. *Trends Food Sci. Technol.* 16 (10): 466–474.

17 Mehta, P.K. and Sehgal, S. (2019). Microbial enzymes in food processing. In: *Biocatalysis* (ed. M.F. Ullah), 255–275. Cham: Springer.

18 Aman, F. and Masood, S. (2020). How nutrition can help to fight against COVID-19 pandemic. *Pak. Med. Sci.* 36 (COVID19-S4): S121.

19 Fan, S., Teng, P., Chew, P. et al. (2021). Food system resilience and COVID-19–lessons from the Asian experience. *Global Food Secur.* 28: 100501.

20 Gurung, N., Ray, S., Bose, S., and Rai, V. (2013). A broader view: microbial enzymes and their relevance in industries, medicine, and beyond. *Biomed Res. Int.* 2013: 329121.

21 Pandey, A., Selvakumar, P., Soccol, C.R., and Nigam, P. (1999). Solid state fermentation for the production of industrial enzymes. *Curr. Sci.* 77: 149–162.

22 Nicholl, D.S. (2008). *An Introduction to Genetic Engineering*. Cambridge University Press.

23 Sanchez, S. and Demain, A.L. (2017). Useful microbial enzymes—an introduction. In: *Biotechnology of Microbial Enzymes* (ed. G. Brahmachari, A.L. Demain, and J.L. Adrio), 1–11. Academic Press.

24 Burton, S.G., Cowan, D.A., and Woodley, J.M. (2002). The search for the ideal biocatalyst. *Nat. Biotechnol.* 20 (1): 37–45.

25 Headon, D.R. and Walsh, G. (1994). The industrial production of enzymes. *Biotechnol. Adv.* 12 (4): 635–646.

26 Sheldon, R.A. and Woodley, J.M. (2018). Role of biocatalysis in sustainable chemistry. *Chem. Rev.* 118 (2): 801–838.

27 Arnold, F.H. and Volkov, A.A. (1999). Directed evolution of biocatalysts. *Curr. Opin. Chem. Biol.* 3 (1): 54–59.

28 Packer, M.S. and Liu, D.R. (2015). Methods for the directed evolution of proteins. *Nat. Rev. Genet.* 16 (7): 379–394.

29 Arnold, F.H. (1998). Design by directed evolution. *Acc. Chem. Res.* 31 (3): 125–131.

30 Ray, L., Pramanik, S., and Bera, D. (2016). Enzymes- an existing and promising tool of the food processing industry. *Recent Pat. Biotechnol.* 10 (1): 58–71.

31 Vuorisalo, T., Arjamaa, O., Vasemägi, A. et al. (2012). High lactose tolerance in North Europeans: a result of migration, not in situ milk consumption. *Perspect. Biol. Med.* 55 (2): 163–174.

32 Law, J. and Haandrikman, A. (1997). Proteolytic enzymes of lactic acid bacteria. *Int. Dairy J.* 7 (1): 1–1.

33 Kongo, J.M. (2013). Lactic acid bacteria as starter-cultures for cheese processing: past, present and future developments. In: *Lactic Acid Bacteria-R & D for Food, Health, and Livestock Purposes* (ed. J.M. Kongo), 1–22. IntechOpen.

34 Abada, E.A. (2019). Application of microbial enzymes in the dairy industry. In: *Enzymes in food biotechnology* (ed. M. Kuddus), 61–72. Academic Press, Elsevier.

35 Feijoo-Siota, L., Blasco, L., Luis Rodriguez-Rama, J. et al. (2014). Recent patents on microbial proteases for the dairy industry. *Recent Adv. DNA Gene Sequences* 8 (1): 44–55.

36 Zolnere, K. and Ciprovica, I. (2017). The comparison of commercially available β-galactosidases for dairy industry. *Res. Rural Dev.* 1: 215–222.

37 Kieliszek, M. and Misiewicz, A. (2014). Microbial transglutaminase and its application in the food industry: a review. *Folia Microbiol.* 59 (3): 241–250.

38 Jooyandeh, H., Amarjeet, K., and Minhas, K.S. (2009). Lipases in dairy industry: a review. *J. Food Sci. Technol. (Mysore)* 46 (3): 181–189.

39 Jaganmai, G. and Jinka, R. (2017). Production of lipases from dairy industry wastes and its applications. *Int. J. Curr. Microbiol. Appl. Sci.* 5: 67–73.

40 Choudhury, P. and Bhunia, B. (2015). Industrial application of Lipase: a review. *Biopharm. J.* 1 (2): 41–47.

41 Younus, H. (2019). Oxidoreductases: overview and practical applications. In: *Biocatalysis* (ed. M.F.U. Qayyum), 39–55. Springer.

42 Seifu, E., Buys, E.M., and Donkin, E.F. (2005). Significance of the lactoperoxidase system in the dairy industry and its potential applications: a review. *Trends Food Sci. Technol.* 16 (4): 137–154.

43 Palai, T. and Dubey, K.K. (2022). Valorization of dairy industry waste into functional foods using lactase. In: *Thermochemical and Catalytic Conversion Technologies for Future Biorefineries* (ed. P. Verma), 161–183. Singapore: Springer.

44 Zhu, Y. and Tramper, J. (2008). Novel applications for microbial transglutaminase beyond food processing. *Trends Biotechnol.* 26: 559–565.

45 Brown, J. (1993). Advances in breadmaking technology. In: *Advances in Baking Technology* (ed. B.S. Kamel and S.E. Stauffer), 38–87. Boston, MA: Springer.

46 Keramat, J., LeBail, A., Prost, C., and Jafari, M. (2011). Acrylamide in baking products: a review article. *Food Bioprocess Technol.* 4: 530–543.

47 Ţain, A.E., Zincă, G., and Banu, I. (2008). Studies about obtaining safe and healthy bakery products using the beneficial properties of enzymes. *Chem. Bull. POLITEHNICA Univ. (Timisoara)* 53 (67): 1–2.

48 Mikus, Ľ., Kovacova, M., Dodok, L. et al. (2013). Effects of enzymes and hydrocolloids on physical, sensory, and shelf-life properties of wheat bread. *Chem. Pap.* 67 (3): 292–299.

49 Zietsman, A.J., Moore, J.P., Fangel, J.U. et al. (2017). Combining hydrothermal pretreatment with enzymes de-pectinates and exposes the innermost xyloglucan-rich hemicellulose layers of wine grape pomace. *Food Chem.* 232: 340–350.

50 Feldman, Z., Bradley, D.G., and Greenberg, D. (2010). The food and beverage industry's efforts regarding obesity prevention. In: *Obesity Epidemiology: From Aetiology to Public Health* (ed. D. Crawford), 409–423. Oxford University Press.

51 Destefanis, G., Brugiapaglia, A., Barge, M.T., and Dal Molin, E. (2008). Relationship between beef consumer tenderness perception and Warner–Bratzler shear force. *Meat Sci.* 78 (3): 153–156.

52 Kaur, H. and Gill, P.K. (2019). Microbial enzymes in food and beverage processing. In: *Engineering Tools in the Beverage Industry* (ed. A.M. Grumezescu and A.M. Holban), 255–282. Woodhead Publishing.

53 Chandrasekaran, M., Basheer, S.M., Chellappan, S. et al. (2015). Enzymes in food and beverage production: an overview. In: *Enzyme Food Beverage Process*, vol. 25 (ed. M. Chandrasekaran), 133–154. CRC Press.

54 Versteeg, C., Rombouts, F.M., Spaansen, C.H., and Pilnik, W. (1980). Thermostability and orange juice cloud destabilizing properties of multiple pectinesterases from orange. *J. Food Sci.* 45 (4): 969–971.

55 Ribeiro, D.S., Henrique, S., Oliveira, L.S. et al. (2010). Enzymes in juice processing: a review. *Int. J. Food Sci. Technol.* 45 (4): 635–641.

56 Aastrup, S., Noel, B., Elmer, J., and Kurt, D. (2004). Choice of Enzyme Solution Should Determine Choice of Raw Materials and Process, Presentation Given at World Brewing Conference, San Diego.

57 Capounova, D. and Drdak, M. (2002). Comparison of some commercial pectic enzyme preparations applicable in wine technology. *Czech. J. Food Sci.* 20 (4): 131–134.

58 Revilla, I. and González-SanJosé, M.L. (2002). Multivariate evaluation of changes induced in red wine characteristics by extracting agents. *J. Agric. Food. Chem.* 50 (16): 4525–4530.

59 Kirk, O., Borchert, T.V., and Fuglsang, C.C. (2002). Industrial enzyme applications. *Curr. Opin. Biotechnol.* 13 (4): 345–351.

60 Ashie, I.N., Sorensen, T.L., and Nielsen, P.M. (2002). Effects of papain and a microbial enzyme on meat proteins and beef tenderness. *J. Food Sci.* 67 (6): 2138–2142.

61 Shahani, K.M., Arnold, R.G., Kilara, A., and Dwivedi, B.K. (1976). Role of microbial enzymes in flavour development in foods. *Biotechnol. Bioeng.* 18 (7): 891–907.

62 Lucke, F.K. (2000). Utilization of microbes to process and preserve meat. *Meat Sci.* 56 (2): 105–115.

63 Singh, P.K., Shrivastava, N., and Ojha, B.K. (2019). Enzymes in the meat industry. In: *Enzymes in Food Biotechnology* (ed. M. Kuddus), 111–128. Academic Press.

64 Haard, N.F. and Simpson, B.K. (1994). Proteases from aquatic organisms and their uses in the seafood industry. In: *Fisheries Processing* (ed. A.M. Martin), 132–154. Springer Science + Business Media.

65 Fernandes, P. (2016). Enzymes in fish and seafood processing. *Front. Bioeng. Biotechnol.* 4: 59.

66 Bayindirli, A. (2010). *Enzymes in Fruit and Vegetable Processing: Chemistry and Engineering Applications*. CRC Press.

67 Nayak, B., Liu, R.H., and Tang, J. (2015). Effect of processing on phenolic antioxidants of fruits, vegetables, and grains—a review. *Crit. Rev. Food Sci. Nutr.* 55 (7): 887–918.

68 Pang, W.C., Ramli, A.N., and Johari, N.D. (2019). Structural properties, production, and commercialization of Invertase. *Sains Malaysiana* 48 (3): 523–531.

69 Pradhan, M. and Panda, S.P. (2022). Applications of industrially important enzymes. In: *Optimization of Sustainable Enzymes Production* (ed. J.S. Eswari and N. Suryawanshi), 19–52. Chapman & Hall.

70 Jozef, S. (2007). The use of starch processing enzymes in the food industry. In: *Industrial Enzymes* (ed. J. Polaina and A.P. MacCabe), 19–34. Springer.

11

Alkane Hydroxylases: Sources and Applications

Sangeeta Negi and Satyapriy Das

Motilal Nehru National Institute of Technology Allahabad, Department of Biotechnology, Prayagraj, Uttar Pradesh 211004, India

11.1 Introduction

Alkane hydroxylases are nonheme iron integral membrane enzymes that belong to the oxidoreductase class of enzymes with EC number (1.14.15.3) [1, 2]. These enzymes utilize NADH as a cofactor to catalyze the insertion of molecular oxygen into inert hydrocarbons, leading to the conversion of various aliphatic hydrocarbons into their primary alcohols. The catalytic process of these enzymes mainly depends on three components such as alkane hydroxylase (AlkB), rubredoxin (AlkG), and rubredoxin reductase (AlkT) [3]. The alkane hydroxylases have enabled a new way for the conversion of petroleum waste into various activated intermediates and fine chemicals. The alkane hydroxylase-mediated conversion of hydrocarbons is considered better than chemical methods because the chemical process is energy-intensive, generates other toxic pollutants, and has a very low biotransformation yield. However, large-scale applications of this enzyme are quite challenging due to its intrinsic properties like the requirement of oxygen and cofactors [4]. Recombinant alkane hydroxylases are the overexpressed form of the alkb gene in the different hosts as a result of cloning and expression. It is quite easy to purify as the expression vector has affinity tags for the purification of recombinant proteins. However, cloning and expression of alkb gene is quite difficult as it has a large number of hydrophobic residues in many strains [5].

11.1.1 Structure and Catalytic Mechanism of Alkane Hydroxylases

Structural information reveals that AlkBs consist of six transmembrane alpha helixes with a set of eight conservative histidine residues that coordinate with iron metal in the active pocket [6]. According to homology modeling, alkane hydroxylases contain substrate channels that extend from the cytoplasm to the inner periplasmic region, limiting the presence of an active site [7]. In some AlkBs, the position of a single R group in the substrate channel can regulate the affinity against

Microbial Enzymes: Production, Purification, and Industrial Applications, First Edition.
Edited by Dinesh Yadav, Pankaj Chowdhary, Gautam Anand, and Rajarshi Kumar Gaur.

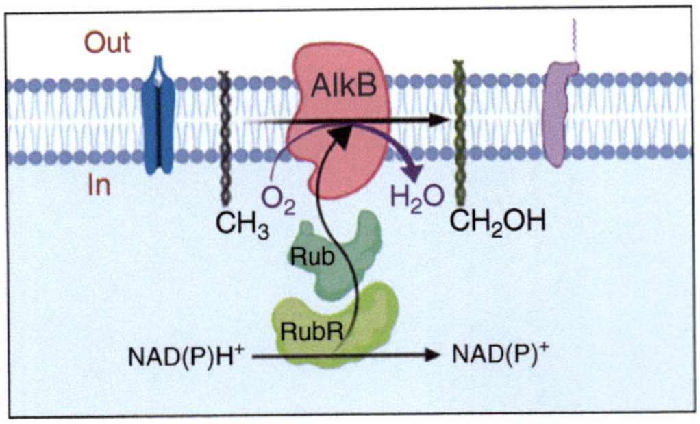

Figure 11.1 Schematic representation of the catalytic process of alkane hydroxylase and its electron transfers cellular mechanism.

specific substrates [8]. However, structural factors that modulate specificity against substrates need to be understood in detail. The substrate specificity of distinct alkane hydroxylases is limited with a different carbon chain length. The catalytic mechanism of alkane hydroxylases is mainly mediated by two accessory proteins (i.e. rubredoxin and rubredoxin reductase) and one cofactor (i.e. nicotinamide adenine dinucleotide phosphate). The catalysis process starts with the simultaneous reduction of rubredoxin and oxidation of NADPH, which is catalyzed by rubredoxin reductase. After that, rubredoxin transfers the electron to activate the alkane hydroxylase and facilitate the O—O bond cleavage. In the end, AlkB inserts one atom from molecular oxygen to the substrate (alkane) and converts it into corresponding primary alcohols and another oxygen atom participates in the release of a water molecule [5] (Figure 11.1).

11.1.2 Classification of Alkane Hydroxylases

Alkane hydroxylases are classified as short-chain, medium-chain, and long-chain alkane hydroxylases based on different properties such as substrate specificity, catalytic characteristics, and substrate range [9].

11.1.2.1 Short-chain Alkane Hydroxylases

The short-chain alkane hydroxylases include methane monooxygenases, propane monooxygenases, and butane monooxygenases, which catalyze the hydroxylation of methane, propane, and butane, respectively, to their respective alcohols (i.e. methanol, propanol, and butanol). Methane monooxygenase is further categorized into soluble monooxygenase (sMMO) and particulate oxygenase (pMMO). sMMO is present in the cytoplasm and can oxidize a variety of substrates such as aliphatic, aromatic, and haloaromatic hydrocarbons [10]. While pMMO has substrate specificity with a particular substrate, including short-chain alkanes, it can epoxidate alkenes [11].

11.1.2.2 Medium-chain Alkane Hydroxylases

This class is the most recognized alkane hydroxylase, which has a substrate range from C_5–C_{12} *n*-alkanes. It has diverse substrate ranges, namely linear, branched, and cyclic hydrocarbons, along with some gaseous alkanes such as propane and *n*-butane [12, 13]. It is well recognized in *Pseudomonas putida* with six alpha-helical segments where N-terminus, two hydrophilic loops, and the C-terminal domain are all located in the cytoplasm [14]. Some researchers have made a fusion protein consisting of a conserved domain of AlkB and a rubredoxin, which can degrade C_8–C_{32} *n*-alkanes to their respective alcohols.

11.1.2.3 Cytochrome P450 Alkane Hydroxylases

Cytochrome P450 is well known for the terminal oxidation of diverse substrate ranges, including alkyl hydrocarbon products, fatty acids, steroids, pesticides, prostaglandins, and carcinogenic materials [15]. Based on the components of P450, they are classified into two classes (i.e. Class I P450s and Class II P450). The electron transfer mechanism of Class I P450s is facilitated by a flavin adenine dinucleotide (FAD)-containing reductase, which received electrons from nicotinamide adenine dinucleotide phosphate (NADPH) and an iron–sulfur protein, while Class II P450s accept electrons via FAD- and flavin mononucleotide (FMN)-containing cytochrome P450 reductase [4, 16]. Although cytochrome P450 alkane hydroxylases have been studied intensively, the specificity against *n*-alkanes is very low. Thus, researchers have employed techniques to modify the substrate-binding pockets of this enzyme to increase its affinity against linear *n*-alkanes.

11.1.2.4 Long-chain Alkane Hydroxylases (LadA)

Long-chain alkane hydroxylases have a substrate range of *n*-alkanes from C_{15} to C_{36}. It utilizes terminal oxidation for the conversion of *n*-alkanes to their corresponding primary alcohols.

It has been revealed that LadA belongs to the subfamily of the bacterial luciferase family, and its structure contains a triosephosphate isomerase barrel fold and an extension at the C-terminus of the polypeptide chain [17, 18]. It can accommodate an FMN, O_2, and part of long-chain *n*-alkane due to the presence of a large pocket at the C-terminal entrance, and therefore, it is also confirmed as flavoprotein monooxygenase.

11.2 Sources of Alkane Hydroxylases

Sources of alkane hydroxylases are well recognized in bacteria, yeast, and fungi, while very few algal species have alkane hydroxylases. The alkane hydroxylases are less identified in animal and plant sources. Some alkane hydroxylases such as cytochrome P450 and its isoforms have been identified in animals and some plants at the genetic level, but the production and yield of the alkane hydroxylases have not been much explored. The major microbial sources are described below and their production strategies for alkane hydroxylases are listed in Table 11.1.

11.2.1 Bacterial Sources

Alkane hydroxylases are distributed in various bacterial strains with unique properties and specific substrate ranges. The most explored bacterial source is

Table 11.1 Different sources of alkane hydroxylases.

Sources	Method of production	Characteristics	References
Pseudomonas oleovorans	Expressed in *Pseudomonas putida* PpSS1 (alcASl)	The strain oxidized C_5–Call linear alkanes to l-alkanols	[19]
Acinetobacter sp. Strain ADP1	Expressed in *Escherichia coli*	—	[20]
Alcanivorax borkumensis	Expressed in *Pseudomonas putida* GPo12	Able to degrade oil-polluted marine environments	[21]
Mycobacterium sp. strain HXN-1500	Coexpressed in *Pseudomonas putida* sp. activity: 3 U/g (dry weight)	Used for production of perillyl alcohol from limonene	[4]
Gordonia sp. strain SoCg	Expressed in *Escherichia coli* BL21 and in *Streptomyces coelicolor* M145 both	Able to degrade alkanes (C_{12}–C_{36}) *n*-triacontane	[22]
Alcanivorax dieselolei strain B-5	Expressed in *Pseudomonas putida* GPo12 (pGEc47ΔB)	Can utilize a broad range of *n*-alkanes (C_5–C_{36}) as the sole carbon source	[23]
Acinetobacter venetianus 6A2	Expressed in *Escherichia coli* DH5α	Capable of degrading paraffin	[24]
Dietzia strain (DQ12-45-1b)	Expressed in *Pseudomonas fluorescens* KOB2Δ1	Able to degrade long-chain *n*-alkanes (such as C_{32})	[25]
Rhodococcus sp. strain TMP2	Expressed in *Escherichia coli* DH5α (*AlkB1–5 genes*)	Degrades a branched alkane	[26]
Pseudomonas putida GPo1	Expressed in *Escherichia coli* DH5α	Specialized in conversion of small C1–C4	[27]
Acinetobacter sp. strain M-1	Expressed in *Escherichia coli*	Able to degrade carbon chain lengths of C20–C44 that are in a solid state	[28]
Pseudomonas aeruginosa Strain SJTD-1	Isolated from oil-contaminated soil and grown on medium	AlkB is involved in the synergetic catabolism of C_{12}–C_{16} alkanes	[29]
Pseudomonas oleovorans	Expressed in *Escherichia coli* and Pseudomonas	AlkB protein contains nine hydrophobic sequences of which eight are sufficiently long to be membrane-spanning segments	[2]
Cyt P450 BM-3 from *Bacillus megaterium*	P450 BM-3 mutated and expressed into *Escherichia coli*	A medium-chain (C12–C18) fatty acid monooxygenase converted into a highly efficient catalyst (AlkB).	[30]
Pseudomonas putida GPo1	Expressed in *Escherichia coli*	Capable of oxidizing aliphatic C_5–C_{12} alkanes to primary alcohols	[31]
Rhodococcus strains (NRRL B-16531 and Q15)	Expressed in *Escherichia coli* and *Pseudomonas* expression system	Possesses eight histidine motifs, two apparent AlkB signature motifs, and six hydrophobic membrane-spanning regions	[32]
Candida guilliermondii	Grown on *n*-alkanes as the only carbon and energy source (5–10 Nm)	—	[33]

pseudomonas sp., which accounts for the degradation of a wide range of substrates. Other bacterial sources, such as Alcanivorax sp., Rhodococcus, *Acinetobacter* sp., *Burkholderia cepacian, Mycobacterium*, and *Achromobacter*, have been well-studied and identified as potential sources of alkane hydroxylases [34]. Vomberg and Klinner (2000) tested 37 bacterial strains for the presence of all genes through Southern blot and observed that Gram-negativities have the strongest signals after hybridization with the alkb gene of *Pseudomonas* sp., which is capable of utilizing short-chain alkanes (up to C_{10}) [35].

11.2.2 Fungal Sources

Fungal alkane hydroxylases are quite less explored when compared with bacterial sources, but they have more capability to produce membrane-bound proteins or enzymes due to their higher biomass production by acquiring large surface area on substrate or media. The genera of some filamentous fungi, such as *Aspergillus, Penicillium, Cladosporium, Dendryphiella, Verticillium, Fusarium*, and *Corollasporium*, are majorly recognized as a fungal source of alkane hydroxylases [34, 36]. The majority of the fungal strains have been identified as producers of Cytochrome P450 monooxygenase [37]. Cytochrome P450s monooxygenases are involved in the bioconversion of many endogenous and xenobiotic compounds [38]. It has been reported that fungal alkane hydroxylases, especially cytochrome P450, provide various physiological traits to fungi in various ecological niches.

11.2.3 Yeast Sources

The yeast sources have also been identified as alkane hydroxylase producers. The major yeast sources for the alkane hydroxylases are *Candida, Cryptococcus, Pichia, Rhodotorula, Saccharomyces, Trichosporon*, etc. reported. The yeast sources are also much recognized for the presence of P450 cytochrome, while some species are identified as producers of medium-chain alkane hydroxylases [34, 36].

11.3 Production, Purification, and Characterization of Alkane Hydroxylases

The microbial production of alkane hydroxylases at an industrial scale is not yet much explored, while at the flask level, it is explored under submerged fermentation. The production process includes various steps, such as inoculum development, selection of appropriate substrate, and incubation at a specific temperature. Significant improvements in the alkane hydroxylase yield through fermentation can be achieved by altering the physicochemical and nutritional process parameters to which AlkB-producing microbes are exposed [39]. Furthermore, the enzyme yield is strongly dependent upon the supplementation of appropriate hydrocarbon substrates. The hydrocarbons (especially alkanes) are being used for the enhanced production of alkane hydroxylase, which includes octane, pentadecane, hexadecane, heptadecane, octadecane, cyclohexane, etc. [6]. The most widely used production strategy for alkane hydroxylase is recombinant DNA technology, which is well-explored for the cloning and expression of alkb gene into the host cell. The cloning strategy for the alkb gene provides many advantages over natural cultivation, which include the overexpression of the AlkB enzyme, easy one-step purification, and easiest identification and characterization of AlkB enzymes, while major disadvantages are high-cost consumption due to costly vectors, restriction enzymes, DNA isolation kit, and PCR (polymerase chain reaction) kits, etc. [40].

Apart from the production process, extraction, and purification are quite crucial in terms of the functionally active and intact AlkB enzyme. Its extraction and

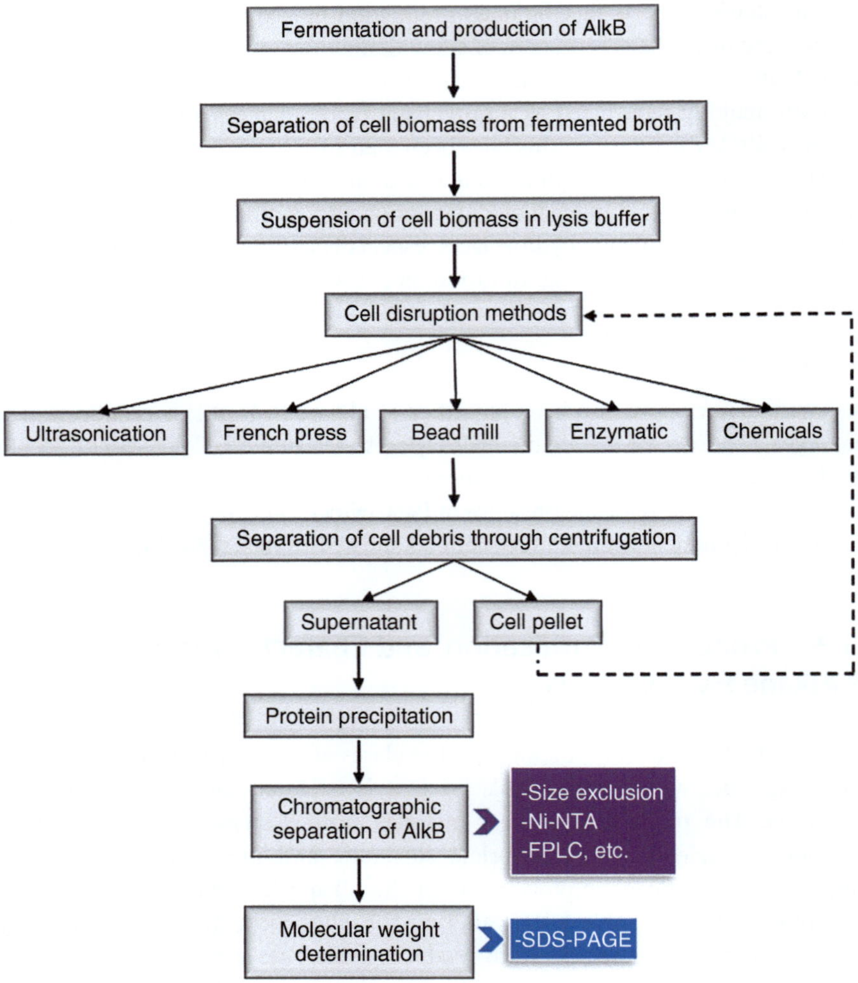

Figure 11.2 Schematic representation of extraction and purification of alkane hydroxylases.

purification process starts with the separation of cell biomass for the fermented broth, which centrifugation, filtration, and flocculation. Alkane hydroxylases are membrane-bound enzymes so their extraction process includes cell disruption techniques such as ultrasonication, cell homogenization, French press, and bead mill in detergent containing lysis buffers. Furthermore, the purification involves protein precipitation (salting out acetone precipitation) and chromatography techniques such as size exclusion chromatography (Superdex 200 resin, Q-Sepharose, and Sephadex resin), affinity chromatography (Ni-NTA resin and Strep-Tactin resin) can be used for the purification of alkane hydroxylases [41]. The molecular weights of alkane hydroxylases can be determined by SDS-PAGE, and protein identification can be done through peptide mass fingerprinting and western blot. The complete process flow chart for the purification of alkane hydroxylase is represented in Figure 11.2.

11.4 Applications of Alkane Hydroxylases

11.4.1 Degradation of Hydrocarbons

Hydrocarbons are hydrophobic, lack functional groups, and are less reactive at room temperature. Diverse microorganisms are capable of utilizing hydrocarbons as carbon sources for their growth. Activation of saturated hydrocarbons occurs due to cleavage of the C—H-bond, while activation of unsaturated hydrocarbons is achieved by co-reactant addition [42]. Alkane hydroxylase increases the low chemical reactivity of inert alkanes [43]. Alkane hydroxylase is categorized based on carbon chain length and their degradation: C_1–C_4 activated by methane monooxygenase, C_5–C_{16} oxidized by integral nonheme iron membrane-bound alkane hydroxylases, and some long-chain alkanes (C_{17} and more) oxidized by new complexes of AlkB [44]. It has been noted that alkanes degrading microorganisms can have multiple alkane hydroxylases, which enable the consumption of different substrates [45]. Hydrocarbon degradation becomes faster due to the presence of O_2 as an electron acceptor [46].

The complete assimilation of hydrocarbons starts with the conversion of *n*-alkanes to their corresponding alcohols through the terminal and subterminal oxidations (Figure 11.3). The primary alcohols from terminal oxidation continued and enter into the beta-oxidation pathway while secondary alcohols from subterminal oxidation, are first converted into primary alcohols then enter into the beta-oxidation pathway [47, 48].

11.4.1.1 Degradation of Short-to-medium Chain Length of Hydrocarbons

The short-chain alkanes (C_1–C_4) are gaseous, while C4–C_9 are liquid and these inert hydrocarbons can be degraded by sequential oxidation at terminal carbon with butane monooxygenase (specific enzyme belongs to alkane hydroxylase) [49–52]. Some strains can utilize propane as the sole carbon source and oxidize it into 2-propanol with the enzyme propane monooxygenase by acting on subterminal

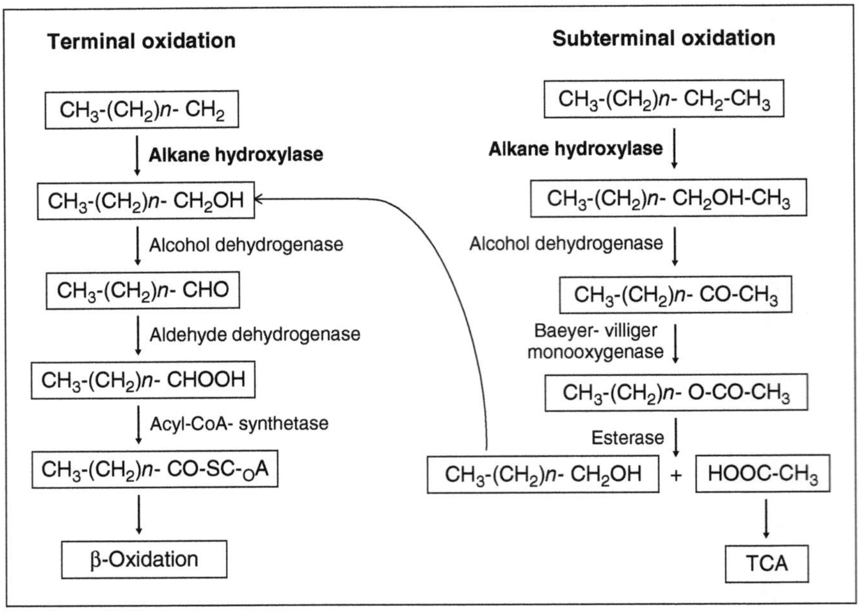

Figure 11.3 Alkane hydroxylase mediated degradation pathway of *n*-alkane.

carbon [53]. The resulting 2-propanol is converted into acetic acid and methanol, including two intermediate products acetone and methyl acetate [54]. Similar enzymes have been reported by Kotani et al. (2006) in *Mycobacterium* sp. TY-6 and *Pseudonocardia* sp. TY-7, which are capable of oxidizing both at the terminal and the subterminal carbon atom in propane [48]. The purified cytochrome P450 from *Mycobacterium* sp. HXN-1500 hydroxylate C_6–C_{11} alkanes to 1-alkanols with high affinity and regioselectivity [55].

11.4.1.2 Degradation of Long-chain *n*-Alkanes

Most of the alkane hydroxylases from *P. putida* GPo1 and *Acinetobacter* sp. EB104 is capable of degradation of alkanes longer than C_{20} into respective primary alcohols. Several bacterial strains can assimilate these alkanes. These alkane hydroxylases are soluble, Cu^{2+}-dependent dioxygenases that are specifically active on C_{10}–C_{30} alkanes and generate *n*-alkyl hydroperoxides [28, 56]. Some flavin-binding monooxygenase (AlmA) from *Acinetobacter* strain, DSM 17874 are reported for oxidation of $C_{20} > C_{32}$ alkanes [57]. The oxidation of C_{15}–C_{36} alkanes into their primary alcohols is reported by LadA from *Geobacillus thermodenitrificans* NG80-2 [58]. The product of terminal oxidation of long-chain alkane such as fatty alcohols are further catalyzed into their respective aldehydes with numerous kinds of aldehydes dehydrogenases for, e.g. *Pseudomonas butanovora* has four and *Acinetobacter calcoaceticus* HO1-N contains two type aldehydes dehydrogenases (one has higher affinity toward decanol and other has an affinity with tetradecanol). Similar enzyme has also been reported in *P. putida* GPo1 [14, 59–61].

11.4.1.3 Degradation of Branched-chain and Aromatic Alkanes

The degradation of branched alkanes is quite difficult compared to alkanes [62]. However, Solano-Serena et al. 2004 has reported the degradation of isooctane into its primary alcohol in many bacterial strains [63]. It has also been reported that isooctane and phytane can be degraded by alkane hydroxylase from *Alcanivorax* sp. [64].

Microorganisms are also reported to degradate aromatic hydrocarbons, such as benzene, xylene, toluene and naphthalene via alkane hydroxylase and in this, these hydrocarbons are first degradated aerobically into catechol or similar compound, then completely degradated into CO_2 through citric acid cycle (TCA) [65].

11.4.1.4 Degradation of Petroleum Pollutants

Increasing demand for petroleum products is the major energy source and vital for economic growth. However, its spills over and improper discharge from various industries becomes a major threat to the environment and lives [66, 67]. Petroleum pollutants consist of many polyaromatic and recalcitrant compounds which are identified as priority pollutants from municipal runoff, petroleum effluent, and oil spills [68]. Marine environments are largely affected by petroleum pollutants; therefore, their remediation/degradation becomes the most concerning issue for petroleum industries [69–71]. The well-known petroleum pollutants are aliphatic, branched, cyclic alkanes, and polycyclic aromatic hydrocarbons (PAHs). PAHs are mostly found in crude oil, which includes naphthalene, fluoranthene, phenanthrene, fluorene, anthracene, pyrene, benzo[*a*]anthracene, benzo[*a*]pyrene, etc. Each constituent of pollutant is composed of numerous hydrocarbons. Thus, each constituent is different in terms of toxicity, degradability, and volatility. These hazardous compounds have the tremendous challenge of designing effective strategies for their bioremediation.

Although enzymatic catalysis/degradation is an emerging tool to achieve useful fine chemicals from petroleum waste [46, 72, 73]. Microbial degradation of petroleum pollutants has been reported to be less effective due to the slow process and accumulation of some toxic compounds inside the microbial cells [74]. The membrane-bound integral AlkB is capable of degrading petroleum hydrocarbons by their terminal or subterminal oxidation [75, 76]. The degradation of toxic petroleum pollutants is commonly carried out by alkane hydroxylase with the insertion of molecular oxygen, which results in the formation of their primary alcohol and later converted into aldehydes, carboxylic acid, and then metabolized by the β-oxidation pathway [76, 77]. In some cases, hydrocarbon oxidation takes place on both termini through ω-hydroxylation and is converted into a dicarboxylic acid [76]. However, those hydrocarbons oxidized by subterminal oxidation are first converted into their respective secondary alcohol, ketones, and ester [78, 79]. Oxidation of petroleum hydrocarbons like diesel, crude oil, *n*-alkanes, and PAHs takes place via terminal oxidation. The degradation of aromatic pollutants started with the cleavage of the ring structure [80]. However, oxidations of aromatic pollutants are quite slower than saturated hydrocarbons [75]. The bacterial alkane hydroxylases are normally involved in the formation of a diol, while fungal alkane hydroxylases are involved in the formation of trans-diol [79]. Cyclic alkanes are converted to cyclic alcohols and dehydrogenated to ketones by an oxidase system.

11.4.2 Pharmaceutical Use

Microbes and enzymes are being used to add functional groups into drugs for many years. Pharmaceutical use of alkane hydroxylases is rising rapidly such as P450 for the hydroxylation of Reichstein S to hydrocortisone [81]. Another example is a synthesis of cortisone from progesterone [3, 82]. Use of P450 alkane hydroxylase for the synthesis of Perillyl alcohol (anticancer drug) from terpenes has also been reported [4]. Similarly, a mutant of P450 (CYP260B1) was used for the conversion of the six steroids drugs (cortisone, cortisol, progesterone, cortodoxone, 17-hydroxyprogesterone, and 11-deoxycorticosterone) and five steroidal drugs (dexamethasone, betamethasone, fluorine, budesonide, and desonide) by [83].

11.4.3 DNA Damage Repair

DNA damage leads to be fundamental problems for cellular mechanisms. Any changes in DNA structure including the addition of chemicals or disruption to a base can be considered as DNA damage. DNA alkylation/methylation occurs by endogenous and exogenous sources; later it leads to cytotoxicity or cancer-linked mutations [10, 84]. Direct repair of the damaged DNA can be done by enzymes, including DNA glycosylases, O^6-methylguanine DNA methyltransferases, etc. AlkB-type oxygenases are also used in the DNA repair process [85]. AlkB family oxygenases catalyze the demethylation of alkylated DNA bases by utilizing 2-oxoglutarate and Fe (II).

Various forms of alkylated DNA have different substrate ranges for the AlkB oxygenases. AlkBH2 has been shown to demethylate duplex dsDNA, but AlkB and AlkBH3 repair damage in single-stranded DNA efficiently [86–88].

Waheed et al. 2020 have recently investigated the catalytic mechanism of AlkB and AlkBH2 for DNA demethylation of ssDNA, and dsDNA by combining molecular dynamics (MD) and molecular mechanics' approaches [89]. Liu et al. 2009 used α-ketoglutarate-Fe(II)-dependent AlkB enzymes for the demethylation of DNA to their native state and proposed that the reaction mechanism consists of four steps. First, the binding of dioxygen to iron which was yielding a ferric-superoxide species. Second, activation of oxygen molecule for the generation of iron–oxygen intermediates, then conformational reorientation of the activated iron–oxygen ligand, and the final step was the oxidative demethylation of nucleotide bases as represented in Figure 11.4 [90].

11.4.4 Role of Alkane Hydroxylases in Polythene Degradation

Polythene waste is highly recognized as one of the major pollutants to the environment and living beings. Microbial and enzymatic degradation of polythene is emerging as eco-friendly tool for the digestion of polythene as well as the generation

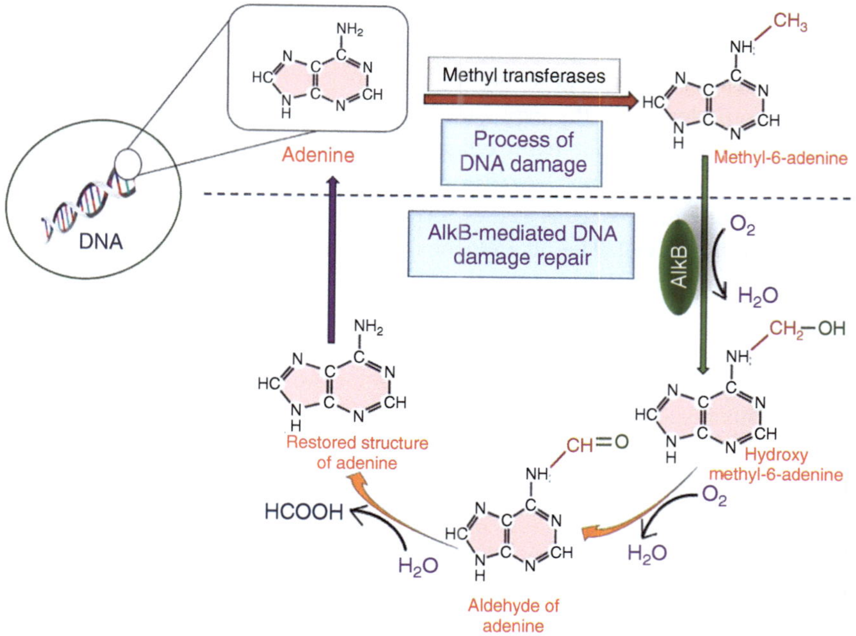

Figure 11.4 Proposed DNA repair mechanism by AlkB with methyladenine as substrate.

of new chemicals. In many microbial strains containing alkane hydroxylase, the enzyme has the ability to degrade a wide range of polythene [91]. The alkane hydroxylases from *Pseudomonas* sp. have shown an important role in the degradation of low molecular weight polyethylene (LMWPE). The mechanism behind the degradation of LMWPEs is explained in the manner that the polythene enters into the plasma membrane of microbes where there are metabolized by alkane hydroxylases and other cascades of enzymes. Yoon et al. (2012) have investigated the mechanism of AlkB1 and AlkB2 hydroxylases from *Pseudomonas aerogenosa* and found that both enzymes are involved in the degradation of polythene [91]. Hou and Majumder reported that cytochrome P450s and AlkBs can degrade polythene by breaking the C—C bonds [92]. Some dioxygenases can also break the side chain of polythene and can oxidize the aromatic hydrocarbons. The recombinant AlkB from *P. aerogenosa* has the potential to mineralize nearly 19.3% of the carbon of polythene waste to CO_2. Alkane hydroxylases having the potential to degrade the polythene are distributed in *Proteobacteria, Actinobacteria, Bacteroidetes*, and *Firmicutes*, suggesting that AlkBs can be explored for the mineralization of polythene waste.

11.5 Future Prospects

Alkane hydroxylases are attractive for bioconversion of a broad range of substrates for industrial interest, especially activation of hydrocarbons, degradation of pollutants, pharmaceutical use, and DNA damage repair. However, despite several applications of alkane hydroxylases, use of this enzyme at present has been largely restricted to lab-scale mainly due to the poor yield of alkane hydroxylases and the requirement of cofactor. Regeneration of NAD(P)H cofactor may resolve these issues and could lead to better exploration of the enzyme. The molecular cloning and overexpression of alkane hydroxylase play an important role in the increased use of AlkBs in different areas. However, alkb genes are found extremely difficult to clone and express into host cells as they form an inclusion body or stop the protein synthesis of the host cell. The heterologous expression of the alkane hydroxylases gene is quite complicated due to the three components of the alkB system, which are necessary for enzyme applications. Fortunately, the alkane hydroxylase system of some strains, such as *P. putida* GPo1, has demonstrated that rubredoxins from diverse alkane degraders bacteria can substitute for the GPo1 rubredoxin in alkane oxidation. This suggests that alternative sources of GPo1 rubredoxin and rubredoxin reductase can act as electron donors for new alkane hydroxylases related to the GPo1 enzyme.

11.6 Conclusion

The AlkB applications discussed in this chapter reveal the potential catalytic importance of AlkB for various applications. However, many challenges associated with alkane hydroxylase uses remain to be resolved before this catalyst can be used in large scales with the same confidence as other oxidoreductases are used in industrial applications. Advancement and investigation in the AlkBs, such as cloning expression systems, and recombinant AlkBs will ensure the expansion of AlkB applications for wider industrial applications.

References

1 McKenna, E.J. and Coon, M.J. (1970). Enzymatic ω-oxidation. *J. Biol. Chem.* 245 (15): 3882–3889. http://dx.doi.org/10.1016/S0021-9258(18)62932-1.

2 Kok, M., Oldenhuis, R., Van Der Linden, M.P.G. et al. (1989). The *Pseudomonas oleovorans* alkBAC operon encodes two structurally related rubredoxins and an aldehyde dehydrogenase. *J. Biol. Chem.* 264 (10): 5442–5451. http://dx.doi.org/10.1016/S0021-9258(18)83565-7.

3 Peterson, J.A., Kusunose, M., Kusunose, E., and Coon, M.J. (1967). Enzymatic ω-oxidation. *J. Biol. Chem.* 242 (19): 4334–4340. http://dx.doi.org/10.1016/S0021-9258(18)99543-8.

4 Van Beilen, J.B. and Funhoff, E.G. (2005). Expanding the alkane oxygenase toolbox: new enzymes and applications. *Curr. Opin. Biotechnol.* 16 (3 SPEC. ISS): 308–314.

5 Eidani, S.Z., Shahraki, M.K., Gasemisakha, F. et al. (2012). Cloning and expression of alkane hydroxylase-1 from *Alcanivorax borkumensis* in *Escherichia coli. Toxicol. Ind. Health* 28 (6): 560–565.

6 Naing, S.H., Parvez, S., Pender-Cudlip, M. et al. (2013). Substrate specificity and reaction mechanism of purified alkane hydroxylase from the hydrocarbon-oclastic bacterium *Alcanivorax borkumensis* (AbAlkB). *J. Inorg. Biochem.* 121: 46–52.

7 Geng, C., Ye, S., and Neese, F. (2010). Analysis of reaction channels for alkane hydroxylation by nonheme iron(IV)-oxo complexes. *Angew. Chem. Int. Ed.* 49 (33): 5717–5720.

8 Yoshizawa, K. (2000). Two-step concerted mechanism for methane hydroxylation on the diiron active site of soluble methane monooxygenase. *J. Inorg. Biochem.* 78 (1): 23–34.

9 Ji, Y., Mao, G., Wang, Y., and Bartlam, M. (2013). Structural insights into diversity and *n*-alkane biodegradation mechanisms of alkane hydroxylases. *Front. Microbiol.* 4 (March): 1–13.

10 Clifton, I.J., McDonough, M.A., Ehrismann, D. et al. (2006). Structural studies on 2-oxoglutarate oxygenases and related double-stranded β-helix fold proteins. *J. Inorg. Biochem.* 100 (4): 644–669.

11 Kitmitto, A., Myronova, N., Basu, P., and Dalton, H. (2005). Characterization and structural analysis of an active particulate methane monooxygenase trimer from *Methylococcus capsulatus* (Bath). *Biochemistry* 44 (33): 10954–10965.

12 Van Beilen, J.B., Holtackers, R., Lüscher, D. et al. (2005). Biocatalytic production of perillyl alcohol from limonene by using a novel *Mycobacterium* sp. cytochrome P450 alkane hydroxylase expressed in *Pseudomonas putida*. *Appl. Environ. Microbiol.* 71 (4): 1737–1744.

13 Johnson, E.L. and Hyman, M.R. (2006). Propane and *n*-butane oxidation by *Pseudomonas putida* GPo1. *Appl. Environ. Microbiol.* 72 (1): 950–952.

14 Van Beilen, J.B., Penninga, D., and Witholt, B. (1992). Topology of the membrane-bound alkane hydroxylase of *Pseudomonas oleovorans*. *J. Biol. Chem.* 267 (13): 9194–9201.

15 Bernhardt, R. (2006). Cytochromes P450 as versatile biocatalysts. *J. Biotechnol.* 124 (1): 128–145.

16 Huang, J.J. and Kimura, T. (1973). Studies on adrenal steroid hydroxylases. Oxidation–reduction properties of adrenal iron–sulfur protein (adrenodoxin). *Biochemistry* 12 (3): 406–409.

17 Ayala, M. and Torres, E. (2004). Enzymatic activation of alkanes: constraints and prospective. *Appl. Catal., A* 272 (1–2): 1–13.

18 Li, L., Liu, X., Yang, W. et al. (2008). Crystal structure of long-chain alkane monooxygenase (LadA) in complex with coenzyme FMN: unveiling the long-chain alkane hydroxylase. *J. Mol. Biol.* 376 (2): 453–465.

19 Bosetti, A., van Beilen, J.B., Preusting, H. et al. (1992). Production of primary aliphatic alcohols with a recombinant *Pseudomonas* strain, encoding the alkane hydroxylase enzyme system. *Enzyme Microb. Technol.* 14 (9): 702–708.

20 Ratajczak, A., Geißdörfer, W., and Hillen, W. (1998). Alkane hydroxylase from Acinetobacter sp. strain ADP1 is encoded by alkM and belongs to a new family of bacterial integral-membrane hydrocarbon hydroxylases. *Appl. Environ. Microbiol.* 64 (4): 1175–1179.

21 Van Beilen, J.B., Marín, M.M., Smits, T.H.M. et al. (2004). Characterization of two alkane hydroxylase genes from the marine hydrocarbonoclastic bacterium *Alcanivorax borkumensis*. *Environ. Microbiol.* 6 (3): 264–273.

22 Lo Piccolo, L., de Pasquale, C., Fodale, R. et al. (2011). Involvement of an alkane hydroxylase system of *Gordonia* sp. strain SoCg in degradation of solid *n*-alkanes. *Appl. Environ. Microbiol.* 77 (4): 1204–1213.

23 Liu, C., Wang, W., Wu, Y. et al. (2011). Multiple alkane hydroxylase systems in a marine alkane degrader, *Alcanivorax dieselolei* B-5. *Environ. Microbiol.* 13 (5): 1168–1178.

24 Throne-Holst, M., Markussen, S., Winnberg, A. et al. (2006). Utilization of *n*-alkanes by a newly isolated strain of *Acinetobacter venetianus*: the role of two AlkB-type alkane hydroxylases. *Appl. Microbiol. Biotechnol.* 72 (2): 353–360.

25 Nie, Y., Liang, J., Fang, H. et al. (2011). Two novel alkane hydroxylase-rubredoxin fusion genes isolated from a Dietzia bacterium and the functions of fused rubredoxin domains in long-chain *n*-alkane degradation. *Appl. Environ. Microbiol.* 77 (20): 7279–7288.

26 Takei, D., Washio, K., and Morikawa, M. (2008). Identification of alkane hydroxylase genes in Rhodococcus sp. strain TMP2 that degrades a branched alkane. *Biotechnol. Lett* 30 (8): 1447–1452.

27 Koch, D.J., Chen, M.M., Van Beilen, J.B., and Arnold, F.H. (2009). In vivo evolution of butane oxidation by terminal alkane hydroxylases AlkB and CYP153A6. *Appl. Environ. Microbiol.* 75 (2): 337–344.

28 Tani, A., Ishige, T., Sakai, Y., and Kato, N. (2001). Gene structures and regulation of the alkane hydroxylase complex in *Acinetobacter* sp. strain M-1. *J. Bacteriol.* 183 (5): 1819–1823.

29 Yang, Y., Liu, J., and Li, Z. (2014). Engineering of P450pyr hydroxylase for the highly regio- and enantioselective subterminal hydroxylation of alkanes. *Angew. Chem. Int. Ed.* 53 (12): 3120–3124.

30 Glieder, A., Farinas, E.T., and Arnold, F.H. (2002). Laboratory evolution of a soluble, self-sufficient, highly active alkane hydroxylase. *Nat. Biotechnol.* 20 (11): 1135–1139.

31 Grant, C., Woodley, J.M., and Baganz, F. (2011). Whole-cell bio-oxidation of *n*-dodecane using the alkane hydroxylase system of *P. putida* GPo1 expressed in *E. coli. Enzyme Microb. Technol.* 48 (6–7): 480–486. http://dx.doi.org/10.1016/j.enzmictec.2011.01.008.

32 Whyte, L.G., Smits, T.H.M., Labbé, D. et al. (2002). Gene cloning and characterization of multiple alkane hydroxylase systems in *Rhodococcus* strains Q15 and NRRL B-16531. *Appl. Environ. Microbiol.* 68 (12): 5933–5942.

33 Schunck, W.H., Riege, P., Blasig, R. et al. (1978). Cytochrome P-450 and alkane hydroxylase activity in Candida guilliermondii. *Acta biologica et medica germanica* 37 (1): K3–K7.

34 Smits, T.H.M., Witholt, B., and van Beilen, J.B. (2003). Functional characterization of genes involved in alkane oxidation by *Pseudomanas aeruginosa. Antonie Van Leeuwenhoek.* 84 (3): 193–200.

35 Vomberg, A. and Klinner, U. (2001). Distribution of alkB genes within *n*-alkane-degrading bacteria. *J. Appl. Microbiol.* 89: 339–348.

36 Van Beilen, J.B., Duetz, W.A., Schmid, A., and Witholt, B. (2003). Practical issues in the application of oxygenases. *Trends Biotechnol.* 21 (4): 170–177.

37 Chen, W., Lee, M.K., Jefcoate, C. et al. (2014). Fungal cytochrome P450 monooxygenases: their distribution, structure, functions, family expansion, and evolutionary origin. *Genome Biol. Evol.* 6 (7): 1620–1634.

38 Moktali, V., Park, J., Fedorova-Abrams, N.D. et al. (2012). Systematic and searchable classification of cytochrome P450 proteins encoded by fungal and oomycete genomes. *BMC Genomics* 13 (1): 525.

39 Das, S. and Negi, S. (2022). Enhanced production of alkane hydroxylase from *Penicillium chrysogenum* SNP5 (MTCC13144) through feed-forward neural network and genetic algorithm. *AMB Express* 12 (1): 1–13. https://doi.org/10.1186/s13568-022-01366-1.

40 Miri, M., Bambai, B., Tabandeh, F. et al. (2010). Production of a recombinant alkane hydroxylase (AlkB2) from *Alcanivorax borkumensis. Biotechnol. Lett* 32 (4): 497–502.

41 Xie, M., Alonso, H., and Roujeinikova, A. (2011). An improved procedure for the purification of catalytically active alkane hydroxylase from *Pseudomonas putida* GPo1. *Appl. Biochem. Biotechnol.* 165 (3–4): 823–831.

42 Holler, T., Widdel, F., Knittel, K. et al. (2011). Thermophilic anaerobic oxidation of methane by marine microbial consortia. *ISME J.* 5 (12): 1946–1956.

43 Rozhkova-Novosad, E.A., Chae, J.C., Zylstra, G.J. et al. (2007). Profiling mechanisms of alkane hydroxylase activity in vivo using the diagnostic substrate norcarane. *Chem. Biol.* 14 (2): 165–172.

44 Van Beilen, J.B. and Funhoff, E.G. (2007). Alkane hydroxylases involved in microbial alkane degradation. *Appl. Microbiol. Biotechnol.* 74 (1): 13–21.

45 Van Hamme, J.D., Singh, A., and Ward, O.P. (2003). Recent advances in petroleum microbiology. *Microbiol. Mol. Biol. Rev.* 67 (4): 503–549.

46 Cao, B., Nagarajan, K., and Loh, K.C. (2009). Biodegradation of aromatic compounds: current status and opportunities for biomolecular approaches. *Appl. Microbiol. Biotechnol.* 85 (2): 207–228.

47 Wentzel, A., Ellingsen, T.E., Kotlar, H.K. et al. (2007). Bacterial metabolism of long-chain *n*-alkanes. *Appl. Microbiol. Biotechnol.* 76 (6): 1209–1221.

48 Kotani, T., Kawashima, Y., Yurimoto, H. et al. (2006). Gene structure and regulation of alkane monooxygenases in propane-utilizing *Mycobacterium* sp. TY-6 and *Pseudonocardia* sp. TY-7. *J. Biosci. Bioeng.* 102 (3): 184–192.

49 Arp, D.J. (1999). Butane metabolism by butane-grown "*Pseudomonas butanovora*". *Microbiology* 145 (5): 1173–1180.

50 Sluis, M.K., Sayavedra-Soto, L.A., and Arp, D.J. (2002). Molecular analysis of the soluble butane monooxygenase from "*Pseudomanas butanovora*". *Microbiology* 148 (11): 3617–3629.

51 Dubbels, B.L., Sayavedra-Soto, L.A., and Arp, D.J. (2007). Butane monooxygenase of "*Pseudomonas butanovora*": Purification and biochemical characterization of a terminal-alkane hydroxylating diiron monooxygenase. *Microbiology* 153 (6): 1808–1816.

52 Kurth, E.G., Doughty, D.M., Bottomley, P.J. et al. (2008). Involvement of BmoR and BmoG in *n*-alkane metabolism in "*Pseudomonas butanovora*". *Microbiology* 154 (1): 139–147.

53 Kotani, T., Yamamoto, T., Yurimoto, H. et al. (2003). Propane monooxygenase and NAD^+-dependent secondary alcohol dehydrogenase in propane metabolism by *Gordonia* sp. Strain TY-5. *J. Bacteriol.* 185 (24): 7120–7128.

54 Kotani, T., Yurimoto, H., Kato, N., and Sakai, Y. (2007). Novel acetone metabolism in a propane-utilizing bacterium, *Gordonia* sp. strain TY-5. *J. Bacteriol.* 189 (3): 886–893.

55 Funhoff, E.G., Bauer, U., García-Rubio, I. et al. (2006). CYP153A6, a soluble P450 oxygenase catalyzing terminal-alkane hydroxylation. *J. Bacteriol.* 188 (14): 5220–5227.

56 Maeng, J.H.O., Sakai, Y., Tani, Y., and Kato, N. (1996). Isolation and characterization of a novel oxygenase that catalyzes the first step of *n*-alkane oxidation in *Acinetobacter* sp. strain M-1. *J. Bacteriol.* 178 (13): 3695–3700.

57 Throne-Holst, M., Wentzel, A., Ellingsen, T.E. et al. (2007). Identification of novel genes involved in long-chain *n*-alkane degradation by *Acinetobacter* sp. strain DSM 17874. *Appl. Environ. Microbiol.* 73 (10): 3327–3332.

58 Feng, L., Wang, W., Cheng, J. et al. (2007). Genome and proteome of long-chain alkane degrading *Geobacillus thermodenitrificans* NG80-2 isolated from a deep-subsurface oil reservoir. *PNAS* 104 (13): 5602–5607.

59 Vangnai, A.S. and Arp, D.J. (2001). An inducible 1-butanol dehydrogenase, a quinohaemoprotein, is involved in the oxidation of butane by "*Pseudomonas butanovora*". *Microbiology* 147 (3): 745–756.

60 Vangnai, A.S., Arp, D.J., and Sayavedra-Soto, L.A. (2002). Two distinct alcohol dehydrogenases participate in butane metabolism by *Pseudomonas butanovora*. *J. Bacteriol.* 184 (7): 1916–1924.

61 van Beilen, J.B., Wubbolts, M.G., and Witholt, B. (1994). Genetics of alkane oxidation by *Pseudomonas oleovorans*. *Biodegradation* 5 (3–4): 161–174.

62 Pirnik, M.P., Atlas, R.M., and Bartha, R. (1974). Hydrocarbon metabolism by *Brevibacterium erythrogenes*: normal and branched alkanes. *J. Bacteriol.* 119 (3): 868–878.

63 Solano-Serena, F., Marchal, R., Heiss, S., and Vandecasteele, J.P. (2004). Degradation of isooctane by *Mycobacterium austroafricanum* IFP 2173: growth and catabolic pathway. *J. Appl. Microbiol.* 97 (3): 629–639.

64 Hara, A., Syutsubo, K., and Harayama, S. (2003). Alcanivorax which prevails in oil-contaminated seawater exhibits broad substrate specificity for alkane degradation. *Environ. Microbiol.* 5 (9): 746–753.

65 Brzeszcz, J. and Kaszycki, P. (2018). Aerobic bacteria degrading both *n*-alkanes and aromatic hydrocarbons: an undervalued strategy for metabolic diversity and flexibility. *Biodegradation* 29 (4): 359–407. https://doi.org/10.1007/s10532-018-9837-x.

66 Deppe, U., Richnow, H.H., Michaelis, W., and Antranikian, G. (2005). Degradation of crude oil by an arctic microbial consortium. *Extremophiles* 9 (6): 461–470.

67 Souza, E.C., Vessoni-Penna, T.C., and De Souza Oliveira, R.P. (2014). Biosurfactant-enhanced hydrocarbon bioremediation: an overview. *Int. Biodeterior. Biodegrad.* 89: 88–94. http://dx.doi.org/10.1016/j.ibiod.2014.01.007.

68 Costa, A.S., Romão, L.P.C., Araújo, B.R. et al. (2012). Environmental strategies to remove volatile aromatic fractions (BTEX) from petroleum industry wastewater using biomass. *Bioresour. Technol.* 105: 31–39. http://dx.doi.org/10.1016/j.biortech.2011.11.096.

69 Ron, E.Z. and Rosenberg, E. (2014). Enhanced bioremediation of oil spills in the sea. *Curr. Opin. Biotechnol.* 27: 191–194. http://dx.doi.org/10.1016/j.copbio.2014.02.004.

70 Varjani, S.J., Rana, D.P., Jain, A.K. et al. (2015). Synergistic ex-situ biodegradation of crude oil by halotolerant bacterial consortium of indigenous strains isolated from on shore sites of Gujarat, India. *Int. Biodeterior. Biodegrad.* 103: 116–124. http://dx.doi.org/10.1016/j.ibiod.2015.03.030.

71 Varjani, S.J. and Upasani, V.N. (2016). Biodegradation of petroleum hydrocarbons by oleophilic strain of *Pseudomonas aeruginosa* NCIM 5514. *Bioresour. Technol.* 222: 195–201. http://dx.doi.org/10.1016/j.biortech.2016.10.006.

72 Boopathy, R. (2000). Factors limiting bioremediation technologies. *Bioresour. Technol.* 74 (1): 63–67.

73 Kumari, A., Ahmad, R., Negi, S., and Khare, S.K. (2017). Biodegradation of waste grease by *Penicillium chrysogenum* for production of fatty acid. *Bioresour. Technol.* 226: 31–38. http://dx.doi.org/10.1016/j.biortech.2016.12.006.

74 Samanta, S.K., Singh, O.V., and Jain, R.K. (2002). Polycyclic aromatic hydrocarbons: environmental pollution and bioremediation. *Trends Biotechnol.* 20 (6): 243–248.

75 Salleh, A.B., Ghazali, F.M., Abd Rahman, R.N.Z., and Basri, M. (2003). Bioremediation of petroleum hydrocarbon pollution. *Indian J. Biotechnol.* 2 (3): 411–425.

76 Abbasian, F., Lockington, R., Mallavarapu, M., and Naidu, R. (2015). A comprehensive review of aliphatic hydrocarbon biodegradation by bacteria. *Appl. Biochem. Biotechnol.* 176 (3): 670–699.

77 Das, N. and Chandran, P. (2011). Microbial degradation of petroleum hydrocarbon contaminants: an overview. *Biotechnol. Res. Int.* 2011: 1–13.

78 Rojo, F. (2009). Degradation of alkanes by bacteria: mini review. *Environ. Microbiol.* 11 (10): 2477–2490.

79 Zhang, Z., Hou, Z., Yang, C. et al. (2011). Degradation of *n*-alkanes and polycyclic aromatic hydrocarbons in petroleum by a newly isolated *Pseudomonas aeruginosa* DQ8. *Bioresour. Technol.* 102 (5): 4111–4116. http://dx.doi.org/10.1016/j.biortech.2010.12.064.

80 Hendrickx, B., Junca, H., Vosahlova, J. et al. (2006). Alternative primer sets for PCR detection of genotypes involved in bacterial aerobic BTEX degradation: distribution of the genes in BTEX degrading isolates and in subsurface soils of a BTEX contaminated industrial site. *J. Microbiol. Methods* 64 (2): 250–265.

81 Petzoldt, K., Annen, K., Laurent, H. et al. (1982). Process for the preparation of 11-beta-hydroxy steroids. Schering Aktiengesellschaft, US Patent No. US 4353985, issued 12 October 1982.

82 Hogg, J.A. (1992). Steroids, the steroid community, and Upjohn in perspective: a profile of innovation. *Steroids* 57 (12): 593–616.

83 Litzenburger, M. and Bernhardt, R. (2017). CYP260B1 acts as 9α-hydroxylase for 11-deoxycorticosterone. *Steroids* 127 (August): 40–45. http://dx.doi.org/10.1016/j.steroids.2017.08.006.

84 Schofield, C.J. and Zhang, Z. (1999). Structural and mechanistic studies on 2-oxoglutarate-dependent oxygenases and related enzymes. *Curr. Opin. Struct. Biol.* 9: 722–731.

85 Samson, L. and Cairns, J. (1977). A new pathway for DNA repair in *Escherichia coli*. *Nature* 267 (5608): 281–283.

86 Fedeles, B.I., Singh, V., Delaney, J.C. et al. (2015). The AlkB family of Fe(II)/α-ketoglutarate-dependent dioxygenases: repairing nucleic acid alkylation damage and beyond. *J. Biol. Chem.* 290 (34): 20734–20742. http://dx.doi.org/10.1074/jbc.R115.656462.

87 Yang, C.G., Yi, C., Duguid, E.M. et al. (2008). Crystal structures of DNA/RNA repair enzymes AlkB and ABH2 bound to dsDNA. *Nature* 452 (7190): 961–965.

88 Zheng, G., Fu, Y., and He, C. (2014). Nucleic acid oxidation in DNA damage repair and epigenetics. *Chem. Rev.* 114 (8): 4602–4620.

89 Waheed, S.O., Ramanan, R., Chaturvedi, S.S. et al. (2020). Role of structural dynamics in selectivity and mechanism of non-heme Fe(II) and 2-oxoglutarate-dependent oxygenases involved in DNA repair. *ACS Cent. Sci.* 6 (5): 795–814.

90 Liu, H., Llano, J., and Gauld, J.W. (2009). A DFT study of nucleobase dealkylation by the DNA repair enzyme AlkB. *J. Phys. Chem. B* 113 (14): 4887–4898.

91 Gyung Yoon, M., Jeong Jeon, H., and Nam, K.M. (2012). Biodegradation of polyethylene by a soil bacterium and AlkB cloned recombinant cell. *J. Biorem. Biodegrad.* 3 (4): 145.

92 Hou, L. and Majumder, E.L.W. (2021). Potential for and distribution of enzymatic biodegradation of polystyrene by environmental microorganisms. *Materials (Basel)* 14 (3): 1–20.

12

An Overview of Production of Bacterial and Fungal Laccases and Their Industrial Applications

Sushil K. Singh[1], *Arya Sahu*[2], *Manish S. Rajput*[1], *and Nand Lal*[3]

[1] *Dr. Ambedkar Institute of Technology for Divyangjan, Department of Biotechnology, Awadhpuri, Kanpur, Uttar Pradesh 208024, India*
[2] *Indian Institute of Technology Ropar, Department of Biomedical Engineering, Ropar, Rupnagar, Punjab 140001, India*
[3] *Chhatrapati Shahu Ji Maharaj University, School of Life Sciences & Biotechnology, Kalyanpur, Kanpur, Uttar Pradesh 208024, India*

12.1 Introduction

Enzymes play a critical role in reducing pollution by allowing for cleaner substance production and they are the biological catalysts with a higher rate of conversion for biochemical reactions. They offer numerous benefits, including reduced energy input, shorter reaction time, no toxicity, excellent substrate specificity, high catalytic efficiency, and moderate reaction conditions. Enzymes break down pollutants from wastewater into a variety of intermediate metabolites since they are proteinaceous in nature [1]. Enzymes are important green, ecofriendly catalytic agents used in several industrial reactions to achieve an economically efficient, cleaner manufacturing process. According to reports, laccases are an intriguing class of oxidative enzymes because they hold great promise for various environmental and biotechnological applications [2, 3].

Laccases are a well-studied subfamily of the multi-copper oxidase (MCO) family of enzymes. MCOs are oxidoreductases that oxidize a wide range of substrates while also reducing oxygen to water. MCOs have four copper ions grouped in two sites. As their name suggests, in type 1 copper, one electron is obtained from a substrate and transferred to the trinuclear center through a histidine-cysteine-histidine motif. In the trinuclear core, which contains one type 2 and two type 3 copper ions, oxygen is reduced to water. One molecule of O_2 receives four electrons from substrate molecules and thus reduces it to two molecules of water [4]. Yoshida discovered laccase from the efflux of *Rhus vernicifera*, which is also known as the Japanese lacquer tree, in the year 1883 [5]. Laccases are known to oxidize various substrates, including aminophenols, phenols, diamines, and some inorganic ions [6]. Laccases serve a wide range of roles in nature, which necessitates their vast substrate range. Plant laccases are important for lignin production [7]. Fungal laccases, on the other

Microbial Enzymes: Production, Purification, and Industrial Applications, First Edition.
Edited by Dinesh Yadav, Pankaj Chowdhary, Gautam Anand, and Rajarshi Kumar Gaur.

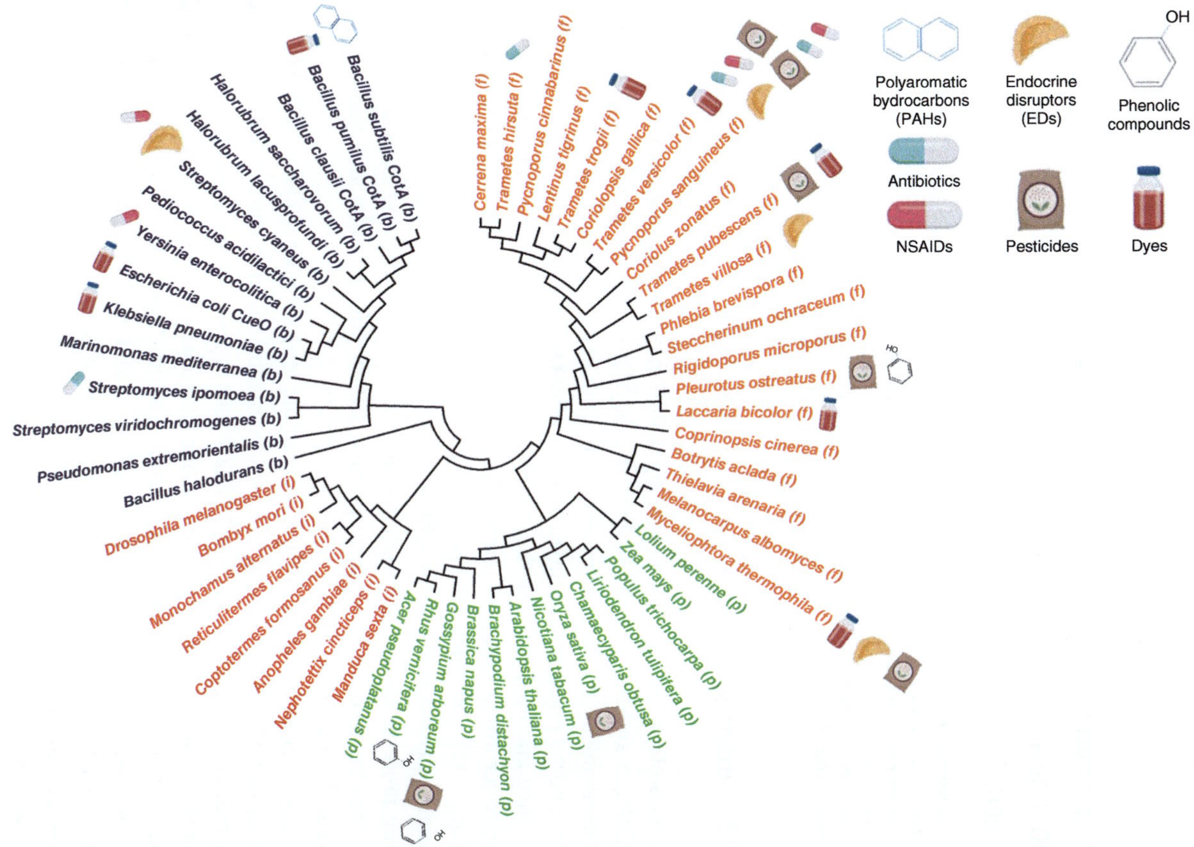

Figure 12.1 Phylogenetic tree depicting some of the different sources of laccases, along with their applications in bioremediation. The sources are colored blue, red, green, or orange depending on whether they are bacterial, insect, plant, or fungal, respectively. Source: Arregui et al. [15]/Springer Nature/CC BY 4.0 DEED. Link: https://microbialcellfactories.biomedcentral.com/articles/10.1186/s12934-019-1248-0/figures/2.

hand, are engaged in lignin breakdown for detoxification, pathogenesis, wood decay, and fungal morphology [6]. These are used by bacteria for copper homeostasis, pigmentation, hazardous chemical breakdown, and lignin degradation [8].

From bacteria to higher plants, laccases are glycoproteins found in a variety of organisms. It is mostly produced by fungi, particularly white-rot species, and has been widely used in industrial operations because of its high redox potential. Industrial investigations of fungal laccases are frequently limited by their long fermentation time, low laccase production, and the fact that they can only be used in acidic and mesophilic reactions. Since most of the industrial operations carried out are in harsh conditions, such as high pH and temperature as well as high salt concentrations, and in these conditions, fungi laccases typically do not work [9, 10]. In the past few years, the application and use of bacterial laccases have exploded because of their numerous advantages over fungal laccases in terms of industrial applications, such as they are able to work in a broad range of temperatures and pH, as well as their extreme stability against various other inhibitory agents [11]. Furthermore, due to their economical advantage in industrial applications, bacterial laccases have several additional advantages, such as ease of cloning and expression in the host with appropriate manipulations, quick enzyme production, and broad substrate specificity [12, 13]. Bacterial laccase is useful for developing biosensors, decolorizing and destroying textile dyes and effluents, and bio-bleaching pulp and paper [14]. Insects, fungi, plants, bacteria, and lichen are just a few of the many organisms that have laccases having unique catalytic properties and sequences (Figure 12.1) [15].

Adding mediators to laccases allows them to be used in more industrial bioremediation processes, such as detoxification of industrial dyes, color removal and delignification of lignocellulosics, explosives, biodegradation of xenobiotic compounds, wastewater treatment, pesticide-contaminated area, and degradation of other contaminants, e.g. polycyclic aromatic hydrocarbons (PAHs) [5]. Inorganic/organic metal complexes, such as Mn^{2+} and $Fe(EDTA)^{2-}$, are other substrates that laccases can reduce [16]. This chapter's goal is to consolidate data on many aspects of bacterial and fungal laccases, such as data on their structure, mechanism of reaction, production, and industrial and biotechnological uses.

12.2 Structure of Laccase

Laccases can be monomeric, multimeric, heterodimeric, and homotetrameric glycoprotein containing four copper atoms in each monomer [16]. Molecular weight ranges from 50 to 130 kDa, depending on the organism from which it has been isolated [17]. Plant laccases have a carbohydrate content of about 45%, whereas fungal laccases have a carbohydrate content of 10–30% of molecular weight [18]. The carbohydrate portion of laccase is thought to ensure the protein part's conformational stability and protect the enzyme against proteolysis and radical inactivation [19]. Laccases are composed of roughly 500 amino acid residues arranged in three successive domains and feature a Greek key beta-barrel structure. The amino acids are divided into three domains: 150 amino acids in the first domain, 150 and 300 amino acids in the second domain, and 300–500 amino acids in the third domain. The laccase structure is stabilized by disulfide bonds between domains I and II, as well as between domains I and III [20–23]. *Melanocarpus albomyces*, on the other hand, has three disulfide bridges: one inside domain I, another between domain I and domain III, and the third between domain II and III [24]. Laccases have four different copper catalytic forms per protein unit. Three types of structures exist for these four Cu ions.

12.2.1 Type 1: Paramagnetic "Blue" Copper

Because of the high electrical absorption generated by the covalent Cu^{2+}–cys bond, type 1 copper gives multi-copper proteins a blue color. The substrate is oxidized at the type 1 Cu^{2+} site, which exhibits a 610 nm absorbance because of its elevated levels of redox potentials of approximately +790 mV [22]. The trigonal coordination of type 1 copper has two histidine residues and a cysteine residue in conserved equatorial ligands and a position that is frequently changeable, whereas the axial ligand in fungal laccases is either leucine or phenylalanine. It's even been suggested that the axial location of the ligand influences the enzyme's oxidation potential, thus providing a way for regulating its activity (Figure 12.2) [22, 25–29].

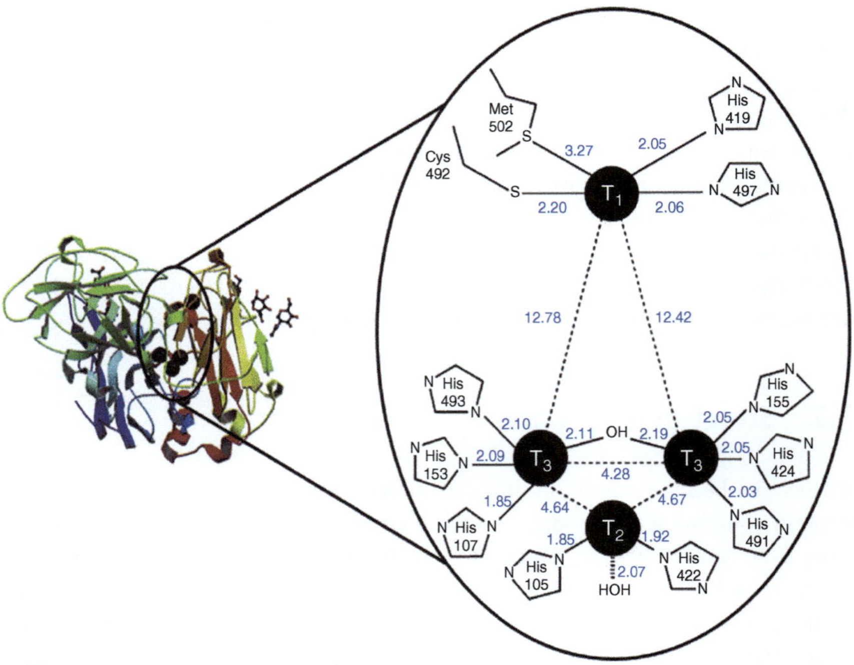

Figure 12.2 The active site of laccase. The orientation of copper atoms and ligand distance (blue, distances in Å). Laccase 2HZH 3-D structure in *Coriolus zonatus* as retrieved from Protein Data Bank (PDB). Source: Adapted from Garavaglia et al. [25].

12.2.2 Type 2: Paramagnetic "Nonblue/Normal" Copper

Type 2 or normal copper site has typical electron paramagnetic resonance (EPR) spectra and lacks substantial absorption characteristics in the visible region [30]. Type 2 Cu^{2+} is positioned close to type 3 Cu^{2+} and is harmonized by two histidine residues.

12.2.3 Type 3: Diamagnetic Spin-coupled Copper–Copper Pair

It has a six-histidine binuclear core with electron adsorption at a wavelength of 330 nm (in oxidized form) and because of strong antiferromagnetic pairing between two type 3 Cu^{2+} atoms, which is linked to the presence of a hydroxyl bridge, there is no EPR signal [22]. A trinuclear cluster created by the combination of copper types 2 and 3 lowers molecular oxygen and releases water [31]. Type 3 copper centers share features with tyrosinases and hemocyanins, which belong to another protein superfamily [32].

12.3 Mode of Action

Polyphenolase, a copper–protein-containing enzyme, oxidizes aromatic compounds. This Cu protein aids in the oxidation of molecules with benzene rings, in which oxygen serves as the last electron acceptor. Laccases (EC 1.10.3.2), cresolase (EC 1.18.14.1), and catechol oxidase (EC 1.10.3.1) are among the enzymes that oxidizes polyphenols [14].

One oxygen molecule loses an electron during the reaction pathway of laccase, which results in the production of two molecules of water. This abstracted electron further facilitates the oxidation of several benzene ring-containing compounds [33, 34]. Laccase's catalytic properties have improved significantly, and it now plays a key role in the breaking down of aromatic compounds, leading to cations formation. In presence of laccase (e.g., quinine from phenol) or non-enzymatic reactions, often less stable cation produced from this reaction, and therefore changed into the stable product (e.g. degradation, hydration, or polymerization) [35]. The presence of four copper atoms triggers the redox process, which makes up the majority of this reaction. Three types of copper are type 1 copper (T_1Cu), type 2 copper (T_2Cu), and type 3 copper (T_3Cu).

The T1-copper center is shallower than the oxygen-binding area, where the substrate molecules are bound. One electron is transported from the substrate to T1 copper via an external-sphere process. As a result of this, free radicals are formed from the substrate molecules, which can then be further radical-coupled or oxidized to produce oligomers or polymers. A cysteine-histidine pathway, which is substantially conserved among all the MCO, is used to transfer the extracted electron from the T1 center to the trinuclear cluster. The redox-active molecular orbitals of T1 coordinating cysteine, backbone atoms, and T3 copper coordinating histidine residues come together to form the so-called super exchange pathway [36].

Type 2 and 3 copper comprise the trinuclear center, which plays a crucial part in the catalytic reaction. When oxygen molecules bind to the trinuclear cluster, then the catalytic process begins and it prevents any other molecules from entering. At the T_2Cu, two molecules of histidine react with one molecule of water, whereas at the T_3Cu site, three histidines and hydroxide molecules react with each other. Laccase transformation is assisted by the formation of water molecules in two different stages using oxygen in the final step. T_2Cu and T_3Cu reduce the first electron, while the peroxide mediator reduces the second electron, which is promptly taken up by the T_2Cu site and T_1Cu coupled to T_3Cu by a covalent His–Cys [34, 37].

12.4 Sources of Laccase

Laccases can be found in a wide-ranging variety of fungi, bacteria, insects, or even in plants [38–41]. Plants that produce laccase include mango, lacquer, mung bean, sycamore, peach, prune, and pine [27]. Most bacterial laccases tend to be produced intracellularly and can be located in periplasmic space of protoplasts, with the exception of a few bacterial laccase [40]. These extracted bacterial laccases are mostly employed in the manufacture of several industrial products. *Azospirillum lipoferum*, a plant root-associated bacterium, was the first bacterial laccase discovered, and it was discovered to be involved in the synthesis of melanin [42]. This enzyme has been isolated from various bacterial species such as *Escherichia coli, Yersinia pestis, Streptomyces griseus, Caulobacter crescentus, Pseudomonas aeruginosa, Bordetella campestris, Mycobacterium tuberculosum, Marinomonas mediterranea, Pseudomonas syringae,* and *Bacillus subtilis* [42–44].

Fungal species have been discovered to be the principal sources of laccase production. Laccase production can be found in a wide variety of fungi. White-rot fungi are among the top laccase producers for fungal species; the majority of fungal laccases come from deuteromycetes, basidiomycetes, and ascomycetes, according to the literature [45–48]. According to recent research, all laccase enzymes have been identified from fungal species, particularly white-rot fungal strains such as *Anthracophyllum discolor, Pleurotus ostreatus, Trichoderma harzianum*, and *Pycnoporus sanguineus* [49]. Laccase enzyme production in lower fungi such *as Pleurotus eryngii, Chaetomium thermophilum, Trametes trogii, Trametes versicolor,* and *Zygomycetes chytridiomycetes* has not been explored. *Trichoderma* species, including *T. harzianum,* have been identified to produce polyphenol oxidase [48, 50]. However, the first fungal laccase was isolated from the ascomycete *Monocillium indicum*, which displayed peroxidative enzyme activity [51]. Among the listed three white-rot fungus species, Basidiomycetes are known to be the most efficient laccase producers [52]. Laccases have also been discovered in different species of insects such as *Manduca, Drosophila, Schistocerca, Oryctes, Papilio, Sarcophaga, Phormia, Calliphora, Tenebrio, Diploptera, Bombyx, Musca, Rhodnius,* and *Lucilia*. It was thought that laccases play an important role in cuticle sclerotization in insects, which was later discovered [53]. A schematic explanation of the sources and uses of this enzyme for more environmentally friendly manufacturing of goods and environmental development are shown in Figure 12.3.

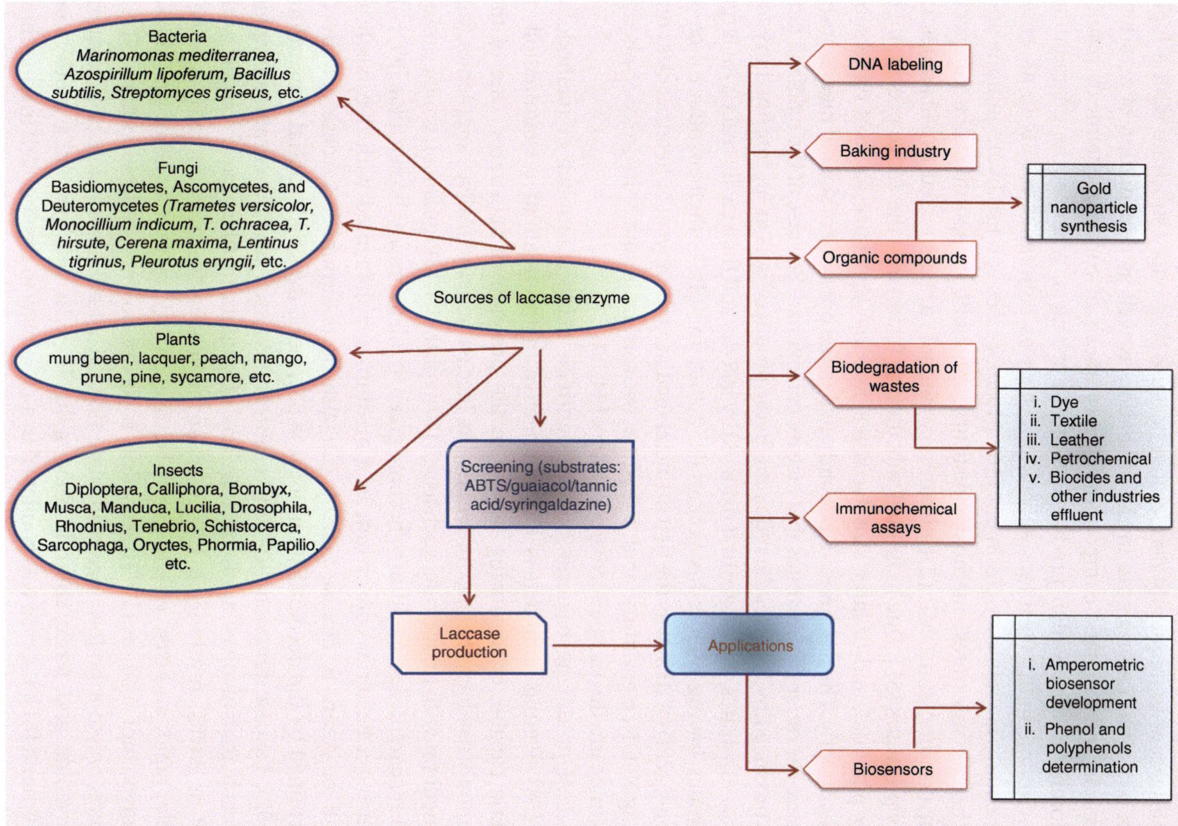

Figure 12.3 Different sources of laccase and its various applications. Source: Adapted from Sharma and Kuhad [54].

12.5 Substrates, Mediators, and Screening of Laccases

Laccases are able to oxidize a wide range of substrates likewise, substrate-specific enzymes, including phenylpropanoids, azo dyes, indigo dyes and phenolic compounds, using the reaction mechanism described above [55]. The reaction mediated by the laccase is frequently decelerated because of a bulky substrate with a high redox potential. Laccases aid in the formation as well as remediation of a variety of organic and aromatic compounds. The synthesis of complex chemicals results in bioremediation, which produces nontoxic products, whereas the degradation of environmentally hazardous substances, such as pollutants, results in an environmentally favorable environment [56]. Most laccases can use hydroquinone and catechol as substrates; methoxy-substituted phenolic compounds like guaiacol, syringaldazine, and DMP (2,4-di-methoxy phenol) are also used as substrates in many processes [57]. Due to limited substrate diffusion into the active pocket, high redox potential, and/or large size, laccase is not able to oxidize some of these substrates directly. The reaction can be conducted in the presence of several mediators to increase the range of substrates that laccase can oxidize. Because of the oxidized radicals produced by laccase, the redox mediator produced acts as an intermediary for laccase substrates, which are first oxidized by laccase and then easily react with large substrates having high redox potentials. 2,20-Azino-bis(3-ethylbenzothiazoline-6-sulfonic acid) (ABTS) was the first artificial mediator employed; N-heterocycles containing N–OH, e.g. violuric acid, *N*-hydroxybenzotriazole, and *N*-hydroxy-*N*-phenyl acetamide are the most effective mediators [34, 37].

Laccase-producing bacteria can be identified using a number of methodologies [58]. Plating approach is highly effective in the qualitative examination of bacteria capable of producing laccase in the presence of substrates. One of the commonly used approaches for identifying laccase activity involves supplementing the medium with a substrate, such as ABTS/naphthol/DMP/guaiacol, which causes the transparent agar medium to become green/reddish brown/ brown/blue [59, 60]. Culturing a bacterial consortium in a medium supplemented with dyes such as Poly-R or Azure-B, laccase activity can also be determined. Laccase activity is determined by the decolorization of these polymeric dyes by bacterial consortium [61, 62]. Laccase functionality can be quickly assessed using a chromatographic approach that involves applying fractions of eluents to filter paper coated with DMP or ABTS, resulting in a blue–green or yellow–brown color [63]. Another simple, rapid, and easy way to assess laccase activity, as well as other peroxidase or polyphenol oxidase (PPO) activities, is to use sodium dodecyl sulfate (SDS). Bacteria create a hollow region in plate flooded with 1% emulsion of potassium ferricyanide and ferric chloride, having lignin as a substrate in a blue–green background [61]. Laccase was employed in a novel way to create a well in a medium containing phenolic substrates such ABTS, 4-hydroxy 3,5-dimethoxybenzaldehyde, guaiacol, and pyrogallol. The presence of laccase is shown by the development of pigmentation in the purlieu of the wells [64]. Colorimetric method, fluorometric method, and voltammetric method can also be used for the screening of bacterial laccases [61, 65, 66].

Soil as well as plant samples collected from industrial wastewater liquidating sites can be used to isolate laccase-producing fungus strains. CBBR G-250, ABTS, guaiacol, DMP, methylene blue, and other azo dyes are examples of phenolic substrates that can be used to screen laccase-producing fungal strains [67]. The following substrates are used to screen fungus for laccase production: (i) C.I. acid blue 113 (decolorization dye), (ii) Bavendam test, (iii) guaiacol, (iv) ABTS, and (v) tannic acid.

12.6 Production of Bacterial Laccases

Laccase is generated extracellularly by a variety of bacteria, while some are unable to do so [39, 68, 69]. Because of low cost and high accessibility agricultural wastes such as rice bran, sawdust, and banana peel are frequently utilized as a substrate for laccase synthesis. Monomeric sugars such as maltose, mannose, fructose, glucose, and lactose are known to make laccase by themselves, but when these carbon sources become scarce, lignin and phenolic chemicals found in agricultural waste help to boost laccase synthesis [70].

Nutritional factors such as carbon to nitrogen ratio, organic salts, and dissolved oxygen along with physical factors such as pH, shaking conditions, optimal growth time, and light intensity have a big impact on laccase synthesis [71–74]. For optimal laccase yield, different bacteria require different times. *Pseudomonas extremorientalis* BU118 has a 24-hour incubation period [61], while *Bacillus tequilensis* SN4 has a 96-hour incubation period [75]. *Geobacillus thermocatenulatus* MS5 is an exceptional bacterial strain, which requires 60 °C to manufacture [76]. Laccase produced from bacteria produces the highest yield at room temperature [8, 60, 76–80].

According to the literature, for maximum laccase production both solid and submerged state fermentations are suited [59, 70, 74]. Statistical techniques, such as response surface methodology (RSM) and Plackett–Burman, can assist to boost laccase production by several folds by careful examination of each factor; laccase activity can be increased to 764-folds or above in *B. tequilensis* SN4, in controlled conditions in simple media [81]. Under optimal conditions, laccase activity from *gamma-proteobacterium* JB can be increased to 9.3-folds [82, 83], whereas *P. aeruginosa* ADN04 generated 46.074 IU/ml of laccase when four variables were optimized (NaCl, NH_4Cl, $MgSO_4$, KH_2PO_4 and Na_2HPO_4) [43]. Using a response surface technique, the laccase production media for *Bacillus cereus* TSS1 were optimized and laccase production was observed to be increased by four times (9.03 U/ml) than in the unoptimized culture conditions (2.05 U/ml) [84]. According to the literature, bacterial laccase works in a wide pH (3–9) and temperature (30–85 °C) range, respectively, with the majority of bacterial laccase having an optimal temperature range between 45 and 60 °C [60, 72, 74, 77, 85]. Laccase from *B. tequilensis* SN4 is beneficial in various industrial processes requiring thermo-alkali stability, such as pulp bio-bleaching in the paper industries because it has a pH of 8.0 and a maximum working temperature of 85 °C [74]. The literature contains very little information regarding the influence of different chemical solvents on the activity of spore laccase. Lu et al. [79] discovered an increase of up to 30% laccase activity in *Bacillus licheniformis* LS04 in optimized culture conditions in the presence of acetonitrile, acetone DMSO (up to 20%), methanol, and ethanol. Laccase obtained from *B. subtilis* WD23 strain retained more than 80% activity in the presence of different organic solvents (50%) such as chloroform, ethyl acetate, petroleum ether, xylene, ether, and acetone [79]. Different inorganic metals and detergents have different effects on laccase yield in different bacteria. Inorganic metals such as Zn^{2+}, Mg^{2+}, and Hg^{2+} suppress laccase enzyme activity to a high degree by modifying protein structure, demonstrating that laccase enzyme yield is independent of cationic ions [70, 74]. It was expected that Hg^{2+} reduces laccase yield, demonstrating the importance of thiol-containing amino acids in laccase activity [86]. Additionally, it has been demonstrated that inorganic minerals such as Co^{2+}, Mn^{2+}, Ca^{2+}, Cu^{2+}, and Ni^{2+} in high concentrations (5 mM) significantly improve laccase activity by changing the substrate's physical state, which directly affects the rate of reaction [70, 74, 77]. Cationic detergents and anionic detergents, like cetyltrimethylammonium bromide (CTAB) and SDS, boost enzyme activity, whereas non-charged detergents, including Tween-80 and Tween-20, have no impact [74, 87]. Laccase activity was not induced by halides such as iodide, bromide, fluoride, and chloride [74].

Using ammonium sulfate precipitation, laccase from *Streptomyces psammoticus* was isolated partially and then immobilized in alginate beads using a copper and calcium entrapment approach. Compared to beads of calcium alginate, which only maintained 42.5% of laccase activity, copper alginate beads have been found to provide greater support for laccase immobilization [88]. Zhang et al. [89] used a shaken liquid culture to produce laccase from *Panus rudis* without using induction. The purified laccase enzyme contained 8% carbohydrate, an isoelectric point of 3.5 and with a molecular weight of 58 kDa. Applying a combination of gel filtration and anion exchange chromatography, McMahon et al. [86] isolated laccase from *Pseudomonas putida* F6 cell extracts isolated from soil and discovered higher laccase activity of 747 and 518 U/mg. Purified laccase has a relative molecular mass of around 59 kDa [87]. Suzuki et al. [90] discovered a laccase-producing strain of *Streptomyces lavendulae* REN-7 (STSL). He obtained a single protein band with a molecular weight of around 73 kDa on a 10% Sodium Dodecyl Sulphate-Polyacrylamide Gel Electrophoresis (SDS-PAGE). Da Cunha et al. [91] used syringaldazine to measure laccase activity and noticed an increase in absorbance during the oxidation of substrates at room temperature. Jhadav et al. [92] in his studies purified laccase produced using guaiacol and glucose-containing medium had lower activity than its crude counterpart, and the efficiency of the purified extract was assessed using a 10% SDS-PAGE. Diamantidis et al. [69] used dialysis to purify *A. lipoferum* laccase proteins, which were then precipitated with ammonium sulfate from the supernatant. Laccase activity, with a molecular mass of 60–70 kDa and an acidic isoelectric point (pI) of about pH 4.0, was found in fractions that were 30–60% saturated [92, 93]. Table 12.1 summarizes all of the information on enzyme sources, production conditions, and bacterial laccase properties.

Table 12.1 Sources, production conditions, and properties of bacterial laccase produced by various microorganisms.

Name of organism	Substrate used in enzyme assay	Temp. optima (°C) of activity	Carbon source/ fermentation conditions	Temp. stability	pH optima of activity	pH stability
Bacillus cereus	Guaiacol	37	MM/37 °C/SF/12–16 h	NR	7.0	NR
Bacillus sp.	ABTO	37	SWN medium/35 °C/SF/ 150 rpm/14 d/pH 7.5	>100%/70 °C/90 min	5.0	NR
Aquisalibacillus elongatus	DMP	40	LB/37 °C/SF/150 rpm/72 h	>80%/25–55 °C/6 h	8.0	>40%/pH 5.0–10.0/6 h
Bacillus licheniformis	ABTS	60	LB/3 °C/SF/200 rpm/48 h	44.56%/60 °C/10 h	4.4	123%/pH 7.0–9.0/10 d/30 °C
Bacillus subtilis	SGZ	60	M9 Medium/37 °C/24–48 h	50%/60 °C/68 h	6.8	50%/pH 5.0–7.0/240 h
γ-Proteobacterium JB	SGZ/ABTS Guaiacol Catechol Hydroquinone L-methyl DOPA Catechin	55	M162 Medium/37 °C/150 rpm/24 h	>60%/50 °C/30 min	6.5	100%/pH 4–10/60 d/4 °C
Azospirillum lipoferum	SGZ	70	Rice rhizosphere/intracellular	100%/70 °C/10 min	6.0	NR
Bacillus HR03	SGZ, DMP	55	NB/37 °C/170 rpm/18 h	NR	5.5	NR
Alteromonas	Tyrosine DOPA DMP SGZ	37	MB/25 °C	NR	6.5	NR
Bacillus subtilis	ABTS	25	NB/37 °C/SF/200 rpm	NR	NR	NR
Streptomyces cyaneus	ABTS	60	GYM/30 °C/SF/140 rpm/96 h/pH 7.2	NR	4.5	50%/pH 9.0/82 d/25 °C
Streptomycetes sp.	ABTS	35	SM/30 °C/24–72 h	NR	6.0	NR
Pseudomonas aeruginosa	ABTS	37	MM/30 °C/60 h/pH 6.0	NR	4.5	NR
Bacillus safenis	NR	37	M162 medium/37 °C/200 rpm/48 h	NR	6.2	NR
Bacillus tequilensis	DMP	85	M162/30 °C/150 rpm/96 h	100%/65 °C/24 h	8.0	75%/pH 9.0/24 h
Bacillus subtilis	Guaiacol	30	NB/37 °C/SF/180 rpm/60 h	100%/30 °C/60 h	5.0	100%/pH 5.0
Bacillus cereus	Guaiacol	37	MM/37 °C/SF/12–16 h	NR	7.0	NR
Geobacillus thermocatenulatus	ABTS	60	NB/60 °C/24–48 h	NR	4.5	NR

12.7 Production of Fungal Laccases

According to the literature, using various production methods and under various atmospheric circumstances, laccase can be produced. The maximum enzyme activity obtained with 2% starch in media is 288 U/ml and when glucose ($C_6H_{12}O_6$) is employed as a carbon source, the enzyme has a maximum activity of 124 U/ml [51]. Laccase enzymes are produced by fungal strains in both submerged and solid-state fermentation using natural as well as synthetic medium to increase yield [94]. Carbon, vitamins, nitrogen, and minerals are all used to make the enzyme production media [95]. Laccase is produced using a variety of carbon and nitrogen sources; ammonium tartrate and glucose are the optimum carbon and nitrogen sources, yielding higher laccase activity [48]. The laccase enzyme's molecular weight ranges between 76 and 79 kDa [48], and from soil samples white-rot fungal strain have been isolated and used for improved laccase production, in varied mineral salt media [3]. Using rice bran as a substrate for solid-state fermentation, a higher enzyme activity was observed. Laccase synthesis was tested on the white-rot fungal strain in a variety of media, including cyanobacterial biomass (algal bloom), groundnut shell (GNS), and synthetic colors [96]. Laccase produced by *Pycnoporus* sp. SYBC-L3 was found to have a maximum activity of 72,000 U/l after six days of incubation in a 65 l air-lift reactor. At both high and low temperatures, this crude laccase showed remarkable thermal stability [97–99]. Maximum activity of 404.23 U/g was observed by laccase produced by *Basidiomycete coriolus* sp. through solid-state fermentation using wheat bran as a substrate after 10 days of incubation. A submerged fermentation approach with statistically optimized medium components was used to extract laccase from *P. ostreatus*, resulting in 2.5 times higher laccase production and enzyme activity than traditional production methods. RSM produced better enzyme activity than the usual optimization method [100, 101].

The use of inducers can boost laccase production. Laccase enzyme synthesis has been stimulated by a variety of inducers in different microorganisms. Among the several inducers, 2,5-xylidine and copper sulfate produced the highest enzyme activities of 692 and 410 U/ml, respectively [51]. Laccase was generated by a number of fungal strains using copper sulfate as an inducer, including *Ganoderma applanatum* (62.5 kDa), *Coriolus versicolor F. antarcticus* (60 kDa), *Pycnoporus sanguineus* (54 kDa), and *Eriophora* sp. (60 kDa) [102]. On the 10th day of culture, maximum enzyme activity was observed using a copper sulfate concentration of 0.5 mM in the presence of *Ganoderma applanatum*. *Pycnoporus sanguineus* exhibited a considerable delayed growth and no growth at all while substituting media with 0.5 and 1 mM copper sulfate, respectively [103]. Isozymes were also induced by copper sulfate in all fungal strains [104]. The molecular weights of the isozymes range from 75 to 120.5 kDa.

12.8 Applications of Laccases

Laccase is significant because it is capable of oxidizing both harmful and harmless substrates. It has found its wide application in pharmaceutical and chemical industries, textile, food, and wood processing industries as well as many others. Laccase is highly specific, an effective catalyst, and environmentally friendly. At an industrial scale, laccases can be used in the following ways.

12.8.1 Bioremediation and Biodegradation

Contamination of water, air and soil occurs as a result of fast industrialization and widespread usage of pesticides for improved agricultural yield, is a severe environmental problem today. Polychlorinated biphenyls (PCB), pentachlorophenol (PCP), PAHs, xylene (BTEX), trinitrotoluene (TNT), benzene, toluene, ethyl benzene and Dichloro Diphenyl Trichloroethane (DDT) are the substances which persist for longer durations in the ecosphere and are also well known for their carcinogenic and mutagenic effects. Fungi refurbish a wide range of harmful substances which is why they piqued the investigator's interests [105]. *T. versicolor* is employed for atrazine bioremediation in soils having low organic and moisture content in semiarid and mediterranean-like environments [106]. Keum and Li [107] degraded PCBs and phenol by using laccase from *P. ostreatus* and *T. versicolor* and discovered that 3-hydroxy biphenyl is more resistant to laccase degradation than 2- or 4-hydroxy counterparts and that the rate of breakdown decreases as chlorination increases. Studies also suggest that after five days of incubation with glucose and fructose as cosubstrates, 56% of protocatechuic acid and 71% of *p*-hydroxy benzoic acid were degraded [108]. Laccase from *Thapsia villosa* helps to clean up the soil by degrading 2,4-DCP (2,4-dichlorophenol). In an experiment conducted by Ahn et al. [109], two types of soil were utilized. In soil 1, both immobilized and free laccase completely removed 2,4-DCP; in soil 2, both immobilized and free laccase completely removed 2,4-DCP (without regard to moisture content). In soil sample 2, approximately 95% more 2,4-DCP was removed using immobilized laccase than free enzyme (55%, 75%, and 90%, respectively, at 30%, 55%, and 100% maximal water holding capacity) [109]. In a low-nitrogen environment, *Cerrena unicolor* produces laccase, which can lower the amount of lignin in sugarcane bagasse by up to 36% in 24 hours at 30 °C [110].

12.8.2 Dye Decolorization

A lot of water and chemicals are used in wet processing in the textile industry. These substances are made up of both inorganic and organic components. In spite of exposure to light, water, and other substances, colors do not fade because of their chemical structure. Due to the fact that laccase degrades dye, laccase-based synthetic dye techniques have been developed and are currently utilized in the industry [111, 112]. *T. versicolor* pellets were used by Blanquez et al. [113] to detoxify and reduce the chemical oxygen demand of a black liquors discharge (COD), as well as color and aromatic chemicals. According to the researchers, COD was reduced by 60%, while color and aromatic compounds were reduced by 70–80%. They discovered that *T. versicolor* may produce laccase. *T. versicolor* completely decolorizes Reactive Black 5, Amaranth, Reactive Blue 15, Tropaeolin O, and Congo Red with no dye sorption, but only partially decolorizes Remazol Brilliant Blue R,

Brilliant Red 3G-P, and Brilliant Yellow 3B-A with dye sorption [114]. Laccase-based hair colors are less irritating and easier to use than traditional hair dyes because H_2O_2 is replaced in the dye composition by laccases [115]. Laccase is also employed in the process of dechlorination. Xylidine is a laccase inducer that reduces dissolved oxygen concentration by increasing dechlorination activity [116]. According to Romero et al. [117], *Stenotrophomonas maltophilia* decolorizes industrial effluent as well as a variety of synthetic dyes, including methylene blue, pink, toluidine blue, Congo red, and methyl orange.

12.8.3 Pulp and Paper Industry

At the industrial level, chlorine and oxygen-based chemical oxidants are employed to separate or degrade lignin, which is an essential requirement for the manufacturing of paper. However, other challenges such as toxicity, cost, and recycling have yet to be resolved. Because laccase mediator system (LMS) results in a partial replacement of ClO_2 in pulp mills, it might be easily integrated into the existing bleaching process [118].

12.8.4 Food Processing Industry

In food processing industries, laccase is used for baking, wine stabilization, juice processing as well as in waste water bioremediation to eliminate undesirable phenolic compounds [119]. A protein's functional and sensory properties are both improved by laccase [19]. In beer industries, laccase is employed to provide stability and increase the shelf life of products. Naturally occurring proanthocyanidins polyphenol stimulates the creation of haze in beer, which results in chill haze. Warming up the beer to room temperature or higher can redissolve this complex. After a certain incubation time, these phenolic rings are replaced by the sulfhydryl group, resulting in a persistent haze that cannot be redissolved. Since laccase can absorb excess oxygen present in beer and hence prolong the shelf life of beer, it has also been used to prevent polyphenol oxidation [120, 121]. Fruit juice is frequently stabilized using laccase. The phenolic compounds and their oxidative byproducts, which are naturally present in fruit juices, give it, its flavor and color. When phenolic or polyphenolic acids oxidize or polymerize, their color and scent change. These modifications, known as enzymatic darkening [122], are brought on by an increase in polyphenol. Using membrane filtering and laccase treatment, phenol and the substrate-enzyme combination are removed, resulting in color stability despite turbidity. In comparison to traditional procedures, laccase treatment is more successful. To increase the freshness of bread, texture, volume, and flavor a number of enzymes are used. Laccase strengthens the gluten structures in dough and baked goods, giving them more volume, a better crumb structure, and improved softness. As a result, the strength and stability increase, laccase addition, stickiness decreases, and machine ability improves, as indicated by the use of low-quality flour [121]. High concentration of polyphenolic and phenolic compounds during the pressing and crushing steps is crucial for the development of wine. Astringency and color are influenced by the high polyphenolic content in the stems, seeds, and skins and depend on the grape variety and also in vinification conditions [123]. Polyphenol oxidation occurs in musts and wines as a result of a complex mechanism, resulting in maderization [120], a change in color and flavor. To stop maderization, polyphenol removal, catalytic factors, polyvinylpolypyrrolidone, clarification, and considerable amounts of sulfur dioxide are used. According to Minussi et al. [123], laccase treatment is practicable, increases storability, and lowers processing costs, while polyphenol removal is selective and has poor organoleptic properties.

12.8.5 Biotechnological Applications of Laccase

Fungus laccases are of particular relevance in terms of potential industrial applications due to their capacity to oxidize a variety of substrates that are relevant to industry. In industrial processes, oxidation reactions are widely employed, e.g. in the pharmaceutical, textile, food, chemical sectors, and wood processing. Enzymatic oxidation could be a viable alternative to chemical oxidation because enzymes are highly specialized and effective catalysts that are also environmentally friendly. Laccases are now being extensively researched for a variety of purposes, and they are already widely employed in the textile industry. Laccases can bleach indigo dye to give denim a desired worn appearance by working with low molecular weight redox-mediator chemicals [124]. Laccase's bleaching potential has been investigated, leading to the fascinating suggestion that laccase could be utilized as a hair color in the presence of hydroxyl stilbenes [125]. Laccases have the potential to oxidase dangerous organic pollutants, including PAHs [126] and chlorophenols [127]; therefore, they could be used in contaminated soil bioremediation. Because isolated enzymes are not cost-effective for large-scale soil remediation, the most effective technique for this application would most likely be to inoculate the soil with laccase-producing fungi. Laccase's current practical applications have prompted a search for an enzyme source derived from white-rot fungus, as well as the use of mediators that stimulate or facilitate enzyme function.

12.8.6 Effluent Treatment

Fungus laccases offer a variety of advantages that make them especially desirable for biotechnological applications of industrial wastewater treatment. They can bleach Kraft pulp and detoxify agricultural wastes like coffee pulp or olive mill waste due to their wide substrate specificity [128]. A fungal isolate called *Flavodon flavus* was reported to have laccase that can decolorize bleach plant effluent from Kraft paper mills [129]. A white-rot basidiomycete called *Trametes villosa's* laccase was identified to break down the endocrine disruptor bisphenol A [130]. Because of their ability to replicate the activity of endogenous hormones in vertebrates, nonylphenols have gotten a lot of attention [131]. They are made up of nonylphenol polyethoxylates (NPEOs), which have been widely utilized as nonionic surfactants in industrial processes but haven't fully degraded. Nonylphenols and NPEOs are both released into the environment as a result of inadequate wastewater treatment facility clearance [131]. Because nonylphenols are more resistant to biodegradation than their parent chemical, they are found in rivers and wastewater treatment plant effluents all over the world [132]. They tend to absorb surface water particles and sediments and accumulate in aquatic organisms as a result of their hydrophobicity. Nonylphenols consequently constitute a serious risk to the environment as well as to human health. It has been demonstrated that the xenoestrogen nonylphenol can be broken down by laccases from the aquatic hyphomycete *Clavariopsis aquatica* [133]. New biotechnological opportunities are made possible by the laccase enzyme, including wastewater treatment and the potential significance of such degrading activities in natural attenuation processes in freshwater environments.

12.8.7 Biofuel Cell – An Eco-friendly Tool to Generate Low-voltage Electricity

A biofuel cell is a type of cell that uses microorganisms to turn chemical energy into electrical energy [134]. It is regarded as a clean method of generating electricity that does not emit greenhouse gases [135]. They have the ability to provide electricity to gadgets that just demand a small amount of energy. The activity can be carried out at room temperature with a neutral pH [136], and the enzyme coat is affordable, practical, and easy to replenish [137]. Because of laccase's capacity to oxidize phenols and convert oxygen to water by four electron transfer at a high redox potential [138], which is a key function of laccase in the cathode compartment of biofuel cells [139], laccase has been used in the creation of biofuel cells. The complex redox centers, laccase's orientation toward the electrodes, and the electrical insulation of the bio-catalytic site produced by the surrounding protein shells, however, prevent direct electron transfer [135]. By using redox mediators like ABTS and osmium-based polymers, the issue of electron shuttling that leads to indirect oxidation is alleviated [138]. The performance of glucose biofuel cells is determined by the materials used for the electrodes and how they are formed on the electrode surface [135].

12.8.8 Biosensor – A New Approach Having Multiple Usages

With the aid of single- or multienzyme systems, biosensors can be built [136]. It is described as an "analytical device that combines biological material, such as enzymes, cells, microorganisms, tissues, etc., with an appropriate transducer, such as an optic, electrochemical, calorimetric, piezoelectric, etc., capable of providing selective/quantitative analytical information" [140]. Guilbault and Lubrano [141] began work on biosensors with amperometric biosensors, which were mostly employed in clinical applications. It has been used in clinical trials to figure out how much dopamine is in your system [142]. Currently, however, research is mainly focused on determining phenols and their regulation [136].

A signal is produced by the biological material inside the biosensor, and this signal is then converted into a response, which could be current, temperature, or something else. Biosensors should have reversibility, speed, sensitivity, selectivity, and a long lifetime with low power consumption and sample volume that are application-dependent [140]. Mousty et al. [143] proposed the use of biosensor devices to detect laccase inhibitors and modulators without the need for reagents. As a result, various laccase-based phenol biosensors have been developed, which exhibit great selectivity, convenience, dependability, and sensitivity [144]. The development of biosensors that use laccase to identify phenols, pesticides, and laccase inhibitors has been the focus of several researchers [145, 146]. Using a two-enzyme system has also had a synergistic impact in the detection of the target product or pollutant.

12.8.9 Clinical Application of Laccase

For example, nonsteroidal anti-inflammatories drugs (NSAIDs) are frequently found in aquatic environments, which harm the liver and kidney of animals consuming water from drug-contaminated sites. Laccases were originally used in biosensors for clinical applications; however, other applications of laccase in the clinical sector have been exploited. Vulture populations in India and Pakistan have plummeted as a result of this. However, NSAIDs that have accumulated in the environment as pollutants, such as naproxen and diclofenac, can be removed using laccase [147]. Urine and primary estrogens, which are produced by male adipose tissues and postmenopausal women and pollute the aquatic environment, are other clinically generated pollutants. Estrogens, the main component of which is estriol, which is formed in the placenta during pregnancy, are another clinically generated pollutant. Laccase can be used to detoxify water bodies that have been contaminated by estrogens or their components [148]. Laccase can provide operational activity at room temperature and cheap treatment, which is advantageous because water treatment plant removal costs are high and require a lot of energy. The other factor is *Agrocybe cylindracea* fungal laccase, which inhibits HIV-1 reverse transcriptase and has antiproliferative properties in cancer cells [149]. Antiproliferative properties of the *Inonotus abaumii* strain against cancer cells have also been discovered [3].

12.8.10 Desulfurization and Bio-solubilization

Laccase can be used to desulfurize hazardous sulfur-containing chemicals that are emitted during the burning of fossil fuels, either post-combustion or precombustion. Bio-solubilization can also assist with the production of liquid fuels from coal and low-grade ores [3].

12.8.11 Cotton and Jute Fiber Quality

Laccase is also used in the cotton and jute industries. After enzymatic treatment with laccase, laccase TEMPO oxidation was employed to graft octadecylamine onto cotton fibers in order to increase the hydrophobic character of the fiber [150]. Jute improves composite binding capability but has a drawback due to its hydrophilic nature, which can be remedied by treating jute with laccase. The treatment enhances the properties of jute fibers by increasing composite synthesis and increasing hydrophobicity. Grafting with dodecyl gallate (DG) and laccase was used in the jute industry to increase the hydrophobicity of the fiber and improve composite reinforcing [151].

12.9 Conclusion and Future Scope

Laccases are multicopper enzymes having potentials to perform oxidation-reduction reactions. These are found in a wide range of higher plants, some insects, bacteria and even in fungi. The ability of laccase to degrade lignin, organic substrates, various dyes, and many other complex compounds has led to laccase as a prominent agent for waste water treatment of effluent discharges by industries like paints, paper and pulp, textiles, chemicals, etc. These help in wastewater treatment by decolorizing and detoxifying these industrial effluents. Laccase has also been used in pharmaceutical industries for the synthesis of antimicrobials, anesthetics, anti-inflammatory, antibiotics, personal-care agents, etc. In food industries, laccase are used for wine stabilization, baking, juice processing, and many applications. Laccases can be employed as biosensors in the xenobiotic degradation, paper and pulp industry, textile industry, and bioremediation. Recently, numerous approaches for immobilizing biomolecules, including as micropatterning, self-assembled monolayers, and layer-by-layer procedures, have been developed to immobilize laccase while preserving its enzymatic function. As a result, laccase is attracting the attention of scientists all around the world.

Laccases offer a wide range of potential applications in a variety of sectors and fields, as demonstrated in this chapter. One of the disadvantages of employing laccase on a large scale is the inability to produce large amounts of this highly active enzyme at a reasonable cost. Studies and technology need to be developed for the production of laccase at lower costs and thus meeting the demands of its requirements. Also, other biotechnological applications of laccase are needed to be explored.

References

1 Filazzola, M.T., Sannino, F., Rao, M.A. et al. (1999). Bioremediation and biodegradation: effect of various pollutants and soil-like constituents on laccase from *Cerrena unicolor*. *J. Environ. Qual.* 28: 1929–1938. https://doi.org/10.2134/jeq1999.00472425002800060032x.

2 Jolivalt, C., Raynal, A., Caminadem, E. et al. (1999). Transformation of *N′*,*N′*-dimethyl-*N*-(hydroxyphenyl) ureas by laccase from the White-rot fungus *Trametes versicolor*. *Appl. Microbiol. Biotechnol.* 51: 676–681. https://doi.org/10.1007/s002530051451.

3 Arora, D.S. and Sharma, R. (2010). Ligninolytic fungal laccase and their biotechnological applications. *Appl. Biochem. Biotechnol.* 160: 1760–1788. https://doi.org/10.1007/s12010-009-8676-y.

4 Mot, A.C. and Silaghi-Dumitrescu, R. (2012). Laccases: complex architectures for one-electron oxidations. *Biochemistry* 77: 1395–1407. https://doi.org/10.1134/S0006297912120085.

5 Desai, S.S. and Nityanand, C. (2011). Microbial laccases and their applications: a review. *Asian J. Biotechnol.* 3: 98–124. https://doi.org/10.3923/ajbkr.2011.98.124.

6 Morozova, O.V., Shumakovich, G.P., Gorbacheva, M.A. et al. (2007). "Blue" laccases. *Biochemistry* 72: 1136–1150. https://doi.org/10.1134/S0006297907100112.

7 Zhao, Q., Nakashima, J., Chen, F. et al. (2013). Laccase is necessary and nonredundant with peroxidase for lignin polymerization during vascular development in *Arabidopsis. Plant Cell* 125: 3976–3987. https://doi.org/10.1105/tpc.113.117770.

8 Singh, G., Bhalla, A., Kaur, P. et al. (2011). Laccase from prokaryotes: a new source for an old enzyme. *Environ. Sci. Biotechnol.* 10: 309–326. https://doi.org/10.1007/s11157-011-9257-4.

9 Du, W., Sun, C., Liang, J. et al. (2015). Improvement of laccase production and its characterization by mutagenesis. *J. Food Biochem.* 39: 101–108. https://doi.org/10.1111/jfbc.12111.

10 Wang, T.N. and Zhao, M. (2016). A simple strategy for extracellular production of CotA laccase in *Escherichia coli* and decolorization of simulated textile effluent by recombinant laccase. *Appl. Microbiol. Biotechnol.* 101: 685–696. https://doi.org/10.1007/s00253-016-7897-6.

11 Guan, Z.B., Shui, Y., Song, C.M. et al. (2015). Efficient secretory production of CotA-laccase and its application in the decolorization and detoxification of industrial textile wastewater. *Environ. Sci. Pollut. Res. Int.* 22: 9515–9523. https://doi.org/10.1007/s11356-015-4426-6.

12 Fernandes, T., Silveira, W., Passos, F. et al. (2014). Laccases from actinobacteria - what we have and what to expect. *Adv. Microbiol.* 4: 285–296. https://doi.org/10.4236/aim.2014.46035.

13 Prins, A.L., Kleinsmidt, N., Khan, B. et al. (2015). The effect of mutations near the T1 copper site on the biochemical characteristics of the small laccase from *Streptomyces coelicolor* A3. *Enzyme Microb. Technol.* 68: 23–32. https://doi.org/10.1016/j.enzmictec.2014.10.003.

14 Mathews, S.L., Smithson, C.E., and Grunden, A.M. (2016). Purification and characterization of a recombinant laccase-like multi-copper oxidase from *Paenibacillus glucanolyticus* SLM1. *J. Appl. Microbiol.* 121: 1335–1345. https://doi.org/10.1111/jam.13241.

15 Arregui, L., Ayala, M., Gómez-Gil, X. et al. (2019). Laccases: structure, function, and potential application in water bioremediation. *Microb. Cell Fact.* 18: 200. https://doi.org/10.1186/s12934-019-1248-0.

16 Thurston, C.F. (1994). The structure and function of fungal laccases. *Microbiology* 140: 19–26. https://doi.org/10.1099/13500872-140-1-19.

17 Mate, D.M. and Alcalde, M. (2015). Laccase engineering: from rational design to directed evolution. *Biotechnol. Adv.* 33: 25–40. https://doi.org/10.1016/j.biotechadv.2014.12.007.

18 Jaiswal, N., Pandey, V.P., and Dwivedi, U.N. (2015). Purification of a thermostable alkaline laccase from papaya (*Carica papaya*) using affinity chromatography. *Int. J. Biol. Macromol.* 72: 326–332. https://doi.org/10.1016/j.ijbiomac.2014.08.032.

19 Baldrian, P. (2006). Fungal laccase - occurrence and properties. *FEMS Microbiol. Rev.* 30: 215–242. https://doi.org/10.1111/j.1574-4976.2005.00010.x.

20 Morozova, O., Shumakovich, G., Shleev, S. et al. (2007). Laccase-mediator systems and their applications: a review. *Appl. Biochem. Microbiol.* 43: 523–535. https://doi.org/10.1134/S0003683807050055.

21 Bertrand, T., Jolivalt, C., Briozzo, P. et al. (2002). Crystal structure of a four-copper laccase complexed with an Arylamine: insights into substrate recognition and correlation with kinetics. *Biochemistry* 41: 7325–7333. https://doi.org/10.1021/bi0201318.

22 Ferraroni, M., Myasoedova, N., Schmatchenko, V. et al. (2007). Crystal structure of a blue laccase from *Lentinus tigrinus*: evidences for intermediates in the molecular oxygen reductive splitting by multicopper oxidases. *BMC Struct. Biol.* 7: 60. https://doi.org/10.1186/1472-6807-7-60.

23 Matera, I., Gullotto, A., Tilli, S. et al. (2008). Crystal structure of the blue multicopper oxidase from the white-rot fungus *Trametes trogii* complexed with *p*-toluate. *Inorg. Chim. Acta* 361: 4129–4137. https://doi.org/10.1016/j.ica.2008.03.091.

24 Plácido, J. and Capareda, S. (2015). Ligninolytic enzymes: a biotechnological alternative for bioethanol production. *Bioresour. Bioprocess.* 2: 23. https://doi.org/10.1186/s40643-015-0049-5.

25 Garavaglia, S., Cambria, M.T., Miglio, M. et al. (2004). The structure of *Rigidoporus lignosus* laccase containing a full complement of copper ions, reveals an asymmetrical arrangement for the T3 copper pair. *J. Mol. Biol.* 342: 1519–1531. https://doi.org/10.1016/j.jmb.2004.07.100.

26 Hakulinen, N., Kiiskinen, L., Kruus, K. et al. (2002). Crystal structure of a laccase from *Melanocarpus albomyces* with an intact trinuclear copper site. *Nat. Struct. Mol. Biol.* 9: 601–605. https://doi.org/10.1038/nsb823.

27 Claus, H. (2004). Laccases: structure, reactions, distribution. *Micron* 35: 93–96. https://doi.org/10.1016/j.micron.2003.10.029.

28 Kumar, S.V., Phale, P.S., Durani, S. et al. (2003). Combined sequence and structure analysis of the fungal laccase family. *Biotechnol. Bioeng.* 83: 386–394. https://doi.org/10.1002/bit.10681.

29 Enguita, F.J. (2011). Structural biology of fungal multicopper oxidases. In: *Mycofactories* (ed. A.L. Leitao), 57–72. Emirate of Sharjah, UAE: Bentham Science Publishers.

30 Rivera-Hoyos, C.M., Morales-Álvarez, E.D., Poutou-Piñales, R.A. et al. (2013). Fungal laccases. *Fungal Biol. Rev.* 27 (3–4): 67–82. https://doi.org/10.1016/j.fbr.2013.07.001.

31 Niku-Paavola, M.L., Fagerström, R., Kruus, K. et al. (2004). Thermostable laccase produced by a white-rot fungus from *Peniophora* species. *Enzyme Microb. Technol.* 35: 100–102. https://doi.org/10.1016/j.enzmictec.2004.03.008.

32 Felby, C., Thygesen, L.G., Sanadi, A. et al. (2004). Native lignin for bonding of fiber boards evaluation of bonding mechanisms in boards made from laccase-treated fibers of beech (*Fagus sylvatica*). *Ind. Crops Prod.* 20: 181–189. https://doi.org/10.1016/j.indcrop.2004.04.020.

33 Decker, H. and Terwilliger, N. (2000). Cops and robbers: putative evolution of copper oxygen-binding proteins. *J. Exp. Biol.* 203: 1777–1782. https://doi.org/10.1242/jeb.203.12.1777.

34 Solomon, E.I., Sundaram, U.M., and Machonkin, T.E. (1996). Multicopper oxidases and oxygenases. *Chem. Rev.* 96: 2563–2605. https://doi.org/10.1021/cr950046o.

35 Chandra, R. and Chowdhary, P. (2015). Properties of bacterial laccases and their application in bioremediation of industrial wastes. *Environ. Sci. Processes Impacts* 17: 326–342. https://doi.org/10.1039/c4em00627e.

36 Rubilar, O., Diez, M.C., and Gianfreda, L. (2008). Transformation of chlorinated phenolic compounds by white rot fungi. *Crit. Rev. Env. Sci. Technol.* 38: 227–268. https://doi.org/10.1080/10643380701413351.

37 Solomon, E.I., Augustine, A.J., and Yoon, J. (2008). O_2 reduction to H_2O by the multicopper oxidases. *Dalton Trans.* 30: 3921–3932. https://doi.org/10.1039/b800799c.

38 Madhavi, V. and Lele, S.S. (2009). Laccase: properties and applications. *BioResources* 4: 1694–1717. https://doi.org/10.15376/BIORES.4.4.1694-1717.

39 Leontievsky, A.A., Vares, T., Lankinen, P. et al. (1997). Blue and yellow laccases of ligninolytic fungi. *FEMS Microbiol. Lett.* 156: 9–14. https://doi.org/10.1111/j.1574-6968.1997.tb12698.x.

40 Mendoza, L. (2011). Laccases from new fungal sources and new promising applications. Ph.D. Thesis. Department of Biotechnology, Lund University, Sweden.

41 Xu, F. (1999). *Encyclopedia of Bioprocess Technology: Fermentation, Biocatalysis, Bioseparation* (ed. M.C. Flickinger and S.W. Drew), 1545–1554. New York, USA: Wiley.

42 Givaudan, A., Effosse, A., Faure, D. et al. (1993). Polyphenol oxidase in *Azospirillum lipoferum* isolated from rice rhizosphere: evidence for laccase activity in non-motile strains of *Azospirillum lipoferum*. *FEMS Microbiol. Lett.* 108: 205–210. https://doi.org/10.1111/j.1574-6968.1993.tb06100.x.

43 Alexandre, G. and Zhulin, I.B. (2000). Laccases are wide spread in bacteria. *Trends Biotechnol.* 18: 41–42. https://doi.org/10.1016/s0167-7799(99)01406-7.

44 Galai, S., Touhammi, Y., and Marzouki, M.N. (2012). Response surface methodology applied to laccase activities exhibited by *Stenotrophomonas maltophilia* AAP56 in different growth conditions. *BioResources* 7: 706–726.

45 Octavio, L.C., Irma, P.P.M.C., Ricardo, B.R.J. et al. (2006). Laccases. In: *Advances in Agricultural & Food Biotechnology* (ed. R.G. Guevara-Gonzalez and I. Torres-Pacheco), 323–340.

46 Assavanig, A., Amornkitticharorn, B., Ekpaisal, N. et al. (1992). Isolation, characterization and function of laccase from *Trichoderma*. *Appl. Microbiol. Biotechol.* 38: 198–202. https://doi.org/10.1007/BF00174468.

47 Aisemberg, G.O., Grorewold, E., Taccioli, G.E. et al. (1989). A major transcript in the response of *Neurospora crassa* to protein synthesis inhibition by cycloheximide. *Exp. Mycol.* 13: 121–128. https://doi.org/10.1016/0147-5975(89)90017-0.

48 Levin, L., Melignani, E., and Ramos, A.M. (2010). Effect of nitrogen sources and vitamins on lignolytic enzyme production by some white-rot fungi dye decolorization by selected culture filtrates. *Bioresour. Technol.* 101: 4554–4563. https://doi.org/10.1016/j.biortech.2010.01.102.

49 Sadhasivam, S., Savitha, S., Swaminathan, K. et al. (2008). Production, purification and characterization of midredox potential laccase from a newly isolated *Trichoderma harzianum* WL1. *Process Biochem.* 43: 736–742. https://doi.org/10.1016/j.procbio.2008.02.017.

50 Singh, S.K., Khajuria, R., and Kaur, L. (2017). Biodegradation of ciprofloxacin by white rot fungus *Pleurotus ostreatus*. *3 Biotech* 7: 69. https://doi.org/10.1007/s13205-017-0684-y.

51 Thakker, G.D., Evans, C.S., and Rao, K.K. (1992). Purification and characterization of laccase from *Monocillium indicum*. *Appl. Microbiol. Biotechnol.* 37: 321–323. https://doi.org/10.1007/BF00210986.

52 Revankar, M.S. and Lele, S.S. (2006). Enhanced production of laccase using a new isolate of white rot fungus WR-1. *Process Biochem.* 41: 581–588. https://doi.org/10.1016/j.procbio.2005.07.019.

53 Dittmer, N.T., Suderman, R.J., Jiang, H. et al. (2004). Characterization of cDNA encoding putative laccase-like multicopper oxidases and developmental expression in the tobacco hornworm, *Manduca sexta*, and the malaria mosquito, *Anopheles gambiae*. *Insect Biochem. Mol. Biol.* 34: 29–41. https://doi.org/10.1016/j.ibmb.2003.08.003.

54 Sharma, K.K. and Kuhad, R.C. (2008). Laccase: enzyme revisited and function refined. *Indian J. Microbiol.* 48: 309–316. https://doi.org/10.1007/s12088-009-0039-4.

55 Senthivelan, T., Kanagaraj, J., and Panda, R.C. (2016). Recent trends in fungal laccase for various industrial applications: an eco-friendly approach – a review. *Biotechnol. Bioprocess Eng.* 21: 19–38. https://doi.org/10.1007/s12257-015-0278-7.

56 Christopher, L.P., Yao, B., and Ji, Y. (2014). Lignin biodegradation with laccase-mediator systems. *Front. Energy Res.* 2: 12. https://doi.org/10.3389/fenrg.2014.00012.

57 Canãs, A.I. and Camarero, S. (2010). Laccases and their natural mediators: biotechnological tools for sustainable eco-friendly processes. *Biotechnol. Adv.* 28: 694–705. https://doi.org/10.1016/j.biotechadv.2010.05.002.

58 Niladevi, K.N., Sheejadevi, P.S., and Prema, P. (2008). Strategies for enhancing laccase yield from *Streptomyces psammoticus* and its role in mediator-based decolorization of azo dyes. *Appl. Biochem. Biotechnol.* 151: 9–19. https://doi.org/10.1007/s12010-008-8175-6.

59 Kameshwar, A.K.S. and Qin, W. (2016). Qualitative and quantitative methods for isolation and characterization of lignin-modifying enzymes secreted by microorganisms. *Bioenergy Res.* 10: 248–266. https://doi.org/10.1007/s12155-016-9784-5.

60 Neifar, M., Chouchane, H., Mahjoubi, M. et al. (2016). *Pseudomonas extremorientalis* BU118: a new salt-tolerant laccase-secreting bacterium with biotechnological potential in textile azo dye decolourization. *3 Biotech* 6: 107. https://doi.org/10.1007/s13205-016-0425-7.

61 Devasia, S. and Nair, J.A. (2016). Screening of potent laccase producing organisms based on the oxidation pattern of different phenolic substrates. *Int. J. Curr. Microbiol. Appl. Sci.* 5: 127–137. https://doi.org/10.20546/ijcmas.2016.505.014.

62 Pointing, S.B. (1999). Qualitative methods for the determination of lignocellulolytic enzyme production by tropical fungi. *Fungal Diversity* 2: 17–33.

63 Archibald, F.S. (1992). A new assay for lignin-type peroxidases employing the dye azure B. *Appl. Environ. Microbiol.* 58: 3110–3116. https://doi.org/10.1128/aem.58.9.3110-3116.1992.

64 Dekker, R., Ling, K.L., and Barbosa, A.M. (2000). A simple method for monitoring chromatography column eluates for laccase activity during enzyme purification. *Biotechnol. Lett.* 22: 105–108. https://doi.org/10.1023/A:1005680027798.

65 Pardo, I., Chanaga, X., Vicente, A.I. et al. (2013). New colorimetric screening assays for the directed evolution of fungal laccases to improve the conversion of plant biomass. *BMC Biotech.* 13: 90. https://doi.org/10.1186/1472-6750-13-90.

66 Lonergan, G., Mew, E., Schliephake, K. et al. (1997). Phenolic substrates for fluorometric detection of laccase activity. *FEMS Microbiol. Lett.* 153: 485–490. https://doi.org/10.1111/j.1574-6968.1997.tb12614.x.

67 Klis, M., Rogalski, J., and Bilewicz, R. (2007). Voltammetric determination of catalytic reaction parameters of laccase based on electrooxidation of hydroquinone and ABTS. *Bioelectrochemistry* 71: 2–7. https://doi.org/10.1016/j.bioelechem.2006.09.008.

68 Gochev, V.K. and Krastanov, A.I. (2007). Isolation of laccase producing *Trichoderma* spp. *Bulg. J. Agric. Sci.* 13: 171–176.

69 Diamantidis, G., Effosse, A., Potier, P. et al. (2000). Purification and characterization of the first bacterial laccase in the rhizospheric bacterium *Azospirillum lipoferum*. *Soil Biol. Biochem.* 32: 919–927. https://doi.org/10.1016/S0038-0717(99)00221-7.

70 Chauhan, P.S., Puri, N., Sharma, P. et al. (2012). Mannanases: microbial sources, production, properties and potential biotechnological applications. *Appl. Microbiol. Biotechnol.* 93: 1817–1830. https://doi.org/10.1007/s00253-012-3887-5.

71 Muthukumarasamy, N.P., Jackson, B., Raj, J.A. et al. (2015). Production of extracellular laccase from *Bacillus subtilis* MTCC 2414 using agroresidues as a potential substrate. *Biochem. Res. Int.* 765190. https://doi.org/10.1155/2015/765190.

72 George, N., Chauhan, P.S., Puri, N. et al. (2014). Statistical optimization of process parameters for production of alkaline protease from *Vibrio metschnikovii* NG155 having application in leather industry. *Int. J. Pharma. Bio. Sci.* 5: 509–517.

73 Narayanan, M.P., Murugan, S., Eva, A.S. et al. (2015). Application of immobilized laccase from *Bacillus subtilis* MTCC 2414 on decolourization of synthetic dyes. *Res. J. Microbiol.* 10: 421–432.

74 Rezaei, S., Shahverdi, A.R., and Faramarzi, M.A. (2017). Isolation, one-step affinity purification, and characterization of a polyextremotolerant laccase from the halophilic bacterium *Aquisalibacillus elongatus* and its application in the delignification of sugar beet pulp. *Bioresour. Technol.* 230: 67–75. https://doi.org/10.1016/j.biortech.2017.01.036.

75 Sondhi, S., Sharma, P., Saini, S. et al. (2014). Purification and characterization of an extracellular, thermo-alkali-stable, metal tolerant laccase from *Bacillus tequilensis* SN4. *PLoS One* 9: e96951. https://doi.org/10.1371/journal.pone.0096951.

76 Verma, A. and Shirkot, P. (2014). Purification and characterization of thermostable laccase from thermophilic *Geobacillus thermocatenulatus* MS5 and its applications in removal of textile dyes. *Scholars Acad. J .Biosci.* 2: 479–485.

77 Sheikhi, F., Ardakani, M.R., Enayatizamir, N. et al. (2012). The determination of assay for laccase of *Bacillus subtilis* WPI with two classes of chemical compounds as substrates. *Indian J. Microbiol.* 52: 701–707. https://doi.org/10.1007/s12088-012-0298-3.

78 Mongkolthanaruk, W., Tongbopit, S., and Bhoonobtong, A. (2012). Independent behavior of bacterial laccases to inducers and metal ions during production and activity. *Afr. J. Biotechnol.* 11: 9391–9398. https://doi.org/10.5897/AJB11.3042.

79 Lu, L., Zhao, M., Wang, N.Y. et al. (2012). Characterization and dye decolorization ability of an alkaline resistant and organic solvents tolerant laccase from *Bacillus licheniformis* LS04. *Bioresour. Technol.* 115: 35–40. https://doi.org/10.1016/j.biortech.2011.07.111.

80 Wang, C., Zhao, M., Lu, L. et al. (2011). Characterization of spore laccase from *Bacillus subtilis* WD23 and its use in dye decolorization. *Afr. J Biotechnol.* 10: 2186–2192. https://doi.org/10.5897/AJB10.937.

81 Sondhi, S., Sharma, P., George, N. et al. (2015). An extracellular thermo-alkali-stable laccase from *Bacillus tequilensis* SN4, with a potential to biobleach softwood pulp. *3 Biotech* 5: 175–185. https://doi.org/10.1007/s13205-014-0207-z.

82 Singh, G., Bhalla, A., Capalash, N. et al. (2010). Characterization of immobilized laccase from *c-proteobacterium* JB: approach towards the development of biosensor for the detection of phenolic compounds. *Indian J. Sci. Technol.* 3: 48–53. https://doi.org/10.17485/ijst/2010/v3i1.8.

83 Singh, G., Ahuja, N., Batish, M. et al. (2008). Biobleaching of wheat straw-rich soda pulp with alkalophilic laccase from *gamma-proteobacterium*

JB: optimization of process parameters using response surface methodology. *Bioresour. Technol.* 99: 7472–7479. https://doi.org/10.1016/j.biortech.2008.02.023.

84 Arunkumar, T., Alexanand, D., and Narendrakumar, G. (2014). Application of response surface methodology (RSM)-CCD for the production of laccase using submerged fermentation. *Int. J. Pharm. Biol. Sci.* 5: 429–438.

85 Rajeswari, M., Vennila, K., and Bhuvaneswari, V. (2015). Optimization of laccase production media by *Bacilllus cereus* TSS1 using BoxBehnken design. *Int. J. Chem. Pharma. Sci.* 6: 95–101.

86 McMahon, A.M., Doyle, E.M., Brooks, S. et al. (2007). Biochemical characterisation of the coexisting tyrosinase and laccase in the soil bacterium *Pseudomonas putida* F6. *Enzyme Microb. Technol.* 4: 1435–1441. https://doi.org/10.1016/j.enzmictec.2006.10.020.

87 Liu, H., Cheng, Y., Du, B. et al. (2015). Overexpression of a novel thermostable and chloride tolerant laccase from *Thermus thermophilus* SG0.5JP17-16 in *Pichia pastoris* and its application in synthetic dye decolorization. *PLoS One* 10: e0119833. https://doi.org/10.1371/journal.pone.0119833.

88 Dalfard, A.B., Khajeh, K., Soudi, M.R. et al. (2006). Isolation and biochemical characterization of laccase and tyrosinase activities in a novel melanogenic soil bacterium. *Enzyme Microb. Technol.* 39: 1409–1416. https://doi.org/10.1016/j.enzmictec.2006.03.029.

89 Zhang, M., Wu, F., Wei, Z. et al. (2006). Characterization and decolorization ability of a laccase from *Panus rudis*. *Enzyme Microb. Technol.* 39: 92–97. https://doi.org/10.1016/j.enzmictec.2005.09.012.

90 Suzuki, T., Endo, K., Ito, M. et al. (2003). Thermostable laccase from *Streptomyces lavendulae* REN-7: purification, characterization, nucleotide sequence and expression. *Biosci., Biotechnol., Biochem.* 67: 2167–2175. https://doi.org/10.1271/bbb.67.2167.

91 Da Cunha, M.A.A., Barbosa, A.M., Giese, E.C. et al. (2003). The effect of carbohydrate carbon sources on the production of constitutive and inducible laccases by *Botryosphaeria* sp. *J. Basic Microbiol.* 43: 385–392. https://doi.org/10.1002/jobm.200310250.

92 Jhadav, A., Vamsi, K.K., Khairnar, Y. et al. (2009). Optimization of production and partial purification of laccase by *Phanerochaete chrysosporium* using submerged fermentation. *Int. J. Microbiol. Res.* 1: 9–12. https://doi.org/10.9735/0975-5276.1.2.9-12.

93 De Souza, C.G.M. and Peralta, R.M. (2003). Purification and characterization of the main laccase produced by the white-rot fungus *Pleurotus pulmonarius* on wheat bran solid state medium. *J. Basic Microbiol.* 43: 278–286. https://doi.org/10.1002/jobm.200390031.

94 Shleev, S.V., Morozova, O.V., Nikitina, O.V. et al. (2004). Comparison of physico-chemical characteristics of four laccases from different basidiomycetes. *Biochimie* 86: 693–703. https://doi.org/10.1016/j.biochi.2004.08.005.

95 Chefetz, B., Chen, Y., and Hadar, Y. (1998). Purification and characterization of laccase from *Chaemotomium thermophilum* and its role in humification. *Appl.*

Environ. Microbiol. 64: 3175–3179. https://doi.org/10.1128/AEM.64.9.3175-3179.1998.

96 Galhaup, C., Wagner, H., Kulbe, K.D. et al. (2001). Efficient production of laccase activity by the white-rot fungus *Trametes pubescens. Proceedings of the 8th International Conference on Biotechnology in the Pulp and Paper Industry*, Helsinki, Finland (4–8 June 2001).

97 Mishra, A., Kumar, S., and Pandey, A.K. (2011). Laccase production and simultaneous decolourization of synthetic dyes in unique expensive medium by new isolates of white-rot fungus. *Int. Biodeterior. Biodegrad.* 65: 487–493. https://doi.org/10.1016/j.ibiod.2011.01.011.

98 Wang, Z.X., Cai, Y.J., Liao, X.R. et al. (2010). Purification and characterization of two thermostable laccases with high cold adapted characteristics from *Pycnoporus* sp. SYBC-L1. *Process Biochem.* 45: 1720–1729. https://doi.org/10.1016/j.procbio.2010.07.011.

99 Liu, J., Cai, Y., Liao, X. et al. (2013). Efficiency of laccase production in a 65 L airlift reactor for potential green industrial and environmental application. *J. Cleaner Prod.* 39: 154–160. https://doi.org/10.1016/j.jclepro.2012.08.004.

100 Patel, H., Gupte, S., Gahlout, M. et al. (2014). Purification and characterization of an extracellular laccase from solid state culture of *Pleurotus ostreatus* HP-1. *3 Biotech* 4: 77–84. https://doi.org/10.1007/s13205-013-0129-1.

101 Chiranjeevi, P.V., Pandian, M.R., and Sathish, T. (2014). Enhancement of laccase production from *Pleurotus ostreatus* PVCRSP-7 by altering the nutritional conditions using response surface methodology. *BioResources* 9: 4212–4225. https://doi.org/10.15376/BIORES.9.3.4212-4225.

102 Jordaan, J., Pletschke, B.I., and Leukes, W.D. (2004). Purification and partial characterization of a thermostable laccase from an unidentified basidiomycete. *Enzyme Microb. Technol.* 34: 635–641. https://doi.org/10.1016/j.enzmictec.2004.02.003.

103 Fonseca, M.I., Shimizu, E., Zapata, P.D. et al. (2010). Copper inducing effect on laccase production of white rot fungi native from Misiones (Argentina). *Enzyme Microb. Technol.* 46: 534–539. https://doi.org/10.1016/j.enzmictec.2009.12.017.

104 Boron, F. and Yesilada, O. (2011). Enhanced production of laccase by fungi under solid substrate fermentation condition. *BioResources* 6: 4404–4416. https://doi.org/10.15376/BIORES.6.4.4404-4416.

105 Riva, S. (2006). Laccases: blue enzymes for green chemistry. *Trends Biotechnol.* 24: 219–226. https://doi.org/10.1016/j.tibtech.2006.03.006.

106 Bastos, A.C. and Magan, N. (2009). *Trametes versicolor*: potential for atrazine bioremediation in calcareous clay soil, under low water availability conditions. *Int. Biodeterior. Biodegrad.* 63: 389–394. https://doi.org/10.1016/j.ibiod.2008.09.010.

107 Keum, Y.S. and Li, Q.X. (2004). Fungal laccase-catalyzed degradation of hydroxy polychlorinated biphenyls. *Chemosphere* 56: 23–30. https://doi.org/10.1016/j.chemosphere.2004.02.028.

108 Udayasoorian, C. and Prabu, P.C. (2005). Biodegradation of phenols by lignolytic fungus *Trametes versicolour*. *J. Biol. Sci.* 5: 824–827. https://doi.org/10.3923/jbs.2005.824.827.

109 Ahn, M.Y., Dec, J., Kim, J.E. et al. (2002). Treatment of 2,4-dichlorophenol polluted soil with free and immobilized laccase. *J. Environ. Qual.* 31: 1509–1515. https://doi.org/10.2134/jeq2002.1509.

110 D'Souza-Ticlo, D., Sharma, D., and Raghukumar, C. (2009). A thermostable metal-tolerant laccase with bioremediation potential from a marine-derived fungus. *Mar. Biotechnol.* 11: 725–737. https://doi.org/10.1007/s10126-009-9187-0.

111 Domìnguez, A., Couto, S.R., and Sanroman, M.A. (2005). Dye decolorization by *Trametes hirsuta* immobilized into alginate beads. *World J. Microbiol. Biotechnol.* 21: 405–409. https://doi.org/10.1007/s11274-004-1763-x.

112 Hou, H., Zhou, J., Wang, J. et al. (2004). Enhancement of laccase production by *Pleurotus ostreatus* and its use for the decolorization of anthraquinone dye. *Process Biochem.* 39: 1415–1419. https://doi.org/10.1016/S0032-9592(03)00267-X.

113 Blanquez, P., Casas, N., Font, X. et al. (2004). Mechanism of textile metal dye biotransformation by *Trametes versicolor*. *Water Res.* 38: 2166–2172. https://doi.org/10.1016/j.watres.2004.01.019.

114 Ramsay, J.A. and Nguyen, T. (2002). Decolourization of textile dyes by *Trametes versicolour* and its effect on dye toxicity. *Biotechnol. Lett.* 24: 1757–1761. https://doi.org/10.1023/A:1020644817514.

115 Roriz, M.S., Osma, J.F., Teixeira, J.A. et al. (2009). Application of response surface methodological approach to optimise Reactive Black 5 decolouration by crude laccase from *Trametes pubescens*. *J. Hazard. Mater.* 169: 691–696. https://doi.org/10.1016/j.jhazmat.2009.03.150.

116 Unal, A. and Kolankaya, N. (2001). Dechlorination of bleached kraft pulp by laccase enzyme produced from some white rot fungi. *Turk. Electron. J. Biotechnol.* 25: 67–72.

117 Romero, S., Blanquez, P., Caminal, G. et al. (2006). Different approaches to improving the textile dye degradation capacity of *Trametes versicolor*. *Biochem. Eng. J.* 31: 42–47. https://doi.org/10.1016/j.bej.2006.05.018.

118 Kunamneni, A., Ballesteros, A.O., Plou, F.J., and Alcalde, M. (2007). Fungal laccase - a versatile enzyme for biotechnological applications. In: *Communicating Current Research and Educational Topics and Trends in Applied Microbiology*, vol. 1 (ed. A. Mendez-Vilas), 233–245. Badajoz, Spain: Formex.

119 Couto, S.R. and Toca Herrera, J.L. (2006). Industrial and biotechnological applications of laccases: a review. *Biotechnol. Adv.* 24: 500–513. https://doi.org/10.1016/j.biotechadv.2006.04.003.

120 Mathiasen, T.E. (1995). Laccase and beer storage. PCT International Application, WO 9521240 A2.

121 Minussi, R.C., Pastore, G.M., and Duran, N. (2002). Potential applications of laccase in the food industry. *Trends Food Sci. Technol.* 13: 205–216. https://doi.org/10.1016/S0924-2244(02)00155-3.

122 Ribeiro, D.S., Henrique, S.M.B., Oliveira, L.S. et al. (2010). Enzymes in juice processing: a review. *Int. J. Food Sci. Technol.* 45: 635–641. https://doi.org/10.1111/j.1365-2621.2010.02177.x.

123 Minussi, R.C., Rossi, M., Bologna, L. et al. (2007). Phenols removal in musts: strategy for wine stabilization by laccase. *J. Mol. Catal. B: Enzym.* 45: 102–107. https://doi.org/10.1016/j.molcatb.2006.12.004.

124 Onuki, T., Nogucji, M., and Mitamura, J. (2000). Oxidative hair dye composition containing laccase. Pat Int Appl WO 0037, 030. *Chem. Abstr.* 133: 78994m.

125 Manzanares, P., Fajardo, S., and Martin, C. (1995). Production of ligninolytic activities when treating paper pulp effluents by *Trametes versicolor*. *J. Biotechnol.* 43: 125–132. https://doi.org/10.1016/0168-1656(95)00125-8.

126 Reddy, C.A. and Mathew, Z. (2001). Bioremediation potential of white rot fungi. In: *Fungi in Bioremediation* (ed. G.M. Gadd), 52–78. Cambridge, UK: Cambridge University Press.

127 Marbach, I., Harel, E., and Mayer, A.M. (1985). Pectin, a second inducer for laccase production by *Botrytis cinerea*. *Phytochemistry* 24: 2559–2561. https://doi.org/10.1016/S0031-9422(00)80667-6.

128 Heemken, O.P., Reincke, H., Stachel, B. et al. (2001). The occurrence of xenoestrogens in the Elbe river and the North Sea. *Chemosphere* 45: 245–259. https://doi.org/10.1016/S0045-6535(00)00570-1.

129 Soares, G.M.B., Costa-Ferreira, M., and Pessoa de Amorim, M.T. (2001). Decolorization of an anthraquinone-type dye using a laccase formulation. *Bioresour. Technol.* 79: 171–177. https://doi.org/10.1016/S0960-8524(01)00043-8.

130 Raghukumar, C. (2000). Fungi from marine habitats: an application in bioremediation. *Mycol. Res.* 104: 1222–1226. https://doi.org/10.1017/S095375620000294X.

131 Lyons, J.I., Newell, S.Y., Buchan, A. et al. (2003). Diversity of ascomycete laccase gene sequences in a southeastern US salt marsh. *Microb. Ecol.* 45: 270–281. https://doi.org/10.1007/s00248-002-1055-7.

132 Bermek, H., Li, K., and Eriksson, K.E.L. (2002). Studies on mediators of manganese peroxidase for bleaching of wood pulps. *Bioresour. Technol.* 85: 249–252. https://doi.org/10.1016/S0960-8524(02)00132-3.

133 Calvo, M., Copa-Patino, J.L., Alonso, O. et al. (1998). Studies of the production and characterization of laccase activity in the basidiomycete *Coriolopsis gallica*, an efficient decolorizer of alkaline effluents. *Arch. Microbiol.* 171: 31–36. https://doi.org/10.1007/s002030050674.

134 Chaturvedi, V. and Verma, P. (2016). Microbial fuel cell: a green approach for the utilization of waste for the generation of bioelectricity. *Bioresour. Bioprocess.* 3: 38. https://doi.org/10.1186/s40643-016-0116-6.

135 Zebda, A., Gondran, C., Cinquin, P. et al. (2012). Glucose biofuel cell construction based on enzyme, graphite particle and redox mediator compression. *Sens. Actuators, B* 173: 760–776. https://doi.org/10.1016/j.snb.2012.07.089.

136 Kulys, J. and Vidziunaite, R. (2003). Amperometric biosensors based on recombinant laccase for phenols determination. *Biosens. Bioelectron.* 18: 319–325. https://doi.org/10.1016/S0956-5663(02)00172-0.

137 Nazaruk, E., Smoliński, S., Swatko-Ossor, M. et al. (2008). Enzymatic biofuel cell based on electrodes modified with lipid liquid-crystalline cubic phases. *J. Power Sources* 183: 533–538. https://doi.org/10.1016/j.jpowsour.2008.05.061.

138 Zheng, W., Zhou, H.M., Zheng, Y.F. et al. (2008). A comparative study on electrochemistry of laccase at two kinds of carbon nanotubes and its application for biofuel cell. *Chem. Phys. Lett.* 457: 381–385. https://doi.org/10.1016/j.cplett.2008.04.047.

139 Quan, D. and Kim, Y. (2004). Characterization of an amperometric laccase electrode covalently immobilized on platinum surface. *J. Electroanal. Chem.* 561: 181–189. https://doi.org/10.1016/j.jelechem.2003.08.003.

140 Leite, O., Lupetti, K., Fatibelloflho, O. et al. (2003). Synergic effect studies of the bi-enzymatic system laccase–peroxidase in a voltammetric biosensor for catecholamines. *Talanta* 59: 889–896. https://doi.org/10.1016/S0039-9140(02)00650-1.

141 Guilbault, G.G. and Lubrano, G.J. (1973). An enzyme electrode for the amperometric determination of glucose. *Anal. Chim. Acta* 64 (3): 439–455. https://doi.org/10.1016/S0003-2670(01)82476-4.

142 Xiang, L., Lin, Y., Yu, P. et al. (2007). Laccase-catalyzed oxidation and intramolecular cyclization of dopamine: a new method for selective determination of dopamine with laccase/carbon nanotube-based electrochemical biosensors. *Electrochim. Acta* 52: 4144–4152. https://doi.org/10.1016/j.electacta.2006.11.040.

143 Mousty, C., Vieille, L., and Cosnier, S. (2007). Laccase immobilization in redox active layered double hydroxides: a reagentless amperometric biosensor. *Biosens. Bioelectron.* 22: 1733–1738. https://doi.org/10.1016/j.bios.2006.08.020.

144 Mei, L.P., Feng, J.J., Wu, L. et al. (2015). Novel phenol biosensor based on laccase immobilized on reduced graphene oxide supported palladium-copper alloyed nanocages. *Biosens. Bioelectron.* 74: 347–352. https://doi.org/10.1016/j.bios.2015.06.060.

145 Nazari, M., Kashanian, S., and Rafpour, R. (2015). Laccase immobilization on the electrode surface to design a biosensor for the detection of phenolic compound such as catechol. *Spectrochim. Acta, Part A* 145: 130–138. https://doi.org/10.1016/j.saa.2015.01.126.

146 Lloret, L., Eibes, G., Moreira, M. et al. (2013). On the use of a high-redox potential laccase as an alternative for the transformation of non-steroidal anti-infammatory drugs (NSAIDs). *J. Mol. Catal. B: Enzym.* 97: 233–242. https://doi.org/10.1016/j.molcatb.2013.08.021.

147 Ueda, M., Shintani, K., Nakanishi-Anjyuin, A. et al. (2012). A protein from *Pleurotus eryngii* var. *tuoliensis* C.J. Mou with strong removal activity against the natural steroid hormone, estriol: purification, characterization, and identification as a laccase. *Enzyme Microb. Technol.* 51: 402–407. https://doi.org/10.1016/j.enzmictec.2012.08.010.

148 Hu, D., Zhang, R., Zhang, G. et al. (2011). A laccase with antiproliferative activity against tumor cells from an edible mushroom, white common *Agrocybe* *cylindracea*. *Phytomedicine* 18: 374–379. https://doi.org/10.1016/j.phymed.2010.07.004.

149 Sun, J., Chen, Q.J., Zhu, M.J. et al. (2014). An extracellular laccase with antiproliferative activity from the sanghuang mushroom *Inonotus baumii*. *J. Mol. Catal. B: Enzym.* 99: 20–25. https://doi.org/10.1016/j.molcatb.2013.10.004.

150 Yu, Y., Wang, Q., Yuan, J. et al. (2016). Hydrophobic modification of cotton fabric with octadecylamine via laccase/TEMPO mediated grafting. *Carbohydr. Polym.* 137: 549–555. https://doi.org/10.1016/j.carbpol.2015.11.026.

151 Dong, A., Yu, Y., Yuan, J. et al. (2014). Hydrophobic modification of jute fiber used for composite reinforcement via laccase-mediated grafting. *Appl. Surf. Sci.* 301: 418–427. https://doi.org/10.1016/j.apsusc.2014.02.092.

13

Magic of Microbial Enzymes: Earthworm's Gut as a Bioreactor

Jayanta K. Biswas[1,2] *and Anurupa Banerjee*[1]

[1] *University of Kalyani, Department of Ecological Studies, Kalyani, Nadia, West Bengal 741235, India*
[2] *University of Kalyani, International Centre for Ecological Engineering, Kalyani, West Bengal 741235, India*

13.1 Introduction

Every living creature on this planet possesses unique qualities that contribute to maintaining holism, harmony, and homeostasis at different scales of ecosystems. Ecologists have explored and identified organisms having major influences and impacts on the abiotic factors governing the environment. The non-trophic relationships between biota and their environment are greatly influenced by the diverse metabolic activities that these organisms possess, thereby impacting the biogeochemical processes occurring in the ecosystem [1].

The wide range of different kinds of activities that organisms carry out are contributed by special types of proteins. In all living cells, tremendous biochemical activity goes on continuously. The majority of all the biochemical reactions are not spontaneous. All the metabolic activities occurring in living organisms are feasible due to the phenomenon of catalysis [2]. All sorts of biological processes, from structural support to triggering, signaling, and regulating several pathways, are accomplished by proteins [3, 4]. Among the various types of proteins, enzymes are the ones able to accelerate chemical reactions, thereby making the perfect biological catalysts, capable of catalyzing all biochemical reactions in a time scale appropriate for the preservation of life [4, 5]. Life would have been impossible without enzymes; the evolutionary synthesis of enzymes solved nature's challenges of catalysis [6], and over billions of years, more powerful and dynamic enzymes have evolved [7]. Exploiting the catalytic power of these amazing natural pieces of bio-machinery for nonnatural chemical transformations provides enormous practical opportunities [8]. The entire biotic world, ranging from the microscopic organisms to the macroscopic ones, possess enzymes. The soil biota largely comprises diverse microbial communities such as bacteria, fungi, protozoa, actinomycetes, and algae, and macrofauna such as earthworms, ants, and termites [9]. Among the macrofaunal groups earthworms play a key role linking the bacteria–organic–inorganic triangle of the nutrient dynamics. The biogeochemical cycling of nutrients and/or essential

Microbial Enzymes: Production, Purification, and Industrial Applications, First Edition.
Edited by Dinesh Yadav, Pankaj Chowdhary, Gautam Anand, and Rajarshi Kumar Gaur.

elements is governed by the biotic enzyme systems, of which the most crucial role is played by the microbial enzymes [10].

A large group of microorganisms inhabit the gut of the earthworms, and their survival wholly depends upon the capacity of the inhabitants to resist the existing environment of the earthworm gut [11]. Apart from the earthworms' digestive enzymes, the enzymatic activities associated with the earthworm gut originate mostly from the microbes that have been ingested and activated [12]. The biological transformations of native and foreign components in soil, and also the different biogeochemical and nutrient cycles operating in nature are a direct consequence of the varying enzymatic activities. Thus, a keen study of the enzymatic activities could act as an index and reveal the state of the condition of the ecosystem [13]. The present chapter will provide information about the complex interrelationship between earthworms and soil microorganisms, and provide an insight into the closely associated enzymes in the earthworm–microbe consortium.

13.2 Classification of Enzymes

Enzymes are proteins that acts as biocatalysts, enabling the acceleration of metabolic reactions in a highly specific manner. The average molecular weight of enzymes ranges from 10 to 2000 kDa [14]. All enzymes are unique. While assuming tertiary and or quaternary structures, enzymes acquire different identifiable sites called the active sites, which act as the main centre for catalytic activity. The active site is highly protected by a hydrophobic boundary and is specifically designed for particular substrates only [15].

To provide a rationale nomenclature to the enzymes identified (over 3000 enzymes have been identified till now), the International Union of Biochemistry and Molecular Biology (IUMB) formed the Enzyme Commission (EC) for classifying, naming, and numbering enzymes [16]. The enzymes are identified by the nomenclature system according to a distinctive four-digit code, the Enzyme Commission, or EC, number. Seven classes of enzymes have been identified based on the kind of reactions they catalyze [17, 18].

Oxidoreductases (EC 1) are capable of catalyzing the oxidation or reduction of substrate(s). For example, reductases, oxidases, peroxidases, oxygenase, and dehydrogenases.

Transferases (EC 2) are capable of catalyzing the transfer of a specific functional group from one molecule to another molecule. For example, peptidyl transferase, transaminase, acetyltransferase, methyltransferase, transaldolase, glycosyltransferase, transketolase, formyl transferase, transaminase, kinase, sulfotransferase, etc.

Hydrolases (EC 3) catalyze the breakdown of larger molecules into relatively smaller molecules by cleaving bonds by reaction with water. For example, proteases/peptidases, amylases, glycosidase, lipase, phospholipases, lactase, acylase, etc.

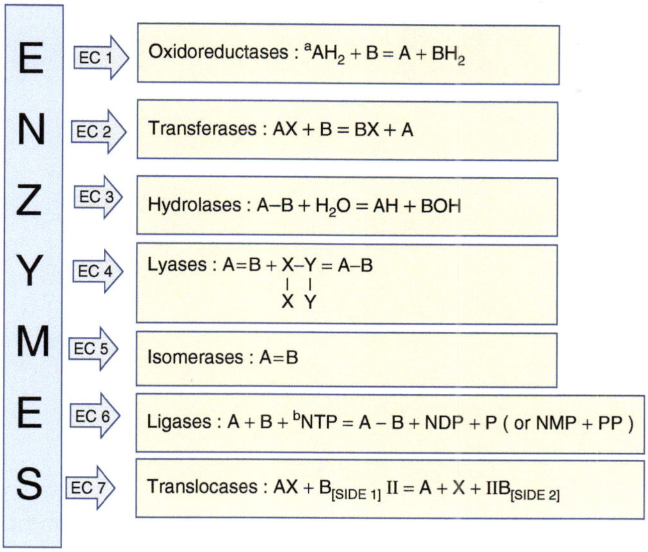

Figure 13.1 The classification of enzymes based on the reaction catalyzed. Where [a] indicates the acceptors nicotinamide adenine dinucleotides (NAD^+ and $NADH + H^+$) by convention. [b]NTP is nucleoside triphosphate. In translocases, || represents a membrane.

Lyases (EC 4) catalyze elimination or addition reactions without requiring hydrolysis or oxidation. For example, decarboxylases, pectolyase, aldehyde lyase, dehydratases, adenylyl cyclase, hydratases, etc.

Isomerases (EC 5) catalyze the conversion of a parent molecule to its isomeric form by breaking a bond intramolecularly and or forming new bonds. For example, racemases, epimerases, cis-trans isomerases, etc.

Ligases (EC 6) catalyze the reaction which involves the formation of a new bond and a new molecule by joining two or more molecules. ATP hydrolysis or energy-rich phosphate bonds provide the energy required by the enzymes. For example, synthetases, chelatases, DNA ligase, carboxylases, etc.

Translocases (EC 7) catalyze the translocation of ions and/or molecules across membranes. For examples, carnitine-acylcarnitine translocase, ADP/ATP translocase, translocase of the inner membrane (TIM), and translocase of the outer membrane (TOM). Translocases were classified in the year 2018 by EC and hence are the latest class of enzymes [17, 19].

Figure 13.1 [18] depicts the classification of enzymes and the reactions they catalyze.

13.3 Earthworms: Intestines of the Earth

The soil itself represents an interactive system comprising its structural components including organic matter, physical and chemical properties, and biological activities [20]. The physical properties of soil are highly influenced by the macroinvertebrates.

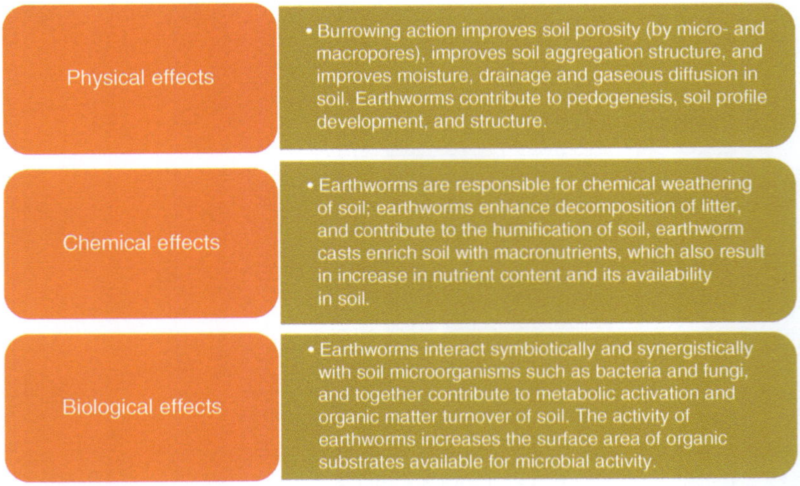

Figure 13.2 Physical, chemical, and biological effects of earthworms on soil environment.

The instinct of ants, termites, and earthworms to continuously excavate the soil in order to create nests, mounds, macro-voids, etc., has a great impact on the soil organic matter turnover, which in turn influences the nutrient cycling in the ecosystem [21]. Earthworms constitute the largest terrestrial macrofaunal biomass worldwide. Earthworms' contribution toward nourishing soil biodiversity, soil fertility, and the overall well-being of the ecosystem make them the "keystone species" of soil ecosystem [22, 23]. Earthworms feed on plant debris, and soil components, which are partially digested through their passage in the gut and are released as casts. This biological conversion of organic matter in the earthworm gut results in the release of nutrient-rich, enzymatically active end product capable of boosting soil productivity (Figure 13.2) [24–26]. The ability of earthworms to ingest soil components allows the earthworm gut to become hosts for a wide variety of microorganisms from different levels of soil strata [27, 28]. The gut of the earthworm possesses dynamic physicochemical regime where the ingested soil microorganisms' experiences mobility, anoxic, and nutrient-rich environment [29, 30]. Earthworm gut resembles a bioreactor where there is a constant variation in nutrient levels; organic acids; oxygen, nitrogen, and hydrogen content; salinity, pH, etc. thereby permitting the ingested microbial taxa to diversify their metabolic processes [31–35].

Earthworms exert a significant impact on soil microbial communities. The amount of ingestion and assimilation by earthworms relies on the type of earthworm species, the type of substrate on which they are thriving, the nature of the existing ecosystem in which the earthworms are residing etc. Each time the earthworms feed, the organisms ingested by the earthworms act as the inoculum to the existing organic matter and partially digested matter in the gut of the earthworm. Each new casts released by the earthworms contain new vibrant microbial species. Many of these microorganisms released are activated during their passage through the earthworm intestine. This shows the existence of an evolutionary relationship between earthworm gut, its burrowing, feeding habits, and the soil microbiota [36, 37]. Therefore, earthworms' role in controlling nutrient cycling and enhancing plant growth is not only mediated by the earthworms alone but also by the earthworm-associated changes brought to the microbial communities present in soil. In this entire process, enzymes play a vital role since there exists a complex mutualistic metabolic relationship between earthworms and the ingested microorganisms [1, 36].

13.4 Earthworms and Their Relation with Microbes and Enzymes

The temperature prevailing in the gut of the earthworm supports all biological processes to continue without hindrance. The temperature control mechanisms in the earthworm gut prevent the inactivation of enzymes due to any temperature fluctuations [2, 38]. Enzymes necessary for enhancing the process of decomposition as well as humification are very common in organisms that feed on litter. Oligochaetes belong to those organisms that rely on organic soil debris for their appetite. The passage of comminuted organic matter through the gut of the earthworm results in the increase in surface area to volume ratio; in that case, the chances of interaction of the microorganisms present in the gut along with their digestive enzymes to act upon the substrate increases. The matter finally leaves the gut in partially digested form as casts [39]. Worm casts have a higher incidence of potassium, manganese, phosphorus, and calcium in their bioavailable forms and are therefore capable of boosting the productivity of soil [11, 40]. As compared to the surrounding soil, earthworm casts are enriched with nutrients, enzymatic activities, and increasing microbial activities, mainly with cellulolytic, nitrifying, denitrifying, and phosphate solubilizing abilities. Enzymatic activities of cellulases, amylases, invertases, proteases, peroxidases, ureases, phosphatases, and dehydrogenases are highly prevalent in worm casts [41–44]. The gut of the earthworm has also been described as a "mutualistic digestive system" [45, 46] where the ingested microorganisms produce exoenzymes capable of enhancing the degradation of complex organic matter during their passage through the gut; as a result, the worm's ability to assimilate the nutrients increases. Many groups of organisms take shelter in the gut of earthworms, and their survival within the gut exclusively depends upon the capability of the inhabitants to resist actions of intra- and intercellular digestive enzymes, intestinal mucus, and other microbial substances [11]. The activity of enzymes within earthworms is influenced by the physiological state, age of earthworms, and also the microorganisms ingested [47].

Earthworm's alimentary canal houses a wide array of digestive enzymes, which are contributed by the earthworms as well as the ingested microbes [48]. Transformation of waste and the process of composting process all involve the work of enzymes [2]. The enzymatic activities commonly associated with earthworms are those involved in the cycling of carbon, nitrogen, and phosphorus. The increased incidence of these enzymatic activities is directly proportional to the presence of microorganisms [2, 38].

Thus, earthworm activities, together with the microbial communities, increase the nitrogen, phosphorus, potassium, and calcium concentrations, and are responsible for the increased mineralization and chelation activities in the soil [49].

Earthworms obtain their nourishment from the breakdown of complex biopolymers (such as starch, cellulose, galactine, and xylan) occurring in plant debris [50]. A strong interaction occurs between the available substrate in the gut of the earthworm along with the joint enzymatic activities of that of the ingested microflora and the earthworm itself. The complete breakdown of such complex polymers requires a synergistic action of enzymes, the larger part of which is provided by the ingested microflora, as compared to the earthworm gut epithelial enzymes [51, 52]. The biological catabolism of soil organic matter and other mineral components is directly mediated by enzymes produced by microorganisms [53].

13.5 Importance of Enzymes Related to Earthworms and the Associated Microorganisms

The earthworms and their associated gut microflora jointly collaborate to create a major impact on the biogeochemical processes of the ecosystem [37, 54].

Some of the earthworm–microbe-associated enzymes having a direct impact on the biogeochemical cycling and catabolism of soil organic matter have been discussed here; these include phosphatases, nitrate reductases, cellulases, amylases, invertases, and xylanases (Figure 13.3).

13.5.1 Phosphatases

Cycling of phosphorus, particularly its solubilization and mineralization, is very important in natural ecosystems [55]. Inorganic phosphorus solubilization and organic phosphorus mineralization can be carried out by microorganisms [56]. Phosphorus solubilization is carried out by using different mechanisms like pH decrease, organic acid release, and proton extrusion [12, 57]. Organic phosphates constitute about 20–30% of total phosphorus in soil. Enzymatic mineralization of organic phosphates can be acquired by phytases, phosphatases, and carbon/phosphorus lyases [58]. The enzyme phosphatases are highly related to earthworms and related microbes. Significantly high phosphatase activities have been observed in the casts of earthworms. The microorganisms inhabiting the earthworm gut are known to contribute the major portion of the enzymes as compared to earthworms' own enzymatic activities [59].

There are two types of phosphatases depending on the optimum pH conditions: one is the acid phosphatases and the second one is the alkaline phosphatases. Phosphate solubilizing microorganisms are known to possess these enzymes and are therefore capable of mineralizing phosphates. The highest rate of enzymatic activities of any enzyme can only be observed when they are in their optimum environmental conditions; therefore, the maximum activity rate for acid phosphatases occurs when they are in acidic soil, while alkaline phosphatases work best

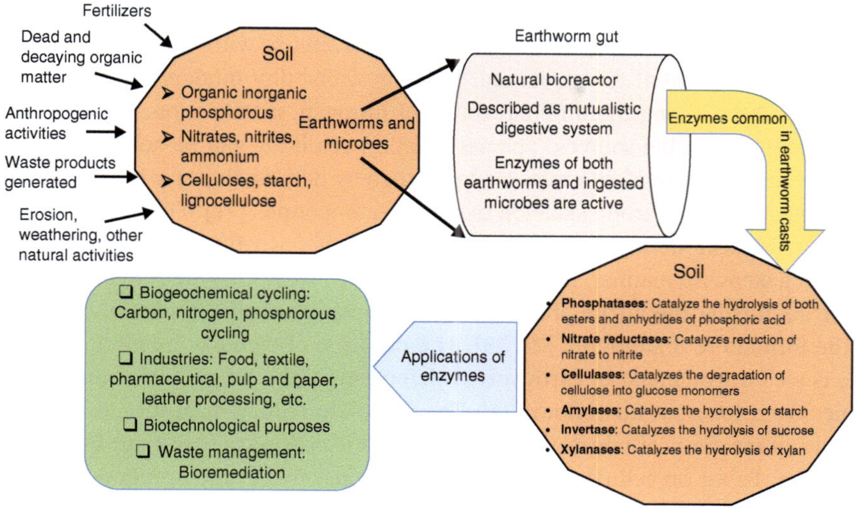

Figure 13.3 Schematic representation showing the complex interrelationship between soil earthworms and microorganisms with the available nutrient sources, the most important enzymes involved, and the applications of these enzymes.

in alkaline to neutral soil [2]. In the microbial world, both prokaryotes (bacteria) as well as eukaryotes (fungi) are able to produce phosphatases. Bacteria of the genus *Bacillus*, *Pseudomonas*, *Staphylococcus*, *Serratia*, etc. are potent phosphatase producers [60, 61]; fungi of the genus *Aspergillus*, *Penicillin*, *Talaromyces*, and *Rhizophagus* have been documented [62]. The enzyme phosphatases are capable of dephosphorylating esters or anhydrides of phosphoric acids by the process of hydrolysis.

Phosphorus is an essential nutrient that is limited in supply and limited in function due to its ability to react strongly with other elements available in soil, such as calcium, iron, and aluminum, making its obtainability very poor. Therefore, the poor availability of phosphorus heavily impacts the nourishment and growth of plants [63, 64]. Depending on the pH conditions of the area where mineralization of organic phosphorus is necessary, the characteristic phosphatases are produced by the microorganisms. Acidic soil plants benefit from acid phosphatases, while neutral or alkaline soil plants rely on alkaline phosphatases [61]. The presence of phosphatases results in the mineralization of the soil's organic phosphorus pool, which results in an increase in the available form of phosphorus, making it readily available to plants. Phosphatases, therefore, not only play a very important role in the agricultural sector by improving plant growth but also prevent environmental pollution caused by the huge amount of use of phosphorus fertilizer [12, 65, 66]. Phosphatases are also very important in the biogeochemical cycling of phosphorus [65, 67].

13.5.2 Nitrate Reductases

Nitrogen is indispensable for the biotic community; the biogeochemical cycling of nitrogen is mediated by essential conversions of different forms of nitrogen with the help of various enzymes [68]. Nitrogen is the important constituent of amino acids, which in turn are the main ingredient in proteins, so without doubt, nitrogen is very much essential for plants and its poor availability hinders their development [69, 70]. Among the different forms of nitrogen, nitrate is one of its significant readily available sources. The assimilation of nitrate can be achieved easily by the systematic use of different enzymes, thereby helping the easy incorporation of nitrogen into the carbon skeleton of organic compounds [71]. The enzymes that enhance the assimilation of nitrate involve the action of two different enzymes operating in a stepwise manner. Initially, the nitrate reductase enzyme converts nitrate to nitrite; further the nitrite produced is acted upon by nitrite reductase, resulting in the formation of ammonia [72, 73]. The presence of the enzyme nitrate reductase is well documented in earthworm microcosms and a large of its contribution comes from ingested microflora [74]. The complete reduction of nitrate involves a chain of reactions of which the initial enzymatic action is carried out by nitrate reductase. Based on cellular location and function, prokaryotic nitrate reductases are divided into three classes: assimilatory nitrate reductase (Nas), which is cytoplasmic; respiratory nitrate reductase (Nar), which is membrane-bound; and dissimilatory nitrate reductase (Nap), which is periplasmic [75]. Bacterial assimilatory nitrate reductases are classified into two types, one ferredoxin (flavodoxin) dependent Nas while the other is NADH dependent Nas [76]. Some of the common strains possessing nitrate reductases are *Bacillus, Escherichia, Streptomyces, Pseudomonas, Xanthomonas, Caulobacter,* etc. [71]. Nitrate reductases have huge importance in the proper cycling of nitrogen in the ecosystem [77]. Another important issue that requires huge attention is the excessive increase in nitrate concentration in the environment leading to nitrate pollution. Nitrate, being highly soluble and mobile, can percolate potentially to groundwater, thereby contaminating drinking water [78]. A huge amount of nitrate accumulation in the soil is injurious to plants. This condition is referred to as "salt stress" Nitrate pollution also has severe negative impact on human health. Apart from this air pollution and climate change are other consequences of high amounts of nitrate. To combat nitrate pollution, utilization of nitrate reductase from prokaryotic origin could be a very good option [71, 79].

13.5.3 Cellulases

Cellulose is one of the most abundant polysaccharides on earth and is the most dominating agricultural waste obtained [80]. β-1,4-Glycosidic linkages join the glucose residues in cellulose [81]. The enzymes capable of hydrolyzing the β-glycosidic linkages of cellulose into its glucose monomer are the cellulases [82]. The complete hydrolysis of cellulose is possible by the action of three different types of cellulases namely, endoglucanase (1,4-D-glucan-4-glucanohydrolase), exocellobiohydrolase (1,4-D-glucan glucohydrolase), and β-glucosidase (D-glucoside glucohydrolase). The endoglucanases carry out the random hydrolysis of glycosidic linkages within the cellulosic polymer, forming smaller units of polysaccharides. Exocellobiohydrolases are capable of hydrolyzing the glycosidic linkages present toward the end of cellulose forming cellobiose. β-glucosidases converts cellobiose to glucose [83, 84]. Several bacterial and fungal species are known for their ability to produce cellulases. Fungal groups are known to possess the best cellulase systems, producing higher cellulase activity than other microbes. Fungal genera such as *Aspergillus* and *Trichoderma* are well-known cellulase producers. A few other fungal strains known to exhibit potential cellulase activity include *Penicillium*, *Rhizopus*, and *Myceliophthora* [5, 85–87]. The most common bacterial strains known to produce cellulase are from *Bacillus* sp., *Pseudomonas* sp., *Cellulomonas* sp., *Cellvibrio* sp., *Microbispora* sp., *Thermomonospora* sp., *Clostridium* sp., *Ruminococcus* sp., etc. [88].

Cellulose is most commonly obtained from agricultural residues and household residues (kitchen waste) in large quantities. These agro-based residues, which are mostly rejected, can be made useful by the enzymatic degradation of cellulose and hemicellulose present in these substrates. Most earthworms are capable of cellulose degradation through the combined action of their own digestive cellulases and the associated microflora [2]. Apart from the major role in the global recycling of cellulose, cellulases have a wide range of applications in food, biofuel production, textile, paper, and animal feed-producing industries. In food industry, cellulases are utilized in making clarified fruit juices, treating beverages, extracting olive oils, etc. [5]. The action of cellulase on lignocellulosic materials enables biofuel (such as bioethanol) generation [87]. In textile industries, denim biostoning, and cellulosic fiber polishing is carried out by the action of cellulases [89]. Paper and pulp industries require high input of cellulosic materials, and reusage of these cellulosic substrates is done with the help of cellulases. The presence of cellulases in animal feed products helps improve the digestibility potential of animal feed [90, 91].

13.5.4 Amylases

Plants, algae, and cyanobacterial species are capable of storing carbohydrate and energy in the form of starch, making it the second-highest renewable resource in nature [92]. Starch is a polymer of glucose linked by glycosidic linkages. Starch consists of both linear and branched glucose polymers. The unbranched linking of glucose units is called amylose, where the glucose units are linked by α-1,4-D-glucosidic bonds; the branched linkage of glucose is called amylopectin in which glucose units are joined by both α-1,4-D-glucosidic and α-1,6-D-glucosidic bonds [93]. The enzyme amylase is capable of catalyzing the hydrolysis of glycosidic linkage present in starch molecules, resulting in the production of dextrins and oligosaccharides [94, 95]. There are three types of amylases α-amylase, β-amylase, and γ-amylase [96]. α-Amylase is an endohydrolase capable of hydrolyzing the α-1,4 linkages in a random manner within the chain and forms smaller fragments; this amylase also can bypass α-1,6 branch points. β-Amylase is an exohydrolase whose action begins from the nonreducing end of the polymer, where each time the enzyme removes two glucose molecules. Formation of disaccharides, β-maltose, and limit dextrin is common after the enzymatic action of β-amylase [97]. γ-Amylases are capable of hydrolyzing both α-1,4- and α-1,6-glycosidic linkages thereby releasing monomeric units of glucose [98]. Several microbial species are known to produce amylases. Earthworms' digestive system together with their associated microorganisms can produce amylases [2]. Among the bacterial strains *Bacillus* sp., *Cladimonas* sp., *Corynebacterium* sp., *Pseudomonas* sp., *Lactobacillus* sp., etc., are potent amylase producers. Fungal strains *Aspergillus* sp. and *Penicillium* sp. are powerful fungal amylase producers [99, 100]. Amylases have huge applications in the industrial front. Amylases are used in the food industry for preparing beverages, fruit juices, cakes, etc. The process of desizing in textile industries is performed with the help of amylases. In paper and pulp industries, amylases are used to alter the starch used for coated paper. The treatment of coating in the paper industry to make smooth and strong paper is done with the help of amylase [95].

13.5.5 Invertases

The disaccharide sucrose consists of two monosaccharides: D-glucose and D-fructose connected by α-1,4-glycosidic linkage [101]. The complete breakdown of sucrose into its monomeric subunits by hydrolyzing the glycosidic bond is carried out by the enzyme invertase. Apart from hydrolyzing bonds, invertase is also capable of transferring a subunit from one molecule to another. The αβ-D-O-fructofuranoside residue can be transferred to an acceptor substrate by invertase [102]. At conditions of higher sucrose concentration, invertase can show hydrolase as well as transferase type of enzymatic activity [103].

Invertases are extensively dispersed among different organisms, yet the most common sources of invertase are bacteria and fungi [104]. Among the fungal strains, *Aspergillus* sp. and *Penicillium* sp. produce high-efficiency invertases; other fungal strains include *Sclerotinia* sp., *Cladosporium* sp., and *Rhodotorula* sp. Bacterial strains such as *Bacillus* sp., *Pseudomonas* sp., *Bifidobacterium* sp., *Arthrobacter* sp., etc., are potent invertase producers [5]. Earthworm-associated microbes are also involved in producing invertase. The enzyme invertase has a great extent of application in the industrial sector. The invertase sugar produced in food industries is used in different ways such as in preparing different types of confectioneries, in infant food preparation, in making artificial honey, and in preparing tablets for supportive digestive disabilities. Apart from the food industry, invertases are also used widely in pharmaceutical industries for the preparation of drugs, digestive tablets, cough syrup, nutraceuticals, etc. [5, 103].

13.5.6 Xylanases

Polysaccharides cellulose and hemicellulose, along with aromatic polymer lignin, together make up the major constituents of lignocellulosic materials [105]. A good portion of the plant cell wall is made up of the polysaccharide hemicellulose; the sugar units of hemicellulose include pentoses, hexoses, and xyloses. When xylose is produced upon hydrolysis of a polymer, it is called xylan. Xylans are structurally complex and the xylose units are connected to one another by β, 1-4, glycosidic linkages [106]. The polymer xylan can be broken down into smaller and monomeric subunits by the glycosidic hydrolase family of enzymes called xylanases [5]. Synergistic action of different exohydrolases and an endohydrolase is required to release xylose subunits from the xylan polymer [2]. Endoxylanases can release short xylooligosaccharides by hydrolyzing glycosidic linkages in the polymer xylan. β-xylosidase an exohydrolase is required to release the monomeric xylose residue from the nonreducing ends of the xylooligosaccharides obtained [107]. A group of other exohydrolases, namely acetyl xylan esterase, glucuronidase, and arabinosidase, are necessary for the liberation of the other side chains from the backbone of xylan polymer [108]. Xylanases can be derived from microorganisms, both fungal and bacterial strains. Earthworms and their associated microbes are highly potent in producing xylanases as earthworms are highly exposed to plant materials. Among the bacterial strains, the most important bacterial genera producing xylanase include *Bacillus, Arthrobacter, Cellulomonas, Micrococcus, Paenibcillus, Staphylococcus, Thermotoga, Microbacterium, Pseudoxanthomonas,* and *Rhodococcus.* Among the fungal strains, *Aspergillus, Fusarium, Penicillium, Geotrichum, Paecilomyces, Cephalosporium,* and *Trichoderma* are well-known xylanase producers. Actinomycetes such as *Streptomyces, Thermomonospora,* and *Thermoactinomycetes* have been reported for xylanase production [109, 110].

Xylanases are extensively used in the industrial sector. In the food industry, xylanases have been used for clarification of fruit and vegetable juices, improving the quality of bread, etc. In the paper industry, xylanases are used to treat pulp to upgrade the quality of paper. This enzyme is used for the treatment of hemicellulose waste. The industrial production of ethanol and xylitol relies on the action of xylanases on the substrate. The process of degumming of bast fibers obtained from certain plants requires the activity of xylanase. Forage crops are treated with xylanases so that there is an improvement in the feed digestibility of ruminant animals [5, 111].

13.6 Conclusions and Future Perspectives

Enzymes are the biocatalysts that execute biochemical reactions and are responsible for upholding life. Microorganisms can break down and transform complex organic matter into simpler forms that can be reused by other organisms. These transformations are carried out by the enzyme systems that the organisms possess. The microbial enzyme systems are therefore considered the key engines driving the earth's biogeochemical cycles. From among the soil organisms, earthworms' role as ecological engineers has been long established. There exists a complex relationship between the earthworm gut and the colonized microbiota, maintaining the earthworm's metabolism and facilitating nutrient transformation; this relationship between earthworms and their ingested soil microflora plays a key role in enhancing the enzymatic activities in soil. The enzymatic activities of the earthworms, together with their enteric microflora, are indicators of microorganisms' contribution toward carbon-, nitrogen-, and phosphorus-cycling. Microbial enzymes have enormous applications in several industries such as in food and beverages, pharmaceuticals, textile, leather processing, paper making, detergents, animal feed, and biotechnological. With the advancement of research, enzymes are also utilized in waste management sectors. Thus, the magic of microbial enzymes affects several aspects of life, and the close association of earthworms and the ingested microflora together with their micro-, meso-, and macro-scale enzymatic system provides an enormous contribution toward environmental sustainability.

The wide application of enzymes in different sectors has resulted in exploring different enzymes, their isolation from novel sources, and knowing their potential. There is still a necessity for exploring the enzymes associated with earthworms in combination with the associated microflora to know the exact contribution of earthworm gut enzymes and the gut microflora. Studying the enzymatic properties of selectively isolated earthworm gut microflora and distinguishing their enzymatic properties from that of the earthworm gut enzymes can help in understanding the individual contribution of earthworms and associated gut microflora in the ecosystem as ecological engineers.

References

1 Le Bayon, R.C., Weber, G.B., Schomburg, A. et al. (2017). Earthworms as ecosystem engineers: a review. In: *Insects and Other Terrestrial Arthropods: Biology, Chemistry and Behaviour. Earthworms Types, Roles and Behaviour* (ed. C.G. Horton), 129–177. New York: Nova Science Publishers.

2 Kiyasudeen, K., Ibrahim, M.H., Quaik, S., and Ismail, S.A. (2016). Important digestive enzymes of earthworm. In: *Prospects of Organic Waste Management and the Significance of Earthworms. Applied Environmental Science and Engineering for a Sustainable Future* (ed. V.J. Jegatheesan et al.), 105–122. Cham: Springer.

3 Mak, W.S. and Siegel, J.B. (2014). Computational enzyme design: transitioning from catalytic proteins to enzymes. *Curr. Opin. Struct. Biol.* 27: 87–94.

4 Iglesias, J.P., Marques, S.M., Pinto, G.P. et al. (2021). Computational design of enzymes for biotechnological applications. *Biotechnol. Adv.* 47: 107696.

5 Singh, R.S., Singh, T., and Pandey, A. (2019). Microbial enzymes – an overview. In: *Biomass, Biofuels, Biochemicals: Advances in Enzyme Technology*, 1–40. Netherland: Elsevier.

6 Wolfenden, R. (2014). Massive thermal acceleration of the emergence of primordial chemistry, the incidence of spontaneous mutation, and the evolution of enzymes. *J. Biolumin. Chemilumin.* 289: 30198–30204.

7 Bunzel, A.H., Anderson, J.L.R., and Mulholland, A.J. (2021). Designing better enzymes: insights from directed evolution. *Curr. Opin. Struct. Biol.* 67: 212–218.

8 Hughes, G. and Lewis, J.C. (2018). Introduction: biocatalysis in industry. *Chem. Rev.* 118: 1–3.

9 Ruiz, N., Mathieu, J., Celini, L. et al. (2011). A synthetic index of soil quality based on soil macro-invertebrate communities. *Soil Biol. Biochem.* 43: 2032–2045.

10 Gougoulias, C., Clark, J.M., and Shaw, L.J. (2014). The role of soil microbes in the global carbon cycle: tracking the below-ground microbial processing of

plant-derived carbon for manipulating carbon dynamics in agricultural systems. *J. Sci. Food Agric.* 94: 2362–2371.

11 Wani, K.A., Mamta, Shuab, R., and Lone, R.A. (2017). Earthworms and associated microbiome: natural boosters for agro-ecosystems. In: *Probiotics in Agro-ecosystem* (ed. V. Kumar et al.), 469–489. Springer Nature, Singapore Pte Ltd.

12 Biswas, J.K., Banerjee, A., Rai, M. et al. (2018a). Potential application of selected metal resistant phosphate solubilizing bacteria isolated from the gut of earthworm (*Metaphire posthuma*) in plant growth promotion. *Geoderma* 330: 117–124.

13 Aira, M., Monroy, F., and Domınguez, J. (2007). *Eisenia foetida* (Oligochaeta: *Lumbricidae*) modifies the structure and physiological capabilities of microbial communities improving carbon mineralization during vermicomposting of pig manure. *Microb. Ecol.* 54: 662–671.

14 Worthington, C.C., Worthington, V., and Worthington, A. (2019). Introduction to Enzymes. https://www.worthington-biochem.com/introBiochem/Enzymes.pdf.

15 Robinson, P.K. (2015). Enzymes: principles and biotechnological applications. *Essays Biochem.* 59: 1–41.

16 Patel, A.K., Singhania, R.R., and Pandey, A. (2017). Production, purification and application of microbial enzymes. In: *Biotechnology of Microbial Enzymes: Production, Biocatalysis and Industrial Applications* (ed. G. Brahmachari), 13–41. Cambridge: Academic Press.

17 Nomenclature Committee of the International Union of Biochemistry and Molecular Biology (NC-IUBMB) (2021). Enzyme Nomenclature. https://iubmb.qmul.ac.uk/enzyme/

18 McDonald, A.G. and Tipto, K.F. (2021). Enzyme nomenclature and classification: the state of the art. The. *FEBS J.* 1–18.

19 Okpara, M.O. (2022). Microbial enzymes and their applications in food industry: a mini review. *Adv. Enzyme Res.* 10: 23–47.

20 Lemtiri, A., Colinet, G., Alabi, T. et al. (2018). Short-term effects of tillage practices and crop residue exportation on soil organic matter and earthworm communities in silt loam arable soil. In: *Soil Management and Climate Change* (ed. M.Á. Muñoz and R. Zornoza), 53–71. Elsivier.

21 Wurst, S., Sonnemann, I., and Zaller, J.G. (2018, 2018). Soil macro-invertebrates: their impact on plants and associated aboveground communities in temperate regions. In: *Aboveground-Belowground Community Ecology. Ecological Studies (Analysis and Synthesis)* (ed. T. Oghushi, S. Wurst, and S. Johnson), 175–200. Cham: Springer.

22 Liu, D., Lian, B., Wu, C., and Guo, P. (2017). A comparative study of gut microbiota profiles of earthworms fed in three different substrates. *Symbiosis*. https://doi.org/10.1007/s13199-017-0491-6.

23 Zhu, D., An, X.L., Chen, Q.L. et al. (2018). Antibiotics disturb the microbiome and increase the incidence of resistance genes in the gut of a common soil collembolan. *Environ. Sci. Technol.* 52 (5): 3081–3090.

24 Hickman, Z.A. and Reid, B.J. (2008). Earthworm assisted bioremediation of organic contaminants. *Environ. Int.* 34 (7): 1072–1081.

25 Fusaro, S., Gavinelli, F., Lazzarini, F., and Paoletti, M.G. (2018). Soil biological quality index based on earthworms (QBS-e). A new way to use earthworms as bioindicators in agroecosystems. *Ecol. Indic.* 93: 1276–1292.

26 Blouin, M., Hodson, M.E., Delgado, E.A. et al. (2013). A review of earthworm impact on soil function and ecosystem services. *Eur. J. Soil Sci.* 64: 161–182.

27 Eisenhauer, N., Cesarz, S., Koller, R. et al. (2012). Global change below ground: impacts of elevated CO_2, nitrogen, and summer drought on soil food webs and biodiversity. *Global Change Biol.* 18: 435–447.

28 Ali, U., Sajid, N., Khalid, A. et al. (2015). A review on vermicomposting of organic wastes. *Environ. Prog. Sustain.* 34: 1050–1062.

29 Aria, M. and Dominguez, J. (2014). Changes in nutrient pools, microbial biomass and microbial activities in soil after transit through gut of three endogeic earthworm species of genus *Prostandilus Qui* and *Bouche*, 1998. *J. Soils Sediments* 14: 1335–1340.

30 Clause, J., Barot, S., and Forey, E. (2015). Effects of cast properties and passage through the earthworm gut on seed germination and seedling growth. *Appl. Soil Ecol.* 96: 108–113.

31 Meier, A.B., Hunger, S., and Drake, H.L. (2018). Differential engagement of fermentative taxa in gut contents of the earthworm *Lumbricus terrestris. Appl. Environ. Microbiol.* 84 (5): 01851–01817.

32 Singleton, D.R., Hendrix, P.F., Coleman, D.C., and Whitman, W.B. (2003). Identification of uncultured bacteria tightly associated with the intestine of the earthworm *Lumbricus rubellus* (*Lumbricidae*; *Oligochaeta*). *Soil Biol. Biochem.* 35: 1547–1555.

33 Byzov, B.A., Tikhonov, V.V., Nechitailo, T.Y., and Demin, V.V. (2015). Taxonomic composition and physiological and biochemical properties of bacteria in the digestive tracts of earthworms. *Eur. J. Soil Sci.* 48: 268–275.

34 Hussain, N., Singh, A., Saha, S. et al. (2016). Excellent N-fixing and P- solubilizing traits in earthworm gut isolated bacteria: a vermicompost based assessment with vegetable market waste and rice straw feed mixtures. *Bioresour. Technol.* 222: 165–174.

35 Biswas, J.K., Banerjee, A., Majumder, S. et al. (2019). New extracellular polymeric substance producing enteric bacterium from earthworm, *Metaphire posthuma*: modulation through culture conditions. *Proc. Zool. Soc.* 72 (2): 160–170.

36 Ahmed, N. and Al-mutairi, K.A. (2022). Earthworms effect on microbial population and soil fertility as well as their interaction with agricultural practices. *Sustainability* 14: 7803.

37 Dey, K.K., Talukdar, N.C., Nongkhlaw, F.M.W., and Thakuria, D. (2018). Isolation, characterization and practical significance of cellulose degrading bacteria from the gut wall of two ecologically distinct earthworms. *Curr. Sci.* 114 (7): 1474–1484.

38 Medina-Sauza, R.M., Alvarez-Jimenez, M., Delhal, A. et al. (2019). Earthworms building up soil microbiota, a review. *Front. Environ. Sci.* 7 (81): 1–20.

39 Lazcano, C., Gomez-Brandon, M., and Dominguez, J. (2008). Comparison of the effectiveness of composting and vermicomposting for the biological stabilization of cattle manure. *Chemosphere* 72: 1013–1019.

40 Singh, J. (2018). Role of earthworm in sustainable agriculture. In: *Sustainable Food Systems: From Agriculture to Industry 2018* (ed. C. Galanakis), 83–122. USA: Academic Press.

41 Bhatnagar, T. (1975). Earthworms and humification: a new aspect of microbial nitrogen incorporation induced by earthworms. In: *Biodegradation and Humification* (ed. G. Kilbertus et al.), 169–182. Sarreguemines, France: Pierron.

42 Sharpley, A.N. and Syers, J.K. (1976). Potential role of earthworm casts for the phosphorus enrichment of run off waters. *Soil Biol. Biochem.* 8: 341–346.

43 Edwards, C.A. and Bohlen, P.J. (1996). The role of earthworms in organic matter and nutrient cycles. In: *Biology and Ecology of Earthworms* (ed. C.A. Edwards and N.Q. Arancon), 155–180. New York: Chapman and Hall.

44 Piya, S., Shrestha, I., Gauchan, D.P., and Lamichhane, J. (2018). Vermicomposting in organic agriculture: influence on the soil nutrients and plant growth. *Int. J. Res* 5 (20): 1055–1063.

45 Brown, G.G. and Doube, B.M. (2004). Functional interactions between earthworms, microorganisms, organic matter, and plants. In: *Earthworm Ecology*, 2e (ed. C.A. Edwards), 213–239. Boca Raton, FL: CRC Press.

46 Edwards, C.A., Dominguez, J., and Arancon, N.Q. (2004). The influence of vermicomposts on pest and diseases. In: *Soil Zoology for Sustainable Development in the 21st Century* (ed. S.H. Shakir Hanna and M. WZA), 397–418. Cairo.

47 Sruthy, P.B., Anjana, J.C., Rathinamala, J., and Jayashree, S. (2013). Screening of earthworm (*Eudrilus eugeniae*) gut as a transient microbial habitat. *Adv. Zool. Bot.* 1: 53–56.

48 Pathma, J. and Sakthivel, N. (2012). Microbial diversity of vermicompost bacteria that exhibit useful agricultural traits and waste management potential. *Springer Plus* 1: 26. doi.org/10.1186/2193-1801-1-26.

49 Menezes, A.B.D., Prendergast-Miller, M.T., Macdonald, L.M. et al. (2018). Earthworm-induced shifts in microbial diversity in soils with rare versus established invasive earthworm populations. *FEMS Microbiol. Ecol.* 94 (5): 1–14.

50 Prabha, M.L. and Priya, M.S. (2011). Comparative studies on enzymatic levels of vegetable wastes decomposed by *Eudrilus eugeniae* and *Eisenia fetida*. *Adv. Biotechnol.* 1 (4): 3–5.

51 Sanchez-Hernandez, J.C., Mazzia, C., Capowiez, Y., and Rault, M. (2009). Carboxyl esterase activity in earthworm gut contents: potential (eco) toxicological implications. *Comp. Biochem. Physiol. C* 150 (4): 503–511.

52 Biswas, J.K., Banerjee, A., Rai, M.K. et al. (2018). Exploring potential applications of a novel extracellular polymeric substance synthesizing bacterium (*Bacillus licheniformis*) isolated from gut contents of earthworm (*Metaphire posthuma*) in environmental remediation. *Biodegrad* 29 (4): 323–337. https://doi.org/10.1007/s10532-018-9835-z.

53 Sahu, N., Vasu, D., Sahu, A. et al. (2017). Strength of microbes in nutrient cycling: a key to soil health. In: *Agriculturally Important Microbes for Sustainable Agriculture* (ed. V.S. Meena et al.), 69–86. Springer, Nature Singapore Pte Ltd. https://doi.org/10.1007/978-981-10-5589-8-4.

54 Suna, M., Chao, H., Zheng, X. et al. (2020). Ecological role of earthworm intestinal bacteria in terrestrial environments: a review. *Sci. Total Environ.* 740: 140008.

55 Richardson, A.E. and Simpson, R.J. (2011). Soil microorganisms mediating phosphorus availability update on microbial phosphorus. *Plant Physiol.* 156: 989–996.

56 Kumar Adhya, T., Kumar, N., Reddy, G. et al. (2015). Microbial mobilization of soil phosphorus and sustainable P management in agricultural soils. *Curr. Sci.* 108: 1280–1287.

57 Stefanoni Rubio, P.J., Godoy, M.S., Della Monica, I.F. et al. (2016). Carbon and nitrogen sources influence tricalcium phosphate solubilization and extracellular phosphatase activity by *Talaromyces flavus*. *Curr. Microbiol.* 72: 41–47.

58 Kumar, R. and Shastri, B. (2017). Role of phosphate-solubilising microorganisms in sustainable agricultural development. In: *Agro-Environmental Sustainability* (ed. J. Singh and G. Seneviratne), 271–303. Cham: Springer.

59 Vinotha, S.P., Parthasarathi, K., and Ranganathan, L.S. (2000). Enhanced phosphatase activity in earthworm casts is more of microbial origin. *Curr. Sci.* 79: 1152–1162.

60 Singh, P. and Banik, R.M. (2019). Effect of purified alkaline phosphatase from *Bacillus licheniformis* on growth of *Zea mays* L. *Plant Sci.Today* 6: 1–9.

61 Rawat, P., Das, S., Shankhdhar, D., and Shankhadhar, S.C. (2020). Phosphate-solubilizing microorganisms: mechanism and their role in phosphate solubilization and uptake. *J. Soil Sci. Plant Nutr.* https://doi.org/10.1007/s42729-020-00342-7.

62 Della Monica, I.F., Godeas, A.M., and Scervino, J.M. (2020). In vivo modulation of arbuscular mycorrhizal symbiosis and soil quality by fungal P solubilizers. *Microb. Ecol.* 79: 21–29.

63 Park, J., Bolan, N., Megharaj, M., and Naidu, R. (2010). Isolation of phosphate-solubilizing bacteria and characterization of their effects on lead immobilization. *Pedologist* 53: 67–75.

64 Khan, M.S., Ahmed, E., Zaidi, A., and Oves, M. (2013). Bacteria in agro biology: crop productivity. In: *Bacteria in Agrobiology: Crop Productivity* (ed. D. Maheshwari, M. Saraf, and A. Aeron), 237–265. Berlin, Heidelberg: Springer.

65 Khan, M.S., Zaidi, A., and Ahmed, E. (2014). Mechanism of phosphate solubilization and physiological functions of phosphate-solubilizing microorganisms. In: *Phosphate Solubilizing Microorganisms* (ed. M.S. Khan, A. Zaidi, and J. Mussarat), 31–62. Switzerland: Springer International Publishing.

66 Koch, M., Kruse, J., Eichler-Löbermann, E. et al. (2018). Phosphorus stocks and speciation in soil profiles of a long-term fertilizer experiment: evidence from sequential fractionation, P K-edge XANES, and 31P NMR spectroscopy. *Geoderma* 316: 115–126.

67 Nannipieri, P., Giagnoni, L., Landi, L., and Renella, G. (2011). Role of phosphatase in soil. In: *Phosphorus in Action, Soil Biology* (ed. E.K. Bunemann et al.), 215–243. Berlin, Heidelberg: Springer-Verlag.

68 Bhardwaj, A.K., Rajwar, D., Yadav, R.K. et al. (2021). Nitrogen availability and use efficiency in wheat crop as influenced by the organic-input quality under major integrated nutrient management systems. *Front. Plant Sci.* 12: 634448.

69 Zhang, Z.W., Fu, Y.F., Zhou, Y.H. et al. (2019). Nitrogen and nitric oxide regulate Arabidopsis flowering differently. *Plant Sci.* 284: 177–184.

70 Fu, Y.F., Zhang, Z.W., Yang, X.Y. et al. (2020). Nitrate reductase is a key enzyme responsible for nitrogen-regulated auxin accumulation in Arabidopsis roots. *Biochem. Biophys. Res. Commun.* https://doi.org/10.1016/j.bbrc.2020.08.057.

71 Chu, S., Zhang, D., Wang, D. et al. (2017). Heterologous expression and biochemical characterization of assimilatory nitrate and nitrite reductase reveals adaption and potential of *Bacillus megaterium* NCT-2 in secondary salinization soil. *Int. J. Biol. Macromol.* 101: 1019–1028.

72 Sengupta, S., Shaila, M., and Rao, G. (1996). Purification and characterization of assimilatory nitrite reductase from *Candida utilis*. *Biochem. J.* 317: 147–155.

73 Lin, J.T. and Stewart, V. (1997). Nitrate assimilation by bacteria. *Adv. Microb. Physiol.* 39: 1–30.

74 Ihssen, J., Horn, M.A., Matthies, C. et al. (2003). N_2O-producing microorganisms in the gut of the earthworm *Aporrectodea caliginosa* are indicative of ingested soil bacteria. *Appl. Environ. Microbiol.* 69 (3): 1655–1661.

75 Morozkina, R.Z. (2007). Nitrate reductases: structure, functions, and effect of stress factors. *Biochemistry* 1151–1160.

76 Jepson, B.J., Anderson, L.J., Rubio, L.M. et al. (2004). Tuning a nitrate reductase for function: the first spectropotentiometric characterization of a bacterial assimilatory nitrate reductase reveals novel redox properties. *J. Biolumin. Chemilumin.* 279: 32212–32218.

77 Kamp, A., Høgslund, S., Risgaard-Petersen, N., and Stief, P. (2015). Nitrate storage and dissimilatory nitrate reduction by eukaryotic microbes. *Front. Microbiol.* 6: 1492.

78 Wellman, T.P. and Rupert, M.G. (2016). Groundwater quality, age, and susceptibility and vulnerability to nitrate contamination with linkages to land use and groundwater flow, Upper Black Squirrel Creek Basin, Colorado, 2013 (No. 2016–5020). US Geological Survey.

79 Bhatia, R.R., Setia, H., and Panthania, P. (2019). Role of heterotrophic aerobic denitrifying bacteria in nitrate removal from wastewater. *J. Appl. Microbiol.* 128: 1261–1278.

80 Hussain, A.A., Abdel-Salam, M.S., Abo-Ghalia, H.H. et al. (2017). Optimization and molecular identification of novel cellulose degrading bacteria isolated from Egyptian environment. *J. Genet. Eng. Biotechnol.* 15: 77–85.

81 Gupta, P., Samant, K., and Sahu, A. (2012). Isolation of cellulose-degrading bacteria and determination of their cellulolytic potential. *Int. J. Microbiol.* 1–5. doi:10.1155/2012/578925.

82 Cai, Y.J., Chapman, S.J., Buswell, J.A., and Chang, S.T. (1999). Production and distribution of endoglucanase, cellobiohydrolase, and beta-glucosidase components of the cellulolytic system of *Volvariella volvaceae*, the edible straw mushroom. *Appl. Environ. Microbiol.* 65: 553–559.

83 Yoon, L.W., Ang, T.N., Ngoh, G.C., and Chua, A.S. (2014). Fungal solid-state fermentation and various methods of enhancement in cellulase production. *Biomass Bioenergy* 67: 319–338.

84 Barzkar, N. and Sohail, M. (2020). An overview on marine cellulolytic enzymes and their potential applications. *Appl. Microbiol. Biotechnol.* 104 (16): 6873–6892.

85 Camassola, M. and Dillon, A.J.P. (2014). Effect of different pretreatment of sugar cane bagasse on cellulase and xylanases production by the mutant *Penicillium echinulatum* 9A02S1 grown in submerged culture. *Biomed Res. Int.* 2014: 720740.

86 Kupski, L., Pagnussatt, F.A., Buffon, J.G., and Furlong, E.B. (2014). Endoglucanase and total cellulase from newly isolated *Rhizopus oryzae* and *Trichoderma reesei*: production, characterization, and thermal stability. *Appl. Biochem. Biotechnol.* 172: 458–468.

87 Singh, A., Bajar, S., Devi, A., and Pant, D. (2021). An overview on the recent developments in fungal cellulase production and their industrial applications. *Bioresour. Technol.* 14: 100652.

88 Saranraj, P., Stella, D., and Reetha, D. (2012). Microbial cellulases and its applications: a review. *Int. J. Biochem. Biotech. Sci.* 1: 1–12.

89 de Souza Moreira, L.R., Sciuto, D.L., and Ferreira Filho, E.X. (2016). An overview of cellulose degrading enzymes and their applications in textile industry. In: *New and Future Developments in Microbial Biotechnology and Bioengineering* (ed. A. Rodrigues), 165–175. Elsevier.

90 Zhang, X.Z. and Zhang, Y.H.P. (2013). Cellulases: characteristics, sources, production, and applications. In: *Bioprocessing Technologies in Biorefinery for Sustainable Production of Fuels, Chemicals, and Polymers* (ed. S.T. Yang, H.A. El-Enshasy, and N. Thongchul), 131–146. John Wiley & Sons Inc.

91 Bajaj, P. and Mahajan, R. (2019). Cellulase and xylanase synergism in industrial biotechnology. *Appl. Microbiol. Biotechnol.* 103 (21–22): 8711–8724.

92 Xia, W., Zhang, K., Su, L., and Wu, J. (2021). Microbial starch debranching enzymes: developments and applications. *Biotechnol. Adv.* 50: 107786.

93 Paul, J.S., Gupta, N., Beliya, E. et al. (2021). Aspects and recent trends in microbial α-amylase: a review. *Appl. Biochem. Biotechnol.* https://doi.org/10.1007/s12010-021-03546-4.

94 Sundarram, A., Pandurangappa, T., and Murthy, K. (2014). α-Amylase production and applications: a review. *J. Appl. Environ. Microbiol.* 2: 166–175.

95 Farooq, M.A., Ali, S., Hassan, A. et al. (2021). Biosynthesis and industrial applications of α-amylase: a review. *Arch. Microbiol.* 203: 1281–1292.

96 Gopinath, S.C., Anbu, P., Arshad, M.K. et al. (2017). Biotechnological processes in microbial amylase production. *Biomed Res. Int.* 1–9.

97 Mary, C., Vaj, E.A., Subhash, A., and Paul, N.M. (2021). Comparative study on the extracellular amylase activity of amylolytic bacteria isolated from different soil types and earthworms gut. *Int. J. Bot. Stud.* 6 (2): 115–121.

98 Argyros, A., Barrett, T., Caiazza, N., and Hogsett, D. (2012). Genetically modified *Clostridium thermocellum* engineered to ferment xylose. US Patent ENCHI Corp 9:546, filed 22 December 2011.

99 Erdal, S.E. and Taskin, M.E. (2010). Production of α-amylase by Penicillium expansum MT-1 in solid-state fermentation using waste Loquat (*Eriobotrya japonica* Lindley) kernels as substrate. *Rom. Biotechnol. Lett.* 15: 5342–5350.

100 Haq, I., Ali, S., Javed, M.M. et al. (2010). Production of alpha amylase from a randomly induced mutant strain of *Bacillus amyloliquefaciens* and its application as a desizer in textile industry. *Pak. J. Bot.* 42: 473–484.

101 Songpim, M., Vaithanomsat, P., Vanichsriratana, W., and Sirisansaneeyakul, S. (2011). Enhancement of inulinase and invertase production from a newly isolated *Candida guilliermondii* TISTR 5844. *J. Soc. Sci.* 45: 675–685.

102 Toledo, L.E.T., Garcia, D.M., Cruz, E.P. et al. (2019). Fructosyl transferases and invertases: useful enzymes in the food and feed industries. In: *Enzymes in Food Biotechnology: Production, Applications, and Future Prospects* (ed. M. Kuddus), 451–469. Massachusetts: Academic Press.

103 Manoochehri, H., Hosseini, N.F., Saidijam, M. et al. (2020). A review on invertase: its potentials and applications. *Biocatal. Agric. Biotechnol.* 25: 101599.

104 Nadeem, H., Rashid, M.H., Siddique, M.H. et al. (2015). Microbial invertases: a review on kinetics, thermodynamics, physiochemical properties. *Process Biochem.* 50: 1202–1210.

105 Burlacu, A., Cornea, C.P., and Israel-Roming, F. (2016). Microbial xylanase: a review. *Sci. Bull.* 335–342.

106 Uday, U.S.P., Choudhury, P., Bandopadhyay, T.K., and Bhunia, B. (2016). Classification, mode of action and production strategy of xylanase and its application for biofuel production from water hyacinth. *Int. J. Biol. Macromol.* 82: 1041–1054.

107 Motta, F.L., Andrade, C.C.P., and Santana, M.H.A. (2013). A review of xylanase production by the fermentation of xylan: classification, characterization and applications. In: *Sustainable Degradation of Lignocellulosic Biomass - Techniques, Applications and Commercialization* (ed. A.K. Chandel and S.S. da Silva), 251–266. Croatia: InTech.

108 Dhiman, S.S., Sharma, J., and Battan, B. (2008). Industrial applications and future prospects of microbial xylanases: a review. *Bio Resources* 3 (4): 1377–1402.

109 Kumar, D., Kumar, S.S., Kumar, J. et al. (2017). Xylanases and their industrial applications: a review. *Biochem. Cell. Arch.* 17: 353–360.

110 Thomas, L., Joseph, A., Singhania, R.R. et al. (2017). Xylanases. In: *Current Developments in Biotechnology and Bioengineering: Production, Isolation and*

Purification of Industrial Products, vol. VII (ed. A. Pandey, S. Negi, and C.R. Soccol), 127–148. Amsterdam: Elsevier.

111 Kaushal, J., Khatri, M., and singh G, Arya SK. (2021). A multifaceted enzyme conspicuous in fruit juice clarification: an elaborate review on xylanase. *Int. J. Biol. Macromol.* 193 (Pt B): 1350–1361.

14

Proteases from Thermophilic Bacteria: Their Significant Characteristics and Recombinant Production

Nitin Srivastava[1], *Sumit Kumar*[2], *and Sunil K. Khare*[1]

[1] *Indian Institute of Technology Delhi, Enzyme and Microbial Biochemistry Laboratory, Department of Chemistry, Hauz Khas, New Delhi 110016, India*
[2] *Amity University, Amity Institute of Biotechnology, Noida, Uttar Pradesh 201313, India*

14.1 Introduction

Proteases find valuable applications in various industrial sectors, viz. bakery, brewing, feed, leather, laundry, and detergent industries, besides their utility in the processing of silk, soy, meat, and milk. These are broadly employed in peptide synthesis in non-aqueous media and environmental waste treatment [1, 2]. The chief source of proteases are microbes, especially bacteria and fungi. *Bacillus*, *Pseudomonas*, *Aspergillus*, and *Trichoderma* sp. are the best-known sources of proteases [3]. The major limitation of the proteases recovered from such sources is that they are less stable under harsh industrial processes; hence, their enzymes are less commercially suitable. In combating these challenges, the thermophilic microbes could be an efficient reservoir to harvest extracellular proteases with improved stability [4]. These microbes could thrive under extreme temperatures, which impart tolerance to their enzymes, to function better under extremes [3, 4].

Thermophiles include microbes in all three domains of life: Archaea, Bacteria, and Eukarya. These organisms grow abundantly above 45 °C. Thermophilic properties of eukaryotes are comparatively less extreme than those of archaea and bacteria. Archaea is undoubtedly the most suitable life form, thriving in thermophilic and hyperthermophilic conditions. Yet, these organisms possess an obligate metabolism adapted to such an environment. Hence, utilizing such microbes for recombinant production in *Escherichia coli* results in less-stable products, whereas utilizing a more suitable host remains a tedious method for industrial implementation [3, 5]. On the other hand, bacteria are widespread in most thermal environments. The major difference between bacteria and archaea is that the tolerance temperature of bacteria is not as high as archaea (>80 °C). The bacteria generally thrive in temperatures ranging from 40 to 80 °C. Examples of thermophilic bacteria thriving in acidic environments is *Hydrogenobacullum* sp., neutral environments are *Sulfurihydrogenibium*, *Chloroflexus*, *Chromatium*,

Microbial Enzymes: Production, Purification, and Industrial Applications, First Edition.
Edited by Dinesh Yadav, Pankaj Chowdhary, Gautam Anand, and Rajarshi Kumar Gaur.

Spirulina, *Thermomicrospira* sp., and alkaline environments are *Thermotoga*, *Thermus*, *Bacillus*, *Synechococcus*, *Phormidium*, *Clostridium*, and *Oscillatoria* sp. [3] (see Figure 14.1).

Owing to such attributes, many attempts have been made to harvest thermophilic bacteria for stable proteases under extremes. The major drawback in producing native thermophilic proteases is the strict maintenance of higher temperatures. The thermophilic metabolism remains unique regarding higher enzymatic rates, but these are always accompanied by low cellular yields that result in lower protease production [3, 6]. Moreover, purification processes are tedious, and the protease is often rendered to lose its stability. As an alternative, several attempts have been made at the heterologous expression of thermophilic proteases, particularly in the *E. coli* host. Various thermophile genomes have been employed for the recombinant production of different proteases. Among the above, only a few strains showed successful heterologous expression of proteases [6]. Some examples of such recombinant heat-stable proteases are from the genome of *Thermus thermophilus* (serine protease) [7], *Thermophilum indigenous* (cysteine protease) [8], *Thermoascus aurantiacus* var. *levisporus* (serine protease) [9], *Bacillus* sp. (neutral protease) [10], *Coprothermobacter proteolyticus* (serine protease) [11], *Thermoanaerobacter tengcongenesis* (alkaline) [12], *Thermus* sp. (alkaline-serine protease) [13], *Bacillus thermoproteolyticus* (thermolysin) [14], *T. thermophilus* (serine protease) [15], *Thermoanaerobacter yonseiensis* (subtilisin like protease) [16], *Bacillus stearothermophilus* (alkaline protease) [17], and *Melghiribacillus thermohalophilus* (subtilisin) [18].

However, the contemporary literature lacks a comprehensive discussion on the employed approaches toward recombinant production of thermostable proteases from thermophilic bacteria. The current chapter describes thermophilic proteases' source, unique properties, and applications and presents insights into the major approaches in their recombinant production and related challenges (see Table 14.1).

14.2 Thermophilic Bacteria

Thermophilic bacteria are organisms that require high temperatures to thrive. Such organism exhibits optimum growth and functional attributes at temperatures beyond 45 °C [19]. The thermophilic bacteria were discovered in the year 1970 [20]. Since then, it has been an interesting research area. These bacteria are generally found in the thermal springs and show the potential to grow up to temperatures as high as 75 °C. Due to their unique properties, the thermophilic bacteria were observed as peculiar harbors for significant biological macromolecules. These are considered lucrative sources due to their smaller life cycle and higher yields of relatively stable enzymes [21]. The most studied bacteria among these are members of *Bacillus* (e.g. *B. stearothermophilus*) and *Clostridium* (e.g. *Clostridium thermosaccharolyticum*) spp. [20, 21]. These organisms were considered to

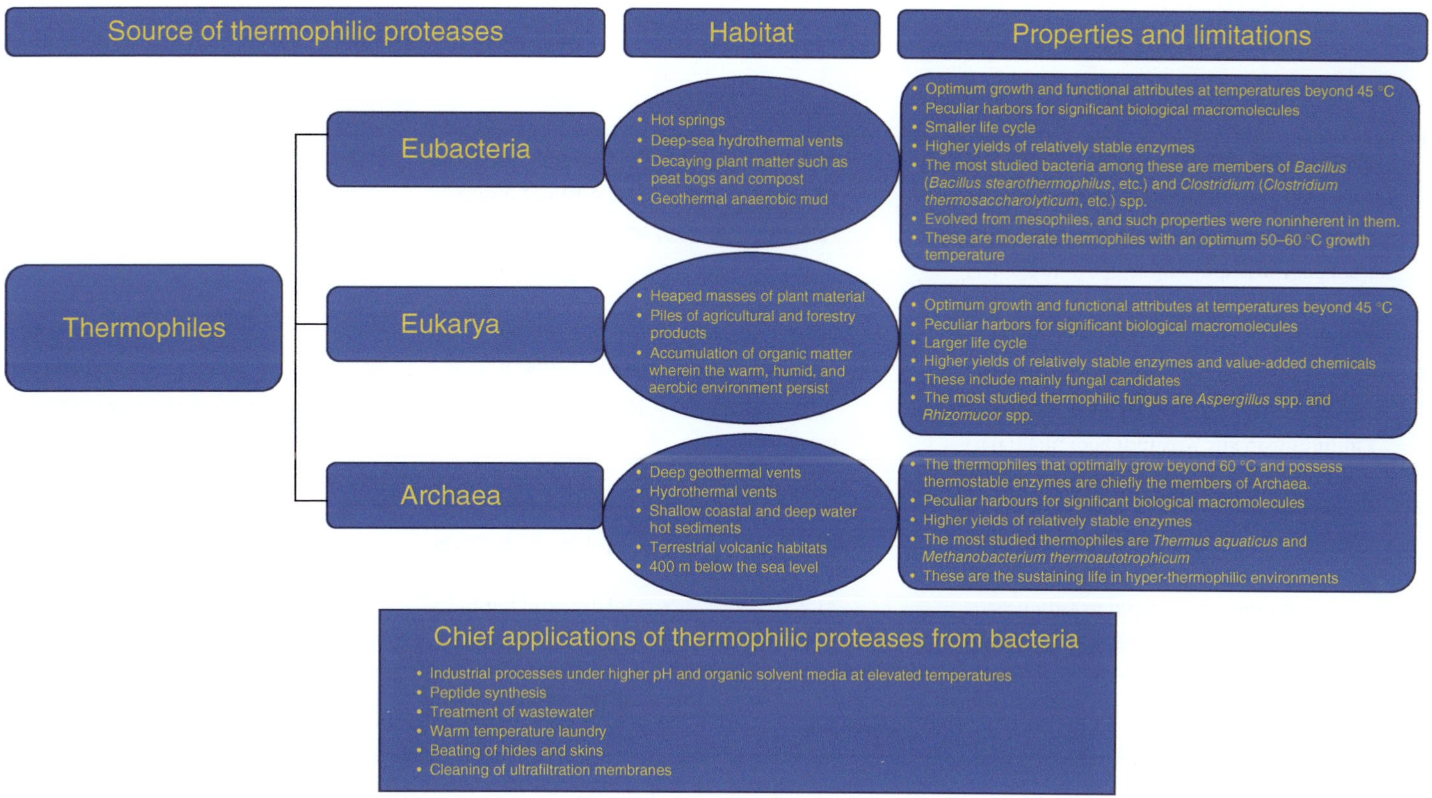

Figure 14.1 Thermophiles and their significance.

Table 14.1 Recombinant proteases from thermophilic bacteria and their applications.

Thermophilic bacteria	Type of recombinant protease	Production (IU/ml)	Applications
Thermus thermophilus	Serine protease [7]	0.25	Detergent, silk degumming
Thermophilum indigenous	Cysteine protease [8]	2.15	Digestibility of proteins and amino acids, feed additives
Thermascus aurantiacus var. *levisporus*	Serine protease [9]	1.05	Detergent, textile industry
Bacillus sp.	Neutral protease [10]	1.8	Upgrade proteins of animal and vegetable origin and food waste degradation
Coprothermobacter proteolyticus	Serine protease [11]	0.38	Detergent, food industry, silk degumming
Thermoanaerobacter tengcongenesis	Alkaline protease [12]	1.5	Detergent, feed, leather industry
Thermus sp.	Alkaline-serine protease [13]	2.2	Leather industry, laundry, food waste processing
Bacillus thermoproteolyticus	Thermolysin [14]	4.3	Reverse biocatalysts, nonaqueous biotransformation reactions, peptide synthesis
Thermus thermophilus	Serine protease [15]	4.0	Detergent, feed, leather industry, food waste
Thermoanaerobacter yonseiensis	Subtilisin like protease [16]	3.5	Detergent, food industry, silk degumming
Bacillus stearothermophilus	Alkaline protease [17]	1.25	Detergent, feed, leather industry, food waste
Melghiribacillus thermohalophilus	Subtilisin [18]	1.5	Detergent, food industry, silk degumming

have evolved from mesophiles, and such properties were non-inherent in them. Such bacteria are moderate thermophiles with an optimum 50–60 °C growth temperature. The thermophiles that optimally grow beyond 60 °C and possess thermostable enzymes are chiefly the members of Archaea. Some of such thermophiles are *Thermus aquaticus* and *Methanobacterium thermoautotrophicum* [20, 21].

Furthermore, the organisms that exhibit optimum growth at temperatures exceeding 80 °C to above 100 °C are hyperthermophiles. Such organisms are *Pyrococcus furiosus*, *Thermotoga neopolitana*, and *Thermotoga maritima*. These microbes are thought to be among the first forms of life to have evolved on Earth. Except for *Thermotogales* and *Aquifex*, all organisms that grow optimally above 80 °C are members of the group Archaea. The maximum industrial demands of robust thermophilic enzymes are chiefly recovered using moderate thermophiles, which possess a smaller life cycle, are cost-effective, and are easy to culture and harvest for enzymes [21, 22].

14.3 Thermophilic Proteases

The proteases are reported to contribute toward 60% of the total world enzyme production [1]. These find substantial applications in various industries, viz. bakery, brewing, feed, pharmaceutical, agricultural, and detergent industries. Apart from their applicability in processing silk, soy, and milk, these are also utilized for waste treatment and peptide synthesis [1, 23]. Such endeavors necessitate the enzyme's high purity and stability (under harsh conditions). Most of the proteases implemented in the industrial sectors are derived from thermophilic microbes, viz. *Bacillus*, *Clostridium*, etc. These are extremely tolerant to harsh conditions, viz., high salinity, organic solvents, temperature, and metal ion concentration [21, 22]. The enzymes sourced from mesophilic microbes are prone to proteolysis and denaturation under such extreme conditions; hence, thermozymes are efficient candidates for industrial applications [24].

There are various mechanisms through which these proteases have evolved to possess greater relative stability. These include high packing density, optimum charge patterns or ion pairs, minimization of accessible hydrophobic surface area, helix stabilization, and subunit assembly. Other factors that add to such enzymes' stability are oligomer formation and environmental factors. Moreover, the thermophilic proteases remain active at higher temperatures due to their physical features, especially the electrostatic interactions [6, 25]. The thermophilic proteases are applied in various industrial sectors, chiefly peptide synthesis and DNA modifications. Besides, the bio-detergents also include proteases, which are stable at high temperatures and in harsh conditions of surfactants. Also, meat and leather processing employ proteases under high temperatures to enhance efficiency. Moreover, the pharmaceutical and agricultural industry also demands large quantities of high-efficiency proteases [6, 25].

14.4 Stability of Thermophilic Proteases and Underlying Mechanisms

The stability of these proteases is a function of two kinds of forces: stabilizing and destabilizing forces. A delicate equilibrium between these forces is the reason for the high stability of these enzymes under extremes. A relatively small change in stabilizing or destabilizing forces can cause large changes in protease stability. A small number of extra salt bridges, hydrophobic interactions, or hydrogen bonds can confer this extra degree of stabilization. There are, therefore, no systematic structural differences between extremely stable and normal proteins [26, 27]. The stability of enzymes is interesting from a fundamental and industrial point of view. Thermozymes can function as examples of improved stability. A better understanding of the stability of thermozymes could reveal ways to stabilize other enzymes. Engineering of mesophilic enzymes might be an option when specific functionality cannot be found among thermozymes. The first studies on thermostability focused on amino acid sequences. More recently, crystal structures of thermozymes have been compared with those of their mesophilic counterparts. This gives extra insight into their mechanism of stability [26, 27].

The conformational stability of proteins results from a compromise between two opposing factors: flexibility for the enzyme's catalytic function and rigidity for conformational stability. Thermozymes are significantly more rigid than their mesophilic counterparts at room temperature. Their high rigidity protects them from unfolding and preserves their catalytically active structure. Therefore, they can be optimally active under more denaturing conditions (e.g. higher temperatures) [28–31].

Basic stability mechanisms are high packing density, optimum charge patterns or ion pairs, minimization of accessible hydrophobic surface area, helix stabilization, and subunit assembly. Oligomer formation and other environmental factors can further stabilize the enzyme [32, 33].

14.4.1 Internal Stabilization

Maximum packing efficiency of an enzyme can be achieved by filling cavities in of the molecular structure and increasing core hydrophobicity. Higher levels of isoleucine, alanines, and prolines are suggested, providing tighter packing in hydrophobic cores and extra stability to loops. Vieille et al. [34] listed several thermozymes with increased hydrophobicity, but only two have increased packing efficiency. Enhanced helix stabilization can contribute to thermostability in various ways. Most important is the loss of conformational entropy of amino acid residues in helical arrangements. Amino acids branched on Cβ (i.e. valine, isoleucine, and threonine) cause more conformational restraints, and, therefore, they occur less frequently in thermozymes. Additionally, specific amino acid compositions at the helical ends can influence stability, but this phenomenon is not unique to thermozymes [34–36]. Another way to stabilize enzymes is to increase stabilizing interactions in the folded protein. Disulfide bridges can stabilize the enzyme by increasing the conformational rigidity [37]. Hydrogen bonds might also stabilize the enzyme. The increasing number of known three-dimensional structures has made it possible to see the importance of ion pairs organized in large networks [38]. These networks at the surface of proteins are believed to be a major stabilizing factor for thermostability. Arginines frequently occur in ion-pair networks and, indeed, in higher numbers in enzymes from hyperthermophiles [37, 38].

Stabilizing interactions between domains and subunits also contribute significantly to the intrinsic stability of proteins. Enzymes from (hyper)thermophilic organisms are known to exist as higher-order association states than their mesophilic analogs, suggesting that the formation of oligomers increases thermostability [34–36]. At temperatures above 100 °C, inactivation of enzymes is mainly caused by chemical modification of the protein rather than by irreversible unfolding. Examples of non-enzymatic irreversible reactions or irreversible covalent modifications are the deamidation of asparagine and glutamine and the oxidative degradation of cysteine, methionine, and tryptophan [37, 38]. Enzymes with lower levels of asparagine, glutamine, cysteine, methionine, and tryptophan are less susceptible to degradation by chemical modification [36–38].

14.4.2 Environmental Factors

Although most enzymes from (hyper)thermophilic organisms are intrinsically very stable, some intracellular enzymes obtain their thermostability from intracellular environmental factors. Salts, high-protein concentrations, coenzymes, substrates, activators, or general stabilizers such as thermamine, sorbitol, or cyclic polyphosphates can stabilize the enzyme. By manipulating the environmental conditions, one can sometimes achieve higher thermostability than by applying genetic engineering [37, 39, 40]. Cell-bound thermozymes such as saccharidases and proteases are active at temperatures (far) above the optimal growing temperature of the organism and are, as a rule, highly stable. Some other environmental factors that can be important are chemical cross-linking, immobilization, and glycosylation. Glycosylation has various effects, but only in some cases is protein stability improved [41].

Glycosylation can also improve the efficiency of tertiary protein assembly. The latter effect involves the stabilization of the nascent rather than the native protein. A final method for enzyme stabilization is using ultrahigh pressure (up to 50 MPa), which may lead to more compact structures and, thus, higher thermostability [41, 42].

14.5 Significance of Thermophilic Proteases

The main reason for selecting enzymes from thermophiles is their high stability, which makes them attractive for several industrial processes. It is useful in many applications because of its thermostability and greater stability under extreme conditions, such as high pH or low water concentrations. Stable enzymes are also more likely to allow organic solvents and detergents and are more resistant to proteolytic attack [43–46]. For example, proteases are used as an additive in household laundry detergents, which must resist denaturation by surfactants and alkaline conditions [45, 46].

A further advantage of using higher temperatures is the reduced risk of contamination. Temperatures above 70 °C are sufficiently high to kill almost all pathogenic bacteria and greatly reduce the numbers of the bacteria most likely to cause troublesome contamination of food processes. Another advantage of applying thermostable enzymes for production is the lower viscosity of process fluids. At higher temperatures, viscosity is usually reduced, lowering shear and, consequently, the costs of pumping, filtration, and centrifugation or allowing lower water levels during processing. Heat and mass transfer rates are also improved [43, 44].

At higher temperatures, diffusion rates will increase, and mass transfer is less limiting. In addition, more substrate will dissolve at higher temperatures, shifting the equilibrium to a higher product yield. This is the case, e.g. in reversed hydrolysis reactions in water [43, 44]. It is often speculated that thermozymes should have higher maximal catalytic rates since classic reaction rate theory states that the rate of a chemical reaction increases with temperature. These higher maximal catalytic rates, however, are not found experimentally [44, 45]. Despite their activity at high temperatures, thermophilic enzymes catalyze reactions with K_m and V_{max} values similar to those of their mesophilic counterparts at their optimal temperature [44]. As expected, thermozyme activity is driven by temperature-dependent substrate kinetic energy variation alone. If the enzyme structure changed significantly with different temperatures, one would expect to find non-linear Arrhenius plots, which is not the case. However, thermozymes do have a broader temperature range in which they are active [43–46].

An important disadvantage of enzymatic processes at higher temperatures is the loss of selectivity and formation of by-products. Furthermore, possible required cofactors, substrates, or products might be unstable, and side reactions, such as Maillard reactions in sugar–enzyme mixtures, may occur. Some processes will have higher costs due to additional heating, and others are less likely to need cooling. Whether operation at higher temperatures is beneficial depends on the overall process and implementation. Applications with thermozymes are often found when the enzymatic process is compatible with existing (high-temperature) process conditions [43, 45, 46].

14.6 Recombinant Thermophilic Protease Production Strategies and Related Challenges

In the current scenario, overexpression of proteases from thermophiles in standard *E. coli* or other organisms such as *Saccharomyces cerevisiae* allows the production of much larger quantities of enzymes that are easy to purify by heat treatment. Thermal denaturation will affect only the host's mesophilic enzymes, and the precipitated proteins can be eliminated by centrifugation, leaving the thermophilic enzyme in solution. Despite being synthesized in a mesophilic host, recombinant thermophilic enzymes usually have kinetic and thermal characteristics identical to the native protein [47, 48]. The influence of strong promoters like T7, etc., through the *E. coli* host channel plays a major role in the recombinant production of putative proteases from the genome of thermophilic bacteria. A few studies show the successful production of proteases from thermophilic sources [47, 49, 50]. In particular, the genera *Bacillus* spp. and *Thermus* spp. strains are utilized for heterologous expression of thermostable proteases. Different proteases, such as metallo, serine, cysteine, and neutral proteases, have been reported from the genomes of thermophilic bacteria. Researchers reported a heat-stable cysteine protease from *T. thermophilus* [7]. This yielded an overall production of 0.25 IU/ml. Another similar research reported alkaline proteases from thermophiles viz. *T. tengcongenesis* (1.5 IU/ml) [12], and *Thermus* sp. (2.2 IU/ml) [13].

Many such studies described the production of serine proteases from *T. thermophilus* (4.3 IU/ml), *Thermus aurantiacus* (4.0 IU/ml), *Thermus* sp. (3.5 IU/ml), and *M. thermohalophilus* (1.23 IU/ml). A single study reported the production of thermolysin, a zinc metalloprotease (1.5 IU/ml) [15–18]. The studies presented very limited attempts at protease production from thermophilic bacteria. Hence, it needs to be explored more for such an endeavor. However, the protease production yielded less through heterologous expression methods, while the productivity was enhanced due to the less time for the enzyme production. This could be a major limitation restricting contemporary research toward this aspect of enzyme production methods. This instigates studies to develop techniques for enhancing the production of such heat-stable proteases with high yields.

In light of the above, methods such as response surface methodology, media engineering, and enzyme engineering were incorporated to enhance the yield to better levels. Combining heterologous expression systems with the proper selection of media conditions and enzyme engineering techniques leads to highly improved yields of thermophilic proteases, which are equally active and stable under harsh industrial conditions [51]. Media engineering and response surface methodology correspond to the right choice of production media, constituting the optimum amount of salts and substrates for higher, active, and stable protease yields [51, 52]. The enzyme engineering approach is undertaken for the dramatic fold-enhancement in protease yield and higher stability. This technique is mainly attempted to improve the characteristics and yield of the thermophilic proteases [51, 52].

14.7 Enzyme Engineering Strategies

Research into the mechanisms of thermostability provides fundamental knowledge of enzyme structure. It allows us to modify enzymes to improve their stability specifically. Enzymes with specific catalytic functions that cannot be found among thermozymes may be engineered from the appropriate mesophilic enzymes [4, 53]. Different approaches can be used to stabilize a (mesophilic) enzyme against inactivation by unfolding. Promising strategies are often directed at protein surface loops and turns. Surface residues typically involve fewer intermolecular interactions than internal residues and are less likely to create volume interferences. Stabilizing or creating ion pairs and reducing conformational strain in helices can be successful. Additional disulfide bridges have been introduced with varying success. They should be introduced where they put less strain on the protein structure. Also, cysteine residues are unstable at about or above 100 °C, rendering them less suitable for this purpose [38, 54, 55]. Various strategies to improve core packing, such as stabilization of α-helices, have shown varying results, and the gain in stability is usually small.

To stabilize thermophilic enzymes further, the inactivation mechanism must first be identified. As discussed, inactivation above 100 °C is often caused by covalent modification rather than unfolding, as with mesozymes. This type of inactivation may be prevented by substituting specific surface amino acids such as asparagine, glutamine, cysteine, methionine, and tryptophan with residues less susceptible to degradation [4, 38, 56]. Until now, protein engineering of thermozymes has mainly focused on improving and understanding thermostability. The main goal is to improve the activity of (mesophilic) enzymes at higher temperatures and other extreme conditions. Less attention is given to engineering thermozymes to change activity or enlarge selectivity. This can be further extended to other proteases of industrial importance. Several attempts have been made to enhance the yield and stability of the proteases [38, 56, 57]. For instance, a structural gene from *B. stearothermophilus* was cloned in the pTB90 plasmid and expressed in the *B. subtilis* strain. The results exhibited a 15-fold increase in protease production than the wild-type strain. Other studies focus on determining specific gene sequences responsible for heat stability in the proteases to engineer such genes for improved stability successfully [58]. A study used a sequence of a serine protease from a thermophilic bacteria, *Aquifex pyrophiles*, to determine residues in the catalytic sites [59]. Another study targeted an "npr" gene from *B. thermoproteolyticus* encoding for thermolysin. It was expressed in *B. subtilis* to deduce the enzyme's primary structure for future genetic manipulation studies [60].

Site-directed mutagenesis approach has been employed to improve the performance of trypsin and carboxypeptidase. This can be further extended to other proteases of industrial importance [9, 61, 62].

14.8 Applications

Proteases hydrolyze proteins into amino acids and peptides. Thermostable proteases are already used in several industrial processes. They function in various industrial processes under higher pH and organic solvent media at elevated temperatures. Daniel et al. listed several thermostable proteases. The best-characterized thermostable protease is probably thermolysin, produced by *B. thermoproteolyticus* [63]. Using proteases at higher temperatures raises a specific problem: heat enhances autolysis, i.e. self-digestion of proteases. The resulting conformational unfolding leads to much faster autolysis because the (partially) unfolded form of the enzyme is a particularly good substrate for the protease molecules that are still active. The better susceptibility of the substrate to proteolytic attack results in higher specific activities for the proteases from the thermophilic origin [63, 64]. Because most commercial protease substrates are mesophilic proteins, proteases have a high industrial potential. A method to prevent autolysis might be the immobilization of the enzyme [65, 66]. Thermostable proteases are used in peptide synthesis mainly because of their compatibility with organic solvents. The major currently used thermostable protease is thermolysin, which is used in the synthesis of the dipeptide *N*-CBZ-L-Asp-L-Phe-methyl-ester, which is the precursor in the preparation of the sweetener aspartame [66]. In the process that employs immobilized thermolysin, the enzyme's compatibility with organic solvents is more crucial than its use at high temperatures [65, 66]. Another actively marketed thermostable protease is a Thermus protease, Pretaq, used to clean up DNA before amplifying the polymerase chain reaction (PCR). The commercial success of this application may be owing to the relatively cost-intensive nature of the application. Proteases resistant to alkalinity and anionic or non-ionic surfactants are additives in domestic laundry detergents. Improved stability is desirable, but thermostable proteases must still be produced sufficiently to be cost-competitive [67].

Moreover, current trends in laundering processes toward lower temperatures may present another barrier. The use of thermozymes in laundry detergents for institutional (e.g. hospital) use may be a future application because especially high temperatures are required in those processes. A larger application might be thermophilic enzymes in (domestic) dishwashing detergent. In this case, much higher pHs are applied (about 9), combined with temperatures of about 60 °C [65, 66].

A thermostable protease would easily withstand this pH and temperatures above 60 °C. Proteases showing high keratinolytic and elastolytic activities are used for soaking in the leather industry. Thermophilic proteases could better be applied to the beating of hides and skins at acid (pH 2.5–5.0) and alkaline (pH 12.0–13.0) conditions. Several proteases have been tested for application in cleaning ultrafiltration membranes [32]. Thermostable proteases at high temperatures (and low viscosities) may allow these products to be reused, which may lead to reduced chemical use and waste production. Presently, no thermophilic proteases are available for this application. Other potential applications are found in meat tenderizing, in which the ideal meat-tenderizing enzyme would be active only during preparation and not storage [65–67].

14.9 Conclusion and Future Perspectives

Thermozymes are already found in several existing processes and have the potential for much wider application (mention proteases in the conclusion). They can replace enzymes from mesophiles in processes that benefit from a higher operating temperature. Synthesis processes can be operated at higher temperatures at other beneficial conditions, such as higher substrate concentrations. In addition, thermozymes play a central role in newly developed processes, such as PCR, that could not be efficiently performed before the discovery of thermozymes. Thermozymes can be applied as biocatalysts in existing industrial processes to replace presently used, often polluting, chemical reagents. This is especially true for the pulp and paper industry, which has problems with aggressive waste from the bleaching process. Daniel et al. state that the theoretical upper limit of enzyme thermal stability might be well above 130 °C [63]. If these enzymes cannot be found in nature, engineering might develop them. This, and the enhanced stability under other extreme conditions, will further broaden the field in which thermozymes can be used. The production of thermozymes in mesophilic organisms makes large-scale production and easy purification of these enzymes possible. Therefore, it is expected that with wider availability and lower costs, thermophilic enzymes will be increasingly applied in industry.

References

1 Srivastava, N., Shiburaj, S., and Khare, S.K. (2023). Pan-genomic comparison of a potential solvent-tolerant alkaline protease-producing *Exiguobacterium* sp. TBG-PICH-001 isolated from a marine habitat. *3 Biotech* 13 (11): 1–17.

2 Srivastava, N., Kumar, S., Shiburaj, S. et al. (2021). Cellular adaptation responses in a halotolerant *Exiguobacterium* exhibiting organic solvent tolerance with simultaneous protease production. *Environ. Technol. Innov.* 23: 101803.

3 Ferrera, I., Aristegui, J., González, J.M. et al. (2015). Transient changes in bacterioplankton communities induced by the submarine volcanic eruption of El Hierro (Canary Islands). *PLoS One* 10 (2): 118–136.

4 Kumar, S., Dangi, A.K., Shukla, P. et al. (2019). Thermozymes: adaptive strategies and tools for their biotechnological applications. *Bioresour. Technol.* 278 (January): 372–382.

5 Kishishita, S., Fujii, T., and Ishikawa, K. (2015). Heterologous expression of hyperthermophilic cellulases of archaea *Pyrococcus* sp. by fungus *Talaromyces cellulolyticus. J. Ind. Microbiol. Biotechnol.* 42 (1): 137–141.

6 Vaidya, A., Nair, V., Georrge John, J., and Singh, S.P. (2018). Comparative analysis of thermophilic proteases. *Life Sci. Inf. Publ.* 4 (November): 65–91.

7 Xie, G., Shao, Z., Zong, L. et al. (2019). Heterologous expression and characterization of a novel subtilisin-like protease from a thermophilic *Thermus thermophilus* HB8. *Int. J. Biol. Macromol.* 138: 528–535.

8 Tarrahimofrad, H., Meimandipour, A., Arjmand, S. et al. (2020). Structural and biochemical characterization of a novel thermophilic Coh01147 protease. *PLoS One* 15 (6): 1–29.

9 Li, S., Zhang, L., Wu, Q. et al. (2011). Increasing the refolding efficiency in vitro by site-directed mutagenesis of Cys383 in rat procarboxypeptidase B. *Enzyme Microb. Technol.* 49 (2): 139–145.

10 Peek, K., Veitch, D.P., Prescott, M. et al. (1993). Some characteristics of a proteinase from a thermophilic Bacillus sp. expressed in *Escherichia coli*: comparison with the native enzyme and its processing in *E. coli* and in vitro. *Appl. Environ. Microbiol.* 59 (4): 1168–1175.

11 Toplak, A., Wu, B., Fusetti, F. et al. (2013). Proteolysin, a novel highly thermostable and cosolvent-compatible protease from the thermophilic bacterium *Coprothermobacter proteolyticus*. *Appl. Environ. Microbiol.* 79 (18): 5625–5632.

12 Koma, D., Yamanaka, H., Moriyoshi, K. et al. (2007). Overexpression and characterization of thermostable serine protease in *Escherichia coli* encoded by the ORF TTE0824 from *Thermoanaerobacter tengcongensis*. *Extremophiles* 11 (6): 769–779.

13 Munro, G.K.L., McHale, R.H., Saul, D.J. et al. (1995). A gene encoding a thermophilic alkaline serine proteinase from *Thermos* sp. strain Rt41A and its expression in *Escherichia coli*. *Microbiology* 141 (7): 1731–1738.

14 Inouye, K., Minoda, M., Takita, T. et al. (2006). Extracellular production of recombinant thermolysin expressed in *Escherichia coli*, and its purification and enzymatic characterization. *Protein Expression Purif.* 46 (2): 248–255.

15 Li, H., Sun, Y., Jiao, X. et al. (2016). Purification and characterization of thermostable serine proteases encoded by the genes ttha0099 and ttha01320 from *Thermus thermophilus* HB8. *Extremophiles* 20 (4): 493–502.

16 Hyeung, J.J., Byoung, C.K., Yu, R.P., and Yu, S.K. (2002). A novel subtilisin-like serine protease from *Thermoanaerobacter yonseiensis* KB-1: its cloning, expression, and biochemical properties. *Extremophiles* 6 (3): 233–243.

17 Fu, Z., Hamid, S.B.A., Razak, C.N.A. et al. (2003). Secretory expression in *Escherichia coli* and single-step purification of a heat-stable alkaline protease. *Protein Expr. Purif.* 28 (1): 63–68.

18 Mechri, S., Zaraî Jaouadi, N., Bouacem, K. et al. (2021). Cloning and heterologous expression of subtilisin SAPN, a serine alkaline protease from *Melghiribacillus thermohalophilus* Nari2AT in *Escherichia coli* and *Pichia pastoris*. *Process Biochem.* 105 (January): 27–41.

19 Oztas Gulmus, E. and Gormez, A. (2020). Identification and characterization of novel thermophilic bacteria from Hot Springs, Erzurum, Turkey. *Curr. Microbiol.* 77 (6): 979–987.

20 Zeikus, J.G. (1979). Thermophilic bacteria: ecology, physiology and technology. *Enzyme Microb. Technol.* 4 (1): 243–252.

21 Lakra, U., Lincoln Singh Munda, V., Nigam, V.K., and Sharma, S.R. (2023). Optimisation, characterization, and biological evaluation of novel exopolysaccharide from *Bacillus licheniformis* (BITSL006). *Nat. Prod. Res.* 1–10. https://doi.org/10.1080/14786419.2023.2265041.

22 Chen, S., Gu, J., Zhang, S., and Yu, R. (2023). Application of hyperthermophiles in sludge composting: a review. *Environ. Chem. Lett.* 22: 445–460.

23 Kumar, S.S., Jithin, V., Jijeesh, V. et al. (2018). Production and purification of alkaline protease from *Exiguobacterium indicum* TBG-PICH-001 isolated from soil samples of Pichavaram Estuary (Tamil Nadu). *Indian J. Geo-Mar. Sci.* 47 (3): 580–586.

24 Hassan, M.M., Li, H., Ahmad, W. et al. (2019). Au@Ag nanostructure based SERS substrate for simultaneous determination of pesticides residue in tea via solid phase extraction coupled multivariate calibration. *Lwt* 105: 290–297.

25 Cowan, D., Daniel, R., and Morgan, H. (1985). Thermophilic proteases: properties and potential applications. *Trends Biotechnol.* 3 (3): 68–72.

26 Kumar, S., Tsai, C.J., and Nussinov, R. (2000). Factors enhancing protein thermostability. *Protein Eng.* 13 (3): 179–191.

27 Razvi, A. and Scholtz, J.M. (2006). Lessons in stability from thermophilic proteins. *Protein Sci.* 15 (7): 1569–1578.

28 Bommarius, A.S. and Paye, M.F. (2013). Stabilizing biocatalysts. *Chem. Soc. Rev.* 42 (15): 6534–6565.

29 Jaenicke, R. (1999). Stability and folding of domain proteins. *Prog. Biophys. Mol. Biol.* 71 (2): 155–241.

30 Isaksen, G.V., Åqvist, J., and Brandsdal, B.O. (2016). Enzyme surface rigidity tunes the temperature dependence of catalytic rates. *Proc. Natl. Acad. Sci. U. S. A.* 113 (28): 7822–7827.

31 Karshikoff, A., Nilsson, L., and Ladenstein, R. (2015). Rigidity versus flexibility: the dilemma of understanding protein thermal stability. *FEBS J.* 282 (20): 3899–3917.

32 Samanta, D., Govil, T., Saxena, P. et al. (2022). Extremozymes and their applications. *Extrem. Ind. Appl.* 90: 1–39.

33 Auerbach, G., Ostendorp, R., Prade, L. et al. (1998). Lactate dehydrogenase from the hyperthermophilic bacterium *Thermotoga maritima*: the crystal structure at 2.1 Å resolution reveals strategies for intrinsic protein stabilization. *Structure* 6 (6): 769–781.

34 Vieille, C., Burdette, D.S., and Zeikus, J.G. (1996). Thermozymes. *Biotechnol. Annu. Rev.* 2 (C): 1–83.

35 Herning, T., Yutani, K., Inaka, K. et al. (1992). Role of proline residues in human lysozyme stability: a scanning calorimetric study combined with X-ray structure analysis of proline mutants. *Biochemistry* 31 (31): 7077–7085.

36 Kanchi, P.K. and Dasmahapatra, A.K. (2021). Destabilization of the Alzheimer's amyloid-β peptide by a proline-rich β-sheet breaker peptide: a molecular dynamics simulation study. *J. Mol. Model.* 27 (12): 1–15.

37 Li, W.F., Zhou, X.X., and Lu, P. (2005). Structural features of thermozymes. *Biotechnol. Adv.* 23 (4): 271–281.

38 Wu, H., Chen, Q., Zhang, W., and Mu, W. (2023). Overview of strategies for developing high thermostability industrial enzymes: discovery, mechanism, modification and challenges. *Crit. Rev. Food Sci. Nutr.* 63 (14): 2057–2073.

39 Rakshit, S.K. (2006). Thermozymes. In: *Enzyme Technology*, vol. 23(4) (ed. A. Pandey, C. Webb, C.R. Soccol, and C. Larroche), 603–614.

40 Hamdan, S.H., Maiangwa, J., Ali, M.S.M. et al. (2021). Thermostable lipases and their dynamics of improved enzymatic properties. *Appl. Microbiol. Biotechnol.* 105 (19): 7069–7094.

41 Atalah, J., Cáceres-Moreno, P., Espina, G., and Blamey, J.M. (2019). Thermophiles and the applications of their enzymes as new biocatalysts. *Bioresour. Technol.* 280: 478–488.

42 Sardiña-Peña, A.J., Mesa-Ramos, L., Iglesias-Figueroa, B.F. et al. (2023). Analyzing current trends and possible strategies to improve sucrose isomerases' thermostability. *Int. J. Mol. Sci.* 24 (19): 14513.

43 Xu, Y., Xuan, X., and Gao, R. (2023). Increased expression levels of thermophilic serine protease TTHA0724 through signal peptide screening in bacillus subtilis and applications of the enzyme. *Int. J. Mol. Scie.* 24: 15950.

44 Finore, I., Feola, A., Russo, L. et al. (2023). Thermophilic bacteria and their thermozymes in composting processes: a review. *Chem. Biol. Technol. Agric.* 10 (1): 1–22.

45 Valenzuela, B., Solís-Cornejo, F., Araya, R., and Zamorano, P. (2023). Isolation and characterization of *Thermus thermophilus* strain ET-1: an extremely thermophilic bacterium with extracellular thermostable proteolytic activity isolated from El Tatio Geothermal Field, Antofagasta, Chile. *Int. J. Mol. Sci.* 24 (19): 1–16.

46 E Ibrahim, N. and Ma, K. (2017). Industrial applications of thermostable enzymes from extremophilic microorganisms. *Curr. Biochem. Eng.* 4 (2): 75–98.

47 Turner, P., Mamo, G., and Karlsson, E.N. (2007). Potential and utilization of thermophiles and thermostable enzymes in biorefining. *Microb. Cell Fact.* 6: 1–23.

48 Yang, Z., Gao, X., Xie, H. et al. (2017). Enhanced itaconic acid production by self-assembly of two biosynthetic enzymes in *Escherichia coli*. *Biotechnol. Bioeng.* 114 (2): 457–462.

49 Wang, C., Dong, D., Wang, H. et al. (2016). Metagenomic analysis of microbial consortia enriched from compost: new insights into the role of Actinobacteria in lignocellulose decomposition. *Biotechnol. Biofuels* 9 (1): 1–17.

50 Manikandan, S., Subbaiya, R., Biruntha, M. et al. (2022). Recent development patterns, utilization and prospective of biofuel production: emerging nanotechnological intervention for environmental sustainability – a review. *Fuel* 314: 122757.

51 Adetunji, A.R., Isadare, D.A., Akinluwade, K.J., and Adewoye, O.O. (2015). Waste-to-wealth applications of cassava – a review. *Study Ind. Agric. Appl.* 4 (4): 212–229.

52 Zhang, Y., Hu, J., Zhang, Q. et al. (2023). Enhancement of alkaline protease production in recombinant *Bacillus licheniformis* by response surface methodology. *Bioresour. Bioprocess.* 10 (1): 27.

53 Rigoldi, F., Donini, S., Redaelli, A. et al. (2018). Review: engineering of thermostable enzymes for industrial applications. *APL Bioeng.* 2 (1): 011501.

54 Han, H., Ling, Z., Khan, A. et al. (2019). Improvements of thermophilic enzymes: from genetic modifications to applications. *Bioresour. Technol.* 279 (January): 350–361.

55 Frock, A.D. and Kelly, R.M. (2012). Extreme thermophiles: moving beyond single-enzyme biocatalysis. *Curr. Opin. Chem. Eng.* 1 (4): 363–372.

56 Janeček, Š. (1993). Strategies for obtaining stable enzymes. *Process Biochem.* 28 (7): 435–445.

57 Xu, Z., Xue, Y.P., Zou, S.P., and Zheng, Y.G. (2020). Enzyme engineering strategies to confer thermostability. *Biomass, Biofuels, Biochemicals* 1 (1): 67–89.

58 Bhatt, K., Lal, S., Ramakrishnan, S., and Joshi, B. (2020). Bioconversion of agriculture wastes to produce α-amylase from *Bacillus velezensis* KB 2216: purification and characterization. *Biocatal. Agric. Biotechnol.* 28 (August): 101703.

59 Kori, L.D. (2011). Extremozymes of the hot and salty *Halothermothrix orenii* Statement of Originality.

60 Bach, H.J., Hartmann, A., Schloter, M., and Munch, J.C. (2001). PCR primers and functional probes for amplification and detection of bacterial genes for extracellular peptidases in single strains and in soil. *J. Microbiol. Methods* 44 (2): 173–182.

61 Xiong, K., Liu, J., Wang, X. et al. (2021). Engineering a carboxypeptidase from *Aspergillus niger* M00988 by mutation to increase its ability in high Fischer ratio oligopeptide preparation. *J. Biotechnol.* 330: 1–8.

62 Ventura, S., Villegas, V., Sterner, J. et al. (1999). Mapping the pro-region of carboxypeptidase B by protein engineering: cloning, overexpression, and mutagenesis of the porcine proenzyme. *J. Biol. Chem.* 274 (28): 19925–19933.

63 Daniel, R.M., Toogood, H.S., and Bergquist, P.L. (1996). Thermostable proteases. *Biotechnol. Genet. Eng. Rev.* 13 (1996): 87–100.

64 Guo, Y., Tu, T., Zheng, J. et al. (2019). Improvement of BsAPA aspartic protease thermostability via autocatalysis-resistant mutation. *J. Agric. Food Chem.* 67 (37): 10505–10512.

65 Barzkar, N., Homaei, A., Hemmati, R., and Patel, S. (2018). Thermostable marine microbial proteases for industrial applications: scopes and risks. *Extremophiles* 22 (3): 335–346.

66 Satyanarayana, T., Kawarabayasi, Y., and Littlechild, J. (2013). *Thermophilic Microbes in Environmental and Industrial Biotechnology: Biotechnology of Thermophiles*, 1–956. Springer.

67 Kochhar, N., Kavya, I.K., Shrivastava, S. et al. (2022). Perspectives on the microorganism of extreme environments and their applications. *Curr. Res. Microb. Sci.* 3: 100134.

15

Mining and Redesigning of Microbial Enzymes for the Degradation of Organophosphorus Pesticides

Fauzia Parween and Rinkoo D. Gupta

South Asian University, Faculty of Life Sciences and Biotechnology, Rajpur Road, Maidan Garhi, New Delhi 110068, India

15.1 Introduction

Organophosphorus (OP) compounds are commonly used esters of phosphate having a general molecular formula of $O{=}P(OR)_3$. They are the product of the reaction between phosphoric acid and alcohol [1]. Despite a ban on their use, they are persistently used to fulfill both constructive and heinous purposes due to their ease of use, low production cost, and high efficiency [2]. The OPs, which include pesticides, nerve agents (NAs), and chemical warfare agents (CWAs), are highly toxic compounds [3]. OPs compounds account for 38% of the total pesticides used around the globe [4]. They are ubiquitously employed and still an integral part of agriculture. These compounds pose significant health threats, pollute the surrounding environment, and are responsible for numerous death cases each year [5, 6]. Reportedly, 25 school children in India died due to the contamination of their mid-day meals with an agricultural pesticide, monocrotophos [7]. Furthermore, there are three million cases of pesticide poisoning every year according to the World Health Organization (WHO) report [8]. There is evidence of its misuse by terrorists or extremist government organizations as ordnance of mass destruction even today [9]. The Syrian government bombarded the cities of Ghouta (in 2013) and Khan Shaykhun (in 2017) within their borders to conquer insurgency with sarin gas, a human-made NA [10]. Therefore, these compounds never completely disappear into ambiguity. The credit for the first time synthesis of the OP compounds goes to Wladimir Moschnin and Phillipe de Clemont in the late nineteenth century [11, 12]. Since then, the OP compounds have evolved promptly from CWAs to pesticides and are used commercially worldwide [2]. NAs are more toxic than pesticides, about 100–10,000 times [3]. In 2017, NAs were used for the murder of a North Korean leader's half-brother. Again in 2018, the NA, Novichok was used in the attempted murder of a former Russian spy [13, 14].

Although OP pesticides and CWAs are diverse in structure and composition, they function through a similar mechanism. Most of them disrupt the enzyme acetylcholinesterase (AChE), a critical component of the neuromuscular junction [6, 15].

Microbial Enzymes: Production, Purification, and Industrial Applications, First Edition.
Edited by Dinesh Yadav, Pankaj Chowdhary, Gautam Anand, and Rajarshi Kumar Gaur.

This leads to a cholinergic crisis due to the accumulation of acetylcholine (ACh), a neurotransmitter, in the synaptic cleft. As a result, there is overstimulation of ACh receptors characterized by various abnormal neurological symptoms [16, 17]. Likewise, their long-term impact on the environment due to prolonged usage needs attention. Recent and continuous studies on OP compounds have fueled scientific research in the development of novel pesticides that are safer. For ensuring public safety emphasis is laid on the innovation of economical and accessible technologies for the detection and detoxification of OPs from the environment [18].

OP hydrolyzing enzymes or OP hydrolase (OPH) are emerging as appealing targets due to their potential to hydrolyze both NAs and pesticides [19]. They are biologically derived, environment friendly, and do not leave a long-lasting impact on underground water, soil, vegetation, or animal life [2]. The use of OPH offers significant advantages for environmental decontamination. Administration of microbes, natively expressing OPH or engineered to express it constitutes whole cell-based remediation [20]. However, researchers are looking for alternative strategies for OP bioremediation as the delivery of genetically engineered organisms is not accepted universally. Moreover, there are other challenges to the whole cell-based bioremediation like the release of enzymes from the cells [4]. Therefore, the focus is now on cell-free enzyme systems [21]. Nature has evolved a diverse group of enzymes that are proficient in degrading the OP compounds. Extensive research with a diverse approach is being carried out to improve the activity, substrate tolerance, and stability of OPH [22]. Thus, enhancing their interest as detoxifying agents [23].

In this chapter, we have described the protein engineering techniques for the designing of novel enzymes with enhanced enzymatic activity. First, we have described the selection of a starting gene, which includes *in silico* designing, wild-type gene, and metagenomic approach. Second, various methods of mutagenesis have been described. Once the mutant gene library is ready, a high-throughput screening (HTS) and selection procedures are required to expand the repository of improved biocatalysts feasible for industrial applications. The dearth of effective screening assay hinders the success of these efforts. Thus, in the last decade, number of screening and selection strategies that have been developed has increased dramatically [24]. An overview of the protein engineering technique is depicted here in Figure 15.1.

15.2 Selection of the Starting Gene

Moonlighting and promiscuity are two natural dimensions of enzyme evolution that can form the basis of the study of redesigning of enzymes [25]. There are multiple examples that show enzymes involved in natural product biosynthesis possess several features that promote enzyme promiscuity [26]. Gene duplication and divergence are the key mechanisms by which enzymes have evolved a varied number of new metabolic and regulatory activities [27]. For the selection of the starting gene, various approaches taken are discussed below. However, the major challenge lies

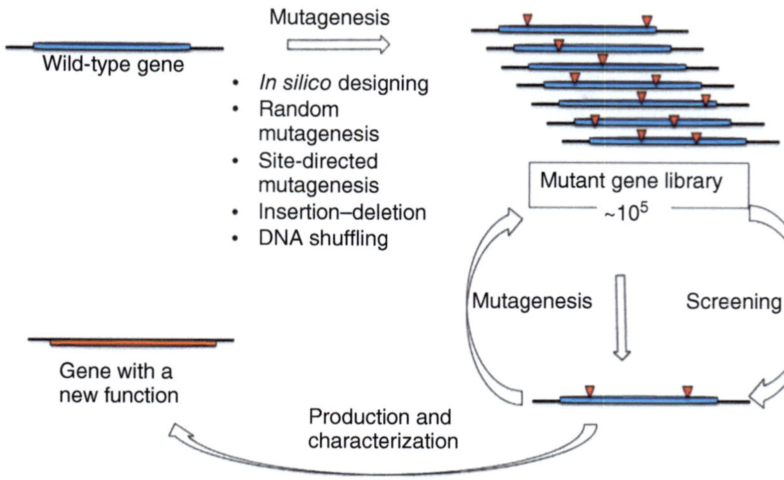

Figure 15.1 An overview of protein engineering. Different strategies may be adopted for the evolution of the selected wild-type gene. A library of mutants is obtained, which is further screened and selected based on the desired function.

in the exhibition of biodegradative capabilities by native microorganisms at sites contaminated with diverse groups of OP compounds or where multiple biodegradation traits are required [28]. A wild-type gene exhibiting detectable level of OP hydrolyzing property can be selected as a starting gene. The source of the gene can be a well-characterized gene, an isolate from the metagenomic library or a synthetic gene designed *in silico* by bioinformatic analysis.

15.2.1 Metagenomics Approach

Microorganisms make use of natural evolution to obtain the desired bioconversion activity. Exploring the environments that most probably host those microorganisms with the required characteristics would be valuable [29]. Considering this, the soil microorganisms are found to be a good source of OP hydrolase enzyme due to their direct exposure to pesticides in the agricultural fields. However, less than 1% of all microorganisms present in the environmental samples are culturable [30]. Besides, it is hardly possible to investigate the number of functional genes present in libraries available [31]. Such limitations are overcome by the recent advancements made in the field of metagenomics [32]. Thus, generating metagenomic libraries is an excellent resource for subsequent screening and selection of novel biocatalysts [33].

15.2.2 *In Silico* Designing

Bioinformatic tools and database are helpful in the designing of a new gene with desirable function. A probable functional gene can be predicted using sequence alignment and gene annotation. For further validation, structural modeling of the predicted gene and docking analysis with different derivatives of the substrates are performed. Further, computational molecular evolution can also be explored to obtain new enzymes by creating gene library and virtual screening. This involves *in silico* variations in the gene, structure modeling, and screening by docking analysis. Some of the best-selected variants can be cloned in a bacterial expression vector, express and purify the protein, and verify the enzymatic activity experimentally. However, functional mis-annotation may cause *in silico* sequence-based library screening to be dubious and biased, preventing the discovery of novel enzymes [34].

15.3 DNA Level Processes for the Creation of Gene Library

Emulating the natural process of genetic variation through processes such as mutations, and selecting the improved variants is called directed evolution [35]. Such protein engineering technique gives rise to functional proteins with improved enzymatic activity and specificity [36]. The success of directed evolution is decisive of the library type [37]. Increasing the diverseness and the trait of the gene library is, therefore, the major focus of the research so that the probability of identifying new and improved variants is increased [38]. Essentially, directed evolution comprises diverse gene library creation through techniques such as random mutagenesis and gene recombination [39]. The repetitive process of mutagenesis, selection, and screening continues until a new generation of improved and the desired variant of an enzyme is produced [40].

15.3.1 Random Mutagenesis

Random mutagenesis is a classical genetic approach where mutations are introduced deliberately to improve the desired enzymes' efficiency and production (Figure 15.2) [41]. It is frequently the preferred choice because of being an economical, simple, effective, and reliable technique for the development of short-term strain [42]. Several mutagenic chemicals such as ethyl methane sulfonate are used and the mutant with desired characteristics is selected [43]. A high concentration of Mg^{++} or Mn^{++} in PCR reaction also causes random mutations. Lately, several techniques have been developed for generating random mutations such as error-prone PCR using nucleotide analogs [44]. For the generation of an effective gene library, it is crucial that all types of nucleotide changes, i.e., transversions and transitions should occur at equal frequency.

15.3.2 Targeted Mutagenesis

Site-directed or targeted mutagenesis is one of the rational methods of generating genetic diversity in the field of directed enzyme evolution [45]. It involves manipulating the catalytic mechanism of an enzyme in a more specific and targeted

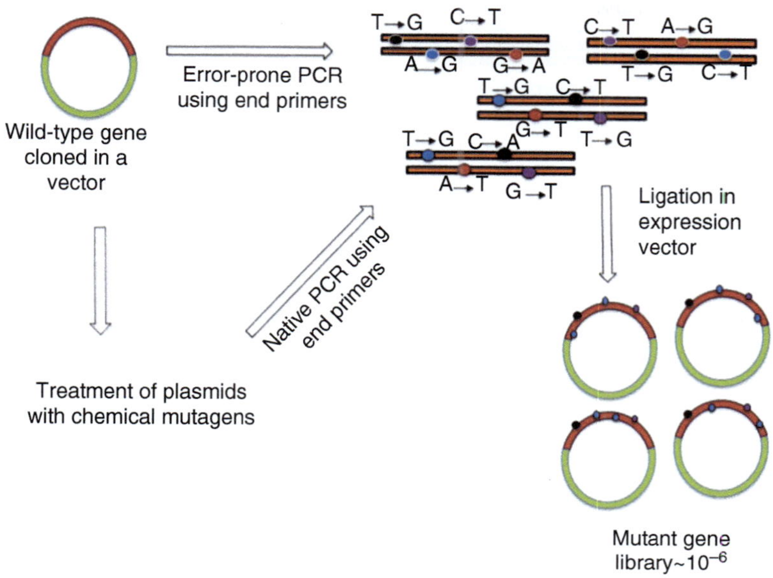

Figure 15.2 Schematic representation of random mutagenesis by error-prone PCR and chemical mutagen. After introducing the mutation by PCR, the mutated DNA is ligated into the expression vector, transformed, and the desired variant is screened.

manner. It was successfully used to boost the activity of OPH against OP compounds by remodeling the shape and size of the substrate-binding sites [46, 47]. However, due to unwanted consequences put forth by substituted amino acids, site-directed mutagenesis may sometimes fail or may give rise to the progressive natural evolution of the enzyme. This emphasizes that the change of amino acids in the active site may affect the efficiency of enzyme and is influenced by several factors [48, 49]. Site-directed mutagenesis can be manipulated by the *in silico* approach, where the three-dimensional structure of enzymes can be modeled to study its catalytic properties and mechanisms [50]. However, irrational approaches such as random mutagenesis and DNA shuffling are preferred because in a rational approach, only a narrow sequence space can be recognized at once [51].

15.3.3 Gene Recombination

DNA shuffling or gene recombination is widely endorsed for the creation of a gene library of high quality [52]. Unlike random mutagenesis, where accumulation of mutations occurs on a single parental gene, DNA shuffling requires a gene pool, i.e., multiple gene sequences encoding proteins of similar function (Figure 15.3) [53].

15.3.4 Insertion–Deletion Mutagenesis

Though, frequently observed in natural protein evolution, the potential of insertions and deletions (InDels) remain unexplored in laboratory evolution. Most directed

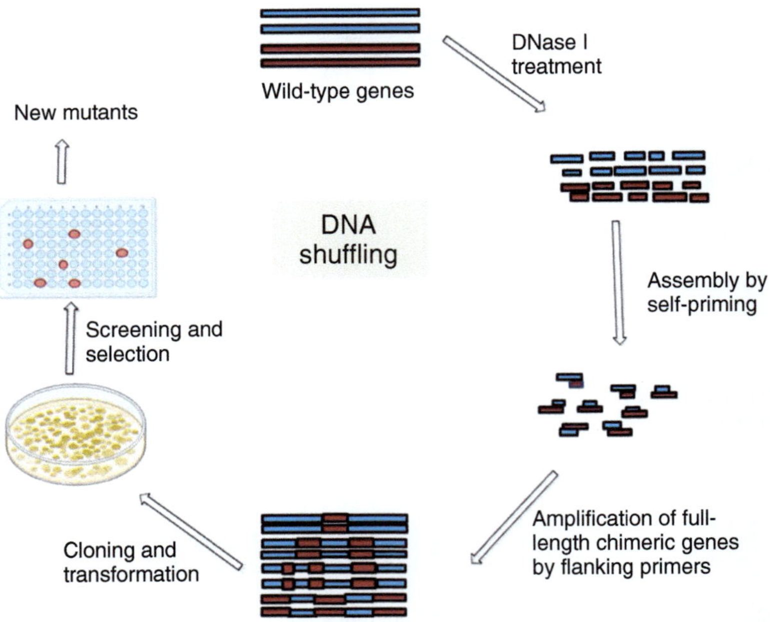

Figure 15.3 DNA shuffling. This mutagenesis method allows the recombination of sequences from different and related genes. It is advantageous in combining the beneficial mutations and the removal of deleterious mutations simultaneously.

evolution so far has been performed using point substitutions [54]. InDels show many limitations with respect to the diversity and quality of the library despite the development of various methods for incorporating them randomly within the gene of interest, most probably due to a change in the reading frame. As a result, non-functional variants are obtained, which must be removed by HTS [55]. InDel could be highly beneficial to study the specificity determining short peptide loops present in some enzymes like bacterial phosphotriesterase [47], by altering the size of the loop or by replacing it with a newly designed loop.

15.3.5 Other Approaches for Library Creation

The generation of small, targeted, and high-quality libraries of mutants is the most effective strategy of enzyme engineering. The evolution of a technique mainly focuses on features that differ from previous point mutagenesis campaigns. For the successful generation of high-quality libraries more sophisticated methods have been developed. A few of them are discussed below.

Transposon-based random insertion and deletion (TRIAD) mutagenesis is an adaptation of InDel mutagenesis wherein the introduction of random one, two, or three nucleotide triplets of single short InDels maintains the overall protein reading frame [56]. Screening the libraries generated by such InDel mutagenesis revealed several hits with improved and diverse enzyme activity that would have been unattainable using conventional point substitution mutagenesis techniques [54].

Recently, iterative saturation mutagenesis (ISM) has evolved for directed evolution, which uses targeted combinatorial approaches. It is a successful and extensively applied technique for protein engineering that can efficiently and simultaneously alter specific protein residues [57].

A yet more advanced Structure-based Optimization of Combinatorial Mutagenesis (SOCoM) is a general-purpose method that utilizes the computational protein design and optimizes arbitrarily large combinatorial mutagenesis libraries directly based on the structural energies of their constituents [58]. It promises to increase the hit rate of discovering beneficial variants.

Golden Gate mutagenesis allows the rapid (performed within one day), straightforward, reliable, and low-cost construction of mutagenesis libraries [59]. It utilizes the restriction enzymes that cut outside of their recognition domain. Multiple gene fragments obtained by PCR amplification can thus be assembled without altering the open reading frame of the reconstituted gene in a highly specific manner [60]. Simultaneously, one to five amino acid positions could be altered within a coding sequence. Therefore, golden gate mutagenesis enables broad applicability in the field of multiple site-directed mutagenesis [61, 62]. Since only a limited portion of sequence space can be experimentally tested and created, it is more logical to use computational protein design at the same time, to focus libraries on a productive portion of the space.

15.4 Screening of the Gene Library

The application of HTS methods greatly benefits in evaluating large, diverse combinatorial libraries for obtaining protein variants with improved characteristics such as binding affinity, catalytic activity, thermostability, etc. While screening of point-mutant libraries is readily done, ingenious solutions must be explored to screen combinatorial sequences.

15.4.1 High-throughput Screening Using Multi-well Microplate

The screening of the gene library is challenging. HTS is the bottleneck in the field of directed evolution research [63]. The study of binding interactions include HTS techniques such as two-hybrid systems, and various *in vitro* display technologies [64–66]. However, selection for enzymatic activities is a more arduous task as after catalytic reaction, a substrate is converted to the product, and the enzyme does not remain linked with the substrate or product molecule. Hence, classical enzymatic activity is assayed on microtiter plates from isolated bacterial colonies on agar and is mostly based on colorimetric and fluorometric assays. Therefore, a handful of variants is screened despite advances in automation (Figure 15.4) [67]. The throughput can be enhanced using robotic systems enormously [68].

Digital imaging (DI) is an HTS method that provides the screening of colonies on a solid-phase through the integration of single-pixel imaging spectroscopy. DI also depends on simple, universally known colorimetric activity assays. It has been

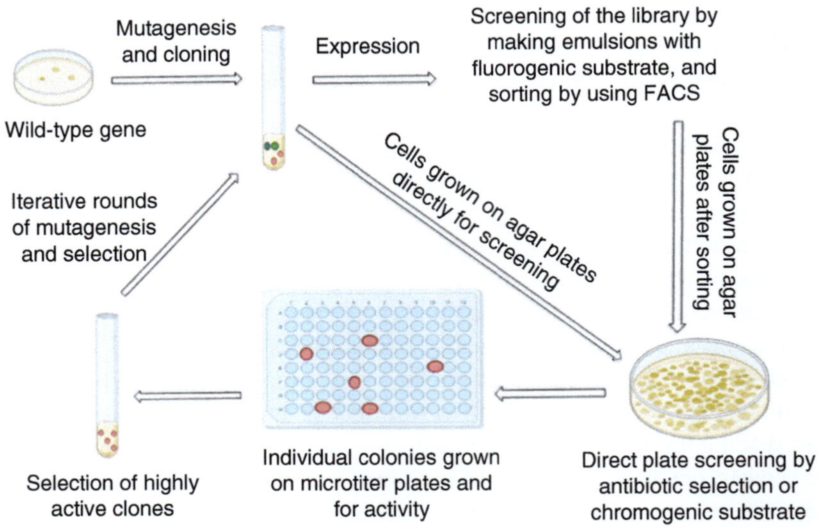

Figure 15.4 Different methods of high-throughput screening. Colorimetric screening in microtiter plates is a classical approach based on enzymatic activities.

advantageous in screening of enzyme variants on substrates that have problematic physical properties [69, 70].

Fluorescence-activated cell sorting (FACS) technology is also highly promising as an HTS method. Its screening approaches for enzyme activities include green fluorescent protein-reporter assays, *in vitro* compartmentalization (IVC), product entrapment, and cell surface display [71–73]. For HTS, among several display technologies, cell surface display is the most compliant. It has been developed in bacteria, yeast, and mammalian cells and has become a significant procedure for fluorescence resonance energy transfer as well as FACS-based screening methods [74].

Pooling of genetic variants of high-diversity libraries facilitates large-scale screening. The screening is done from the pooled library members, based on desired phenotypes such as fluorescent proteins with increased lifetime, enhanced brightness, and reversible photo-switching. Sequencing is then done to determine their corresponding genotypes [75]. HTS of genetic variants is important in expanding the comprehension of biological systems and also assisting the progress of biotechnology applications.

15.4.2 *In Vitro* Compartmentalization

Artificial compartments are made for isolation of individual DNA molecules, in independent reactors for the synthesis of protein as well for the enzyme reaction to take place in a cell-free system [76]. This is called IVC and includes water-in-oil (W/O) emulsion droplets. The product molecules generated by the encoded enzymes are compartmentalized and the cells are then sorted [77]. There are several advantages of IVC over *in vivo*-based HTS methods. First, it eliminates the possibility of off-target mutations since it bypasses the regulatory network of the

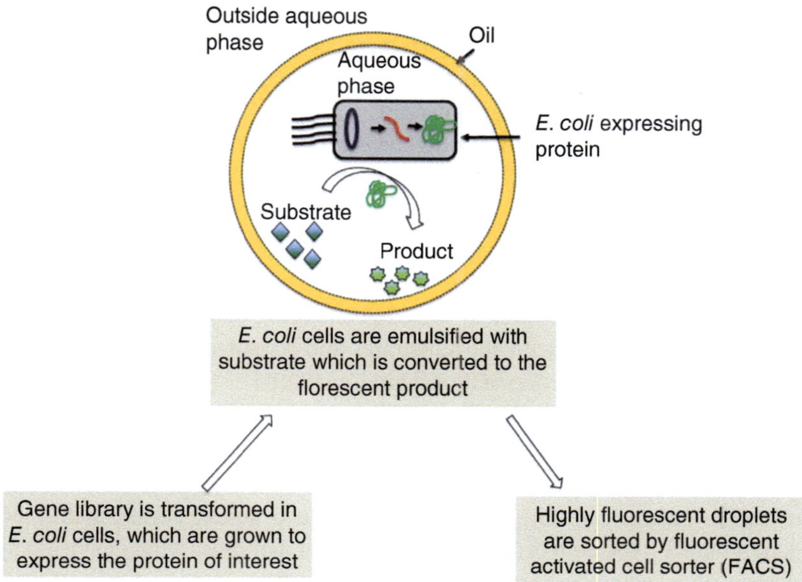

Figure 15.5 High-throughput screening by double emulsion method using whole cell expression system, i.e., *E. coli* cells expressing protein of interests.

in vivo system. Second, it avoids transformation; thus, the library size is limited [73]. Thus, widening the scope of this technology. One of the limitations of IVC is that many enzymes are incompatible with the method because of the varying conditions between transcription–translation and screening. However, combining IVC with FACS is a promising approach for screening activity during the directed evolution of enzymes [77, 78].

15.4.3 Double Emulsion

The double emulsion technique is a variation of the IVC method where fluorescent water-in-oil-in-water (w/o/w) emulsions are sorted by FACS [78]. The double emulsions are prepared from the primary water-in-oil (w/o) emulsion as non-aqueous suspensions are incompatible with FACS (Figure 15.5) [79]. FACS of double emulsions can potentially widen the range of screening enzymes as it can recover hits from as many alternative droplets as in a sea of 10^6-fold. Moreover, it relies on using fluorogenic substrates, which need not be coupled to the gene and are available for many different enzymes. Thus, the high throughput of this method is highly suitable for directed evolution due to the speed as well as the broad dynamic range of the screening [79, 80].

HTS by double emulsions has many advantages as it can be utilized for either cell-free expression system or whole-cell double emulsion (Figure 15.5). The cell-free double emulsion is completely *in vitro* and there is no need to transform the cells. Therefore, instantaneously different cycles of mutation, recombination, and selection are carried out. Moreover, the use of a highly purified cell-free translation system and the product need not remain inside or trapped on the surface of the enzyme. Therefore, toxic enzymatic activities for a cell are no more a hindrance [78, 81]. On the other hand, whole cell double emulsion comprises bacterial expression system for the transcription and translation. The expressed enzymes convert the substrates, present in the droplet, to the fluorescent product, which is analyzed and sorted by the FACS.

15.4.4 Microbead Display

In this approach, proteins are linked to the DNA encoding them using microbeads, which are further emulsified with the substrates and screened using FACS. It has several advantages for the selection of ligand binding [82, 83]. The beads are specially designed for the gene, the encoded enzyme, and the enzyme product in a coupled manner. To segregate the genes, the beads are compartmentalized in w/o/w emulsions and the proteins are expressed on the surface [84]. With the recent advancements in the field of microfluidics, highly uniform w/o/w double emulsion droplets can be generated with the help of a microfluidic chip or a microcapillary device [85]. The Microbead display method proves to be beneficial in the discovery and engineering of new biocatalysts. No transformation or cloning is required as it is completely formed *in vitro* [86]. As much as 10^6-fold enrichment of the gene of interest can be obtained after two rounds of selection [82]. Moreover, multivalence display can be achieved, providing a potential advantage in the selection of low-affinity ligands. A total of 3000–5000 DNA molecules and 9000–15,000 protein molecules can be carried by a single bead [87]. Multivalent displays can multiply the signal difference between the beneficial and nonbeneficial mutants [88]. Recently, for the evolution and selection of membrane proteins, a liposome display is designed. A pure cell-free translation system encapsulates the DNA encoding the membrane proteins of interest, which are displayed on the surface of liposome membranes after being translated [89]. The microbead display technology is highly successful and efficient in the selection of binding proteins [65]. Though the throughput is relatively high, flow cytometry has certain limitations. It imposes an upper limit on the size of the libraries that can be selected $\sim 10^9$. However, it is probably necessary to select the microbead display libraries by affinity purification for unbiased selection relative to compartment size [82].

15.5 Characterization of Designed Enzymes

15.5.1 Protein Production

The production expense is usually a decisive factor in the accomplishment of enzyme-based tools for bioremediation [2]. To overcome the cost of production, many researchers purify the enzymes from the media of the bacterial culture directly. Throughout their life cycle, bacteria release fragments of proteins, nucleic acids, and other biomolecules from their outermost membrane, which have various implications such as pathogenesis and community communication [90, 91]. Outer membrane vesicles as part of the parental bacterium's membrane can be exploited to cargo proteins of interest. These proteins can be purified directly from the bacterial culture media and checked for activity subsequently [92]. Purification can also be conveniently obtained from growth media in bulk using an engineered 6xHis affinity tag expressed on the surface of the vesicle [93]. Recently, various research groups have shown several benefits of this strategy. The stability of the encapsulated enzyme was improved significantly. Moreover, the enzyme activity was preserved over a range of pH conditions, in high salt solutions, and under elevated temperatures [94, 95]. Therefore, OMVs allowed for a one-step purification protocol that is simple and cost-effective. Additionally, it allows large-scale enzyme production and diffusion in bacteria like *Escherichia coli*, which can be grown in fermenters. Moreover, this technique lessens the trouble related to manufacturing and downstream processing required for commercial enzyme production significantly [2].

15.5.2 Enzyme Activity and Specificity

One of the critical applications of directed evolution is improving enzyme activity under well-defined conditions [96]. This could be determined by the enzyme kinetic parameters such as $V_{max}/K_m/K_{cat}$, i.e., through kinetic characterization. The effectiveness of the enzyme generated through directed evolution can be measured through these parameters. The rate of the release of the product from the enzyme complex is determined by the initial rate of reaction (v_0) or K_{cat} [45]. The structure, as well as the binding affinity of the active site, is determined by the ionic groups of amino acids such as amino, carboxyl, thiol, imidazole, and phenolic groups. Subsequently, the catalytic activity is affected by the dissociation state of active site amino acids [97]. The mutations in the catalytic site binding pocket are reported for boosting the rate of the reaction as well as accelerating the turnover frequency of the enzyme dramatically [98].

15.5.3 Protein Stability

Once taken out of their biological surroundings, enzymes unfold into non-functional amino acid chains. Therefore, enzyme stability is one of the crucial factors that focus to maintain their intricately folded structure and prevent their activity [48]. Thus, preventing the loss of function as well as enhancing the functional stability of the enzymes are the major areas of research. Loss of function occurs when the enzyme is subjected to excessive temperature, extreme pH, and proteases [99]. The commercial success of enzymes in terms of stability is achieved through various strategies such as the use of soluble additives, storage formulation, protein engineering, immobilization, and other chemical modifications [100, 101]. The most popular approach is the covalent binding of appropriate modifiers to the enzyme's surface residues. Polysaccharides as modifiers have proved to be distinguishing for the improvements in enzyme characteristics [102]. Researchers in the last decade have focused much on the improvement of enzyme stability. Many fascinating results have been reported. Enzyme stability can have multiple advantages: enzymatic reactions can be carried out at higher temperatures if the enzymes are heat-resistant [103, 104]. Additionally, conversion rates and solubility of the substrates are increased and the risk of microbial growth and the viscosity of the reaction medium is decreased [105]. Hydrophilic/hydrophobic balance of protein surface plays a major role in its thermal stability, solubility, activity, specificity as well as stability toward pH. Due to the difficulty in characterizing active sites of enzymes, their optimum pH is determined experimentally [106–108]. Several strategies may be applied to assess the stability of enzymes. The half-life of an enzyme at a certain temperature provides information about enzyme residual activity [109, 110].

15.5.4 Mode of Application

In addition to the aforementioned factors, an ideal enzyme for bioremediation must be capable of decontaminating any surface and rapidly detoxifying the toxic chemicals. Moreover, they should be environmentally friendly. DNA-based scaffolds and nanostructures are used these days for the display of enzymes in a more consistent and reproducible manner. They are designed computationally concerning Watson-Crick base pairing [111, 112]. Similarly, quantum dots scaffolds and OMV encapsulation can potentially improve the applicability of enzymes as field-conveyable materials. Some of these enzymes are under investigation for their *in vivo* efficacy [94, 113]. For *in vivo* use, the addition of polyethylene glycol (PEG) molecules remarkably improves the benefits of an enzyme [114]. For improving the kinetic and biophysical properties, enzyme immobilization on solid supports is found to be beneficial. In all of the strategies of enzyme application, it should be taken care that enzyme structure and the active site are not perturbed [115, 116].

15.6 Conclusion and Future Perspectives

Enzymatic detoxification of OPs has become the subject of numerous studies because current methods of removing them, such as bleach treatments and incineration, are slow, expensive, and cause environmental concerns. Several enzymes have evolved in nature with the capability of degrading the OP compounds. Extensive research is underway to improve their stability, activity, substrate specificity, and overall efficacy and thus enhance their appeal as decontamination agents. The use of OPH as agents of bioremediation presents potential benefits due to their distinct characteristics such as rapid hydrolysis of the NAs, environment-friendly, nonflammable, noncorrosive, and easy and safe disposal. While significant benefits have been made in developing enzymes as candidate biocatalysts, there are still miles to go. Further validations are required for their use as both personal and industry-scale decontamination in the same manner. Essentially impelling collaborations between the academy, government, and industry are required. Each of them can contribute parallelly to the recognition of enzymes as bioremediation machinery. The most essential is the change in the perception of society and institutions against the use of these lethal compounds and their long-lasting impacts.

List of Abbreviations

ACh	acetylcholine
AChE	acetylcholinesterase
CWA	chemical warfare agent
DI	digital imaging
DNA	deoxyribonucleic acid
FACS	fluorescence-activated cell sorting
HTS	high-throughput screening
InDels	insertions and deletions
ISM	iterative saturation mutagenesis
IVC	*in vitro* compartmentalization
NA	nerve agent
OP	organophosphorus
OPH	organophosphate hydrolase
PCR	polymerase chain reaction
SOCoM	structure-based optimization of combinatorial mutagenesis
TRIAD	transposon-based random insertion and deletion
WHO	World Health Organization

References

1 Adeyinka, A., Muco, E., and Pierre, L. (2021). Organophosphates. In: *Hazard Chem Agents Risk Chang 1800–2000* (ed. StatPearls) [Internet] 2023 May 29, 267–293. StatPearls Publishing.

2 Thakur, M., Medintz, I.L., and Walper, S.A. (2019). Enzymatic bioremediation of organophosphate compounds—progress and remaining challenges. *Front. Bioeng. Biotechnol.* 7: 289.

3 Matula, M., Kucera, T., Soukup, O., and Pejchal, J. (2020). Enzymatic degradation of organophosphorus pesticides and nerve agents by EC: 3.1.8.2. *Catalysts* 10 (12): 1365.

4 Singh, B.K. and Walker, A. (2006). Microbial degradation of organophosphorus compounds. *FEMS Microbiol. Rev.* 30 (3): 428–471.

5 Jayaraj, R., Megha, P., and Sreedev, P. (2016). Organochlorine pesticides, their toxic effects on living organisms and their fate in the environment. *Interdiscip. Toxicol.* 9 (3–4): 90.

6 Kaushal, J., Khatri, M., and Arya, S.K. (2021). A treatise on Organophosphate pesticide pollution: current strategies and advancements in their environmental degradation and elimination. *Ecotoxicol. Environ. Saf.* 207: 111483.

7 Krause, K.H., Van Thriel, C., De Sousa, P.A. et al. (2013). Monocrotophos in Gandaman village: India school lunch deaths and need for improved toxicity testing. *Arch. Toxicol.* 87 (10): 1877–1881.

8 Srinivas Rao, C., Venkateswarlu, V., Surender, T. et al. (2005). Pesticide poisoning in South India – opportunities for prevention and improved Medical Management Europe PMC Funders Group. *Trop. Med. Int. Health* 10 (6): 581–588.

9 Williams, M. and Sizemore, D.C. (2019). Biologic, Chemical, and Radiation Terrorism Review [Internet]. StatPearls. StatPearls Publishing.

10 Brooks, J., Erickson, T.B., Kayden, S. et al. (2018). Responding to chemical weapons violations in Syria: legal, health, and humanitarian recommendations. *Confl. Health* 12 (1): 1–7.

11 Franjesevic, A.J., Sillart, S.B., Beck, J.M. et al. (2019). Resurrection and reactivation of acetylcholinesterase and butyrylcholinesterase. *Chemistry* 25 (21): 5337–5371.

12 Costa, L.G. (2018). Organophosphorus compounds at 80: some old and new issues. *Toxicol. Sci.* 162 (1): 24–35.

13 Greathouse, B., Zahra, F., and Brady, M.F. (2021). Acetylcholinesterase Inhibitors Toxicity. StatPearls.

14 Chai, P.R., Hayes, B.D., Erickson, T.B., and Boyer, E.W. (2018). Novichok agents: a historical, current, and toxicological perspective. *Toxicol. Commun.* 2 (1): 45–48.

15 Naughton, S.X. and Terry, A.V. (2018). Neurotoxicity in acute and repeated organophosphate exposure. *Forensic Toxicol.* 408: 101.

16 Pereira, E.F.R., Aracava, Y., DeTolla, L.J. et al. (2014). Animal models that best reproduce the clinical manifestations of human intoxication with organophosphorus compounds. *J. Pharmacol. Exp. Ther.* 350 (2): 313.

17 Jokanović, M. (2018). Neurotoxic effects of organophosphorus pesticides and possible association with neurodegenerative diseases in man: a review. *Forensic Toxicol.* 410: 125–131.

18 Gupta, R.D. (2016). Recent advances in enzyme promiscuity. In: *Sustainable Chemical Processes*, vol. 4, 1–7. Springer.

19 Mukherjee, S. and Gupta, R.D. (2020). Organophosphorus nerve agents: types, toxicity, and treatments. *J. Toxicol.* 2020: 1–16.

20 Gupta, R.D., Goldsmith, M., Ashani, Y. et al. (2011). Directed evolution of hydrolases for prevention of G-type nerve agent intoxication. *Nat. Chem. Biol.* 7 (2): 120–125.

21 Karbelkar, A.A., Reynolds, E.E., Ahlmark, R., and Furst, A.L. (2021). A microbial electrochemical technology to detect and degrade organophosphate pesticides. *ACS Cent. Sci.* 7: 1718–1727.

22 Ashani, Y., Gupta, R.D., Goldsmith, M. et al. (2010). Stereo-specific synthesis of analogs of nerve agents and their utilization for selection and characterization of paraoxonase (pon1) catalytic scavengers. *Chem. Biol. Interact.* 187 (1–3): 362.

23 Parween, F., Sarker, A., and Gupta, R.D. (2022). Chlorpyrifos and parathion regulate oxidative stress differentially through the expression of paraoxonase 2 in human neuroblastoma cell. *Neurotoxicology* 93: 60–70.

24 Yi, D., Bayer, T., Badenhorst, C.P.S. et al. (2021). Recent trends in biocatalysis. *Chem. Soc. Rev.* 50 (14): 8003–8049.

25 Copley, S.D. (2003). Enzymes with extra talents: moonlighting functions and catalytic promiscuity. *Curr. Opin. Chem. Biol.* 7 (2): 265–272.

26 Fewer, D.P. and Metsä-Ketelä, M. (2020). A pharmaceutical model for the molecular evolution of microbial natural products. *FEBS J.* 287 (7): 1429–1449.

27 Copley, S.D. (2020). Evolution of new enzymes by gene duplication and divergence. *FEBS J.* 287 (7): 1262–1283.

28 Mishra, S., Lin, Z., Pang, S. et al. (2021). Recent advanced technologies for the characterization of xenobiotic-degrading microorganisms and microbial communities. *Front. Bioeng. Biotechnol.* 9: 31.

29 Thomas, T., Gilbert, J., and Meyer, F. (2012). Metagenomics - a guide from sampling to data analysis. *Microb. Inf. Exp.* 2 (1): 3.

30 Schloss, P.D. and Handelsman, J. (2005). Metagenomics for studying unculturable microorganisms: cutting the Gordian knot. *Genome Biol.* 6 (8): 1–4.

31 Ngara, T.R. and Zhang, H. (2018). Recent advances in function-based metagenomic screening. *Genomics Proteomics Bioinf.* 16 (6): 405–415.

32 Gupta, R.D. and Sharma, R. (2011). Metagenomics for environmental and industrial microbiology. *Sci. Cult.* 77 (1–2): 5.

33 Adrio, J.L. and Demain, A.L. (2014). Microbial enzymes: tools for biotechnological processes. *Biomolecules* 4 (1): 117.

34 Li, X., Zhang, Z., and Song, J. (2012). Computational enzyme design approaches with significant biological outcomes: progress and challenges. *Comput. Struct. Biotechnol. J.* 2 (3): e201209007.

35 Packer, M.S. and Liu, D.R. (2015). Methods for the directed evolution of proteins. *Nat. Rev. Genet.* 16 (7): 379–394.

36 Engqvist, M.K.M. and Rabe, K.S. (2019). Applications of protein engineering and directed evolution in plant research. *Plant Physiol.* 179 (3): 907.

37 Gupta, R.D. and Tawfik, D.S. (2008). Directed enzyme evolution via small and effective neutral drift libraries. *Nat. Methods* 5 (11): 939–942.

38 Qu, G., Li, A., Acevedo-Rocha, C.G. et al. (2020). The crucial role of methodology development in directed evolution of selective enzymes. *Angew. Chem. Int. Ed.* 59 (32): 13204–13231.

39 Cobb, R.E., Chao, R., and Zhao, H. (2013). Directed evolution: past, present, and future. *AlChE J.* 59 (5): 1432–1440.

40 Yuan, L., Kurek, I., English, J., and Keenan, R. (2005). Laboratory-directed protein evolution. *Microbiol. Mol. Biol. Rev.* 69 (3): 373.

41 Labrou, N. (2010). Random mutagenesis methods for in vitro directed enzyme evolution. *Curr. Protein Pept. Sci.* 11 (1): 91–100.

42 Rowlands, R.T. (1984). Industrial strain improvement: mutagenesis and random screening procedures. *Enzyme Microb. Technol.* 6 (1): 3–10.

43 Latif, A., Iqbal, M., and Asgher, M. (2018). Ethyl methane sulfonate chemical mutagenesis of *Bacillus subtilis* for enhanced production of protease. *Org. Med. Chem. Int. J.* 5 (3): 91–98.

44 Rezaie, E., Latifi, A.M., and Mirzaei, M. (2018). Activity improvement of organophosphorus hydrolase enzyme by error prone PCR method. *J. Appl. Biotechnol. Rep.* 5 (3): 100–104.

45 Nannemann, D.P., Birmingham, W.R., Scism, R.A., and Bachmann, B.O. (2011). Assessing directed evolution methods for the generation of biosynthetic enzymes with potential in drug biosynthesis. *Future Med. Chem.* 3 (7): 809.

46 Raushel, F.M. (2002). Bacterial detoxification of organophosphate nerve agents. *Curr. Opin. Microbiol.* 5 (3): 288–295.

47 Chen-Goodspeed, M., Sogorb, M.A., Wu, F., and Raushel, F.M. (2001). Enhancement, relaxation, and reversal of the stereoselectivity for phosphotriesterase by rational evolution of active site residues. *Biochemistry* 40 (5): 1332–1339.

48 Xie, Y., An, J., Yang, G. et al. (2014). Enhanced enzyme kinetic stability by increasing rigidity within the active site. *J. Biol. Chem.* 289 (11): 7994–8006.

49 Damián-Almazo, J.Y. and Saab-Rincón, G. (2013). Site-directed mutagenesis as applied to biocatalysts. In: *Genetic Manipulation of DNA and Protein–Examples from Current Research*, 303–330. Rijeka, Croatia: InTech.

50 Steiner, K. and Schwab, H. (2012). Recent advances in rational approaches for enzyme engineering. *Comput. Struct. Biotechnol. J.* 2 (3): e201209010.

51 Chen, R. (2001). Enzyme engineering: rational redesign versus directed evolution. *Trends Biotechnol.* 19 (1): 13–14.

52 Coco, W.M., Levinson, W.E., Crist, M.J. et al. (2001). DNA shuffling method for generating highly recombined genes and evolved enzymes. *Nat. Biotechnol.* 19 (4): 354–359.

53 Meyer, A.J., Ellefson, J.W., and Ellington, A.D. (2013). Library generation by gene shuffling. *Curr. Protocol. Mol. Biol.* 105 (1): 15.

54 Emond, S., Petek, M., Kay, E.J. et al. (2020). Accessing unexplored regions of sequence space in directed enzyme evolution via insertion/deletion mutagenesis. *Nat. Commun.* 11 (1): 1–14.

55 Kashiwagi, K., Isogai, Y., Nishiguchi, K.I., and Shiba, K. (2006). Frame shuffling: a novel method for in vitro protein evolution. *Protein Eng. Des. Sel.* 19 (3): 135–140.

56 Tizei, P.A.G., Harris, E., Withanage, S. et al. (2021). A novel framework for engineering protein loops exploring length and compositional variation. *Sci. Rep.* 11 (1): 9134.

57 Acevedo-Rocha, C.G., Hoebenreich, S., and Reetz, M.T. (2014). Iterative saturation mutagenesis: a powerful approach to engineer proteins by systematically simulating Darwinian evolution. *Methods Mol. Biol.* 1179: 103–128.

58 Verma, D., Grigoryan, G., and Bailey-Kellogg, C. (2015). Structure-based design of combinatorial mutagenesis libraries. *Protein Sci.* 24 (5): 895–908.

59 Püllmann, P., Ulpinnis, C., Marillonnet, S. et al. (2019). Golden mutagenesis: an efficient multi-site-saturation mutagenesis approach by Golden Gate cloning with automated primer design. *Sci. Rep.* 9 (1): 1–11.

60 Engler, C., Gruetzner, R., Kandzia, R., and Marillonnet, S. (2009). Golden gate shuffling: a one-pot DNA shuffling method based on type IIs restriction enzymes. *PLoS One* 4 (5): e5553.

61 Dennig, A., Shivange, A.V., Marienhagen, J., and Schwaneberg, U. (2011). OmniChange: the sequence independent method for simultaneous site-saturation of five codons. *PLoS One* 6 (10): e26222.

62 Quaglia, D., Ebert, M.C.C.J.C., Mugford, P.F., and Pelletier, J.N. (2017). Enzyme engineering: a synthetic biology approach for more effective library generation and automated high-throughput screening. *PLoS One* 12 (2): e0171741.

63 Aharoni, A., Amitai, G., Bernath, K. et al. (2005). High-throughput screening of enzyme libraries: thiolactonases evolved by fluorescence-activated sorting of single cells in emulsion compartments. *Chem. Biol.* 12 (12): 1281–1289.

64 Wong, J.H., Alfatah, M., Sin, M.F. et al. (2017). A yeast two-hybrid system for the screening and characterization of small-molecule inhibitors of protein-protein interactions identifies a novel putative Mdm2-binding site in p53. *BMC Biol.* 15 (1): 1–17.

65 Wittrup, K.D. (2001). Protein engineering by cell-surface display. *Curr. Opin. Biotechnol.* 12 (4): 395–399.

66 Bazan, J., Całkosiński, I., and Gamian, A. (2012). Phage display—a powerful technique for immunotherapy: 1. Introduction and potential of therapeutic applications. *Hum. Vaccines Immunother.* 8 (12): 1817.

67 Aharoni, A., Griffiths, A.D., and Tawfik, D.S. (2005). High-throughput screens and selections of enzyme-encoding genes. *Curr. Opin. Chem. Biol.* 9 (2): 210–216.

68 Xiao, H., Bao, Z., and Zhao, H. (2015). High throughput screening and selection methods fordirected enzyme evolution. *Ind. Eng. Chem. Res.* 54 (16): 4011.

69 Delagrave, S., Murphy, D.J., Pruss, J.L.R. et al. (2001). Application of a very high-throughput digital imaging screen to evolve the enzyme galactose oxidase. *Protein Eng.* 14 (4): 261–267.

70 Koné, F.M.T., Le Béchec, M., Sine, J.P. et al. (2009). Digital screening methodology for the directed evolution of transglycosidases. *Protein Eng. Des. Sel.* 22 (1): 37–44.

71 Feldhaus, M.J., Siegel, R.W., Opresko, L.K. et al. (2003). Flow-cytometric isolation of human antibodies from a nonimmune *Saccharomyces cerevisiae* surface display library. *Nat. Biotechnol.* 21 (2): 163–170.

72 Becker, S., Schmoldt, H.U., Adams, T.M. et al. (2004). Ultra-high-throughput screening based on cell-surface display and fluorescence-activated cell sorting for the identification of novel biocatalysts. *Curr. Opin. Biotechnol.* 15 (4): 323–329.

73 Tawfik, D.S. and Griffiths, A.D. (1998). Man-made cell-like compartments for molecular evolution. *Nat. Biotechnol.* 16 (7): 652–656.

74 Limsakul, P., Peng, Q., Wu, Y. et al. (2018). Directed evolution to engineer monobody for FRET biosensor assembly and imaging at live-cell surface. *Cell Chem. Biol.* 25 (4): 370–379.e4.

75 Emanuel, G., Moffitt, J.R., and Zhuang, X. (2017). High-throughput, image-based screening of pooled genetic variant libraries. *Nat. Methods* 14 (12): 1159.

76 Stapleton, J.A. and Swartz, J.R. (2010). Development of an in vitro compartmentalization screen for high-throughput directed evolution of [FeFe] hydrogenases. *PLoS One* 5 (12): e15275.

77 Miller, O.J., Bernath, K., Agresti, J.J. et al. (2006). Directed evolution by in vitro compartmentalization. *Nat. Methods* 3 (7): 561–570.

78 Mastrobattista, E., Taly, V., Chanudet, E. et al. (2005). High-throughput screening of enzyme libraries: in vitro evolution of a beta-galactosidase by fluorescence-activated sorting of double emulsions. *Chem. Biol.* 12 (12): 1291–1300.

79 Zinchenko, A., Devenish, S.R.A., Kintses, B. et al. (2014). One in a million: flow cytometric sorting of single cell-lysate assays in monodisperse picolitre double emulsion droplets for directed evolution. *Anal. Chem.* 86 (5): 2526.

80 Menghiu, G., Ostafe, V., Prodanović, R. et al. (2021). A high-throughput screening system based on fluorescence-activated cell sorting for the directed evolution of Chitinase A. *Int. J. Mol. Sci.* 22 (6): 1–15.

81 Shimizu, Y., Inoue, A., Tomari, Y. et al. (2001). Cell-free translation reconstituted with purified components. *Nat. Biotechnol.* 19 (8): 751–755.

82 Sepp, A., Tawfik, D.S., and Griffiths, A.D. (2002). Microbead display by in vitro compartmentalisation: selection for binding using flow cytometry. *FEBS Lett.* 532 (3): 455–458.

83 Contreras-Llano, L.E. and Tan, C. (2018). High-throughput screening of biomolecules using cell-free gene expression systems. *Synth. Biol.* 3 (1): ysy012.

84 Yang, G. and Withers, S.G. (2009). Ultrahigh-throughput FACS-based screening for directed enzyme evolution. *ChemBioChem* 10 (17): 2704–2715.

85 Vladisavljević, G.T., Al Nuumani, R., and Nabavi, S.A. (2017). Microfluidic production of multiple emulsions. *Micromachines* 8 (3): 75.

86 Griffiths, A.D. and Tawfik, D.S. (2003). Directed evolution of an extremely fast phosphotriesterase by in vitro compartmentalization. *EMBO J.* 22 (1): 24.

87 Gan, R., Yamanaka, Y., Kojima, T., and Nakano, H. (2008). Microbeads display of proteins using emulsion PCR and cell-free protein synthesis. *Biotechnol. Progr.* 24 (5): 1107–1114.

88 Steiner, D., Forrer, P., Stumpp, M.T., and Plückthun, A. (2006). Signal sequences directing cotranslational translocation expand the range of proteins amenable to phage display. *Nat. Biotechnol.* 24 (7): 823–831.

89 Fujii, S., Matsuura, T., Sunami, T. et al. (2014). Liposome display for in vitro selection and evolution of membrane proteins. *Nat. Protoc.* 9 (7): 1578–1591.

90 Deatherage, B.L., Lara, J.C., Bergsbaken, T. et al. (2009). Biogenesis of bacterial membrane vesicles. *Mol. Microbiol.* 72 (6): 1395.

91 Schwechheimer, C., Sullivan, C.J., and Kuehn, M.J. (2013). Envelope control of outer membrane vesicle production in Gram-negative bacteria. *Biochemistry* 52 (18): 3031.

92 Alves, N.J., Turner, K.B., Daniele, M.A. et al. (2015). Bacterial nanobioreactors – directing enzyme packaging into bacterial outer membrane vesicles. *ACS Appl. Mater. Interfaces* 7 (44): 24963–24972.

93 Alves, N.J., Turner, K.B., DiVito, K.A. et al. (2016). Affinity purification of bacterial outer membrane vesicles (OMVs) utilizing a His-tag mutant. *Res. Microbiol.* 168 (2): 139–146.

94 Alves, N.J., Moore, M., Johnson, B.J. et al. (2018). Environmental decontamination of a chemical warfare simulant utilizing a membrane vesicle-encapsulated phosphotriesterase. *ACS Appl. Mater. Interfaces* 10 (18): 15712–15719.

95 Alves, N.J., Turner, K.B., Medintz, I.L., and Walper, S.A. (2016). Protecting enzymatic function through directed packaging into bacterial outer membrane vesicles. *Sci. Rep.* 6: 24866–24866.

96 Amitai, G., Gupta, R.D., and Tawfik, D.S. (2007). Latent evolutionary potentials under the neutral mutational drift of an enzyme. *HFSP J.* 1 (1): 67–78.

97 Miyanaga, K. and Unno, H. (2014). Reaction kinetics and stoichiometry. *Compr. Biotechnol.* 47–60.

98 Mayer, C., Dulson, C., Reddem, E. et al. (2019). Directed evolution of a designer enzyme featuring an unnatural catalytic amino acid. *Angew. Chem. Int. Ed.* 58 (7): 2083–2087.

99 Longo, M.A. and Combes, D. (1998). Analysis of the thermal deactivation kinetics of α-chymotrypsin modified by chemoenzymatic glycosylation. *Prog. Biotechnol.* 15 (C): 135–140.

100 Osbon, Y. and Kumar, M. (2019). Biocatalysis and strategies for enzyme improvement. In: *Biophysical Chemistry - Advance Applications*, 1–22. IntechOpen.

101 Gupta, M.N. (1992). Enzyme function in organic solvents. *Eur. J. Biochem.* 203 (1–2): 25–32.

102 Sulej, J., Jaszek, M., Osińska-Jaroszuk, M. et al. (2021). Natural microbial polysaccharides as effective factors for modification of the catalytic properties of fungal cellobiose dehydrogenase. *Arch. Microbiol.* 203 (7): 4433.

103 Mozhaev, V.V., Berezin, I.V., Martinek, K., and Nosoh, Y. (1988). Structure-stability relationship in proteins: fundamental tasks and strategy for the development of stabilized enzyme catalysts for biotechnology. *CRC Crit. Rev. Biochem.* 23 (3): 235–281.

104 Vieille, C. and Zeikus, G.J. (2001). Hyperthermophilic enzymes: sources, uses, and molecular mechanisms for thermostability. *Microbiol. Mol. Biol. Rev.* 65 (1): 1.

105 Mauerhofer, L.M., Pappenreiter, P., Paulik, C. et al. (2018). Methods for quantification of growth and productivity in anaerobic microbiology and biotechnology. *Folia Microbiol.* 64 (3): 321–360.

106 Panja, A.S., Maiti, S., and Bandyopadhyay, B. (2020). Protein stability governed by its structural plasticity is inferred by physicochemical factors and salt bridges. *Sci. Rep.* 10 (1): 1–9.

107 Bowman, L., Motamed, R., Lee, P. et al. (2020). A simple and reliable method for determination of optimum pH in coupled enzyme assays. *Biotechniques* 68 (4): 200–203.

108 Longo, M.A. and Combes, D. (1997). Influence of surface hydrophilic/hydrophobic balance on enzyme properties. *J. Biotechnol.* 58 (1): 21–32.

109 Binner, R., Menath, V., Huber, H. et al. (2011). Comparative study of stability and half-life of enzymes and enzyme aggregates implemented in anaerobic biogas processes. *Biomass Convers. Biorefin.* 1 (1): 1–8.

110 Zhang, X.F., Yang, G.Y., Zhang, Y. et al. (2016). A general and efficient strategy for generating the stable enzymes. *Sci. Rep.* 6: 33797.

111 Saha, U., Todi, K., and Malhotra, B.D. (2021). Emerging DNA-based multifunctional nano-biomaterials towards electrochemical sensing applications. *Nanoscale* 13 (23): 10305–10319.

112 Bui, H., Díaz, S.A., Fontana, J. et al. (2019). Utilizing the organizational power of DNA scaffolds for new nanophotonic applications. *Adv. Opt. Mater.* 7 (18): 1900562.

113 Ellis, G.A., Dean, S.N., Walper, S.A., and Medintz, I.L. (2020). Quantum dots and gold nanoparticles as scaffolds for enzymatic enhancement: recent advances and the influence of nanoparticle size. *Catalysts* 10 (1): 83.

114 Banerjee, S.S., Aher, N., Patil, R., and Khandare, J. (2012). Poly(ethylene glycol)-prodrug conjugates: concept, design, and applications. *J. Drug Delivery* 2012: 1–17.

115 Mohamad, N.R., Marzuki, N.H.C., Buang, N.A. et al. (2015). An overview of technologies for immobilization of enzymes and surface analysis techniques for immobilized enzymes. *Biotechnol. Biotechnol. Equip.* 29 (2): 205.

116 Yamaguchi, H., Kiyota, Y., and Miyazaki, M. (2018). Techniques for preparation of cross-linked enzyme aggregates and their applications in bioconversions. *Catalysts* 8 (5): 174.

16

Use of Omics Tools Toward the Discovery of Fungal Enzymes and Secondary Metabolites

Neelam A. Kungwani[1], *Simran Dani*[2], *and Gunjan Sharma*[2]

[1] *Gujarat Biotechnology University, Department of Environmental Biotechnology, Gujarat International Finance Tec-City, Gandhinagar, Gujarat 382355, India*
[2] *Gujarat Biotechnology University, Department of Plant Biotechnology, Gujarat International Finance Tec-City, Gandhinagar, Gujarat 382355, India*

16.1 Introduction

Enzymes from natural sources such as plants and animals have been in use since ancient times. The use of the fermentation process to produce cheese, bread, and wine has been in practice since the beginning of civilization. In the current industrial era, the traditional sources are not able to suffice the growing demands and hence, microbial enzymes are more prevalent. With the development of biotechnological techniques, research on microbial enzymes has flourished. In recent years, fungi have gained the attention of researchers due to their diversity, and biosynthesis of versatile enzymes and metabolites. Upscaling, purification, and economical feasibility have made fungal enzymes profitable and marketable. Fungal enzymes exhibit high specificity and can tolerate high pH and temperature conditions. The adaptability of fungi under extreme conditions makes them feasible for industrial-scale operations.

The drive toward sustainability has created a massive increase in demand for bioactive compounds. Agricultural waste, organic waste, and industrial by-products are used as a substrate for fungal growth and metabolite production [1]. Fungal enzymes represent more than 50% of commercial enzymes in food, textile, leather, and pharmaceutical industries [2]. Fungal enzymes are also used for bioremediation and biofuel production [3]. Based on the catalytic reaction, fungal enzymes are classified as: (i) oxidoreductases, (ii) transferases, (iii) hydrolases, (iv) lyases, (v) isomerases, (vi) ligases, and (vii) translocases.

Bioinformatic tools have revolutionized multiple facets of research, including fungal biology. The traditional methods are resource-intensive and slow. The challenging purification of the protein, dynamic interaction, and limited scalability are major drawbacks in fungal enzyme research, due to which researchers are leaning toward *in silico* approaches. Several bioinformatic tools have emerged for the fungal biosynthetic gene cluster identification within genomes using machine

Microbial Enzymes: Production, Purification, and Industrial Applications, First Edition.
Edited by Dinesh Yadav, Pankaj Chowdhary, Gautam Anand, and Rajarshi Kumar Gaur.

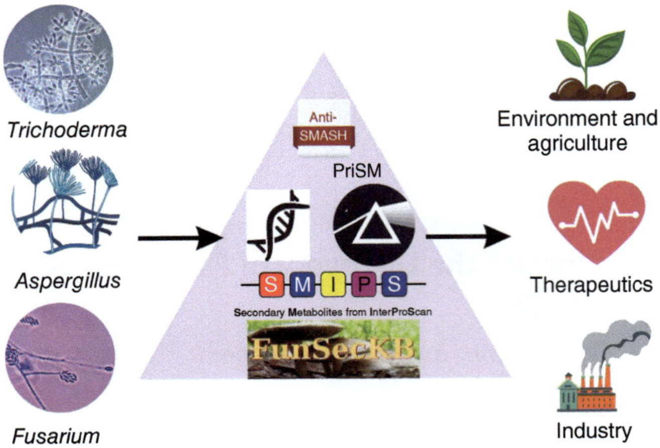

Figure 16.1 Graphical abstract of the applications of the fungal enzymes/secondary metabolites in various research areas and the representative predictive bioinformatics tools. Source: US Department of Agriculture/Wikimedia Commons/Public domain; U.S. Federal Government/Wikimedia Commons/Public domain; with permission of Fungal Secretome KnowledgeBase.

learning based on homology studies of known fungal enzymes and their accessory genes. With the help of multi-omics approaches, the protein–protein interaction, structure, annotation, functional analysis, possible mode of action, and initial screening can be carried out within a few days [4]. Databases for fungal proteins and enzymes, such as FunSecKB, have been established for data storage and easy access. Genome-wide analysis for identification and annotation of gene clusters for metabolites has now become easier and more accessible for all [5]. Several *in silico* tools such as Fungipath assist in the study of metabolite biosynthesis pathway conservation among fungi and specific pathways. *In silico* tools are important for fungal enzymes and secondary metabolite studies as they provide fundamental information before the onset of experimental investigations (Figure 16.1).

16.2 Biotechnological Applications of Key Fungal Enzymes

Fungal enzymes are a significant component among the industrial enzymes, playing an important role in the new economy [2]. Fungal enzymes have significant applications in different industries such as food, pharmaceutical, agricultural, and environmental industries (Table 16.1). Fungal enzymes are used in the food industry as a shelf-life enhancer without affecting the nutritional content of the food. For example, L-asparaginase is the most commonly used enzyme in the food and beverage industries [13]. It is used to minimize the acrylamide level in food by generation of nontoxic L-aspartic acid from L-asparagine [2]. L-Asparaginase is also used as a therapeutic agent in acute lymphoblastic leukemia [14]. In the biomedical field,

Table 16.1 List of commercially important fungal enzymes.

Enzymes	Industrial applications	Sources	References
Cellulase	Paper, textile, detergent, biofuel	*Aspergillus niger, Trichoderma atroviride*	[6]
Laccase	Bioremediation, biofuel, synthetic detergent	*Cotiolos versicolor, Pycnoporus sanguineus, Trametes pubescens*	[6]
Amylase	Beverage industry, baking industry, leather industry	*Aspergillus niger, Aspergillus oryzae*	[7]
Phytase	Animal feed, agriculture	*Myceliophthora, Mucor, Penicillium, Rhizopus*	[8]
Lipase	Pulp industry, cosmetic industry, dairy industry	*Aspergillus niger, Aspergillus oryzae*	[9]
Protease	Dairy, detergent, pharmaceutical	*Aspergillus niger*	[10]
Xylanase	Biorefinery, paper industry, biofuel	*Aspergillus niger, Aspergillus nidulans*	[11]
Chitinase	Waste management, Health care application	*Metarhizium anisopliae, Ustilago maydis, Coprinopsis cinerea, Trichoderma harzianum, Xenorhabdus nematophila*	[9, 12]

fungal enzymes and metabolites are used for their antimicrobial, therapeutic, and antioxidative properties. In the environmental field, fungal enzymes and metabolites are used for bioremediation and biodegradation of toxic waste materials.

In this section, different categories of fungal enzymes that are of industrial interest are presented.

16.2.1 Proteases

Proteases are the enzymes that hydrolyze the peptide bond in protein molecules. Fungal proteases are extremely important from an industrial perspective as they are routinely used in the pharmaceutical, detergent, leather, waste, and food industries. Protease is the most widely used additive used in the detergent industry. In the textile industry, alkaline and protease-based detergents are commonly used to remove tough stains from fabrics. Industrially important proteases are widely produced from filamentous fungal strains such as *Aspergillus*. In the food industry, fungal proteases are used for the clarification of beer, coagulation of cheese, and baking. *Penicillium roqueforti* and *Penicillium caseicolum* proteases are used for the cheese ripening process. As compared to the bacterial protease, fungal protease can remain active at a wide range of pH. Due to the invaluable use of fungal proteases in pharmaceuticals and the medical field, their market demand has increased. *Aspergillus flavipes* protease is used to produce bioactive peptides [15]. Aspartic proteases and L-glutaminase are used to produce digestive aids and to treat leukemia, respectively [16].

16.2.2 Amylase

Fungal amylases such as α-amylase, β-amylase, and glucoamylase have applications in industries related to food, textile, detergent, paper, and pharmaceutical sectors [17]. In the baking industry, α-amylase is used to improve the fermentation rate and the texture of the dough. *Aspergillus* sp. is the most common source of industrially important amylases [18]. Fungi are a potential source of cold-active amylase suitable for health, industrial, and environmental applications. Amylase derived from *Paecilomyces variotii* ATHUM 8891 has better stability and catalytic activity under diverse temperatures and has great potential for use in starch-based industries [7]. β-Amylases are of plant origin, but few fungal strains have been reported to produce them, such as *Rhizopus* sp., *Helminthosporium oxysporium*, and *Penicillium frequestans* [19]. Glucoamylase hydrolyzes glucose monomers from nonreducing ends of amylose and amylopectin and is a common catalyst used in the food industry for saccharification [15].

16.2.3 Cellulase

Cellulase is an industrially important enzyme used in textile, detergent, paper, and food industries as well as biofuel production. Fungi from genera *Penicillium*, *Trichoderma*, and *Aspergillus* are commonly used to produce cellulase on an industrial scale. The market size of cellulase was US$ 9.9 billion in 2019, which is expected to be US$ 14.9 billion by 2027 [6]. The enzyme is grouped into three categories, which include (i) endocellulases, (ii) exocellulases/cellobiohydrolases, and (iii) cellobiases/β-glucosidase. It is an enzyme complex that works on different parts of cellulose by hydrolysis. This property is utilized in the textile industry for the softening of fabric [6].

16.2.4 Lipases

Lipases are enzymes that break triglycerides into fatty acids and glycerol. Fungal lipases are very stable substrate-specific enzymes, which work efficiently under diverse conditions. Commercially lipases are produced from fungi such as *Aspergillus niger*, *Humicola lanuginose, Rhizopus arrhizus, Rhizopus japonicus, Rhizopus oryzae*, and *Mucor miehei*. Fungal lipases have applications in paper and pulp industry, cosmetic industry, dairy industry, biodiesel production, bioremediation of wastewater, etc. [9]. Lipolase, a commercially used lipase enzyme, was first produced by Novozymes company using *Thermomyces lanuginosus* and is a popular choice for detergents and cleaning applications [15].

16.2.5 Phytase

Phytase enzyme catalyzes the hydrolysis of phytic acid, resulting in the release of phosphorous. Fungal phytase is used in animal feed to increase the bioavailability of phosphorous as a mineral. Fungal phytases are extremophilic enzymes that can work at broad pH and temperature ranges. Filamentous fungi, such as *Aspergillus, Mucor, Penicillium,* and *Trichoderma*, are common sources of phytase enzymes. The fungal phytase is widely used in agricultural and environmental sectors, as animal feed supplement, and plant growth promoter [8].

16.3 Biotechnological Potential of Fungal Metabolites

Fungi produce an array of secondary metabolites that are of great importance to mankind. There are four major groups of fungal secondary metabolites: polyketides (PKS), terpenoids, nonribosomal peptides (NRP), and hybrid NRPs/polyketides. Polyketides and terpenoids are derivatives of acetyl-CoA, whereas other metabolites are derived from amino acids [20]. The secondary metabolite biosynthetic genes are in clusters and are significant in the biosynthesis pathways. Multi-omics approaches indicate that fungi are treasure troves of secondary metabolites, with several environmental and medical implications [21]. The secondary metabolites are involved in the fungal metabolism or establishment of contact with other species [22]. Secondary metabolites from fungi can be a source of novel therapeutic drugs. Fungal genera that are well-studied for the synthesis of secondary metabolites include *Aspergillus, Beauveria, Cephalosporium, Micromonospora, Monascus, Penicillium, Streptomyces*, and *Tolypocladium* [23]. A summary of fungal secondary metabolites and their biological activities is listed in Table 16.2.

16.3.1 Polyketides

Polyketides are synthesized from acetyl-CoA by polyketide synthases (type I, II, and III) and are important fungal secondary metabolites that have biocidal, anticancer, immunosuppressive, and neurotoxic activities. They have various structures and biological activities. Most of the studied polyketides from fungi are mycotoxins. Patulin, citrinin, and ochratoxins A and B are some secondary metabolites that are reported from the genus *Penicillium* [20, 32]. Asperochrins A–C obtained from *Aspergillus ochraceus* are active against aquatic pathogenic bacteria *Aeromonas hydrophila* and *Vibrio anguillarum* [33]. Polyketides are also known to be carcinogenic such as fumonisins from *Fusarium verticillioides* [34]. T-toxin from *Cochliobolus heterostrophus* is a phytotoxic fungal secondary metabolite that affects maize by causing mitochondrial toxicity [27, 35].

16.3.2 Terpenoids

Terpenoids are the most diverse group of secondary metabolites found in plants and fungi, having wide applications. Fungi produce a myriad of biologically active terpenoids, which include mycotoxins, antibiotics, antitumor compounds, and phytohormones. Structurally terpenoids are derived from $(C_5)_n$ isoprene units, thus classified as hemiterpenoids, monoterpenoids, sesquiterpenoids, diterpenoids,

Table 16.2 Secondary metabolites from fungi and their biological activities.

Class of secondary metabolite	Metabolites	Source	Activity	References
Polyketides	Statins	*Aspergillus terreus*	Hypo-cholesterolemic agents	[24]
	Aflatoxins	*Aspergillus arachidicola, Aspergillus austwickii, Aspergillus cerealis*	Hepatotoxicity, teratogenicity, and immunotoxicity	
	Ochratoxin	*Aspergillus carbonarius, Aspergillus niger, Aspergillus ochraceus*	Immunosuppression, cancer induction	
	Fumonisins	*Fusarium verticillioides* and *Fusarium proliferatum*	Carcinogenic, genotoxic, teratogenic	
	Zearalenone	*Fusarium cerealis, Fusarium crookwellense, Fusarium culmorum*	Reproduction and fertility disorders	
	Patulin	*Penicillium, Aspergillus,* and *Byssochlamys*	Mitochondrial apoptosis	
	Melanin	*Aspergillus fumigatus, Aspergillus nidulans*	Pathogenicity	
Nonribosomal peptides	Gliotoxin	*Aspergillus fumigatus*	Immunosuppression activity	[24–26]
	Siderophores	*Aspergillus fumigatus*	Virulence, anticancer	
	Cyclosporine A	*Trichoderma polysporum*	Immunosuppressant	
	Penicillin G	*Penicillium chrysogenum*	Antibiotic	
Terpenoids	Fusicoccin A	*Phomopsis amygdali*	Plant disease	[20, 27, 28]
	Sarcodonin G	*Sarcodon scabrosus*	Antiproliferative	
	Hypnophilin	*Pleurotellus hypnophilus*	Antitumor activity	
	Helvolic acid	*Aspergillus novofumigatus, Aspergillus terreus*	Antibiotic	
	Gibberellic acid	*Fusarium fujikuroi*	Phytohormone	
	Deoxynivalenol	*Fusarium* spp.	Mycotoxin	
Others	Ergosterol	*Claviceps purpurea*	Mycotoxin	[29–31]
	Fusarin C	*Fusarium* spp.	Mycotoxin	
	Ochratoxin A	*Aspergillus ochraceus, Aspergillus carbonarius, Aspergillus niger*, and *Penicillium verrucosum*	Mycotoxin	

sesterterpenoids triterpenoids, and tetraterpenoids. Sesquiterpenoids from fungi *Laccaria bicolor,* promote lateral root production in *Arabidopsis* sp. [36]. Diterpenoids from endophytic fungi *Trichoderma atroviride* possess antibacterial and cytotoxic activity [37]. Some terpenoids are famous antibiotics such as fusidic acid and helvolic acid from *Fusidium coccineumis* and *Aspergillus novofumigatus,* respectively (Table 16.2).

16.3.3 Nonribosomal Peptides

NRPs are majorly studied from filamentous fungi and identified as virulence factors. NRP are produced by multidomain enzymes known as NRP synthetases. NRPs display a broad range of biological actions, i.e., insecticidal, antiviral, nematicidal, phytotoxic, and antimicrobials [38]. The well-recognized NRPs are penicillin and cephalosporin, and immunosuppressants such as cyclosporines [22]. Siderophores, iron-chelating compounds produced by both fungi and bacteria, are chemically NRPs. Commonly known fungal siderophores are chemically hydroxamate-type in nature, e.g., ferrichromes, fusarinines, coprogens, and rhodotorulic acid [39, 40]. NRPs are crucial for host interaction, fungal development, and stress tolerance [39].

Some secondary metabolites are produced due to the joint activity of polyketides and NRPs are known as hybrid secondary metabolites. The common hybrid secondary metabolites are fusaristatin A and ochratoxin A produced by *Fusarium graminearum* and *Aspergillus* sp. [20]. Structurally, ochratoxin is a pentaketide derived from dihydrocourmarins. Indole alkaloids (IA) are also pharmacologically important fungal secondary metabolites. Fumigaclavines and fumitremorgens reported from *Aspergillus fumigatus* are IAs derived from tryptophan [24]. Ergot alkaloids are vasoconstrictor compounds derived from *Claviceps purpurea* [41].

16.4 *In Silico* Tools for Fungal Enzymes and Secondary Metabolites Prediction

In this section, user-friendly *in silico* tools and webservers for fungal enzymes and secondary metabolites prediction (Table 16.3) are discussed, which can be helpful to beginners as well as experienced researchers.

16.4.1 antiSMASH (http://antismash.secondarymetabolites.org/)

antiSMASH stands for – "antibiotics & Secondary Metabolite Analysis Shell" [42]. The key enzymes for bioactive secondary metabolite biosynthesis are highly conserved despite their structural and chemical diversity. antiSMASH identifies biosynthetic gene cluster based on gene prediction, annotation, domain analysis using different tools such as ClusterFinder, CASSIS, MIBiG, NRPSpredictor2, PhytoClust, antiSMASH DB, CRISPy-Web, ClusterMine360, JGI-IMG/ABC [54, 55]. Thus, it is a rapid and comprehensive, computational pipeline that helps in mining

Table 16.3 List of the bioinformatic resources that can be applied for fungal biology studies.

Tool	Website	References
antiSMASH	http://antismash.secondarymetabolites.org/	[42]
PRISM	https://prism.adapsyn.com/	[43]
SeMPI	http://sempi.pharmazie.uni-freiburg.de/	[44, 45]
SMURF	http://smurf.jcvi.org/index.php	[46]
FungiPath	http://fungipath.i2bc.paris-saclay.fr/	[47]
MultiGeneBlast	https://multigeneblast.sourceforge.net/	[48]
FunSecKB	http://proteomics.ysu.edu/secretomes/fungi.php	[49]
SMIPS-CASSIS	https://sbi.hki-jena.de/cassis/	[50]
SBSPKS	http://www.nii.ac.in/sbspks2.html	[51]
DoBISCUIT	https://www.nite.go.jp/en/nbrc/genome/dobiscuit.html	[52]
NP.searcher	https://dna.sherman.lsi.umich.edu/	[53]

secondary metabolite biosynthetic gene clusters in microbial (bacteria and fungi) and plant genome sequences. It is also one of the most popular choices for the prediction of secondary metabolite biosynthetic gene clusters. The users may upload the genome sequence from their study or use an already existing genome (NCBI accession number) for the analysis.

16.4.2 PRISM (https://prism.adapsyn.com/)

PRISM stands for "PRediction Informatics for Secondary Metabolomes" (PRISM) [43]. It is an open-source algorithm for biosynthetic gene clusters identification and prediction of polyketides (type I and II), and NRPs from microbial genomes. PRISM also helps in the chemical structure prediction of secondary metabolites [43, 56, 57].

16.4.3 ClustScan

ClustScan stands for "Cluster Scanner" [58]. It is a combined package for the prediction and annotation of secondary metabolite synthetic clusters such as polyketides and NRP sequences from genomic and metagenomic data [58, 59].

16.4.4 SeMPI (http://sempi.pharmazie.uni-freiburg.de/)

SeMPI is used for biosynthetic gene cluster identification of NRPs and polyketides (type I modular) from microbial genomes [44, 45]. The advantage of SeMPI tool is the detection of partial as well as incomplete clusters based on homology. This tool is developed by the researchers at the Institute of Pharmaceutical Sciences, University of Freiburg, Germany, for the prediction of novel drug agents.

16.4.5 SMURF (http://smurf.jcvi.org/index.php)

SMURF stands for "Secondary metabolite unique regions finder" [46]. This web-based software tool developed at J. Craig Venter Institute (JCVI), USA, helps in the prediction of secondary metabolites biosynthesis genes within fungal genomes/supercontigs.

16.4.6 FungiPath (http://fungipath.i2bc.paris-saclay.fr/)

FungiPath is a tool for the prediction of fungal metabolic pathways based on orthology [47]. FungiPath uses MaRiO (Meta-Approach Requiring Intersections for Orthologs predictions) program [60] for the prediction of orthologous proteins. Currently, 155 KEGG pathways, 2387 Metacyc pathways, and 165 fungal genomes are incorporated in FUNGIpath analysis.

16.4.7 MultiGeneBlast (https://multigeneblast.sourceforge.net/)

MultiGeneBlast is an NCBI-BLAST-based program that performs a homology search for operons and gene clusters. The algorithm used for this program is adapted from antiSMASH. It is an intuitive tool that can be used for comparative genomic analysis, the study of evolutionary history, and bimolecular diversity [48].

16.4.8 FunSecKB (http://proteomics.ysu.edu/secretomes/fungi.php)

FunSecKB stands for "Fungal secretome knowledgebase" [49]. It is a collection of all the secreted fungal proteins derived from the NCBI-RefSeq fungal protein data. The integrated computational pipeline comprises bioinformatic tools related to the prediction of secretome, such as SignalP, WolfPsort, Phobius, TMHMM, and PS-Scan [61].

16.4.9 SMIPS-CASSIS (https://sbi.hki-jena.de/cassis/)

SMIPS stands for "Secondary Metabolites by InterProScan" and CASSIS stands for "Cluster Assignment by Islands of Sites" [50]. SMIPS is an online tool for the genome-wide prediction of backbone genes encoding secondary metabolites (such as polyketide synthases, NRP synthetases, and dimethylallyl tryptophan synthases). CASSIS identifies gene clusters around such backbone genes. SMIPS-CASSIS also considers the coregulation possibility of secondary metabolite gene clusters.

16.4.10 SBSPKS (http://www.nii.ac.in/sbspks2.html)

SBSPKS stands for "structure-based sequence analysis of polyketide synthases" [51]. It is an online tool that helps in the prediction and structure analysis of polyketide synthases and NRP synthetases [51, 62]. SBSPKSv2 is a recent version [62], that provides two different interfaces: Genomic Space and Chemical Space. Genomic space provides an interface for the sequence-based analysis and modeling of polyketide synthases and NRP synthetases. Chemical space provides a database of polyketide synthases and NRP synthetase pathways and a comparison of chemical structures.

16.4.11 DoBISCUIT (https://www.nite.go.jp/en/nbrc/genome/dobiscuit.html)

DoBISCUIT is developed by Biological Resource Center, NITE (NBRC), Japan. DoBISCUIT stands for "Database of BIoSynthesis clusters CUrated and InTegrated" [52]. It is a curated database of biosynthetic gene clusters and related literature. DoBISCUIT has applications in genome mining, combinatorial biosynthesis, and assessing the novelty of the gene clusters [52].

16.4.12 NP.searcher (https://dna.sherman.lsi.umich.edu/)

NP.searcher is a simplified tool that processes DNA sequences to predict polyketide and NRP sequences and generates "Simplified Molecular Input Line Entry Specifications" (SMILES) as output data [53] that can be further converted to a 2D or 3D structure using chemical drawing software, and used for docking studies.

16.5 Use of *In Silico* Tools for the Prediction of Fungal Enzymes and Secondary Metabolites

Various *in silico* tools for the prediction of candidate enzymes and secondary metabolites are useful in experimental as well as bioinformatic studies. In the broad range fungal plant pathogen *Sclerotinia sclerotiorum*, eighty secondary metabolite clusters were identified using *in silico* analysis tools anti-SMASH and SMURF [63]. In a similar study, antiSMASH was used to identify twenty-five gene clusters for secondary metabolites in the plant pathogenic fungus *Verticillium dahliae* [5]. In phytopathogenic fungus, *Chrysoporthe cubensis* secretome prediction and functional annotation were conducted using various bioinformatic databases and tools to analyze biomass hydrolysis potential [64]. In phytopathogenic fungi *Ganoderma boninense,* which causes basal stem rot in coconuts and oil palms, SeMPI v.2 and antiSMASH programs were used to detect sequences or gene clusters that are potentially responsible to produce NRPs [65]. The anti-inflammatory activity of marine fungal metabolite butyrolactone I was studied using the ADMETlab tool [66]. The bioinformatic analysis of α-amylase gene acquired from *A. niger* strain CSA45 was carried out using BLASTp, ClustalW2 [67]. Santacruz-Juárez et al. [68] studied fungal enzymes for polyethylene degradation using *in silico* tools. In the phytopathogenic fungi *Bipolaris sorokiniana* that attacks grasses and cereals, the secretome analysis was performed using various *in silico* tools [69].

16.6 Implications and Limitations of the *In Silico* Studies in Fungal Biology

In silico approaches facilitate fungal biology research by speeding up the predictions and annotation process. Once the desired information is identified it becomes easier to experimentally validate it and saves a lot of time for the researchers. However, since most of the bioinformatic tools rely on a standard dataset that is used to set up the prediction algorithms, sometimes the results can be erroneous. Thus, it is recommended that the *in silico* predictions must be verified by laboratory experiments.

16.7 Conclusions and Prospects

The rise of cost-effective next-generation sequencing technologies has assisted researchers with a rapid generation of sequencing data, which further requires various *in silico* tools for processing and annotation. However, it is very critical to know about the requirements for an experiment and its analysis approaches. Based on the background information provided in this chapter, by now the readers must be acquainted with the importance of fungal enzymes and metabolites in industries and the bioinformatic tools that can be applied in fungal biology research.

References

1 Lange, L. (2017). Fungal enzymes and yeasts for conversion of plant biomass to bioenergy and high-value products. *Microbiol. Spectrum* 5 (1): 5–1.

2 El-Gendi, H., Saleh, A.K., Badierah, R. et al. (2022). A comprehensive insight into fungal enzymes: structure, classification, and their role in mankind's challenges. *J. Fungi* 8 (1): 23.

3 Østergaard, L.H. and Olsen, H.S. (2011). Industrial applications of fungal enzymes. In: *Industrial Applications* (ed. M. Hofrichter), 269–290. Berlin, Heidelberg: Springer.

4 Doyle, S. (2011). Fungal proteomics: from identification to function. *FEMS Microbiol. Lett.* 321 (1): 1–9.

5 Shi-Kunne, X., Jové, R.D., Depotter, J.R. et al. (2019). *In silico* prediction and characterisation of secondary metabolite clusters in the plant pathogenic fungus *Verticillium dahliae*. *FEMS Microbiol. Lett.* 366 (7): fnz081.

6 Singh, A., Bajar, S., Devi, A., and Pant, D. (2021). An overview on the recent developments in fungal cellulase production and their industrial applications. *Bioresour. Technol. Rep.* 14: 100652.

7 Apostolidi, M.E., Kalantzi, S., Hatzinikolaou, D.G. et al. (2020). Catalytic and thermodynamic properties of an acidic α-amylase produced by the fungus *Paecilomyces variotii* ATHUM 8891. *3 Biotech* 10 (7): 311.

8 Jatuwong, K., Suwannarach, N., Kumla, J. et al. (2020). Bioprocess for production, characteristics, and biotechnological applications of fungal phytases. *Front. Microbiol.* 11: 188.

9 Kumar, A., Verma, V., Dubey, V.K. et al. (2023). Industrial applications of fungal lipases: a review. *Front. Microbiol.* 14: 1142536.

10 Dhevagi, P., Ramya, A., Priyatharshini, S. et al. (2021). Industrially important fungal enzymes: productions and applications. In: *Recent Trends in Mycological Research: Volume 2: Environmental and Industrial Perspective* (ed. A.N. Yadav), 263–309. Springer, Cham.

11 Gawande, P.V. and Kamat, M.Y. (1999). Production of *Aspergillus* xylanase by lignocellulosic waste fermentation and its application. *J. Appl. Microbiol.* 87 (4): 511–519.

12 Gomaa, E.Z. (2021). Microbial chitinases: properties, enhancement and potential applications. *Protoplasma* 258 (4): 695–710.

13 Wang, Y., Xu, W., Wu, H. et al. (2021). Microbial production, molecular modification, and practical application of L-asparaginase: a review. *Int. J. Biol. Macromol.* 186: 975–983.

14 Egler, R.A., Ahuja, S.P., and Matloub, Y. (2016). L-Asparaginase in the treatment of patients with acute lymphoblastic leukemia. *J. Pharmacol. Pharmacother.* 7 (2): 62–71.

15 McKelvey, S.M. and Murphy, R.A. (2017). Biotechnological use of fungal enzymes. In: *Fungi: Biology and Applications* (ed. K. Kavanagh), 201–225. Wiley.

16 Naeem, M., Manzoor, S., Abid, M.U. et al. (2022). Fungal proteases as emerging biocatalysts to meet the current challenges and recent developments in biomedical therapies: an updated review. *J. Fungi* 8 (2): 109.

17 Souza, P.M. (2010). Application of microbial α-amylase in industry - a review. *Braz. J. Microbiol.* 41: 850–861.

18 Saranraj, P. and Stella, D. (2013). Fungal amylase—a review. *Int. J. Microbiol. Res.* 4 (2): 203–211.

19 Adeniran, H.A., Abiose, S.H., and Ogunsua, A.O. (2010). Production of fungal β-amylase and amyloglucosidase on some Nigerian agricultural residues. *Food Bioprocess Technol.* 3: 693–698.

20 Avalos, J. and Limón, M.C. (2021). Fungal secondary metabolism. *Encyclopedia* 2 (1): 1–13.

21 Aghdam, S.A. and Brown, A.M. (2021). Deep learning approaches for natural product discovery from plant endophytic microbiomes. *Environ. Microbiomes* 16 (1): 1–20.

22 Brakhage, A.A. (2013). Regulation of fungal secondary metabolism. *Nat. Rev. Microbiol.* 11 (1): 21–32.

23 Devi, R., Kaur, T., Guleria, G. et al. (2020). Fungal secondary metabolites and their biotechnological applications for human health. In: *New and Future Developments in Microbial Biotechnology and Bioengineering* (ed. A.A. Rastegari, A.N. Yadav, and N. Yadav), 147–161. Elsevier.

24 Roy, A., Ahuja, S., and Garg, S. (2021). Fungal secondary metabolites: biological activity and potential applications. In: *Recent Trends in Mycological Research: Volume 1: Agricultural and Medical Perspective* (ed. A.A. Rastegari, A.N. Yadav, and N. Yadav), 159–188.

25 Anjum, T., Azam, A., and Irum, W. (2012). Production of cyclosporine A by submerged fermentation from a local isolate of *Penicillium fellutanum*. *Indian J. Pharm. Sci.* 74 (4): 372–374.

26 Ziemons, S., Koutsantas, K., Becker, K. et al. (2017). Penicillin production in industrial strain *Penicillium chrysogenum* P2niaD18 is not dependent on the copy number of biosynthesis genes. *BMC Biotech.* 17: 1–1.

27 Pusztahelyi, T., Holb, I.J., and Pócsi, I. (2015). Secondary metabolites in fungus-plant interactions. *Front. Plant Sci.* 6: 573.

28 Marra, M., Camoni, L., Visconti, S. et al. (2021). The surprising story of Fusicoccin: a wilt-inducing phytotoxin, a tool in plant physiology and a 14-3-3-targeted drug. *Biomolecules* 11 (9): 1393.

29 Rodrigues, M.L. (2018). The multifunctional fungal ergosterol. *MBio* 9 (5): e01755-18.

30 Kleigrewe, K., Aydin, F., Hogrefe, K. et al. (2012). Structure elucidation of new fusarins revealing insights in the rearrangement mechanisms of the *Fusarium* mycotoxin fusarin C. *J. Agric. Food. Chem.* 60 (21): 5497–5505.

31 Bui-Klimke, T.R. and Wu, F. (2015). Ochratoxin A and human health risk: a review of the evidence. *Crit. Rev. Food Sci. Nutr.* 55 (13): 1860–1869.

32 Kumar, A., Asthana, M., Gupta, A. et al. (2018). Secondary metabolism and antimicrobial metabolites of *Penicillium*. In: *New and Future Developments in Microbial Biotechnology and Bioengineering* (ed. V.K. Gupta and S. Rodriguez-Couto), 47–68. Elsevier.

33 Liu, Y., Li, X.M., Meng, L.H., and Wang, B.G. (2015). Polyketides from the marine mangrove-derived fungus *Aspergillus ochraceus* MA-15 and their activity against aquatic pathogenic bacteria. *Phytochem. Lett.* 12: 232–236.

34 Siddiquee, S. (2018). Recent advancements on the role of biologically active secondary metabolites from *Aspergillus*. In: *New and Future Developments in Microbial Biotechnology and Bioengineering* (ed. V.K. Gupta and S. Rodriguez-Couto), 69–94. Elsevier.

35 Stergiopoulos, I., Collemare, J., Mehrabi, R., and De Wit, P.J. (2013). Phytotoxic secondary metabolites and peptides produced by plant pathogenic Dothideomycete fungi. *FEMS Microbiol. Rev.* 37 (1): 67–93.

36 Ditengou, F.A., Müller, A., Rosenkranz, M. et al. (2015). Volatile signalling by sesquiterpenes from ectomycorrhizal fungi reprogrammes root architecture. *Nat. Commun.* 6 (1): 6279.

37 Galindo-Solís, J.M. and Fernández, F.J. (2022). Endophytic fungal terpenoids: natural role and bioactivities. *Microorganisms* 10 (2): 339.

38 Le Govic, Y., Papon, N., Le Gal, S. et al. (2019). Non-ribosomal peptide synthetase gene clusters in the human pathogenic fungus *Scedosporium apiospermum*. *Front. Microbiol.* 10: 2062.

39 Oide, S. and Turgeon, B.G. (2020). Natural roles of nonribosomal peptide metabolites in fungi. *Mycoscience* 61 (3): 101–110.

40 Winkelmann, G. (1992). Structures and functions of fungal siderophores containing hydroxamate and complex one type iron binding ligands. *Mycol. Res.* 96 (7): 529–534.

41 Hodgson, E. (2012). Toxins and venoms. *Prog. Mol. Biol. Transl. Sci.* 112: 373–415.

42 Medema, M.H., Blin, K., Cimermancic, P. et al. (2011). antiSMASH: rapid identification, annotation and analysis of secondary metabolite biosynthesis gene clusters in bacterial and fungal genome sequences. *Nucleic Acids Res.* 39 (suppl_2): W339–W346.

43 Skinnider, M.A., Merwin, N.J., Johnston, C.W., and Magarvey, N.A. (2017). PRISM 3: expanded prediction of natural product chemical structures from microbial genomes. *Nucleic Acids Res.* 45 (W1): W49–W54.

44 Zierep, P.F., Padilla, N., Yonchev, D.G. et al. (2017). SeMPI: a genome-based secondary metabolite prediction and identification web server. *Nucleic Acids Res.* 45 (W1): W64–W71.

45 Zierep, P.F., Ceci, A.T., Dobrusin, I. et al. (2020). SeMPI 2.0—a web server for PKS and NRPS predictions combined with metabolite screening in natural product databases. *Metabolites* 11 (1): 13.

46 Khaldi, N., Seifuddin, F.T., Turner, G. et al. (2010). SMURF: genomic mapping of fungal secondary metabolite clusters. *Fungal Genet. Biol.* 47 (9): 736–741.

47 Grossetête, S., Labedan, B., and Lespinet, O. (2010). FUNGIpath: a tool to assess fungal metabolic pathways predicted by orthology. *BMC Genomics* 11: 81.

48 Medema, M.H., Takano, E., and Breitling, R. (2013). Detecting sequence homology at the gene cluster level with MultiGeneBlast. *Mol. Biol. Evol.* 30 (5): 1218–1223.

49 Lum, G. and Min, X.J. (2011). FunSecKB: the fungal secretome knowledgebase. *Database* 2011: bar001.

50 Wolf, T., Shelest, V., Nath, N., and Shelest, E. (2016). CASSIS and SMIPS: promoter-based prediction of secondary metabolite gene clusters in eukaryotic genomes. *Bioinformatics* 32 (8): 1138–1143.

51 Anand, S., Prasad, M.V., Yadav, G. et al. (2010). SBSPKS: structure based sequence analysis of polyketide synthases. *Nucleic Acids Res.* 38 (suppl_2): W487–W496.

52 Ichikawa, N., Sasagawa, M., Yamamoto, M. et al. (2012). DoBISCUIT: a database of secondary metabolite biosynthetic gene clusters. *Nucleic Acids Res.* 41 (D1): D408–D414.

53 Li, M.H., Ung, P.M., Zajkowski, J. et al. (2009). Automated genome mining for natural products. *BMC Bioinf.* 10 (1): 185.

54 Blin, K., Kim, H.U., Medema, M.H., and Weber, T. (2019). Recent development of antiSMASH and other computational approaches to mine secondary metabolite biosynthetic gene clusters. *Briefings Bioinf.* 20 (4): 1103–1113.

55 Blin, K., Shaw, S., Augustijn, H.E. et al. (2023). antiSMASH 7.0: new and improved predictions for detection, regulation, chemical structures and visualisation. *Nucleic Acids Res.* 51: W46–W50.

56 Skinnider, M.A., Dejong, C.A., Rees, P.N. et al. (2015). Genomes to natural products prediction informatics for secondary metabolomes (PRISM). *Nucleic Acids Res.* 43 (20): 9645–9662.

57 Skinnider, M.A., Johnston, C.W., Gunabalasingam, M. et al. (2020). Comprehensive prediction of secondary metabolite structure and biological activity from microbial genome sequences. *Nat. Commun.* 11 (1): 6058.

58 Starcevic, A., Zucko, J., Simunkovic, J. et al. (2008). ClustScan: an integrated program package for the semi-automatic annotation of modular biosynthetic gene clusters and *in silico* prediction of novel chemical structures. *Nucleic Acids Res.* 36 (21): 6882–6892.

59 Cullum, J., Starcevic, A., Diminic, J. et al. (2011). ClustScan: an integrated program package for the detection and semiautomatic annotation of secondary metabolite clusters in genomic and metagenomic DNA datasets. In: *Handbook of Molecular Microbial Ecology I: Metagenomics and Complementary Approaches* (ed. F.J. de Bruijn), 423–432. John Wiley & Sons.

60 Pereira, C., Denise, A., and Lespinet, O. (2014). A meta-approach for improving the prediction and the functional annotation of ortholog groups. *BMC Genomics* 15 (6): 1–8.

61 Meinken, J., Asch, D.K., Neizer-Ashun, K.A. et al. (2014). FunSecKB2: a fungal protein subcellular location knowledgebase. *Comput. Mol. Biol.* 4 (4): 1–17.

62 Khater, S., Gupta, M., Agrawal, P. et al. (2017). SBSPKSv2: structure-based sequence analysis of polyketide synthases and non-ribosomal peptide synthetases. *Nucleic Acids Res.* 45 (W1): W72–W79.

63 Graham-Taylor, C., Kamphuis, L.G., and Derbyshire, M.C. (2020). A detailed *in silico* analysis of secondary metabolite biosynthesis clusters in the genome of the broad host range plant pathogenic fungus *Sclerotinia sclerotiorum*. *BMC Genomics* 21 (1): 1–20.

64 Tavares, M.P., Morgan, T., Gomes, R.F. et al. (2021). Secretomic insight into the biomass hydrolysis potential of the phytopathogenic fungus *Chrysoporthe cubensis*. *J. Proteomics* 236: 104121.

65 Shokrollahi, N., Ho, C.L., Zainudin, N.A. et al. (2021). Identification of non-ribosomal peptide synthetase in *Ganoderma boninense* Pat. that was expressed during the interaction with oil palm. *Sci. Rep.* 11 (1): 16330.

66 Nie, Y., Yang, J., Zhou, L. et al. (2022). Marine fungal metabolite butyrolactone I prevents cognitive deficits by relieving inflammation and intestinal microbiota imbalance on aluminum trichloride-injured zebrafish. *J. Neuroinflammation* 19 (1): 1–7.

67 Avwioroko, O.J., Anigboro, A.A., Unachukwu, N.N., and Tonukari, N.J. (2018). Isolation, identification and *in silico* analysis of alpha-amylase gene of *Aspergillus niger* strain CSA35 obtained from cassava undergoing spoilage. *Biochem. Biophys. Rep.* 14: 35–42.

68 Santacruz-Juárez, E., Buendia-Corona, R.E., Ramírez, R.E., and Sánchez, C. (2021). Fungal enzymes for the degradation of polyethylene: molecular docking simulation and biodegradation pathway proposal. *J. Hazard. Mater.* 411: 125118.

69 Pathak, G.M., Gurjar, G.S., and Kadoo, N.Y. (2020). Insights of *Bipolaris sorokiniana* secretome-an *in-silico* approach. *Biologia* 75: 2367–2381.

17

Bioprospecting of Microbial Enzymes with Application in Environmental Biotechnology: An Omic Approach

Maricy R. L. Bonfá[1], *Rodrigo M. Pereira*[1], *Francine A. Piubeli*[2], *Caio C. A. do Prado*[3], *and Lucia R. Grossman*[4]

[1] *Universidade Federal da Grande Dourados, Faculty of Biological and Environmental Science, Rodovia Dourados/Itahum, Km 12, Cidade Universitária, Dourados/MS, 79.804-970, Dourados, MS, Brazil*
[2] *University of Seville, Department of Genetics, Faculty of Biology, C/PROFESOR GARCÍA GONZÁLEZ, S/N CP 41012, Seville, Spain*
[3] *Universidade Federal de São Paulo Unifesp, Institute of Marine Science, Dona Maria Máximo 168, 11070-100 Santos, SP, Brazil*
[4] *Hocking College, School of Natural Resources, 3301 Hocking Pkwy. Nelsonville, Nelsonville, OH 45764, USA*

17.1 Introduction

Environmental biotechnology is a multidisciplinary science that involves microbiology, chemistry, biochemistry, molecular biology, engineering, and geology, among others. The principle that guides this science is the use of living beings (mainly microorganisms, plants, or parts of them) to restore contaminated environments and prevent new pollution, in addition to using sustainable bioproducts from these organisms. Thus, the main objective of this science is to preserve the environment and its resources from the negative impact of anthropic activities.

Since its inception, environmental biotechnology has brought many advantages over conventional methods, particularly in the areas of bioremediation, phytoremediation, and wastewater treatment, which have operating costs much lower than conventional methods. In addition to the lower cost, it also opens the possibility of using living beings, in an integrated beneficial cycle of treatment/sustainable production, in which the processes that produce waste are used as a base (raw material) for new processes.

Physicochemical methods , on the other hand, can generate other wastewater and residues that later require treatment or disposal. There are numerous environmental problems, such as excess waste, contamination by pesticides, oil disasters, and industrial waste, where environmental biotechnology can help, using methods such as biodegradation and bioremediation, biological treatment of effluents, production of bioplastics, biopesticides, biofertilizers, production of renewable energy, and others.

Microbial Enzymes: Production, Purification, and Industrial Applications, First Edition.
Edited by Dinesh Yadav, Pankaj Chowdhary, Gautam Anand, and Rajarshi Kumar Gaur.

Environmental pollution can be organic or inorganic, and the origin of these pollutants varies according to the anthropogenic processes that occur in each place. For example, inorganic compounds can come from agriculture (fertilizers and pesticides), mining, and industrial activities (heavy metals, nitrates, and phosphates). Organic compounds, in turn, can come from accidents with oil and solvents, military activities, use of pesticides and fertilizers in agriculture, and places without domestic sewage treatment.

The main organisms used in environmental biotechnology are bacteria, archaea, fungi, protozoa, algae, and plants. These can be applied both in environmental restoration processes and in the production of sustainable bioproducts.

Microorganisms have incredible enzymatic machineries that they use to biodegrade toxic and recalcitrant compounds, transforming them into less-toxic substances or, more desirably, CO_2 and water. In addition to toxic compounds, microorganisms play a fundamental role in the biogeochemical balance, since they are the ones who decompose all organic matter on the planet with their enzymatic system.

In this way, the biodegradation that is innate to microorganisms is used to restore contaminated environments and assist in effluent and waste treatment processes. Therefore, it can be defined that a bioremediation process is a monitored and controlled biological decontamination.

The fantastic microorganism's system of enzymes and variety of metabolism are also responsible for the synthesis of bioproducts. Biofuels can be produced through enzymatic transesterification or also by the accumulation of lipids from yeasts and microalgae, in addition to the production of methane gas obtained through the anaerobic biodigestion of effluents and residues by methanogenic archaea. These are some of the examples of biofuels that can be obtained, but other possibilities exist such as genetically modified microorganisms (GMO) that are transformed to have the ability to produce these bioproducts.

Another important bioproduct is biopolymers that can be used as an environmentally sustainable replacement for plastics of fossil origin for applications in the food, oil, medical, and pharmaceutical industries. These compounds can be obtained in different ways, from bacterial lactic acid, through plants, and also by bacteria that have enzymes such as polyhydroxyalkanoates (PHA) synthase.

Many studies have already been published about the bioprospecting of microorganisms that have these enzymes for environmental applications. However, bioprospecting using classical methods of microbiological cultivation limits the discovery of these enzymes for later environmental and industrial applications. In this way, omics methods such as metagenomics, metatranscriptomics, and synthetic biology can support this search. Furthermore, from the omics data generated, it is possible to genetically transform microorganisms by inserting genes responsible for the synthesis of enzymes of environmental interest.

In this sense, this chapter will present the main enzymes of environmental application both for restoration and to produce environmentally sustainable bioproducts. In addition to presenting and discussing omics and molecular tools for the bioprospecting and production of these enzymes.

17.2 Environmental Biotechnology Areas

Didactically, the areas of environmental biotechnology will be divided into two: environmental restoration and bioproducts.

17.2.1 Environmental Restoration: Biodegradation and Bioremediation

The increase in the generation of domestic, hospital, industrial, and agro-industrial wastes brought great concern, mainly due to the aspects of pollution and environmental contamination. In this way, tools were developed to recover contaminated areas or minimize the various possible damages to nontarget organisms [1]. Among several methods developed, the main ones are derived from three basic models of action: physical, chemical, and biological (Figure 17.1) [2].

17.2.1.1 Biodegradation

Biodegradation is a natural process in which organic chemical compounds are degraded biologically. The term is used to indicate different degrees of degradation, from the loss of some component to complete mineralization resulting in CO_2 and

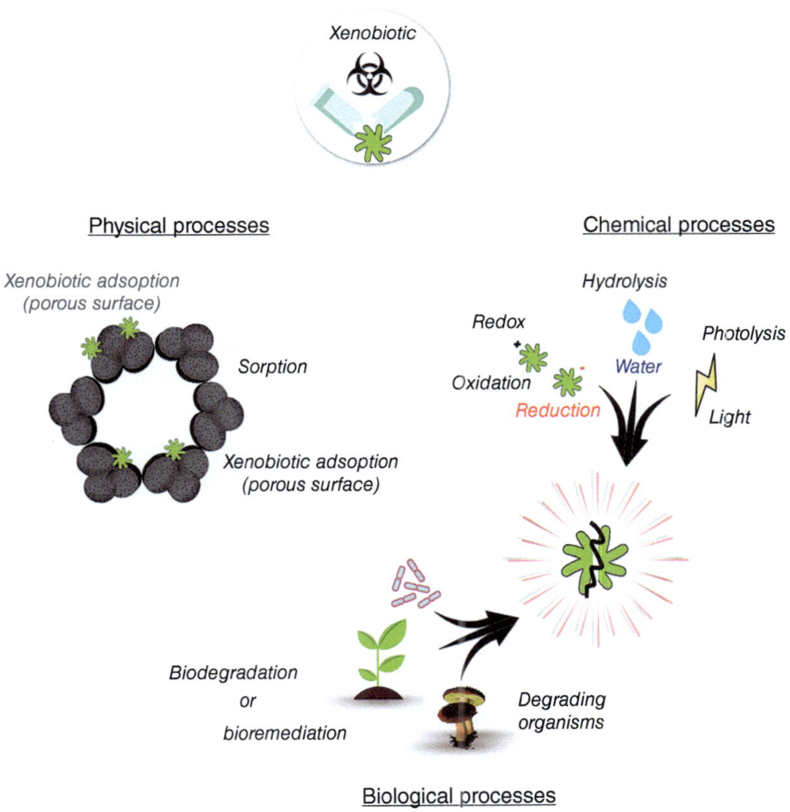

Figure 17.1 Main mechanisms of detoxification of xenobiotics.

water. This degradation only occurs because the microorganisms present in all environments have enzymes. Biodegradation may occur by cometabolism when several microorganisms and several enzymes are required until the compound is completely degraded. Or the complete mineralization of the compound may occur, in which case, the microorganism responsible for the degradation uses the compound as an energy source.

According to studies, the presence of xenobiotics in the environment causes the natural selection of microorganisms capable of metabolizing and using such toxic compounds as an energy source. In this way, bioprospecting for increasingly resistant and high-performance microorganisms becomes the focus for the selection of candidates for bioremediation in environmental recovery [3].

However, one of the major problems involving the removal of these toxic compounds is linked to their recalcitrance (difficulty of being metabolized and degraded) and environmental physicochemical characteristics. Due to their direct influence on the local microbiota, biological processes are the ones with the greatest number of studies on their mechanisms of action, seeking to use wild microorganisms from the environment itself to help carry out these procedures [4].

As biodegradation is the result of enzyme action produced by microorganisms. However, in addition to the presence of a high diversity of microorganisms and metabolic diversity, other factors influence the biodegradation of organic compounds. These factors can be physical, chemical, or biological.

i) **Physical factors:**
   - Place – the physical nature of the location where the compost is contaminating, since depending on the environmental matrix, the compost may be more or less bioavailable.
   - Temperature – although microorganisms and their enzymes may have metabolic adaptations to perform at extreme temperatures, biological reactions will occur more rapidly in mild environments. An example of an inhospitable climate is the Arctic, an environment with a very cold climate, in which the potential for biodegradation of petroleum compounds by indigenous communities has not yet been discovered [5].
   - Light – the incidence of light in contaminated environments can also influence biodegradation, since the compounds can undergo photooxidation, transforming themselves into biodegradable compounds.

ii) **Chemical factors:**
   - pH – the pH influences biodegradation in several ways, since it can reduce or increase the bioavailability of the contaminating compound, as well as in the enzymatic reaction.
   - O_2 – oxygenation is another important factor because in places without oxygen availability, only anaerobiosis can occur, which is generally slower than aerobic biodegradation. Many bioremediation methods consist of aerating the environment to accelerate the biodegradation process.
   - Humidity – the presence of water in contaminated sites contributes positively to biodegradation since biological activities depend on water. However,

different microorganisms act in different concentrations of water. Fungi, e.g., can survive and multiply in drier environments better than bacteria.

- Nutrients – the concentration of organic and inorganic compounds in the contaminated environment can improve biodegradation. This is because, often, the pollutant alone does not provide microorganisms with all the nutrients necessary for growth and metabolism. However, the presence of easily assimilated organic compounds can inhibit the degradation of toxic and recalcitrant compounds.

iii) **Biological factors**

- Microbiota – biodiversity is a very important factor for the biodegradation of contaminants. So that the greater the microbial diversity, the greater the enzymatic metabolic diversity. In cases of bioremediation, species and metabolic biodiversity should always be evaluated, as it is an important point in decision-making about the method to be used. In cases where there are no or few microorganisms, e.g., the process used may be bioaugmentation.
- Abundance – in addition to biodiversity, the abundance of microorganisms is also important. The greater biomass of microorganisms will positively influence biodegradation. In cases where there is biodiversity but low abundance, the bioremediation option may be biostimulation.
- Biosurfactants – these are substances produced by microorganisms that increase the solubility and bioavailability of contaminating compounds, thus facilitating their biodegradation. They work like detergents that transform nonpolar compounds into small micelles, thus facilitating microbial and enzymatic activity.

From these factors discussed above on the biodegradation of contaminants in environments, bioremediation processes can be planned. Several methods can be used depending on the type of environment, location of contamination, and the biological factors already discussed. The methods will be presented below. In addition to the factors presented above, conditions must be studied before the bioremediation process is decided, as shown in Table 17.1.

17.2.1.2 Bioremediation Methods

The applied bioremediation methods can be divided according to the place where they will be applied. Therefore, they can be *in situ* or *ex situ*. Both must consider the location and type of contamination when choosing the method.

In situ methods, which are applied at the site of contamination, can be used for both aquatic and soil environments. They range from the addition of nutrients and oxygen to also adding microorganisms, biosurfactants and pooling immobilized enzymes in products formulated for bioremediation.

Biostimulation is generally used in cases where the existence of microbiota with the potential to biodegrade the polluting compounds is known, but is present in low abundance, or in cases where an improvement in time or percentage of degradation with biostimulation is expected. In this method, nutrients and biosurfactants can be added.

Table 17.1 Main factors affecting biological processes.

Microbial	**Microbial growth**
Growth to log phase	Types of contaminants
Mutation and horizontal gene transfer	Concentration
Induction enzymes	An alternative source of carbon present
Microbiota enrichment production of toxic metabolites	Microbial interaction (competition, succession, and predates)
Environment	**Bioavailability (physical-chemical)**
Development of preferred substrate	Balanced sorption
Lack of nutrients	Irreversible sorption
Injunction environmental conditions	Integration of serious issues
Substrate	**Mass transfer limitation**
Low concentration of contaminants	Solubility and oxygen diffusion
Chemical structure of contaminants	Nutrient diffusion
Contaminant toxicity	Miscibility/solubility in water
Solubility of contaminants	
Biological process (aerobic versus anaerobic)	**Reason**
Redox potential	Importance and size of the procedure
Availability of electron acceptors	Technical information of the studied site
Microbial population present at the site	Knowledge of local microbial diversity

Source: Adapted from Boopathy [6].

Bioaugmentation is the addition of microorganisms to a contaminated environment. In this case, autochthonous microorganisms can be used, and allochthonous, even GMO, microorganisms can be used. Another more recently used form is the use of a pool of microbial enzymes that are added with slow-release dispersants.

Aeration increases the activity of aerobic microorganisms and consequently increases the biodegradation of contaminants. Several forms of aeration can be used, from soil disturbance to injection of air or pure oxygen at the contamination site.

Ex situ bioremediation is restricted to some types of environments such as soil and groundwater. It depends on the extent of the contamination. In soil, methods such as landfarming and biopiles can be used. In the case of groundwater, treatment in bioreactors is recommended.

17.2.1.3 Microbiological Treatment of Wastewater

The biodegradation of organic compounds is also the principle used for the treatment of wastewater. Both domestic and industrial sewage can be treated using biological systems. Again, it is important to emphasize that the enzymes produced by these microorganisms are responsible for reducing organic matter and pollutants in wastewaters.

There are many treatment methods, such as activated sludge, ponds (anaerobic, aerobic, and facultative), bioreactors, and microalgae treatment. It is important to point out that currently, the processes that can still generate bioproducts or energy must be considered, as they are more environmentally sustainable.

17.2.2 Bioproducts

Due to human actions, the Earth is constantly contaminated by xenobiotics; thus, in addition to environmental recovery processes, the processes of production, transport, and disposal of recalcitrant products and waste must be reviewed and modernized. In this sense, biotechnology brings environmentally friendly solutions to produce energy and biopolymers, to replace fossil raw materials. Although the frequency and volume of oil spilled in accidents have decreased in recent decades, they still occur [7]. In addition, the emission of greenhouse gases emitted during the production and burning of fuels is a serious problem for the planet [8].

17.2.3 Fuels and Energy

Currently, there are several processes for obtaining fuel and energy through microbial activity.

17.2.3.1 Enzymatic Transesterification

This process is applied after the extraction of vegetable oil, vegetable oil residues, and downstream microbial production by microalgae, yeast, and even GMO. This process has many advantages over the chemical process, since it generates much less waste and, as it is a specific enzymatic reaction, and it has a high yield. However, it is still not an economically viable process due to low-scale production.

The extraction of vegetable oils, as well as the cultivation of corn and sugar cane to produce biofuels such as biodiesel and ethanol, although they are less polluting than fossil fuels, are still not considered sufficiently sustainable, since they occupy fertile agricultural areas. That would be used for food production.

17.2.3.2 Anaerobic Digestion of Biomass

The production of methane gas from the anaerobic digestion of biomass is considered a great source of energy, generally to be used at the production site or surroundings and is considered reuse of waste from other processes, such as sewage treatment, industrial effluents, lignocellulosic residues, cell debris and sludge from microalgae production. Through the enzymatic activity of methanogenic archaea in the anaerobic process, the gas is produced.

17.2.3.3 Microalgae

Microalgae are considered the most promising and environmentally sustainable source of biofuels and energy, since, in addition to converting atmospheric CO_2 into energy, fertile areas are not required for their cultivation. Through these microorganisms, biodiesel, bioethanol, biomethane, and bio-oil can be produced, also classifying them as the most versatile source of biofuel [9].

17.2.3.4 Biopolymers

According to a recent report by the United Nations Environment Programme, plastic production in 2020 was over 500 million tons and could increase to 1 billion tons by 2050 if plastics from fossil sources are not replaced by other renewable sources [10]. The plastic accumulation from 1950–2017 was 9.2 billion tons, of which 5.3 were discarded, 1.0 were incinerated, 2.9 are still in use, and only 700 million tons were recycled [10].

It is estimated that plastic takes around 450 years to naturally degrade in the environment. But until that happens, the accumulation of plastics can bury the Earth. In addition, plastics over time turn into microplastics (MP) that have accumulated in food chains and are consequently ingested daily by humans, who can ingest through various routes about 0.1–5 g of MP per week [11]. Many studies have suggested that these compounds are associated with many human diseases such as cancer, obesity, developmental, reproductive, and cardiovascular problems [11].

In this sense, it is extremely important to reduce the production of conventional plastics and increase the production of bioplastics. In addition to the development of technologies to accelerate the degradation process of plastics already produced.

Currently, there are some bioplastic production processes such as "green polyethylene" from sugarcane, which, although produced from a renewable source, is not considered a biodegradable plastic, but as it has a high added value, it makes recycling possible. Other sources of biodegradable bioplastics are those produced from starch known as thermoplastic starch (TPS), where starch is polymerized from processes such as extrusion.

Another biodegradable bioplastic is the polyesters produced from the polymerization of lactic acid synthesized by lactic acid bacteria that have anaerobic metabolism and the enzyme lactate dehydrogenase that transforms pyruvic acid into lactic acid.

A metabolic pathway dependent on a specific enzyme is also present in the synthesis of PHA, which are produced by bacteria that accumulate lipids when in culture media-rich in carbon sources and abstinence from some essential nutrient for cell division. Bacteria that can polymerize these lipids have enzymes such as polyhydroxyalkanoate synthase (PHA synthase). This type of biopolymer can be produced in industrial bioreactors and has several applications in the market, mainly medical and pharmaceutical. Some organisms and even plants have already been genetically modified to produce these biopolymers.

Unfortunately, the world production of biopolymers is still low when compared to conventional polymers. However, it is extremely important that this paradigm shift happens, since the problems caused by fossil-based plastics tend to increase even more in the coming decades.

17.3 Microbial Enzymes Applied in Environmental Recovery

For the bioremediation process to be effective and to show results, the microorganisms involved in the process must be able to metabolize xenobiotics through enzymatic mechanisms [12]. Besides being a less expensive technique,

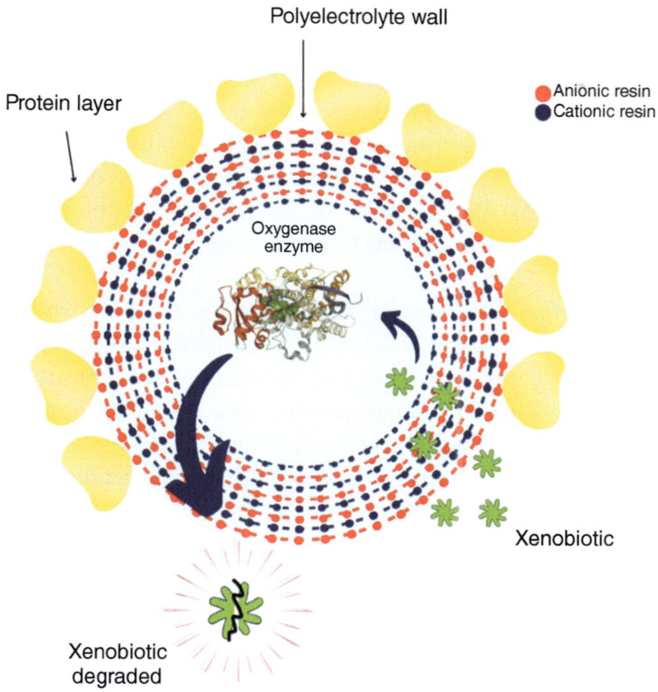

Figure 17.2 Degradation process or enzymes immobilized in layers of ionic resins.

bioremediation has presented excellent performance against several recalcitrant xenobiotic compounds due to the action mainly of monooxygenase enzymes [13, 14] and various other types of enzymatic families [3].

17.3.1 Oxireductases

Oxi-reducing enzymes are responsible for most of the degradation of recalcitrant compounds existent in the environment, being present in several organisms, but mainly in microorganisms such as bacteria and fungi. Enzymes in this family have the ability to oxidize and/or reduce xenobiotic substrates to simple molecules, making them less toxic to living beings [12].

The immobilization of enzymes in polyelectrolyte layers is shown to have excellent performance practice for the industrial area. In Figure 17.2, we can observe the exemplified scheme of the mechanism of action of enzymes of the oxireductase family. The polarity characteristic of the xenobiotic molecule has a great influence on the enzymatic process; for this reason, the polyelectrolyte layer on the outside of the enzyme has the function of permeating and selecting a passage of compound after undergoing reactions of nucleophilic to electrophilic cluster [15].

Within the large family of oxireductases, there are four main classes of enzymes: oxygenases, oxidases, peroxidases, and dehydrogenases.

(i) Oxygenases are the main enzymes involved in the aerobic process of metabolization of xenobiotic compounds. These enzymes act by modifying the solubility of these molecules through oxidation reactions, making them more water-soluble, smaller, and in some cases, less toxic [13]. The chemical process involved in this reaction is based on the oxidation of the substrate (xenobiotic) and catalysis of one or two molecular oxygen molecules (O_2) to the xenobiotic. Oxygenases are catalyzed by structures called cofactors, responsible for electron transfers throughout the chemical reaction (e.g. heme, nicotinamide adenine dinucleotide (NAD), nicotinamide adenine dinucleotide phosphate (NADP), flavin adenine dinucleotide (FAD), flavin mononucleotide (FMN), and metal ions) [15].

(ii) Oxidases are enzymes that catalyze oxidation reactions using O_2 as the ultimate electron acceptor. Its action is linked with mechanisms mediated by metallic cofactors, such as copper and flavin [16]. Enzymes of this class are not found abundantly when compared to other oxireductases. However, due to the simplicity of their chemical reaction's regeneration and the independence of their cofactors, they are of great industrial interest. Its catalytic action allows O_2 molecules to be reduced to highly reactive hydrogen peroxide (H_2O_2) molecules with great oxidative action [17].

(iii) Peroxidases are enzymes present in numerous living organisms, from animals to bacteria to plants, presenting the function of decomposing H_2O_2 among other organic and inorganic molecules [12, 18]. Within the catalytic action, the group found several different types of peroxidases, such as lignin peroxidase (LiP), manganese peroxidase (MnP), versatile peroxidase (VP), and dye bleaching peroxidase (DyP). In environmental biotechnology, the use of these enzymes is intended primarily for the degradation of phenolic compounds. The application of these enzymes is very prominent in the pulp and paper market, seeking to minimize the use of chemical processes and maximize the use of microbial enzymes for this function, culminating in the lower production of toxic residues [19].

(iv) Dehydrogenases are enzymes responsible for the catalysis of redox reactions, mediated by cofactors such as NAD, NADP, FAD, and FMN [20]. The biochemical process occurs by transferring a pair of electrons and protons from a substrate (oxidation) to an acceptor molecule (reduction). These enzymes, like other oxidative enzymes, have a great influence on load flow and energy production [21]. However, due to its restriction of enzymatic activity, occurring only intracellularly, the activity of dehydrogenases in the environment, especially in the soil, is considered as a bioindicator of live microbial activity and available organic matter [22].

17.3.2 Hydrolases

Hydrolytic enzymes are of great importance in the biodegradation of toxic molecules in a natural way. Through the reaction in the presence of water molecules, chemical bonds are broken, mainly between carbon–carbon (C–C), carbon–nitrogen (C–N), and carbon–oxygen (C–O) [23]. These enzymes, in addition to being able to degrade xenobiotics, have catalytic mechanisms necessary for biomass degradation

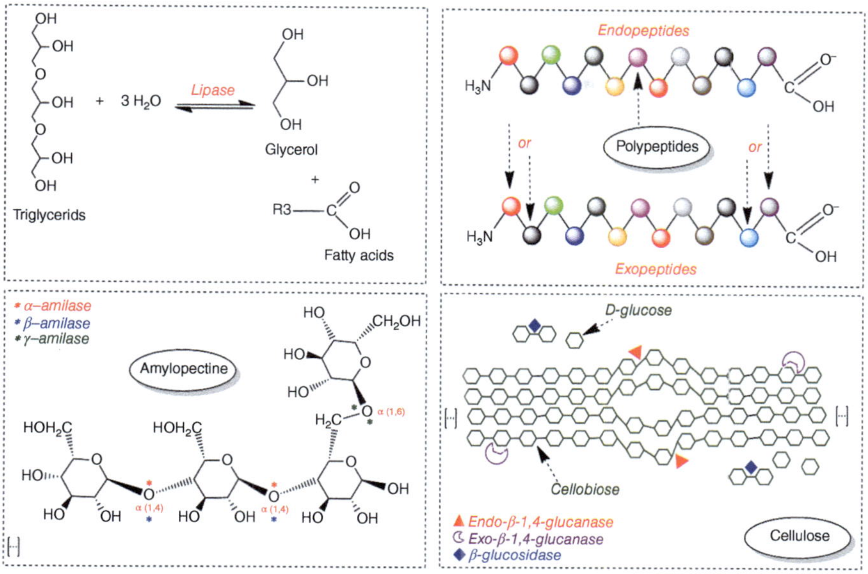

Figure 17.3 Mechanisms of action of hydrolytic enzymes.

(e.g. cellulose), present in the environment. Hydrolases are classified according to their specificity of hydrolytic action (Figure 17.3), and this is the reason for their pharmaceutical, food and chemical industrial use present in various processes (i.e. lipases, proteases, amylases, cellulases, and DNAses). Mechanisms involved in the process of degradation of contaminants have also been identified and characterized, introducing the enzymes carboxylesterase, phosphotriesterase, and haloalkane desalogenase, the most important in the metabolization of organophosphate compounds, carbamates, and chlorinated organic compounds [12]. Hydrolases are enzymes represented by the superfamily α-/β-hydrolases of widely differing phylogenetic origin and catalytic function. The core of each enzyme is an α-/β-sheet containing eight β-strands connected by six α-helices, which catalyze hydrolysis and synthesis of acid bonds [12, 24].

(i) Lipases are enzymes that catalyze the conversion of long-chain triacylglycerols (≥C8) into glycerol molecules and free fatty acids. The lipolytic activity of this group of enzymes is directly associated with the remedial action of long-chain hydrocarbons (oils) present in the environment, as is the case of fossil fuels and crude oil [12]. In addition to their hydrolytic activity, lipases also present esterification and interesterification. Also known as esterases, these lipases present catalytic action in molecules of short-chain fatty acids (≤C8) with commercial value, as esters widely used by the cosmetics industry for serving as an emollient agent and in the production of biodiesel by the transesterification process [12, 23, 25].
(ii) Proteases are enzymes that catalyze protein cleavage through hydrolysis between peptide bonds. The family of peptidase is divided according to its mode of catalytic action, dividing into enzymes that act on amino acids,

aromatic amino acids, and sulfur amino acids [23]. Enzymes that hydrolyze internal regions of proteins or long-chain peptides are called endopeptidases, e.g., trypsin and chymotrypsin. Similarly, enzymes that catalyze terminal (in amino or carboxylic) or nearby (penultimate) regions are called exopeptidases, e.g., carboxypeptidases and aminopeptidases [23]. Proteases have been widely used in various areas, including the pharmaceutical industry, food industry, chemical industry, leather industry, and textile industry [26]. Also used in the biodegradation of polymers, microbial proteases, besides being responsible for more than 60% of commercial production, have great potential for use in the bioremediation of feathers in poultry farms (keratinase) and residues of shells of crustaceans (chitinases) [27].

(iii) Amylases are groups of enzymes produced by archaea, bacteria, plant, animal, and fungi, which have the potential to catalyze the breakdown of starch molecules into glucose monomers or short glucose chains [28]. In addition to amylolytic activity, widely used in biorefineries, recent studies have shown capabilities of amylases in degrading molecules of n-alkanes ($10 \leq n \leq 14$ C) and low-density polyethylenes (LDPE) [29]. Endoamylases are groups of enzymes that cleave the carbon chains of amylose or amylopectin randomly in the internal glycosidic α-1,4, and α-amylases are enzymes totally dependent on metal ions, specifically calcium cofactors (Ca), [30]. Exoamylases represent the second group of amylolytic enzymes, which cleave the bonds from the outside of the carbon chains α-1.4 and α-1.6 by β-amylases, amyloglucosidase, and α-glicosidase. Similar to amyloglucosidase enzymes, γ-amylase can cleave glycosidic bonds α-1.6 and α-1.4 in the non-reducing extremity of the carbon chain, producing glucose monomers. Unlike other amylases, it presents better efficiency in acidic pHs, with an optimal point of 3.0 [31].

(iv) Cellulases are enzymes that hydrolyze the cellulose chain in smaller and fermentable sugars. Cellulase produced by microorganisms can be linked to the cell associated with the cellular and extracellular envelope. Cellulases are mixtures of extracellular enzymes. Three major groups are involved in the cellulose hydrolysis process: endoglucanase, which acts in regions of low crystallinity (amorphous cellulose), producing free chain ends; exoglucanase or cellobiohydrolase are enzymes that bind to the finished regions of the free chains (region created by endoglucanases), producing units glucose or cellobiose; β-glicosidases are enzymes that do the hydrolysis of cellobiose to glucose monomers [32]. In addition to the enzymatic activity already known in the degradation of plant biomass and by-products (residues) of agribusiness, recently [26] discovered the biodegradation of polymer plastics, such as LDPE and high-density polyethylene by cellulases [33–35].

17.4 Microbial Enzymes for Bioproduct Manufacturing

17.4.1 Biofuel

The oil crisis that has been established in recent decades, coupled with increased demand for fuels and growing concern for the environment, has called for the search for alternative energy sources in Brazil and around the world. Research has increasingly focused on the development of new basic inputs to produce biofuels due to the renewable nature, wide availability, biodegradability, and low cost. Thus, the utilization of by-products of the agribusiness industry, mainly plant biomass, has shown promise due to the production of various types of saccharides used in the manufacture of biofuels, as is the case of the biodiesel and bioethanol industries.

17.4.1.1 Biodiesel

Biodiesel is a fuel that can be produced from vegetable oils, animal fats, and oils produced by microorganisms (algae, fungi, and bacteria). The raw materials used are thus converted into biodiesel using a chemical reaction involving a triglyceride molecule, three molecules of alcohol, and a catalyst. This chemical reaction involved in the chemical process is called transesterification or etanolysis (if the alcohol used is ethanol), which is the most common process of obtaining biodiesel that occurs in stages. These materials (raw materials) are used in the transesterification process and react with alcohol and catalysts (KOH or NaOH) (Figure 17.4). The result of this chemical reaction is the production of crude biodiesel and crude glycerin or glycerol [25].

17.4.1.2 Bioethanol

The bioethanol producing market is also linked to products and by-products generated within biorefineries. Unlike biodiesel production that mostly occurs by

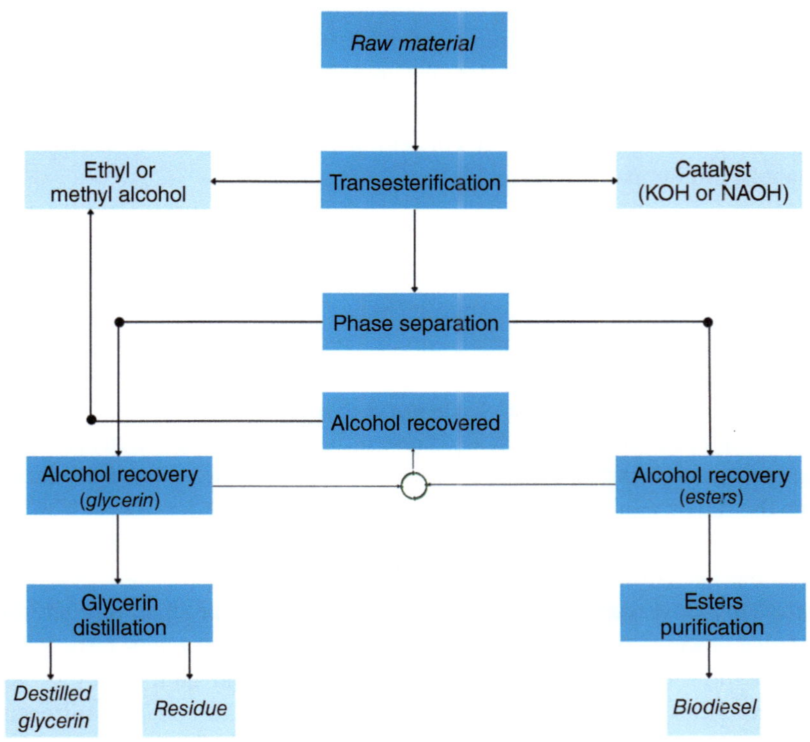

Figure 17.4 Biodiesel biosynthesis process.

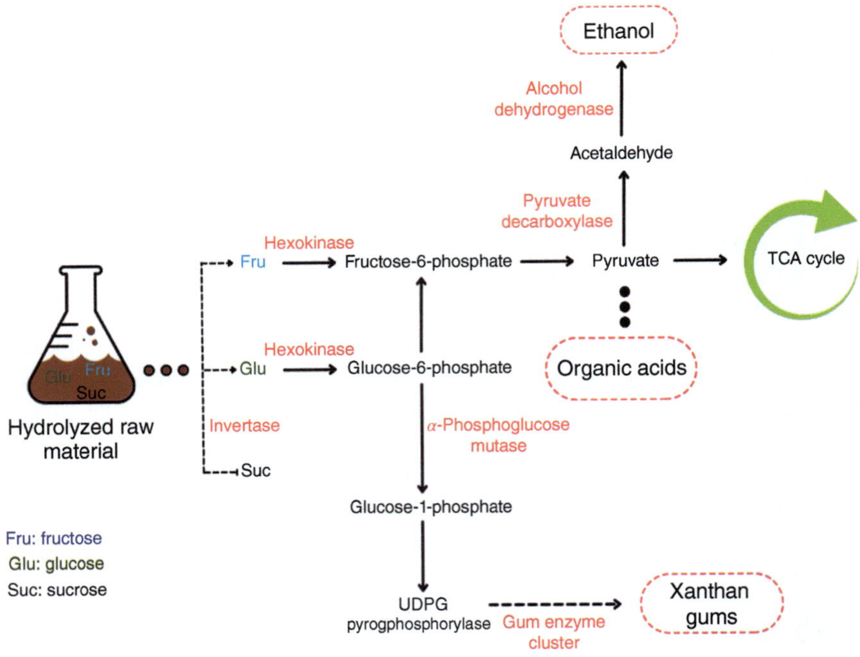

Figure 17.5 Biosynthesis of bioproducts from industrial waste.

chemical reactions, for bioethanol production all raw material must be pretreated for the removal of plant recalcitrant parts, i.e., the fraction of lignin, leaving available all hemicellulose and cellulose for use (Figure 17.5). Historically, the use of chemical processes for biomass pretreatment has been increasingly exchanged for bioprocesses, showing to be more efficient, presenting better cost–benefit and less-catabolic inhibitors [36].

17.4.2 Food Industry

17.4.2.1 Xanthan Gum

With high industrial potential, xanthan gum is a repetitive chain of heteropolysaccharides consisting of glucuronic acid, mannose, and glucose. Its main use is intended for the food industry due to its emulsifying, thickening, and stabilizing action [36, 37]. In addition to food, it also presents broad application in the pharmaceutical and cosmetic industry for favoring the miscibility of insoluble substances, ensuring the stability and homogeneity of the final products.

Originated from microorganisms, xanthan gum is named after its largest known producer, the bacterium of the genus *Xanthomonas* spp., the most studied *Xanthomonas campestres*, capable of transforming sugars into a product, through the fermentative process [38]. Studies have already identified the enzymes responsible for the biosynthesis of xanthan gum (Figure 17.5), through gum family genes. Xanthan gum can be produced with various sources of carbon and nitrogen, as by-products of the food industry; however, being preferable to fermentable sources [36, 39]. However, knowing the raw material to be used has a great influence on gum biosynthesis, because variations in nitrogen content may divert the metabolic route for pyruvate synthesis and not uridine diphosphate glucose, as shown in Figure 17.5 [36].

17.4.2.2 Organic Acids

Organic acids are by-products of metabolic routes of microorganisms, mostly produced by fermentative processes. Leaders in the market of biotechnological products, organic acids are characterized by their nature of weak acid, not completely dissociated in water, such as acetic acid, butyric acid, citric acid, succinic acid, lactic acid, and among others (Figure 17.5) [36]. The oldest products ever listed in the bioprocess industry were acetic acid and citric acid production in 1823 and 1913, respectively [40]. Compared to many other biomasses recovery routes, these reactions are conducted under aerobic, anaerobic, or anoxic conditions. Used in numerous applications, some acids find application in several areas, such as food and feed processing, pharmaceuticals, and bioplastics synthesis, having great importance for the chemical industry [41].

The presence of organic groups and functions found in these acids make them desirable to produce biopolymers, as is the case of keto and hydroxyl groups, capable of synthesizing polyesters and polyamides, respectively [40]. The process of chemical polymerization occurs through polycondensation, a reaction that involves the binding of lactic acid monomers by OH and COOH groups. An example of the use of organic acids is the application of lactic acid in the synthesis of biopolymer, polylactic acid (PLA), with great potential for substitution for polystyrene and petroleum-based polyethylene terephthalate (PET) [42]. Regulated in 1970 by the Food and Drug Administration (FDA) in the United States, PLA was allowed for use in medicine for its high biocompatibility, biodegradability, and thermoplastic [43].

17.4.2.3 Biopolymers

Biopolymers are polymers produced by living organisms and have high biodegradability in the environment. Derived from renewable sources, these polymers have been used as substitutes for synthetic polymers derived from highly recalcitrant and toxic fossil fuels for ecosystems. Biopolymers can be used to produce all types of packaging; however, adjustments according to the rheological properties of the material and proportion must be considered in the processing [44].

The synthesis of these compounds, however, is performed during a stress process induced by the microorganisms, resulting in the production of intracellular energy reserves consisting of large carbonyl chains [45]. Biopolymers can be divided according to their origin and production and can be polymers extracted directly from biomass (polysaccharides), polymers produced by chemical synthesis (lactic polyacid), and polymers produced by microorganisms (PHAs, poly-β hydroxybutyrate – PHB, etc.) [46].

Among all the types of polymers, the family of PHA compounds is the most studied. PHAs are compounds produced by microorganisms that present high biocompatibility and low toxicity to animals and humans, thus highlighting their use in medicine. In 2007, the first marketable PHA product, the absorbable suture, was developed by FDA-approved Tephaflex® in the United States [47]. These biopolymers are made up of large chains of polyesters and are known as second-generation biopolyester compounds, mostly obtained by bacterial fermentation processes [48].

PHA biosynthesis occurs under conditions of nutritional deficiency, mainly C and N. In general, the biochemical process involves the physiological stress of the microorganisms [36, 45, 48]. The enzymes involved in the biochemical route of biosynthesis are called PHA polymerases. However, these stereospecific enzymes are dependent on the bacterial strains used, as a result varying in the length of the final PHA chains occurs and may be short (scl 3–5 C), medium (mcl 6–14 C), or long (lcl above 14 C) [49]. Thus, producing PHA subclasses, as is the case of PHB, which contains a methyl group in its chemical structure, is the most prominent representative of the scl-PHA group [48].

The metabolic route of PHA to date has been defined by three enzymatic pathways, guided according to the number of lateral C available in the biopolymer synthesized by the microorganism. Route I is responsible for the synthesis of scl and mcl PHAs, controlled by the enzymes β-ketothiolase and acetoacetyl CoA reductase, regulated by the *PhaA* and *PhaB* genes, respectively (Figure 17.6), [50] and *PhaC* gene is responsible for adding monomers to the polymer chain. Route II acts exclusively on the mcl PHAs, found mainly in bacteria of the genus *Pseudomonas*. The biochemical mechanism involved is related to catalysis and fatty acid oxidation, and the enzymes such as acile CoA synthase and acile CoA dehydrogenase participate in this synthesis (Figure 17.6). The last route (III) occurs through the glycolytic pathway, converting malonil CoA into (R)-3-hydroziacil CA, where they are polymerized through the *PhaC* gene, as shown in Figure 17.6. [49].

The use of PHA polymers, in particular the class of PHB biopolymers, has gained great visibility over the years [45, 46]. PHB consists of structuring linear chains connected by ester type connections, present in PHA, behaving like a conventional thermoplastic. Its main feature is the high biodegradability at room temperature [51]. The use of these polymers has great potential in medical applications, where flexible or elastomeric materials are very important [46, 51].

17.5 Omics Approaches for Bioprospecting Enzymes

Meta-approaches such as metagenomics and metatranscriptomics have progressed as potential means to characterize the complexity and functionality of the microbial community, respectively, allowing a more complete view of the genetic capacity of a given microbial community. The development of these technologies has provided new insight into the investigation of microbial communities, allowing a better understanding of behavior and interactions in different environments, and providing new knowledge to decipher the molecular mechanisms at both the individual and the community level. This knowledge offers new perspectives in the search for new enzymes with biotechnological potential and, therefore, in the establishment of new strategies in the field of environmental biotechnology.

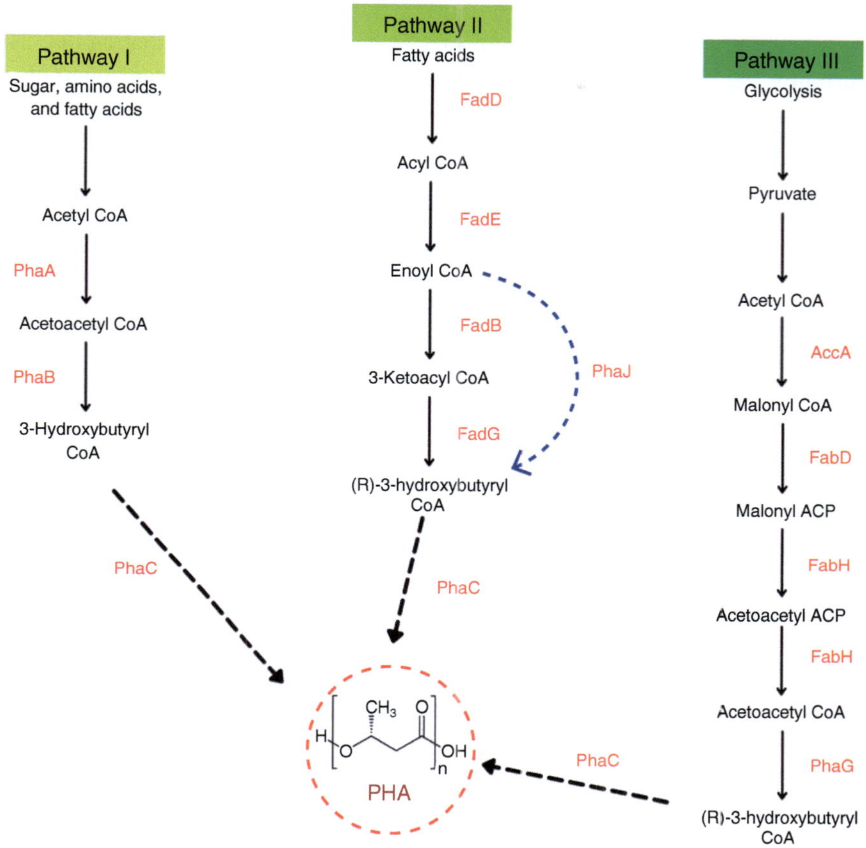

Figure 17.6 PHA biosynthetic metabolic pathway. *PhaA*, β-ketothiolase; *PhaB*, acetoacetyl CoA reductase; *PhaC*, PHA synthase; *FadD*, acetyl CoA synthase; *FadE*, acyl CoA dehydrogenase; *FadB*, enoyl CoA hydratase; *FadG*:3-cetoacyl reductase; *PhaJ*, 3-hydroxiacyl CoA hydratase; *AccA*, acetyl CoA carboxylase; *FabD*, malonyl CoA ACP transacylase; *FabH*:3-cetoacyl ACP synthase III; *PhaG*, 3-cetoacyl ACP reductase.

17.5.1 Metagenomics

In 1998, Handelsman et al. reported the diversity of microorganisms that lived in a soil sample by sequencing the genome of the microbiota, establishing the beginning of the metagenomic technique [52, 53]. This technique has brought a great evolution to the field of microbiology since a great amount of unknown unculturable microorganisms can now be accessed.

The development of more sophisticated DNA sequencing techniques, like next-generation sequencing (NGS), has led to increased accuracy, lower costs, and faster turnaround times [54]. This progress is directly attributable to advancements in next-generation sequencers, which have significantly improved genomic analysis capabilities.

The evolution of the metagenomics technique has expanded the scope of applications beyond soil sampling. In addition to the areas of agriculture, ecology, and food, several other areas are applying metagenomics to deepen knowledge about the microbiota, such as medicine, industry, pollution, and bioremediation [28, 55]. Currently, the most varied environments such as water, air, rhizosphere, plant phyllosphere, and urban environments such as hospitals and subways have been reported [56–58].

There are different ways of carrying out research on the environmental microbiota. It is possible to analyze portions of the microbiota based on specific genes common to the portion to be studied. A very popular example of partial assessment of the environmental microbiota is the sequencing of the 16S rRNA gene present in all prokaryotes. The 18S rRNA gene or the internal transcribed spacer (ITS) region is the most commonly used for studies of eukaryotic diversities. Other genes can also be sequenced depending on the research objectives. For fungi besides 18S rRNA and 28S rRNA, elongation factor-1alpha (ef-1a) and Beta-tubulin can be used, although the ITS1 and ITS2 intergenic regions are the most common or more popular. For bacteria, the most used is the 16S rRNA; however, genes such as rpoB, gyrB, and dnaK can also be used, among others. For animals, the most frequent is cytochrome oxidase 1, also known as COI [59]. Generally, when using this analysis option, the technique is called amplicon sequencing, but it can also be called target gene sequencing (targeted gene sequencing or targeted metagenomic), as well as metataxonomic or metabarcoding [60–63]. The diversity of possible nomenclatures indicates that the scientific community has not yet reached a consensus on which would be the most appropriate nomenclature. When only the Sanger DNA sequencing method was used, any technique that used sequenced environmental DNA was called metagenomics, but after the emergence of next-generation sequencers (NGSs), distinctions began to be made, which has led to the diversity of possible nomenclatures for the same technique. The advantage of amplicon sequencing is that it is faster and cheaper to run, and its analysis can be performed on simpler computers, not requiring larger servers. However, only a fraction of the total diversity of the microbiota will be accessed. In addition, the information obtained will have its taxonomic resolution limited to the genus level.

To access all the diversity of microorganisms in an environmental sample, the most appropriate technique is the metagenomic technique, also known as whole genome shotgun (WGS) or simply shotgun metagenome. This technique achieves taxonomic resolution at the species level, eventually reaching the strain level. Unlike the amplicon sequencing technique, the volume of sequenced DNA and information generated in this technique is immense, requiring many hours of data processing on large servers. Precisely because it analyzes a much larger volume of environmental DNA and consequently a huge amount of information, the metagenomic technique is more expensive than the amplicon sequencing technique. This analysis represents a moment of the diversity existing in the analyzed environment, like a static photo in a moment of time. In the quest to understand how the population of microorganisms varies over time in an environment, it is common to carry out sampling with further study over time.

Another advantage of the metagenomics technique is the possibility of obtaining a glimpse into the functional potential of the microbiota detected in the environment.

For this, different strategies can be adopted, but the simplest of them is based on the use of a combination of programs for translating nucleotides into amino acids, with subsequent comparison to protein databases. A more specific approach would be to implement a functional metagenomics study, which uses the construction of a genomic library using DNA extracted from the environmental microbiota, with subsequent screening of this library through biochemical techniques and finally sequencing. This option, also called culturome by some [64], is much more expensive and time-consuming as it involves long bench work, using many reagents.

Metagenomics answers the question of who is present in the analyzed sample at the time the research is taking place very precisely, but on the question of which genes are being expressed at a given time, the technique does not provide good results; only superficial information can be obtained. Metagenomics can answer which genes are present, but it cannot tell whether they are being expressed or not. Another limitation of the technique is to say whether the microorganisms detected are active or inactive in the analyzed sample. In addition, rare microorganisms are at risk of not being detected if enough DNA is not sequenced. To accurately answer which genes are being expressed at the time of analysis, the most appropriate technique is transcriptomics, which works by analyzing mRNA.

17.5.1.1 Steps for Performing a Metagenomic Study

Experimental Design and Metadata The first step of any metagenomic analysis, should be the experimental design, as this will directly impact the statistical analysis step. It is appropriate to have in mind what questions you want to answer to help with this step and to be able to conduct the experiment in the best possible way. Legal and ethical considerations also need to be made before starting the experiment.

Metadata are important to help interpret the data obtained and allow future comparisons. The location of the sample, as well as information about it or its position relative to other samples, can be included in the analyses. These information can help in the interpretation of the results obtained and how the microorganisms are related in their niches.

Sampling and Storage This stage of the analysis can have a profound impact on the quality and quantity of microbial DNA that will be extracted, which can generate large distortions in the analysis. It is the basis for obtaining good results. For this reason, it must be carried out following protocols that have already been tested and have been proven to be effective in other studies. The collection of samples can vary greatly depending on the environment where it is performed. Each environment and the way that microorganisms are distributed in it has several specificities, e.g., if the samples come from soil, a static environment, however, very complex, due to physical, chemical, and biological interactions, a series of care must be taken. The first measure is to clean the soil surface, removing plant remains that may be covering the site; samples must be collected with sterile equipment to avoid contamination, collections must vary from 15 to 30 cm in depth, and all geolocation data should be annotated to be informed later in the metadata. On the other hand, if the study is carried out in the rhizosphere of a plant, only the soil around approximately 5 mm of the roots should be collected, taking care to avoid collecting pieces of the root that could contaminate the DNA to be extracted. Although in both cases they are soil samples, the way of collection is profoundly different. Extrapolating to other examples such as water and air, the collection mode is radically different due to the much more dynamic nature of these environments. Water samples need to be collected and filtered, usually using filters and membranes from which the DNA of the microbiota trapped in them will be extracted. Both, in the case of water and in the case of soil, physicochemical characteristics must be measured, as well as geolocation, to fill in the metadata.

Although different, both subjects are closely related, and sample storage is just as important as using proper procedures to collect each sample in the environment. These issues may eventually receive less attention and resources than the other stages of analysis, but both are critically important as they will influence all other stages of the analysis. The nature of the sample to be collected will practically guide the equipment needed for collection and storage. It is not always possible to immediately store the collected samples in a freezer, or to extract DNA from the environmental microbiota at the collection site. However, there are other possible solutions such as the use of thermal boxes containing ice, until they are stored in a −80 °C freezer, as well as storage in liquid nitrogen. The best solution is always to proceed with DNA extraction as soon as possible, thus avoiding losing information about the microbial community being studied.

Another important question is: How many samples will be needed? The answer will vary according to the nature of the environment to be analyzed, as well as what analyses will be performed on the collected samples.

DNA Extraction and Sequencing As well as sampling and storing the samples, the microbial DNA extraction step is another essential step in metagenomic analysis. Differences between DNA isolation protocols introduce biases in the taxonomic analysis of the microbiota; this is a known fact. Contaminants can complicate DNA extraction, particularly in environmental samples. For example, the soil can be rich in organic matter, which in turn has many humic acids, which are negatively charged, as well as DNA molecules, so their presence in soil samples directly interferes with the extraction of DNA from the microbiota. For this reason, DNA extraction performed using commercial kits is the most recommended, although variations can also be observed. Although commercial kits are widely used for DNA isolation, they differ in their efficiency in lysing specific microorganisms, e.g., Gram-positive and Gram-negative bacteria such as Firmicutes and Bacteroidetes [65, 66]. Commercial kits with at least one mechanical lysis step, usually using beads, have demonstrated better efficiencies in obtaining high-quality, high-concentration DNA than kits that perform only chemical lysis. Some of the commercial kits used to extract DNA from environmental samples can be seen in Table 17.2.

Among the different next-generation sequencing (NGS) platforms, the most used currently for metagenomes is Illumina, but another DNA sequencing technology that generates short reads, the Ion from ThermoFisher, is also used in metagenome studies, but on a smaller scale. Among the platforms that generate long reads, some

Table 17.2 Commercial kits used to extract DNA from environmental.

DNA extraction kit	Description	Manufacturer	References
Quick-DNA fecal/soil microbe kits	The quick-DNA fecal/soil microbe kits are fecal and soil DNA extraction kits designed for the simple and rapid isolation of inhibitor-free, PCR-quality host cell and microbial DNA from a variety of sample sources.	Zymo Research, USA	[66]
MoBio power soil DNA extraction kit	This kit is designed for isolating genomic DNA from environmental samples. It is intended for use with environmental samples containing a high humic acid content, including difficult soil types such as compost, sediment, and manure	MOBIO, USA	[67]
FastDNA spin kit for soil (FSP)	Designed to isolate bacterial, fungal, plant, and animal genomic DNA from soil and other environmental samples	MP Biomedicals, USA	[66]
DNeasy power soil pro kit	The kit contains streamlined Inhibitor Removal Technology (IRT) to eliminate the challenging inhibitors commonly found in soil and environmental samples in even less time. The kit also has a novel bead tube and optimized chemistry for more efficient lysis of soil bacteria and fungi.	Qiagen, USA	[68]

equipment from Oxford Nanopore has been used, especially for the technique of targeted sequences. A more detailed analysis of the next-generation sequencing (NGS) can be found in the paper by [54].

Bioinformatics Analysis Regardless of the sequencing strategies used, bioinformatics tools such as biological programs and databases are essential to convert DNA sequencing data into useful biological information. Before describing possible ways to analyze sequenced environmental DNA data it is necessary to know the type of analysis previously performed. If the technique adopted was targeted sequencing, then the set of analyses will be one; if it is shotgun metagenomics, the analyses will be different. In both ways, analyzing the quality of the sequences is essential because if the sequenced DNA presents problems, the rest of the analysis will be compromised.

If the option is targeted sequencing, then some of the programs used in the analysis of biological data could be:

- FastQC for gathering information about the quality of reads;
- USEARCH [69] or VSEARCH [70] for clustering if the chosen option is OTUs (Operational taxonomic unit);

- Dada2 [71] or Deblur [72] for clustering if the option chosen is ASV (amplicon sequence variant);
- Quiime2 [73] or mothur [74] have a set of integrated pipelines for amplicon sequencing analyses;
- Diamond [75] for taxonomic classification comparing reads to protein databases.

As for the database, the Ribosomal Database Project (RDP), Silva Database, and Greengenes are generally widely used in taxonomic identification.

On the other hand, if the chosen method is metagenomic shotgun, then the set of steps and programs required will be much larger due to the large volume of data that will need to be analyzed. In a simplified way, the steps of a metagenomic shotgun analysis can be summarized in quality control of reads, binning, assembly, gene prediction, gene annotation, and data sharing. Considering an assembled-based metagenomic shotgun analysis, some alternatives are presented below.

For quality control, the FastQC program can be used to gather information about the quality of the reads. The Trimmomatic programs [76] or Prinseq [77] can be used to remove short reads or reads with poor sequencing qualities.

The Binning step represents an evolution in the sequence clustering technique; in this clustering process, the genomic sequences are assembled into groups so that each subset represents a separate biological taxon. Some program alternatives for this step are DAS tool [78] or MetaWrap [79].

In the assembly stage, which will unite the DNA fragments called reads, into larger fragments called contigs, as well as in the other stages, there is a wide variety of programs that can be used; some of the best known are IDBA-UD [80], MEGAHIT [81], another very popular one is MetaSpades [82]. An assembly program that uses artificial intelligence and that was an evolution of MetaVelvet is MetaVelvet-DL [83]. After the assembly step, a useful program to assess the quality of the assembly is MetaQuast [84]. The assembly of genomes from metagenomes has a specific acronym: MAG (metagenome-assembled genomes), which means exactly what the name says microbial genomes assembled from metagenomic data [85].

The annotation process can be divided between programs that perform the gene prediction and programs that perform the naming of the exon itself, i.e., the gene annotation. For prediction, the MetaGeneMark program [86] does a good job, as does Glimmmer-MG [87]. Some examples of annotation programs are GhostKoala [88] and eggNOG-mapper [89].

Another program that has been widely used in the analysis of metagenomic data is Megan6-CE [90], created in 2007; it continues to receive improvements and updates, which increases confidence in the results obtained by the program. In addition, the program is easy to use, as it only needs two input files and has a user-friendly interface, making it a widely accepted tool in the research community.

In the last step of the metagenomics shotgun analysis, the data will need to be stored and made available to the scientific community and there are some well-known databases/platforms for this purpose. Mg-RAST [91] enables storage, dissemination, and processing and analysis. It is very useful to compare with other works and eventually come up with new answers. Another very useful platform is MGnify [92] from EMBL-EBI (European Molecular Biology). This free platform makes it possible to submit metagenomic data, to later make the analysis and comparison of the DNAs of the microbial community of an analyzed environment. In addition, MGnify allows performing different search modes for the materials deposited on the platform. It is also important to include in this brief description of storage platforms, availability, and analysis of metagenomic data the IMG/M. The IMG/M – Integrated Microbial Genome & Metagenome [93] platform is maintained by the US Department of Energy to support Joint Genome Institute (JGI) research but is also open to all scientists worldwide who need this type of platform.

The speed of evolution of bioinformatics tools is driven by the development of sequencing techniques, as well as by other areas such as computer science and Bioinformatics itself. The creation, comparison and improvement of metagenomic data analysis pipelines is advancing with astonishing speed. Articles on tools, pipelines, and databases in metagenomic data analysis are constantly being published, increasing the knowledge base on the subject [64, 85, 94–97].

17.5.1.2 Enzyme Prospecting Through Metagenomics

The metagenomic shotgun technique makes it possible to answer which microorganisms are present in the analyzed environments with great precision, as it is based on the sequenced DNA. This means of detection made it possible and still allows the discovery of new microorganisms. Exactly for this reason, sequencing the DNA of the microbial community allows the determination of the genetic diversity of the microbial community and accessing the genes of this community present in the environment. Although it is not possible to know if they are being expressed or not, the technique allows a glimpse of the functional potential present in the microbial community. With each new microorganism discovered, a set of new enzymes belonging to it can also be accessed, which generates a lot of useful information.

There are a few possible alternatives to discovering enzymes from the DNA of the environmental microbial community, also called eDNA (environmental DNA). The conventional alternative that requires the isolation and cultivation of microorganisms, known as activity-guided bioassays from cultured organisms, and the culture-free alternatives such as those based on shotgun metagenomics and activity-based screening functional metagenomics, also called polymerase chain reaction (PCR)-based screening [28, 98–100].

Activity-based functional metagenomics consists of extracting DNA from the environmental sample, cloning the fragments of these DNAs into vectors that carry large fragments such as cosmids, BACs (artificial bacterial chromosome) or YACs (artificial yeast chromosome) and building a metagenomic library by inserting vectors in host cells. Then, it is possible to perform a biochemical screening in the library based on the bioactive function to verify the existence of any enzyme of interest. If an enzyme of interest is found, this vector is extracted from the host cell with subsequent PCR amplification, followed by DNA sequencing. This search alternative, however, is expensive, time-consuming, and not always efficient. It is also possible to sequence the entire metagenomic library and proceed with in silico prospecting using the metagenomics tools already mentioned in the bioprospecting section. This classic technique has some disadvantages, such as being limited to microorganisms that grow in some known culture media and only being able to perform the screening of one type of enzyme at a time. Despite this, new discoveries still occur through this classic research method.

In PCR-based functional metagenomics, the search for protein domains of interest is performed by the degenerate primers used in the amplification of these regions in the environmental DNA. Among the positive points, it is possible to mention that sequencing amplicons is cheaper than the metagenomics shotgun technique. In addition, this technique achieves success even with sequences occurring in low abundance, but amplicons that are eventually short can make taxonomic identification difficult.

One of the problems with this technique is that it is limited to homologous sequences only. This characteristic in turn limits the technique, minimizing the possibility of discovering totally new enzymes. Despite this, it is widely used in the discovery of homologous enzymes, but which present physicochemical properties different from those already known.

Another more direct way is to use the metagenomic shotgun and go straight to prospecting using bioinformatics doing in silico screening. In this technique, there is no need for specific primers or cloning in host cells, but sequencing alone will not provide phenotypic information, so cloning and heterologous expression will still be necessary after finding the enzyme with the desired characteristics. In metagenomic shotgun screening, different sequencing techniques can be combined to obtain complementarity between short reads and long reads and thus have access to long BCGs (biosynthetic cluster genes) that encode enzymes in bacteria. Among the advantages of this type of approach, it is possible to mention that the genomic and taxonomic context can be obtained through the assembly and binning steps; in addition, it can provide a broad profile of the microbial community and its enzymes potentially present in the environment. Another great advantage is the growing set of data made available by this technique in databases, which allows for initial prospection in silico. This makes it possible to speed up the search, as very specific targets with the desired characteristics can be quickly found. Subsequently, the adoption of practices used in another approach, such as the design of primers, can be done and, with that, access the desired enzymes in the environmental microbial community.

17.5.2 Metranscriptomic

While genomics and metagenomics deal with the genomic profiles of an individual organism or a microbial community, respectively, transcriptomics and metatranscriptomics focus on the subset of genes that are transcribed in each condition. Consequently, transcriptomics and metatranscriptomics are powerful frameworks for visualizing which genes are active or overexpressed in each environmental condition. In this context, in this section, we focused on the use of metatranscriptomics in the search for new enzymes with biotechnological potential. Thus, here we summarized relevant studies in which this approach was applied in the environmental field.

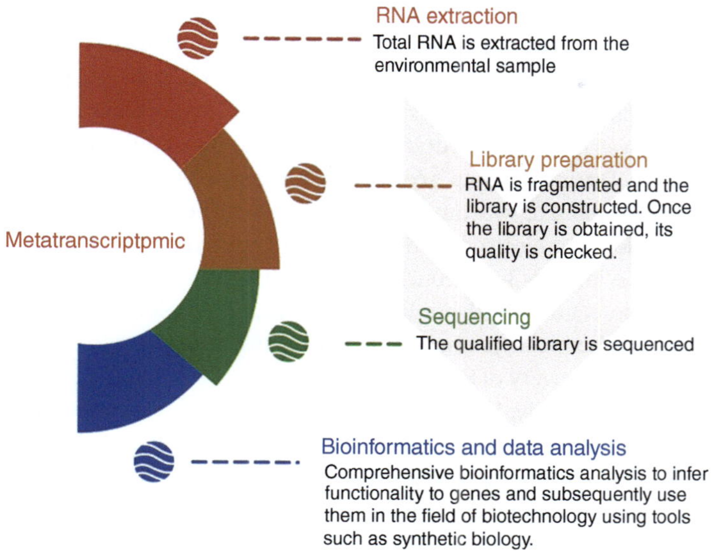

Figure 17.7 Workflow for obtaining the functionality of overexpressed genes in environmental samples using the metatranscriptomics approach.

Metatranscriptomics allows the recovery and sequencing of expressed genes (mRNAs) to profile active metabolic processes to obtain a more accurate picture of their ecology. A distinct advantage of these approaches is that they provide a global view of the diversity and function of the *in situ* community. The general process of metatranscriptomic data is illustrated in Figure 17.7. Briefly, the first step is to extract total RNA from the environmental sample to be investigated. Next, RNA from a given template is fragmented and the corresponding dataset is constructed, the quality of which must be checked. The library is then sequenced. And finally, the generated raw sequence data set is thoroughly analyzed using bioinformatics tools. The analysis of these data provides not only knowledge of the genes overexpressed by a bacterial community in each environmental condition, but also infers their functionality and that information can be key to promoting bioremediation of other contaminated environments. The data obtained through approaches such as metatrasncriptomics can be the starting point for obtaining engineered microorganisms using novel technologies such as Synthetic Biology and, therefore, their implementation in biodegradation can allow the use of microorganisms with greater capacity for degradation and adaptation in hostile environments, opening new horizons in bioremediation strategies.

In this way, several papers have recently been published using this approach, e.g., Li et al. [101] have investigated, using the metatrascriptomic approach, the effect of bioaugmentation in an anaerobic reactor used for the treatment of lignocellulosic cow manure waste. The results showed that bioaugmentation enhanced hydrolysis and methanogenesis because of the metabolism of the endogenous microorganisms. The authors also observed a high activity of different enzymes related to cellulase metabolism, which could underlie the improvement in cellulose degradation.

In another study, Schmidt et al. [102] highlighted the need to develop technologies to convert waste into compounds of interest. In this regard, they have engineered a biotechnological waterfall for the conversion of plant waste into acetoin and electrical energy. For this purpose, they used a dark fermentation effluent of plant residues where compounds such as propionate, butyrate, and acetate were oxidized in a bioelectrochemical system. During this step, acetate and butyrate were eliminated from the effluent, whereas propionate was the major component. The key genes in this process (carbon oxidation and electrode reduction) were determined by metatranscriptomic analysis. The authors have concluded that the effluent proved to be a suitable medium for biotechnological production strains, as propionate from the effluent of the bioelectrochemical system became the chemical platform for acetoin production with a carbon recovery of 86%.

In line with the previous study, Sato et al. [103] used the metatranscriptome to understand the complex microbiological processes intrinsic to activated sludge reactors. This approach was carried out in two types of reactors (high and low throughput). The authors demonstrated that denitrifying microorganisms (nitrite-oxidizing bacteria [NOB] and ammonia-oxidizing bacteria [AOB]) promoted the anaerobic degradation of heavy oil; nevertheless, no notable differences in the gene expression of degradation-related enzymes were found when comparing the results of both reactors. In contrast, nitrification activities verified by metatranscriptomics revealed that genes related to the synthesis of denitrifying enzymes were remarkably high only in the high-throughput reactor. In conclusion, the authors claim to have uncovered an unexpected interplay of nitrogen and carbon metabolisms in the intricate microbiome of activated sludge reactors.

Finally, Alessi et al. [104] have studied the enzymatic mechanisms involved in the degradation of lignocellulose by microbial communities, motivated by those possessing an enzyme complex capable of efficiently degrading plant materials present in nature. In this context, the authors investigated the microbial degradation of straw using metatranscriptomics to identify new mechanisms of lignocellulose conversion that might be useful in the industrial pretreatment of this raw material. The use of this approach allowed the authors to identify the occurrence of multiple active enzymes related to carbohydrate metabolism. The authors explained that this study revealed a broad range of hemicellulases, hydrolytic cellulases, and carbohydrate-binding modules implicated in lignocellulose degradation. The authors concluded that the use of metatranscriptomics has led to the identification of many enzymes related to lignocellulose degradation that can be used in enzyme cocktails to improve the processing of plant-derived feedstocks. Additionally, this study identified many unknown proteins, several of which may provide a key role in the microbial community degradation of lignocellulose.

17.5.3 Application of Synthetic Biology in Environmental Biotechnology

The use of omics approaches applied to the search for new enzymes has contributed to a breakthrough in biotechnology. The improvement in massive sequencing,

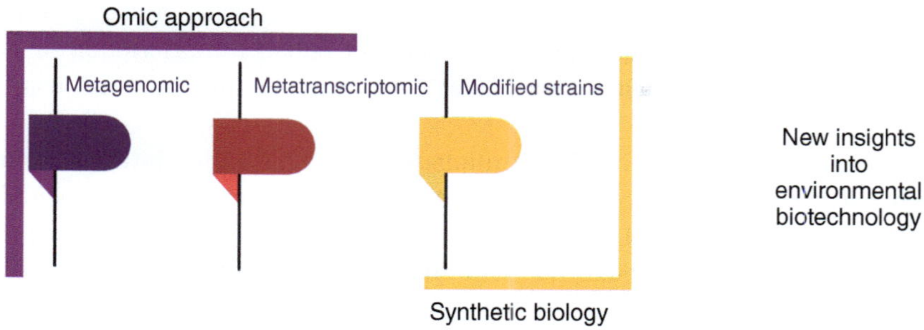

Figure 17.8 Overview of new approaches used to improve environmental biotechnology.

associated with the improvement in gene editing technologies, as well as the development of new bioinformatics platforms for data analysis has brought with it the necessary information for the use of synthetic biology and with it a large number of new opportunities for the development of new biological systems and new tools for environmental biotechnology (Figure 17.8).

Synthetic biology is an emerging field of research with an interdisciplinary approach that allows reconstructing of existing natural biological systems and converts them into a microbial factory, i.e, modifying metabolic pathways by inserting and/or deletion of one or more genes responsible for producing a certain enzyme of interest or improving cell signaling circuits to increase the performance of a certain biological system; furthermore, it allows building new pathways, organisms, or biological devices artificially.

In recent years, with advances in synthetic biology techniques, this methodology has gained ground in the field of microbial remediation and has attracted increasing attention as an excellent tool to improve microorganisms capable of degrading contaminants compared to traditional methods. In the last decade, through top-down and bottom-up engineering approaches, synthetic biology has proven to be a very powerful tool in utilizing and modifying existing genetic materials to reengineer organisms with desired capabilities. The combination of synthetic biology and engineering has been shown to improve the understanding of the mechanism of action of biological components. Therefore, these technologies have made rewarding advances in solving problems in the field of environmental restoration. Thus, in this part of the chapter, we discussed how synthetic biology is being applied in environmental biotechnology, highlighting its use in bioremediation, in the field of biofilms, and in the production of new biofuels.

About the use of synthetic biology in the field of environmental bioremediation, several studies have been carried out, in which engineered bacteria can achieve complete degradation of different compounds. For example, Roldán et al. [105] have proposed different strategies for the bioremediation of cyanide-containing wastes. In this study, the authors highlight that *Pseudomonas pseudoalcaligenes* CECT5344 has the potential to become a model organism for the application of synthetic biology to optimize cyanide remediation using the design-build-test-learn cycle. Without the need to introduce new exogenous functions, development could focus on overflowing metabolic pathways and employ site-directed mutagenesis of specific regulatory genes and/or promoters to either enhance transcription or to improve the enzymatic activity of specific enzymes, such as nitrilase NitC, using protein engineering.

In another study, carried out by Kurumbang et al. [106], they introduced in *Escherichia coli* a synthetic route for the degradation of the recalcitrant compound 1,2,3-trichloropropane (TCP) to obtain glycerol as a product. To do this, the authors used metabolic models to help them infer the best ratios of each enzyme that should be introduced synthetically to promote the degradation of 1,2,3-trichloropropane in *E. coli*. Similar trends have been reported by Gong et al. [107] in their work on the mineralization of 1,2,3-trichloropropane. For this purpose, the authors have introduced a synthetic pathway for the aerobic degradation of 1,2,3-trichloropropane composed of three enzymes (haloalcohol dehalogenases (DhaA) that enhance the dehalogenation of TCP to the (R) and (S) enantiomers of 2,3-dichloropropane-1-ol from *Rhodococcus rhodochrous* NCIMB 13064, haloalcohol dehalogenases (HheC) and epoxide hydrolases (EchA) involved in the conversion of 1,3-dichloro-2-propanol (DCP) to glycerol from *Agrobacterium radiobacter* AD1) were integrated into the chromosome of *Pseudomonas putida* KT2440 by using a previously performed genome assembly approach with upp as a contraselective marker. The resulting modified microorganism (termed KTU-TGVF) was found to be effective in degrading 1,2,3-trichloropropane as the only carbon source for growth. These results were confirmed in bioreactor studies that demonstrated the potential of this modified microorganism for the bioremediation of 1,2,3-trichloropropane.

Another use of synthetic biology in the field of remediation is related to PET, a plastic widely employed in the production of textiles and as a container for different types of products. Several enzymes with the ability to degrade this type of compounds have been described; however, they have a low activity. Recently, a new bacterium, *Ideonella sakaiensis* 201-F6, was recovered from sediments containing PET bottles used for recycling, which showed a high capacity to utilize PET as its carbon and energy source. The two enzymes found in *I. sakaiensis* that allow it to degrade polyethylene terephthalate are a PET hydrolase, that degrades PET into mono (2-hydroxyethyl) terephthalic acid (MHET); and MHET hydrolase, a structurally single enzyme that turns MHET into terephthalic acid and ethylene glycol [108]. Once these enzymes were discovered, several works have been done to optimize the degradation of PET. An instance of this is the research done by Austin et al. [109], who optimized the expression of the gene encoding PETase from *I. sakaiensis* strain 201-F6 in *E. coli*, and for a more efficient depolymerization of PET; the authors also performed a mutation in the active site of PETase to make it more similar to cutinase. The results showed that it is realistic to further engineer the protein to enhance the efficiency of PETase and demonstrate the necessity to develop additional structure-activity relationships for the biodegradation of synthetic polyesters.

Another important field in which synthetic biology is applied in the field of environmental biotechnology is related to the production of biofilms. Biofilms are widespread microbial aggregations that form on several different biological and nonbiotic surfaces. Moreover, they are considered an excellent example of the microbiome, and their study can provide a lot of information related to the interactions between species, evolutionary processes, and gene transfer between different microorganisms. Biofilms are formed by extracellular polymeric substances produced by the microbial community that makes them up. The diversity and stability of these communities are not fully understood. However, they are known to be very complex microbial establishments composed of dead, living, and vegetative bacterial cells, in addition to exocellular products, enzymes, and molecules that mediate cell-to-cell communication [110].

Biofilm formation is intrinsically associated with the degradation processes of recalcitrant compounds. Mohsin et al. [111] affirmed that biofilms are a tool in bioremediation and can help make the use of new technologies applied to environmental cleanup sustainable if they are used correctly. The application of biofilms in the bioremediation process is cost-effective because the final product is clean, which could also help reduce the environmental impact. For this reason, the use of genetic engineering associated with synthetic biology in biofilm-forming bacteria is emerging as a powerful tool to increase the performance of bacteria with the ability to completely degrade recalcitrant compounds and avoid their exposure to the environment.

Li et al. [112] have performed synthetic biology on the biofilm-producing bacterium *Bacillus subtilis* N4 with the aim of efficiently removing acetonitrile in sewage processing to minimize the effluent of this pollutant in nontreated wastewater. To this end, they have engineered *B. subtilis* N4 with the nitrilase enzyme produced by the nit gene of nitrile-degrading bacteria (*R. rhodochrous* BX2). The recombinant bacterium (*B. subtilis* N4-pHT01-nit) formed robust biofilms and was able to degrade nitriles. The authors demonstrated that a bacterium with the ability to form biofilms and genetically modified to degrade nitriles can improve the degradation of pollutants in sewage. The authors further conclude that this emerging strategy provides a new avenue for improving the biological degradation of toxic contaminants in wastewater. In a subsequent study, Li et al. [113] also studied the involvement of *B. subtilis* N4 in the degradation of wastewater containing organonitriles. For this purpose, they used synthetic biology to modify the biofilm-forming bacterium *B. subtilis* N4 by introducing genes that produced the enzymes nitrilohydratase and amidase, which play a critical key role in the degradation of organonitriles. The recombinant bacterium was named *B. subtilis* N4/pHTnha-ami and was able to successfully degrade organonitrites.

17.5.3.1 Synthetic Biology to Biofuels Production

Currently, fossil fuels continue to be the main source of energy for society. However, the eminent scarcity of these products, as well as the concern with the environmental effects that the use of these fossil fuels entails, has motivated the interest of the scientific society in developing new sustainable alternatives to replace this product. In this context, the production of biofuels based on the use of biomass by engineering microorganisms has been playing a leading role in the search for new alternatives.

The attention of researchers has shifted away from the production of biofuels from lignocellulosic biomass, among other reasons because saccharification of these compounds produces high amounts of lignin. As a substitute, biomass gasification was suggested as an option to saccharification, since in this process, the main end products are carbon oxides (CO, CO_2) and hydrogen. Consequently, microorganisms able to utilize carbon oxides have attracted considerable attention to producing these new sustainable fuels, such as butanol and ethanol. In this regard, several studies are being carried out in this field, an example being the studies by Namakoshi et al. [114], who disrupted the glgC genes encoding glucose-1-phosphate adenylyltranferase and phaCE encoding the PHA synthase subunit in *Synechocystis* sp. PCC 6803 and built an ethanol route by inserting the pdc and adh genes from *Zymomonas mobilis*. The consequent strain was able to produce large amounts of ethanol from sodium carbonate.

Finally, also to improve ethanol production, Nishiguchi et al. [115] based on the prediction of a kinetic model, have overexpressed four enzymes (including phosphoribulokinase, phosphoglycerate kinase, enolase and phosphoglycerate kinase, and pyruvate kinase) in *Synechocystis* sp. PCC 6803. The authors have observed that the strain with the overexpressed phosphoglycerate kinase enzyme obtained the highest ethanol produced using sodium carbonate.

This part of the chapter has provided insight into the use of synthetic biology. Research applied to synthetic biology has been carried out in different fields of environmental engineering. Once discovered, various enzymes, genes, and metabolic pathways using omics tools have served as a template for use in this emerging technology. Although much remains to be discovered in the field of synthetic biology, this emerging technology, together with omics technologies, is creating new perceptions and new expectations within environmental biotechnology.

17.6 Conclusion and Perspectives

Due to the current global scenario of environmental contamination and exaggerated waste production, it is of paramount importance to apply the biotechnological approach to solve these problems. As described in this chapter, much knowledge has already been obtained from the research using microorganisms and studying their enzymes both in the aspect of bioremediation and in the development of bioproducts that replace fossil sources.

With the emergence of the omics sciences, new possibilities for studies emerged and with robust generation of data that can be obtained without the need for growing microorganisms. However, transforming this in silico data to generate biotechnological products is a challenge both in the methodological and economic aspect, but with the rapid development of the techniques in biotechnology, It is already becoming.

Transforming in silico data into bioproducts that can be applied to environmental improvement is urgent, since the production of environmentally unsustainable products and the consequent pollution of the environments have occurred in a very accelerated way.

References

1 Lellis, B., Fávaro-Polonio, C.Z., Pamphile, J.A., and Polonio, J.C. (2019). Effects of textile dyes on health and the environment and bioremediation potential of living organisms. *Biotechnol. Res. Innovation* 3: 275–290.

2 Bhatt, P., Gangola, S., Bhandari, G. et al. (2021). New insights into the degradation of synthetic pollutants in contaminated environments. *Chemosphere* 268: 128827.

3 Jaiswal, S. and Shukla, P. (2020). Alternative strategies for microbial remediation of pollutants via synthetic biology. *Front. Microbiol.* 11: 1–14.

4 Verma, J.P., Jaiswal, D.K., and Sagar, R. (2014). Pesticide relevance and their microbial degradation: a-state-of-art. *Rev. Environ. Sci. Biotechnol.* 13: 429–466.

5 Vergeynst, L., Wegeberg, S., Aamand, J. et al. (2018). Biodegradation of marine oil spills in the Arctic with a Greenland perspective. *Sci. Total Environ.* 626: 1243–1258.

6 Boopathy, R. (2000). Factors limiting bioremediation technologies. *Bioresour. Technol.* 74: 63–67.

7 ITOPF (2022). Oil tanker spill statistics 2021. London.

8 EPA (2022). Basic information about oil and natural gas air aollution standards. https://www.epa.gov/controlling-air-pollution-oil-and-natural-gas-industry/basic-information-about-oil-and-natural-gas (accessed 26 April 2024).

9 Siddiki, S.Y.A., Mofijur, M., Kumar, P.S. et al. (2022). Microalgae biomass as a sustainable source for biofuel, biochemical and biobased value-added products: an integrated biorefinery concept. *Fuel* 307: 121782.

10 UNEP (2021). From pollution to solution a global assessment of marine litter and plastic pollution.

11 Senathirajah, K., Attwood, S., Bhagwat, G. et al. (2021). Estimation of the mass of microplastics ingested – a pivotal first step towards human health risk assessment. *J. Hazard Mater.* 404: 124004.

12 Sharma, B., Dangi, A.K., and Shukla, P. (2018). Contemporary enzyme based technologies for bioremediation: a review. *J. Environ. Manage.* 210: 10–22.

13 Dubey, K.K., Kumar, P., Singh, P.K., and Shukla, P. (2014). Exploring prospects of monooxygenase-based biocatalysts in xenobiotics. In: *Microbial Biodegradation and Bioremediation* (ed. Elsevier), 577–614. Elsevier Inc.

14 Girvan, H.M. and Munro, A.W. (2016). Applications of microbial cytochrome P450 enzymes in biotechnology and synthetic biology. *Curr. Opin. Chem. Biol.* 31: 136–145.

15 Behbudi, G., Yousefi, K., and Sadeghipour, Y. (2021). Microbial enzymes based technologies for bioremediation of pollutions. *J. Environ. Treat. Tech.* 9: 463–469.

16 Martin, C., Binda, C., and Fraaije, M.W. (2020). The multipurpose family of flavoprotein oxidases. In: *Flavin-Dependent Enzymes: Mechanisms, Structures and Applications*, 1e (ed. Academic Press), 63–86. Elsevier Inc.

17 Vennestrøm, P.N.R., Christensen, C.H., Pedersen, S. et al. (2010). Next-generation catalysis for renewables: combining enzymatic with inorganic heterogeneous catalysis for bulk chemical production. *ChemCatChem* 2: 249–258.

18 Bansal, N. and Kanwar, S.S. (2013). Peroxidase(s) in environment protection. *Sci. World J.* 2013: 9.

19 Singh, A.K., Bilal, M., Iqbal, H.M.N. et al. (2021). Science of the Total Environment Bioremediation of lignin derivatives and phenolics in wastewater with lignin modifying enzymes: status, opportunities and challenges. *Sci. Total Environ.* 777: 145988.

20 Phale, P.S., Sharma, A., and Gautam, K. (2019). Microbial degradation of xenobiotics like aromatic pollutants from the terrestrial environments. In: *Pharmaceuticals and Personal Care Products: Waste Management and Treatment Technology* (ed. Butterworth-Heinemann), 259–278. Elsevier Inc.

21 Dotaniya, M.L., Aparna, K., Dotaniya, C.K. et al. (2019). Crop production. In: *Enzymes in Food Biotechnology* (ed. Academic Press), 569–589. Elsevier Inc.

22 Mierzwa-Hersztek, M., Wolny-Koładka, K., Gondek, K. et al. (2020). Effect of coapplication of biochar and nutrients on microbiocenotic composition, dehydrogenase activity index and chemical properties of sandy soil. *Waste Biomass Valorization* 11: 3911–3923.

23 Karigar, C.S. and Rao, S.S. (2011). Role of microbial enzymes in the bioremediation of pollutants: a review. *Enzyme Res.* 2011.

24 Dimitriou, P.S., Denesyuk, A., Takahashi, S. et al. (2017). Alpha/beta-hydrolases: a unique structural motif coordinates catalytic acid residue in 40 protein fold families. *Proteins Struct. Funct. Bioinf.* 85: 1845–1855.

25 Zhao, X., Qi, F., Yuan, C. et al. (2015). Lipase-catalyzed process for biodiesel production: enzyme immobilization, process simulation and optimization. *Renewable Sustainable Energy Rev.* 44: 182–197.

26 Sharma, A., Sharma, T., Sharma, T. et al. (2019). Role of microbial hydrolases in bioremediation. In: *Microbes and Enzymes in Soil Health and Bioremediation* (ed. Springer), 149–164.

27 Bhandari, S., Poudel, D.K., Marahatha, R. et al. (2021). Microbial enzymes used in bioremediation. *J. Chem.* 2021: 8849512.

28 Datta, S., Rajnish, K.N., Samuel, M.S. et al. (2020). Metagenomic applications in microbial diversity, bioremediation, pollution monitoring, enzyme and drug discovery. A review. *Environ. Chem. Lett.* 18: 1229–1241.

29 Pinto, É.S.M., Dorn, M., and Feltes, B.C. (2020). The tale of a versatile enzyme: alpha-amylase evolution, structure, and potential biotechnological applications for the bioremediation of n-alkanes. *Chemosphere* 250: 126202.

30 Tiwari, S., Srivastava, R., Singh, C. et al. (2015). Amylases: an overview with special reference to alpha amylase. *J. Global Biosci.* 4: 1886–1901.

31 Kaur, N., Kumar, V., and Kumar, S. (2021). Alpha-amylase as molecular target for treatment of diabetes mellitus: a comprehensive review. *Chem. Biol. Drug Des.* 98: 539–560.

32 Kumar, M., Vivekanand, V., and Pareek, N. (2021). Enzymatic degradation of lignocellulosic waste: bioremediation and industrial implementation. In: *Bioremediation for Environmental Sustainability Toxicity, Mechanisms of Contaminants Degradation, Detoxification, and Challenges* (ed. G. Saxena, V. Kumar, and M.P. Shah), 163–194. Chennai, India: INC.

33 Das, M.P. and Kumar, S. (2015). An approach to low-density polyethylene biodegradation by *Bacillus amyloliquefaciens*. *3 Biotech* 5: 81–86.

34 Ingavale, R.R. and Raut, P.D. (2018). Comparative biodegradation studies of LDPE and HDPE using *Bacillus weihenstephanensis* isolated from garbage soil. *Nat. Environ. Pollut. Technol.* 17: 649–655.

35 Krishnaswamy, V.G., Sridharan, R., Kumar, P.S., and Fathima, M.J. (2022). Cellulase enzyme catalyst producing bacterial strains from vermicompost and its application in low-density polyethylene degradation. *Chemosphere* 288: 132552.

36 Zhang, S., Wang, J., and Jiang, H. (2021). Microbial production of value-added bioproducts and enzymes from molasses, a by-product of sugar industry. *Food Chem.* 346: 128860.

37 Kang, Y., Li, P., Zeng, X. et al. (2019). Biosynthesis, structure and antioxidant activities of xanthan gum from *Xanthomonas campestris* with additional furfural. *Carbohydr. Polym.* 216: 369–375.

38 Habibi, H. and Khosravi-Darani, K. (2017). Effective variables on production and structure of xanthan gum and its food applications: a review. *Biocatal. Agric. Biotechnol.* 10: 130–140.

39 Sworn, G. (2021). Xanthan gum. In: *Handbook of Hydrocolloids*, 3e (ed. G.O. Phillips and P.A. Williams), 833–853. Woodhead Publishing.

40 Becker, J., Lange, A., Fabarius, J., and Wittmann, C. (2015). Top value platform chemicals: bio-based production of organic acids. *Curr. Opin. Biotechnol.* 36: 168–175.

41 Deng, W., Wang, Y., and Yan, N. (2016). Production of organic acids from biomass resources. *Curr. Opin. Green Sustainable Chem.* 2: 54–58.

42 Hamad, K., Kaseem, M., Ayyoob, M. et al. (2018). Polylactic acid blends: the future of green, light and tough. *Prog. Polym. Sci.* 85: 83–127.

43 Singhvi, M.S., Zinjarde, S.S., and Gokhale, D.V. (2019). Polylactic acid: synthesis and biomedical applications. *J. Appl. Microbiol.* 127: 1612–1626.

44 Carvajal-Piñero, J.M., Ramos, M., Jiménez-Rosado, M. et al. (2019). Development of pea protein bioplastics by a thermomoulding process: effect of the mixing stage. *J. Polym. Environ.* 27: 968–978.

45 Al-Battashi, H., Annamalai, N., Al-Kindi, S. et al. (2019). Production of bioplastic (poly-3-hydroxybutyrate) using waste paper as a feedstock: optimization of enzymatic hydrolysis and fermentation employing *Burkholderia sacchari*. *J. Cleaner Prod.* 214: 236–247.

46 Sivakanthan, S., Rajendran, S., Gamage, A. et al. (2020). Antioxidant and antimicrobial applications of biopolymers: a review. *Food Res. Int.* 136: 109327.

47 Liu, H., Kumar, V., Jia, L. et al. (2021). Biopolymer poly-hydroxyalkanoates (PHA) production from apple industrial waste residues: a review. *Chemosphere* 284: 131427.

48 Mehrpouya, M., Vahabi, H., Barletta, M. et al. (2021). Additive manufacturing of polyhydroxyalkanoates (PHAs) biopolymers: materials, printing techniques, and applications. *Mater. Sci. Eng., C* 127: 112216.

49 Sindhu, R., Madhavan, A., Arun, K.B. et al. (2021). Metabolic circuits and gene regulators in polyhydroxyalkanoate producing organisms: intervention strategies for enhanced production. *Bioresour. Technol.* 327: 124791.

50 Zhang, X., Lin, Y., Wu, Q. et al. (2020). Synthetic biology and genome-editing tools for improving PHA metabolic engineering. *Trends Biotechnol.* 38: 689–700.

51 Horue, M., Rivero Berti, I., Cacicedo, M.L., and Castro, G.R. (2021). Microbial production and recovery of hybrid biopolymers from wastes for industrial applications – a review. *Bioresour. Technol.* 340: 125671.

52 Handelsman, J. (2005). Metagenomics: application of genomics to uncultured microorganisms. *Microbiol. Mol. Biol. Rev.* 68: 669–685.

53 Handelsman, J., MichelleR, R., Brady, S.F. et al. (1998). Molecular biological access to the chemistry of unknown soil microbes: a new frontier for natural products. *Chem. Biol.* 5: 245–249.

54 Hu, T., Chitnis, N., Monos, D., and Dinh, A. (2021). Next-generation sequencing technologies: an overview. *Hum. Immunol.* 82: 801–811.

55 Garrido-Cardenas, J.A. and Manzano-Agugliaro, F. (2017). The metagenomics worldwide research. *Curr. Genet* 63: 819–829.

56 Lambais, M.R., Barrera, S.E., Santos, E.C. et al. (2017). Phyllosphere metaproteomes of trees from the Brazilian Atlantic forest show high levels of functional redundancy. *Microb. Ecol.* 73: 123–134.

57 Saran, L.M., Pissarra, T.C.T., Silveira, G.A. et al. (2018). Land use impact on potentially toxic metals concentration on surface water and resistant microorganisms in watersheds. *Ecotoxicol. Environ. Saf.* 166: 366–374.

58 Danko, D., Bezdan, D., Afshin, E.E. et al. (2021). A global metagenomic map of urban microbiomes and antimicrobial resistance. *Cell* 184: 3376–3393.e17.

59 Choudhary, P., Singh, B.N., Chakdar, H., and Saxena, A.K. (2021). DNA barcoding of phytopathogens for disease diagnostics and bio-surveillance. *World J. Microbiol. Biotechnol.* 37: 1–20.

60 Marchesi, J.R. and Ravel, J. (2015). The vocabulary of microbiome research: a proposal. *Microbiome* 3: 1–3.

61 Macedo, G., van Veelen, H.P.J., Hernandez-Leal, L. et al. (2021). Targeted metagenomics reveals inferior resilience of farm soil resistome compared to soil microbiome after manure application. *Sci. Total Environ.* 770: 145399.

62 Semenov, M.V. (2021). Metabarcoding and metagenomics in soil ecology research: achievements, challenges, and prospects. *Biol. Bull. Rev.* 11: 40–53.

63 Zotta, T., Ricciardi, A., Condelli, N., and Parente, E. (2021). Metataxonomic and metagenomic approaches for the study of undefined strain starters for cheese manufacture. *Crit. Rev. Food Sci. Nutr.* 62: 3898–3912.

64 Liu, Y.X., Qin, Y., Chen, T. et al. (2021). A practical guide to amplicon and metagenomic analysis of microbiome data. *Protein Cell* 12: 315–330.

65 Fricker, A.M., Podlesny, D., and Fricke, W.F. (2019). What is new and relevant for sequencing-based microbiome research? A mini-review. *J. Adv. Res.* 19: 105–112.

66 Wegl, G., Grabner, N., Köstelbauer, A. et al. (2021). Toward best practice in livestock microbiota research: a comprehensive comparison of sample storage and DNA extraction strategies. *Front. Microbiol.* 12: 627539. https://doi.org/10.3389/fmicb.2021.627539.

67 Fadiji, A.E. and Babalola, O.O. (2020). Metagenomics methods for the study of plant-associated microbial communities: a review. *J. Microbiol. Methods* 170: 105860.

68 Wang, D.D., Zhao, W., Reyila, M. et al. (2022). Diversity of microbial communities of *Pinus sylvestris* var. mongolica at spatial scale. *Microorganisms* 10: 371.

69 Edgar, R.C. (2010). Search and clustering orders of magnitude faster than BLAST. *Bioinformatics* 26: 2460–2461.

70 Rognes, T., Flouri, T., Nichols, B. et al. (2016). VSEARCH: a versatile open source tool for metagenomics. *PeerJ* 2016: 1–22.

71 Callahan, B.J., McMurdie, P.J., Rosen, M.J. et al. (2016). DADA2: high-resolution sample inference from *Illumina amplicon* data. *Nat. Methods* 13: 581–583.

72 Amir, A., Daniel, M., Navas-Molina, J. et al. (2017). Deblur rapidly resolves single. *Am. Soc. Microbiol.* 2: 1–7.

73 Bolyen, E., Rideout, J.R., Dillon, M.R. et al. (2019). Reproducible, interactive, scalable and extensible microbiome data science using QIIME 2. *Nat. Biotechnol.* 37: 852–857.

74 Schloss, P.D. (2020). Reintroducing mothur: 10 years later. *Appl. Environ. Microbiol.* 86: e02343-19.

75 Buchfink, B., Reuter, K., and Drost, H.G. (2021). Sensitive protein alignments at tree-of-life scale using DIAMOND. *Nat. Methods* 18: 366–368.

76 Bolger, A.M., Lohse, M., and Usadel, B. (2014). Trimmomatic: a flexible trimmer for Illumina sequence data. *Bioinformatics* 30: 2114–2120.

77 Schmieder, R. and Edwards, R. (2011). Quality control and preprocessing of metagenomic datasets. *Bioinformatics* 27: 863–864.

78 Sieber, C.M.K., Probst, A.J., Sharrar, A. et al. (2018). Recovery of genomes from metagenomes via a dereplication, aggregation and scoring strategy. *Nat. Microbiol.* 3: 836–843.

79 Uritskiy, G.V., DiRuggiero, J., and Taylor, J. (2018). MetaWRAP—a flexible pipeline for genome-resolved metagenomic data analysis. *Microbiome* 6: 1–13.

80 Peng, Y., Leung, H.C.M., Yiu, S.M., and Chin, F.Y.L. (2012). IDBA-UD: a de novo assembler for single-cell and metagenomic sequencing data with highly uneven depth. *Bioinformatics* 28: 1420–1428.

81 Li, D., Liu, C.M., Luo, R. et al. (2015). MEGAHIT: an ultra-fast single-node solution for large and complex metagenomics assembly via succinct de Bruijn graph. *Bioinformatics* 31: 1674–1676.

82 Nurk, S., Meleshko, D., Korobeynikov, A., and Pevzner, P.A. (2017). MetaSPAdes: a new versatile metagenomic assembler. *Genome Res.* 27: 824–834.

83 Liang, K.C. and Sakakibara, Y. (2021). MetaVelvet-DL: a MetaVelvet deep learning extension for de novo metagenome assembly. *BMC Bioinf.* 22: 1–21.

84 Mikheenko, A., Saveliev, V., and Gurevich, A. (2016). MetaQUAST: evaluation of metagenome assemblies. *Bioinformatics* 32: 1088–1090.

85 Setubal, J.C. (2021). Metagenome-assembled genomes: concepts, analogies, and challenges. *Biophys. Rev.* 13: 905–909.

86 Zhu, W., Lomsadze, A., and Borodovsky, M. (2010). Ab initio gene identification in metagenomic sequences. *Nucleic Acids Res.* 38: 1–15.

87 Kelley, D.R., Liu, B., Delcher, A.L. et al. (2012). Gene prediction with Glimmer for metagenomic sequences augmented by classification and clustering. *Nucleic Acids Res.* 40: 1–12.

88 Kanehisa, M., Sato, Y., and Morishima, K. (2016). BlastKOALA and GhostKOALA: KEGG tools for functional characterization of genome and metagenome sequences. *J. Mol. Biol.* 428: 726–731.

89 Cantalapiedra, C.P., Hernández-Plaza, A., Letunic, I. et al. (2021). eggNOG-mapper v2: functional annotation, orthology assignments, and domain prediction at the metagenomic scale. *Mol. Biol. Evol.* 38: 5825–5829.

90 Huson, D.H., Beier, S., Flade, I. et al. (2016). MEGAN community edition – interactive exploration and analysis of large-scale microbiome sequencing data. *PLoS Comput. Biol.* 12: 1–12.

91 Wilke, A., Bischof, J., Gerlach, W. et al. (2016). The MG-RAST metagenomics database and portal in 2015. *Nucleic Acids Res.* 44: D590–D594.

92 Mitchell, A.L., Almeida, A., Beracochea, M. et al. (2020). MGnify: the microbiome analysis resource in 2020. *Nucleic Acids Res.* 48: D570–D578.

93 Chen, I.M.A., Chu, K., Palaniappan, K. et al. (2021). The IMG/M data management and analysis system v.6.0: new tools and advanced capabilities. *Nucleic Acids Res.* 49: D751–D763.

94 Pérez-Cobas, A.E., Gomez-Valero, L., and Buchrieser, C. (2020). Metagenomic approaches in microbial ecology: an update on whole-genome and marker gene sequencing analyses. *Microb. Genomics* 6: 1–22.

95 Borchetia, S., Gogoi, M., Pal, R. et al. (2018). Metagenomic study and biodegrading capability of bacterial community in monocrotophos treated tea soil. *J. Adv. Microbiol.* 12: 1–14.

96 Yang, C., Chowdhury, D., Zhang, Z. et al. (2021). A review of computational tools for generating metagenome-assembled genomes from metagenomic sequencing data. *Comput. Struct. Biotechnol. J.* 19: 6301–6314.

97 Breitwieser, F.P., Baker, D.N., and Salzberg, S.L. (2018). KrakenUniq: confident and fast metagenomics classification using unique *k*-mer counts. *Genome Biol.* 19: 198.

98 Kamble, A., Srinivasan, S., and Singh, H. (2019). In-silico bioprospecting: finding better enzymes. *Mol. Biotechnol.* 61: 53–59.

99 Robinson, S.L., Piel, J., and Sunagawa, S. (2021). A roadmap for metagenomic enzyme discovery. *Nat. Prod. Rep.* 38: 1994–2023.

100 Sysoev, M., Grötzinger, S.W., Renn, D. et al. (2021). Bioprospecting of novel extremozymes from prokaryotes—the advent of culture-independent methods. *Front. Microbiol.* 12: 630013. https://doi.org/10.3389/fmicb.2021.630013.

101 Li, Y., Zhao, J., and Zhang, Z. (2021). Implementing metatranscriptomics to unveil the mechanism of bioaugmentation adopted in a continuous anaerobic process treating cow manure. *Bioresour. Technol.* 330: 124962.

102 Schmidt, A., Sturm, G., Lapp, C.J. et al. (2018). Development of a production chain from vegetable biowaste to platform chemicals. *Microb. Cell Fact.* 17: 90. https://microbialcellfactories.biomedcentral.com/articles/10.1186/s12934-018-0937-4.

103 Sato, Y., Hori, T., Koike, H. et al. (2019). Transcriptome analysis of activated sludge microbiomes reveals an unexpected role of minority nitrifiers in carbon metabolism. *Commun. Biol.* 2: 179.

104 Alessi, A.M., Bird, S.M., Oates, N.C. et al. (2018). Defining functional diversity for lignocellulose degradation in a microbial community using multi-omics studies. *Biotechnol. Biofuels* 11: 166.

105 Roldán, M.D., Olaya-Abril, A., Sáez, L.P. et al. (2021). Bioremediation of cyanide-containing wastes. *EMBO Rep.* 22: e53720.

106 Kurumbang, N.P., Dvorak, P., Bendl, J. et al. (2014). Computer-assisted engineering of the synthetic pathway for biodegradation of a toxic persistent pollutant. *ACS Synth. Biol.* 3: 172–181.

107 Gong, T., Xu, X., Che, Y. et al. (2017). Combinatorial metabolic engineering of *Pseudomonas putida* KT2440 for efficient mineralization of 1,2,3-trichloropropane. *Sci. Rep.* 7: 7064.

108 Rylott, E.L. and Bruce, N.C. (2020). How synthetic biology can help bioremediation. *Curr. Opin. Chem. Biol.* 58: 86–95.

109 Austin, H.P., Allen, M.D., Donohoe, B.S. et al. (2018). Characterization and engineering of a plastic-degrading aromatic polyesterase. *PNAS* 115: E4350–E4357.

110 Seghal Kiran, G., Ramasamy, P., Sekar, S. et al. (2018). Synthetic biology approaches: towards sustainable exploitation of marine bioactive molecules. *Int. J. Biol. Macromol.* 112: 1278–1288.

111 Mohsin, M.Z., Omer, R., Huang, J. et al. (2021). Advances in engineered *Bacillus subtilis* biofilms and spores, and their applications in bioremediation, biocatalysis, and biomaterials. *Synth. Syst. Biotechnol.* 6, 180–91.

112 Li, C., Yue, Z., Feng, F. et al. (2016). A novel strategy for acetonitrile wastewater treatment by using a recombinant bacterium with biofilm-forming and nitrile-degrading capability. *Chemosphere* 161: 224–232.

113 Li, C., Sun, Y., Yue, Z. et al. (2018). Combination of a recombinant bacterium with organonitrile-degrading and biofilm-forming capability and a positively charged carrier for organonitriles removal. *J. Hazard Mater.* 353: 372–380.

114 Namakoshi, K., Nakajima, T., Yoshikawa, K. et al. (2016). Combinatorial deletions of glgC and phaCE enhance ethanol production in *Synechocystis* sp. PCC 6803. *J. Biotechnol.* 239: 13–19.

115 Nishiguchi, H., Hiasa, N., Uebayashi, K. et al. (2019). Transomics data-driven, ensemble kinetic modeling for system-level understanding and engineering of the cyanobacteria central metabolism. *Metab. Eng.* 52: 273–283.

18

Recent Trends in Computational Tools for Industrially Important Enzymes

Shweta Srivastava[1,2], *Sakina Bombaywala*[1,2], *Hemant J. Purohit*[1], and *Nishant A. Dafale*[1,2]

[1] *Environmental Biotechnology and Genomics Division, CSIR-National Environmental Engineering Research Institute, Nagpur 440020, India*
[2] *Academy of Scientific & Innovative Research (AcSIR), Ghaziabad 201002, India*

18.1 Introduction

The widespread use of microbe-derived enzymes has led to their high demands in food, pharmaceutical, and chemical industries, including the manufacturing plants of textiles, detergents, pulp, paper, and leather [1]. The processes dependent on enzymes are shown to be more efficient and cost-effective. They allow for enhanced recovery of products, and require less use of toxic chemicals and harsh environments. Animals, plants, and microorganisms are various sources of industrially used enzymes, but the most studied and proficient enzymes are sourced from microorganisms. The microbial enzymes are easily and rapidly produced due to the ease of culture and shorter life span of microorganisms. Synthetic biology can be used to manipulate microorganisms for their enhanced benefits in obtaining desired enzymes.

The important industrial enzymes are amylase, laccase, inulinase, lipase, nitrilase, protease, and xylanase. The microbe-derived enzymes contribute to the most considerable fraction of living matter on Earth. They are present in diverse environmental habitats, including the harshest ones, such as hot springs, salt brines, acid mines, frozen Antarctic ice, and deep-sea hydrothermal vents. The conventional culturable approach allows the identification of only 0.1–1% of the total microbial diversity, limiting the complete knowledge of microbial enzymes.

In the past decades, the collection of total environmental DNA and applications of nonculturable techniques called meta-omics, such as metagenomics, metatranscriptomics, and metaproteomics have resulted in an inclusive understanding of the uncultured microbial population as a source of potent enzymes [2]. Access to novel genome sequences is thought to aid in the process of finding new enzymes for industrial applications. Additionally, the availability of noncultivable microbial DNA from extreme habitats will be helpful in getting insights into their novel potentials. The extent to which the potential can be explored is limited by the current

Microbial Enzymes: Production, Purification, and Industrial Applications, First Edition.
Edited by Dinesh Yadav, Pankaj Chowdhary, Gautam Anand, and Rajarshi Kumar Gaur.

bioinformatics pipelines available, and therefore, the novel enzymatic activities can remain unknown. The screening of genomic libraries thus becomes vital in the wake of the need to uncover the potential of microorganisms. The biocatalytic activities can be studied by screening the genomic libraries against various commercial substrates, especially to know the turnover process of synthetic substances.

The potent and robust commercial enzymes can be harnessed from naturally extremophilic habitats responsible for the diversity of temperature, alkalinity, acidity, pH, and salinity. Consequently, the acceleration in identifying novel enzymes is due to an increase in the number of sequencing projects for DNA belonging to microbial communities of extreme environments.

Among the meta-omic approaches, metagenomics is considered to be the most promising in terms of the identification of innovative catalysts discovered from prokaryotic DNA [2–4]. However, the great potential for metaproteomics has also been recognized by the discovery of cellulases and lipases. Unlike in prokaryotes, where the genes are directly expressed, the eukaryotic genes include large introns spacing the exons, making the metagenomic analysis tricky. However, the pioneering work of Grant et al. on eukaryotic metatranscriptomics for finding novel enzymes involved the enrichment and reversed transcription of selected 3-polyadenylated mRNAs [5]. Several biocatalysts, namely cellulases and phosphatases, were characterized following this approach.

The present chapter emphasizes the application of various in silico tools for mining genomes and metagenomes of prokaryotic DNA for finding novel industrially relevant biocatalysts (Figure 18.1). The chapter includes a comprehensive

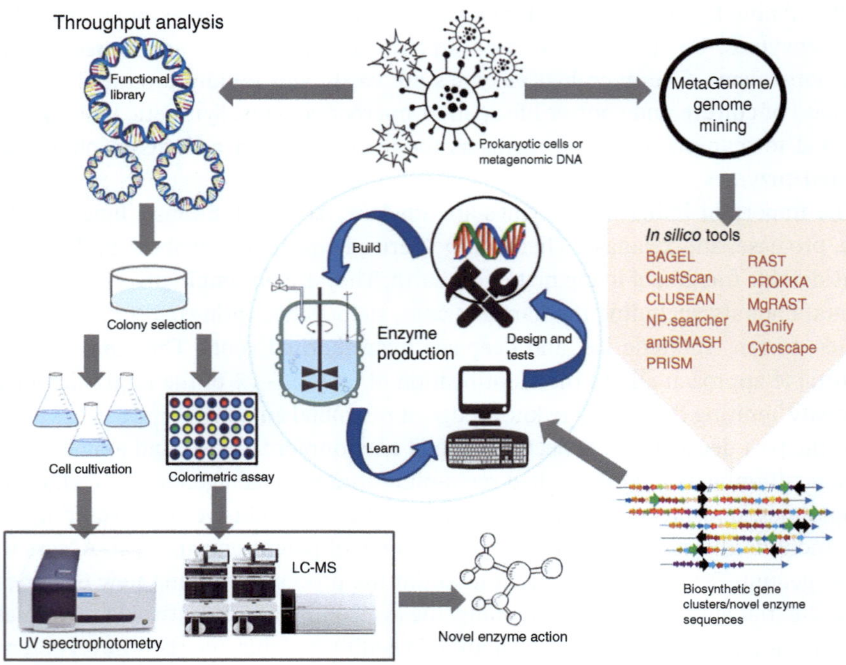

Figure 18.1 Schematic representation of approaches for mining novel enzymes from genomic or metagenomic sequences. Source: Agilent Technologies, Inc.

discussion of innovative ideas and recent trends in the discovery of potential enzymes from diverse microbial communities. The role of computational enzymology and system biology has also been underlined in characterizing potent biocatalysts for their industrial usage.

18.2 Strategies for Discovering Enzymes

Our natural environment is a significant source of microbial enzymes. The depth of exploration of such biodiversity depends on the availability of tools for mining genomes and screening metagenomes. It is also important for tapping into the unknown potentials of extremophiles. The conventional approach to the discovery of novel enzymes starts with screening for potential enzymes in natural sources like soil or waste streams [6–9]. The screening assay is followed by selection of enzymes with desired properties by growing on selective media. The selected isolates are further identified by gene sequence that encodes for desired enzymatic function. For this, either whole genome or targeted sequencing can be done for random mutations created in the gene. Targeted gene amplification can be also done using degenerate primers followed by polymerase chain reaction (PCR) library cloning and screening for clone showing desired properties. Although, screening and identification methods are commonly used, they have low success rates. Therefore, the *in silico* data mining or bioprospecting are straightforward, promising, and complementary approach to the conventional methods for enzyme discovery.

Recent advances in high-throughput next-generation sequencing have generated vast amounts of data. The amount of data present in UniProt database is 60M protein sequence and is increasing tremendously at a pace of 2% per month. Most of these data are obtained from microbiome genome sequencing projects. The diversity of enzymes has increased the difficulty and complexity of discovering novel enzymes. Subsequently, most of the protein sequences in the database are inconsistent or have unknown functions. Thus, the key challenge in enzyme discovery is to devise experimental strategies and *in silico* data mining for determining *in vivo* metabolic functions and in vitro enzymatic activities.

18.2.1 Mining Microbial Genomes

The success in genome sequencing projects has resulted in the availability of vast amounts of DNA sequence data and databases, thereby generating an immense opportunity for finding and characterizing microbial enzymes [10]. The cost-effective and reduced time for sequencing DNA is made possible on next-generation sequencing platforms (SoLid, 454 Roche and, Solexa) [11]. Less than two weeks are now required for completing the sequencing using these cutting-edge technologies [12]. The assembled sequences are generated from raw sequenced data and further annotated for functional proteins and potential enzyme using various in silico tools.

The discovery of novel bioproducts is based on one of the two approaches. The first one involves searching for open reading frames (ORFs) in the genomes [13].

This is followed by annotating putative proteins and their subsequent cloning, overexpression, and screening of the desired bioactivity. The second approach involves searching sequence homology against sequences present in the databases [14]. This search for conserved homologous regions is then identified as putative proteins of concern and is further characterized. Various bioinformatics tools like Basic Local Alignment Search Tool (BLAST) and Hidden Markov Model (HMM) are used for carrying out homology alignments.

The reliable annotations of sequences are tricky in view of huge sequence data. Therefore, approximately 40% of the sequences deposited in public databases are categorized as "uncharacterized proteins"[15]. The homologous alignment approach is thus not a reliable method for understanding the in-depth potential of genome and metagenome data. This approach could be a preliminary to the enhanced identification criteria like finding conserved key enzymes/protein motifs, protein 3D model analysis, thermophily, enzyme features, substrate specificity, and search for isofunctional enzymes.

The study by Wang et al. applied the combination approach of homologous annotation of query sequences and genomic analysis of the putative gene sequence for the identification of a novel acyltransferase from *Fulvivirga* sp. W222. The encoded enzyme was responsible for catalyzing the transfer of the acyl group to a primary amine of the desferrioxamine G compound [16]. In prokaryotes, the genes colocalized in clusters generally encode enzymes that are part of the same metabolic pathway [17]. Therefore, the study of the genes neighboring the gene of interest provides clues to the functional activity of the encoded enzymes. It is known that many ORFs are incorrectly predicted; therefore, text-based approaches hold less importance during extensive research projects. One of the easiest ways to find proteins is by searching query genes by the enzymatic function in public database search options. The drawback of this approach is that only a small fraction of enzymes has been experimentally verified for their functions, and the lack of uniqueness in the protein features limits the search in databases.

18.2.2 Novel Enzymes from Unculturable Microbial Community

Only less than 1% of the microbial diversity of a particular biosphere can be cultured in the laboratory under standard conditions [18]. The metagenomics approach is an alternative to the conventional culturable approach, wherein the genomic library is prepared from environmental DNA [19]. The library is then screened for ORFs that encode potential putative enzymes of interest. The process of screening is based on either sequence or function similarities. The functional screening of genes is a selection of bacterial clones displaying the desired functional activity. This may involve either phenotype detection, induced expression of genes, or heterologous complementation [20]. On the contrary, the screening process based on gene sequences involves the PCR and DNA hybridization. The PCR procedure entails the use of a set of universal primers complementary to consensus sequences in the genes. The activity screening procedure faces problems of insufficient and biased expression of genes in *Escherichia coli*. Contrary to the expression of a particular gene, the overexpression of foreign genes at significant levels needs a completely different approach. The targeted engineering of transcription (ribosome engineering) or translation engineering can be one of the possible solutions. Sequence-based applications can take advantage of synthetic biology, which involves a curated database of possible candidates followed by the synthesis of genes and checking for desired functional activities. The increasing numbers of uncharacterized proteins in public databases are still unexplored for their metabolic and functional potential. Rather than simple BLAST, structure-guided predictions of enzyme functions are important for discovering novel enzymes.

The industrially relevant enzymes like lipases, amidase, amylase, beta-glucosidase, oxidoreductase, epoxide hydrolase, and decarboxylases are derived from extreme habitats. The environmental niches explored to obtain microbial biocatalysts are colonic vents, cow rumen, marine environments, arctic tundra, and termite guts.

18.2.2.1 Activity-guided Functional Metagenomics

The initial metagenome library screening process was based on identifying the desired functional activities of the cloned genes from the library [19]. The gene vectors such as cosmid, fosmid, or artificial chromosome libraries are used to clone the bacterial cells and then phenotypically identify them. The common methods of phenotype detection include a zone of antibiotic and metal inhibition, antibiotic resistance, fluorimetry, and colorimetry. The workflow for the activity-guided screening process does not depend on sequence homology; therefore, it is valuable for the *de novo* discovery of enzymes. This workflow has been efficiently used to expand the pool of industrially relevant enzymes, particularly lipases, cellulases, hemicellulases, amylases, esterases, and chitinases [21]. Numerous drawbacks of using an activity-based screening method subsist for the identification of natural biocatalysts. Because several specific substrates and cofactors are required for the detection of enzymes, the probability of enzyme detection by simple activity assays is less. Additionally, the success in identification is limited because of incompatibility of metabolic requirements, bias in codon usage, and low levels of gene expression in clones. Although limitations for activity-based screening exist, it is widely used for preliminary screening, followed by more specific sequence-dependent methods [22].

18.2.2.2 PCR-based Functional Metagenomics

The sequence-based screening involves the use of degenerate universal primers to amplify the gene sequence of interest in PCR reaction. The PCR-based methods are throughput and sensitive, although they can be improved by discretization and pooling approaches [23, 24]. The amplicon-based screening for domain markers for biosynthetic such as ketosynthase and adenylation domains are commonly used to identify novel Biosynthetic Gene Clusters (BCGs) and other microbial products [25, 26]. The BCGs from a large metagenomic library were cloned in *E. coli* [27]. The *E. coli* clones containing polyketide synthase (PKS) and nonribosomal peptide synthase (NPKS) clusters were screened through PCR. As the approach is based on the homology to known protein domains, the disadvantage of the approach is the difficulty in the identification of unknown gene clusters. An additional disadvantage to the sequences-based approach comes from inherent biases of PCR reactions for amplification of GC-rich sequences and for low abundance microbial count [28]. Further, the amplification of short gene sequences does not provide a complete picture of taxonomy and genes co-occurrence. An innovative approach for combating the drawback is found by Libis et al. The method reported term CONKAT-Seq depends on the co-occurrence analysis of targeted gene amplicon sequences [29]. The methodology involves amplification of position-barcoded sequences followed by identification of novel biosynthetic gene clusters (BGCs) by using statistical analysis for finding co-occurring biosynthetic domains (Table 18.1). Another low-cost approach can be amplicon sequencing. However, as the cost of sequencing decreases, shotgun metagenomics can be an alternative or complementary to functional metagenomics. It can be used to further accelerate the process of enzyme discovery.

18.2.3 High-throughput Metagenomic Screening for Enzymes

Shotgun metagenomics involves the sequencing of entire untargeted eDNA. The methodology involves the preparation of samples, sequencing, assembly, and analysis. The shotgun metagenomics is free of biases of PCR gene amplification, and library cloning is not needed [42–45]. The preparation of fosmid and cosmid libraries is not required; thus, shotgun sequencing is less work-intensive and fast. However, both functional and shotgun metagenomics are usually followed by gene cloning and heterologous gene expression for the characterization of enzymes and getting phenotypic information. The essential requirement of shotgun metagenomics is the extraction of an adequate amount and quality of DNA and sufficient sequencing depth and error corrections of sequence read. The major drawback of shotgun metagenomics comes from the use of widely popular sequencing technology called Illumina Sequencing. It produces short reads while being computationally expensive and has limitations of inaccurate reads assembly and binning [46]. The short read assembly can also be supported by other techniques like Hi-C chromosome capture for assembling short read. Maximum resolution of microbial genomes belonging to cow rumen and the human gut was obtained by using this approach. Alternatively, long reads can be obtained by Oxford Nanopore [47] and PacBio HiFi methods [48]. It is reported to significantly increase the quality of metagenome assembly, especially for repetitive and large BCG sequences [49, 50]. The major advantage of shotgun sequencing is that the metagenomic datasets are deposited in the public (open-access) databases. This is an effective strategy to make metagenomes available to various researchers across the globe. For instance, Tara Oceans is the biggest initiative that works to make metagenomic datasets along with metadata available for public analysis. This initiative started in 2009, and since then, the project members have published over 100 papers. Many groups have further analyzed available datasets to investigate numerous facets of oceanography [51]. It has thus, demonstrated the contribution of a single large-scale meta-omics initiative to research in ecology, biogeochemistry, oceanography,

Table 18.1 Genome mining tools for BGC identification.

Sr. no.	Software tools	Available	Key features	References
1	AntiSMASH	https://antismash.secondarymetabolites.org	Capability to recognize 52 different BGC types using genome sequence data. Prediction of NRPS and PKS substrate specificity is included, as is a comparison to the MIBiG database of curated known BGCs. Versions for online and local installation are available.	[30]
2	PRISM	http://grid.adapsyn.com/prism	From genome sequence data, 22 distinct BGC types were identified. Prediction of NRPS and PKS substrate specificity, as well as graph-based structure analysis for identification of BGCs, is included. Only available online.	[31]
3	BiG-SCAPE	http://bigscape-corason.secondarymetabolites.org/	AntiSMASH predicted BGCs via domain calling were compared across the genome to Pfam models. Allows for the visualization of BGC similarity in terms of synteny and gene content. Only for local installation	[32]
4	ANASTASIA	https://galaxyproject.org/use/anastasia/	It is a web-based framework that has been customized specifically for metagenome bioinformatic analysis and is associated with MariaDB database server via a Web2py web interface.	[33]
5	ClusterFinder	https://github.com/petercim/ClusterFinder	ClusterFinder detects putative gene clusters of secondary metabolite in sequence data using a probabilistic approach. Clusterfinder is available as a standalone program	[34]
6	DeepBGC	https://github.com/Merck/deepbgc	Deep learning is used to detect BGCs in bacterial and fungal genomes. A Bidirectional Long Short-Term Memory Recurrent Neural Network is used, as well as a word2vec-like vector embedding for Pfam family of protein domains. A Random Forest classifier is used to predict the product activity and class of detected BGCs. Only for local installation	[35]

(Continued)

Table 18.1 (Continued)

Sr. no.	Software tools	Available	Key features	References
7	BAGEL	http://bagel4.molgenrug.nl/	BAGEL is a database and mining tool for ribosomally synthesized and posttranslationally modified peptides (RIPPs). It can identify RIPP biosynthetic gene clusters in genomic/metagenomic data	[36]
8	SMURF	http://jcvi.org/smurf/index.php	SMURF is a search platform for secondary metabolite biosynthetic gene clusters in fungi. SMURF searches for conserved domains in NRPS, PKS, hybrid-PKS/NRPS, and terpenoid gene clusters using an HMM-based search strategy.	[37]
9	CLUSEAN CLuster SEquence ANalyzer	https://bitbucket.org/tilmweber/clusean	CLUSEAN is a pipeline for annotating secondary metabolite BGC based on Bioperl. It enables automated homology searches, identification of conserved protein domains in NRPS and PKS gene clusters, enzyme classification, and NRPS A-domain specificity predictions.	[38]
10	eSNaPD	http://esnapd2.rockefeller.edu/	eSNaPD is a tool for surveying secondary metabolite gene cluster diversity in metagenomic DNA sequences while also accounting for data metadata, such as geographic sampling location.	[39]
11	MIBiG	https://mibig.secondarymetabolites.org/	Used for identifying new and novel BGCs. To connect genes and chemical structures and vice versa in order to better understand secondary metabolite biosynthesis can be used to modify existing biosynthetic pathways and design new ones.	[40]
12	IMG-ABC	https://img.jgi.doe.gov/cgi-bin/abc/main.cgi	Approximately 1000 BGCs are related to known structures in the MIBiG database, and approximately 900,000 possible BGCs are of unknown structure. The huge number of BGCs are identified ClusterFinder analysis, as well as fragmented PKS-I BGCs and NRPS identified by Illumina sequencing.	[41]

virology, and enzymology. As compared to biochemical and PCR-based functional metagenomics, the rate of an enzyme discovered is relatively rare from shotgun metagenomics. With the increase in the accessibility of sequence data, enzyme discovery research is gradually shifting toward *in silico* shotgun metagenomics.

18.3 Computational Methods for Enzyme Function Prediction

The prediction of protein function is important for understanding molecular-level mechanisms that are vital for sustaining life on Earth and for vast applications in biomedical and pharmaceuticals for human healthcare. The major difficulty faced in enzyme function prediction is the time and energy requirements for the experimental classification of enzymatic functions. In recent years, computational methods have gained ever-increasing role in guiding and designing experiments for drastically improving the success rate. The computational tools often relied on traditional methods for identification of protein domains or sequences by using BLAST tool. However, a large number of tools have been developed to exploit data from genome sequences and can also be coupled with a large amount of experimental data to generate new opportunities for making functional predictions. The advanced computational tools can perform tasks such as the prediction of protein sequence, evolutionary relationships between proteins, and protein–protein interactions. Nevertheless, comprehensive assessment of the large and diverse amounts of target protein sequences is practically difficult due to problems of accurate annotation of targeted sequences.

Several methods for enzyme engineering involve alterations in the active site and corresponding binding sites and product channels in the enzyme. Alternatively, the rapid advancement in the field of machine learning can be of potential use for accelerating and increasing the success rate of computation-based predictions.

18.3.1 Querying Metagenomic Databases

Initial steps in shotgun metagenomics are the extraction of DNA from collected environment samples and eDNA sequencing [52–55]. This is followed by steps for downstream bioinformatic processing to deposit the metagenome dataset in public repositories such as iMicrobe, MGnify, and JGI IMG/M (Joint Genome Institute Integrated Microbial Genomes and Microbiomes resource) [19]. The MGnify is a resource developed to search the "Microbial Dark Matter" [56]. The MGnify performs metagenome mapping using HMM instead of using Diamond or BLAST, which are based on a sequence-based alignment approach [57]. The BLAST and Diamond are fast and efficient for primary identification, but the HMMs benefit from their ability to identify remote homologs. The HMM profiles use the probabilistic models to detect distantly spaced sequences, therefore enabling the identification of enzymes from a group of protein families. The HMMs build queries of a number of aligned sequences rather than on one single sequence. The custom HMMs are built from a small number of clades based on their evolutionary relationship. For instance, the study by Neubauer et al. made a custom HMM of tryptophan halogenase gene sequences [52]. The custom-made HMM was then queried to metagenomes retrieved from public databases, resulting in the identification of 254 hits to the HMM profile. The study found a flavin-dependent halogenase that catalyzed the conversion of indole to 3-bromoindole. The fact that enzymes preferred bromination over chlorination was found to be interesting. Another observation was the low specific activity (2.5 mU/mg) of the halogenase for indole, suggesting indole as its natural substrate. This underlines the challenge for functional activity and substrate determination by only using the sequence homology approach.

The metagenome-assembled genomes (MAGs) can be reconstructed from metagenome datasets and are reported to give more insight and resolution of genomes. The study by Nayfach et al. reported more than 52,000 MAGs reconstructed from >10,000 metagenomes belonging to various environmental niches [53]. It is estimated that this study has increased the knowledge of bacterial and archaeal phylogenetic diversity by 44% and also predicted potential biosynthetic pathways. The analysis using antiSMASH has resulted in the detection of >100,000 BCGs. This includes the largest BCG having 62 modules for PKS, NPKS belonging to Acidobacterium derived from soil habitat. Although these BCG modules lack functional characterization, it can be emphasized that the opportunities and challenges exist for metagenome dataset due to the sheer quality and quantity of data. Therefore, building on the existing tools like ANASTASIA (automated nucleotide amino acid sequences translational plAtform for systemic interpretation and analysis) and MGnify will facilitate the development of improved platforms for acceleration in the rate of new enzyme discovery.

18.3.2 Enzyme Characterization Through Phylogenetics

Since the time Darwin first proposed the phylogenetic tree, the understanding of evolutionary relationships has been central to the study of living things [54]. The biological advancements involving the cracking of the genetic code have aided in the study of phylogenetic relationships based on DNA and proteins rather than solely dependent on morphological traits. Although at different scales, the overall aim of phylogenetics is to understand the association between functional traits, including functionally related enzymes. As compared to the 16sRNA genes that group depending on the organism, the biosynthetic enzymes classify on the basis of shared functions and preferred substrates [55]. The alignment-based enzyme discovery has been improved due to the involvement of phylogenetics. This approach involves the alignment of gene sequences encoding for known enzymes to the metagenomic reads. Public databases like Protein Data Bank [58] and Swiss-Prot [59] can be used for retrieving seed sequences of characterized enzyme groups. The sequences that group into a phylogenetic clade are interesting as they may represent new functional activity and substrate preference. Such data can be used as a starting point for planning enzyme characterization and validation experiments.

The major drawback of phylogenetic trees construction is its dependency on the accuracy of multiple sequence alignment. Additionally, the phylogenetic analysis is expensive as the computational requirements for the estimation of trees from large sequences are costly. The FastTree algorithm [60] dramatically reduces the time for tree construction using heuristic methods to constrain the tree search and to round up maximum likelihood evaluations to approximate values.

The phylogenetic analysis of genes encoding for protein families and protein sequences can be used to infer the evolution of contemporary proteins from ancestral proteins. For example, the reconstruction of the phylogenetic tree for adenylate-forming enzymes has proposed that the enzymes for secondary metabolisms, such as peptide synthase and β-lactone synthetases, are similar to protein scaffolds of primary metabolic enzymes like ligases and CoA [55]. The study by Hendrikse et al. reported the enzyme diterpene cyclase to be related to ancestral sequences [61]. Further experimental characterization demonstrated that the enzyme enhanced thermal stability and wide substrate preference. Both features are common to ancestral sequences that are reported to promote the development of advanced features. A probability-based web tool called FastML enables tree construction for the nonspecialist [62]. More powerful are the Bayesian algorithm-based phylogenetic methods (*The Bayesian Approach to Molecular Phylogeny – Archive ouverte HAL*). For instance, the Bayesian method was used to study the phylogeny of lanthipeptide synthetase, belonging to RiPP maturases that are responsible for inserting sulfur bridges in peptide bonds [63]. The study performed by Zhang et al. found that the sequence of lanthipeptide BCGs and maturases is crucial as it governs the structure of final products [64]. Overall, the study of phylogeny is one of the prime and fundamental for bioprospecting enzymes from the metagenome.

18.3.3 Sequence Similarity Networking

The sequence similarity networks (SSNs) are recently used for understanding the phylogeny of protein families and superfamilies. The protein superfamily analysis using SSNs was done in 2009 [65], which demonstrated an association between diverse protein families. The SSNs are created by means of a BLAST search of customized sequence dataset and later visually represented wherein nodes are amino acid sequences, and the pair-wise sequence similarity is represented by each edge. Generally, the SSNs are shortened to fit within the threshold limits so that they contain protein subfamilies or small clusters. Like in phylogenetics, the seed sequences of known enzymes are added to the SSNs. It is then used as an anchor point to seek identity between protein subfamilies and families. In a study, soil and vanilla pod metagenomes were screened for potential triesterases using SSNs. The SSNs gave triseterase hits with numerous protein family clusters belonging to three protein superfamilies [66]. SSNs have also been used as complementary to phylogenetics for proposing the radial divergence of the nitroreductase superfamily from a minimal protein scaffold responsible for binding cofactors [67]. Using SSNs, both known and unknown protein families can be used as a starting point for the characterization of enzymes. The SSNs allow the visualization of the relationship between large numbers of protein sequences at the same time in the form of a visual graph. Unlike the maximum likelihood phylogenetic tree method, the SSNs enable fast computation time and the interactive graphs can be accessed through an open-source software called Cytoscape [68]. The drawback of Graphical User Interface in Cytoscape is the reproducibility of the large protein networks containing a multitude of nodes. The Cytoscape API, CyREST, enables the building of reproducible protein interaction networks. Popular computer languages like Python and R can be used easily used with CyREST [69]. SSNs can also be interactively visualized in igraph package that is accessible with R, Python, and C/C++ programs [70]. The Enzyme Function Initiative Enzyme Similarity Tool (EFI-EST) is a web-based application that facilitates automated SSNs generation without the need for knowledge of programming.

18.3.3.1 D-structure-based Methods

The unavailability of protein structures has restricted the incorporation of structural information to understand the enzyme function. It is hypothesized that novel protein domains are likely to pose novel enzyme functions that have led to the initiation of a global campaign for cataloging structural information of protein domains [71]. This initiative has been unintentionally focused on information from a culturable microbial population. Entries from unculturable microorganisms or metagenomes are only 0.3% in the protein database (PDB). Interestingly, high-throughput structural study has resulted in solving thousands of protein structures; however, only rarely have novel protein folds been discovered [72]. It is noted that out of the numerous conformations that a protein molecule can attain, only a handful of these conformations are represented in biological systems studied to date. Thus, much of the functional and structural vastness of proteins remains to be interrogated in an unculturable microbial population. It is identified that even ancient and most conserved protein domains are able to catalyze a vast diversity of biochemical reactions, therefore suggesting only a start of unfolding functional diversity of proteins and their structural space. Despite using effective tools for structural prediction like AlphaFold2, it is not possible to make a significant prediction about the relationship between protein sequence, structure, and function [73]. Nonetheless, compared to the primary structure of proteins, the secondary, tertiary, and quaternary folds are able to provide key insights into functional activities. Protein families implicated in biosynthetic reactions such as RiPP recognition element, thioesterase domains, and adenylate forming enzymes consist of members with dissimilar amino acid sequences but share conserved protein structural folds. It is not surprising that for several protein families, the structure-based alignment yields more significant and accurate results compared to the alignment-based purely on amino acid sequences. Few structure-based alignment tools for enzyme families are MATRAS, Caretta, and MAMMOTH [74–76]. The web-based application for protein structure homology is Phyre2, SWISS-MODEL, and I-TASSER, which are available for predicting structural folds belonging to the metagenomic dataset [77–79]. A study used a deep learning pipeline for protein structure prediction from metagenome samples of Tara Oceans. The study found a ubiquitous protein family

(PF15461) involved in photosynthesis [80]. The active site structure and motifs play a crucial role in determining the functions of proteins. Therefore, structural modeling is an important step toward the detection of amino acid sequences and structural determination of the active site.

18.3.3.2 Motifs and Active Site Residues

The active sites of enzymes occupy only a fraction of the total volume of a complete 3D folded protein. As compared to other protein parts, the active site residues have a conserved identity and have typical architectural types [81]. The Ser-His-Asp catalytic triad is the most common example of active site conservation. They are found as catalytic residues in alpha/beta hydrolases, chymotrypsin, and subtilisin [82]. The triad is responsible for hydrolysis reactions in over 17 different biochemical mechanisms catalyzed by enzymes belonging to almost all the EC classes. Particularly, the multiple functions performed by the Ser-His-Asp triad are attributed to its wide substrate specificity and ability to be involved in several types of chemical reactions at the active sites. The architecture of active sites is predominantly based on substrate chemistry for half of triad-containing enzymes. For the rest of the half, changes at active site involve mostly alteration in hydrogen bonds and/or acid/bases. As the architecture of active site is a determinant of catalytic reactions with chemical diversity. It is challenging to predict the protein function from the architecture of the active site.

It is regarded that the alteration of even one amino acid residue at the active site of an enzyme is able to make changes in substrate specificity or enantiomer selectivity. Therefore, in proteomic engineering, it is often risky to make changes to the active site as it may lead to a dead end in finding novel enzyme activity. The alternative to engineering is to find naturally occurring variations in the active site. The conversed variants of catalytic domains and sites can be explored in the metagenomes. However, very few studies have been done on the discovery of enzymes based on the search for natural active site alterations found in metagenome datasets. Typically, the active site aberration comes into the picture only after initial activity-based screening, followed by enzyme function characterization. For instance, a multi-functional catalytic triad was found in endoglucanase from a metagenomic library of soil during activity-based screening. The determination of amino acid residues at the active site is possible even without the knowledge of enzyme classification and functional activity. Various tools such as CASTp are able to automatically detect active site pockets[83]. The mechanism and catalytic site atlas is an inclusive database that stores the mechanisms and structural features of active sites [84]. It contains approximately 1000 entries that represent >73,000 Swiss-Prot and >15,000 PDB entries [85]. The UniProt provides information on active sites that can be used for the identification of deviating active sites' structural alignments in the metagenome dataset.

The important functional elements of protein are conserved motifs, and sites for cofactor binding can also be detected using tools like ScanProsite [86]. For example, RiPP maturases is a promiscuous enzyme that catalyzes the addition of ornithine in the peptide backbone of the protein. The structural alignment RiPP maturases was done, and it was found to contain the "DXHXD" motif conserved in the enzymes. This was then used to identify and characterize novel RiPP arginases from culturable isolates and metagenome sequences belonging to groundwater. The search for conserved motifs followed by complete sequence alignments for homology search dramatically improves the accuracy of the structure and function prediction of the enzyme.

18.3.4 Extremophiles as a Source of Industrial Enzymes

Microbial populations thriving in extreme environments are interesting to study as a source of industrially useful enzymes. The microbes may be under extremes of temperature (−2 to 12, 60–110 °C), radiation, pressure, pH (<2, >9), and alkalinity (2–5 NaCl) [87]. Recent studies have suggested extremophiles have great potential in terms of the diversity of proteins and enzymes. The limitations to exploiting the potential of extremophiles are due to difficulty with culturing microorganisms and enzyme characterization.

In a study by Yang et al., laccase was isolated from the thermophile bacterium *Trametes trogii* strain S0301 [88]. Further, the gene encoding for laccase was found to have a sequence similar to the lcc3 gene for *T. trogii* strain BAFC463. Enzyme characterization found that the laccase could perform decolorization of dye at 60 °C. This is the first successful report of isolation and characterization of a thermostable laccase from thermophilic bacteria. The enzyme is reported to display better properties for biotechnological applications compared to fungus-derived laccases.

Similarly, cellulases were purified and characterized using metagenomic data belonging to cattle rumen [89]. The cellulases were identified by the annotation approach based on sequence similarity and an organized assembly of learning algorithms. Thus, it is highlighted that the machine learning approach for finding sequence similarities has the potential to predict the functional properties of enzymes. The study by James et al. identified and isolated a new transketolase made up of two polypeptide chains encoded by a "split-gene" from *Carboxydotherms hydrogenoformans, a* hyperthermophilic bacterium [90]. Several thermostable enzymes such as, cellulose, amylase, protease, and lipases have found usefulness in various biotechnological applications. Extreme thermophilic bacteria (thriving at 60–80 °C) are found to largely belong to *Clostridium, Thermotoga, Thermus,* and *Bacillus,* whereas *hyperthermophiles* are distributed in archaeal genera such as *Thermococcus, Methanopyrus*, and *Pyrococcus*. The most commercially used Taq polymerase is isolated from *Thermus aquaticus* with a net worth of $500 million in 2009 [91].

With current efforts to lessen the consumption of energy, biomolecules from psychrophiles have been employed for industrial applications. Examples of cold-active enzymes is amylase, protease, and lipases with commercial applications in the detergent industry and cellulases and xylanase employed in the pulp and paper industry. Cellulase and xylanase are polymer-degrading enzymes; thus, they also find applications for saccharification of lignocellulosic biomass with prospects for the production of alcohol (second-generation biofuel) [9]. Further, the psychrophilic enzymes are employed for bioremediation of oil-polluted water, textile stone washing and polishing, extraction and clarification of fruits juices, and enhancing the quality of bakery products [92].

The salinity-tolerant halophilic bacteria have also been explored for enzyme discovery. The halophilic enzymes consist of negatively charged amino acids in their peptide backbone that help prevent protein precipitation [93]. Thus, this property confers them to functional activity even in nonaqueous media. Examples of salt-tolerant enzymes are amylase, xylanase, protease, and lipases isolated from halophilic bacteria such as *Halobacterium*, *Halothermothrix*, and *Halobacillus* [94–96]. Yang et al. discovered an enzyme responsible for salt tolerance in the microbial community of the gut. The screening of the metagenome library from the fecal sample has resulted in the identification of 48 halophilic strains; 10 out of 48 strains have shown to exhibit enhanced stability and tolerance to a range of salt concentrations [97]. The high-throughput metagenome analysis has demonstrated 91 genes to encode for enzymes that confer salt tolerance [98]. Two genes encoding for trehalose-6-phosphate hydrolase were cloned in *E. coli* for further enzyme characterization. In addition to being salt-tolerant, the activity of the enzyme increased with the increasing concentration of NaCl. Numerous studies have reported that the microbes of the gastrointestinal tract (gut) harbor a large number of salt-tolerant genes and, therefore, can be explored to get new insights into the mechanisms of halophiles [99–102].

Halophilic enzymes like lipases and proteases have found applications as laundry additives and dishwashing detergents. It can be concluded that the study of novel extremozymes has immense potential for in-depth investigation of biochemical diversity. The studies have largely helped to look for enhanced commercial applications and increase the understanding of the microbial world.

18.4 Conclusion

Using computational tools to investigate novel enzymes, researchers discovered several industrially important enzymes such as cellulase, pectinase, xylanase, and others. However, the industrial sector's fierce competition for better-optimized enzymes places a premium on discovering more sustainable enzymes from various extreme niches. Computational progress in mining novel enzymes has shaped the enzymology sector in search of more superior, cost-effective, and natural catalysts to drive processes. The methods and approaches for discovering novel enzymes using genomics and metagenomics tools are discussed in this book chapter. Using homology modeling, advances in sequencing platforms and annotation tools reveal several protein sequences. The number of entries in the UniProt sequence database continues to grow at a rate of nearly four years. A platform that can bring together information on sequences, phylogeny, and chemistry to assign roles and conduct experimental validation is still required for these proteins' functional assignments.

Acknowledgments

Sakina Bombaywala is grateful to the Department of Biotechnology, India, for a Senior Research Fellowship. The manuscript has been checked for plagiarism by Knowledge Resource Centre, CSIR-NEERI, Nagpur, India, and the assigned KRC number is CSIR-NEERI/KRC/2022/DEC/EBGD/4.

References

1 Okpara, M.O. (2022). Microbial enzymes and their applications in food industry: a mini-review. *Adv. Enzym. Res.* 10: 23–47. https://doi.org/10.4236/AER.2022.101002.

2 Parmar, K.M., Hathi, Z.J., and Dafale, N.A. (2017). Control of multidrug-resistant gene flow in the environment through bacteriophage intervention. *Appl. Biochem. Biotechnol.* 181: 1007–1029. https://doi.org/10.1007/s12010-016-2265-7.

3 Bohra, V., Dafale, N.A., and Purohit, H.J. (2019). Understanding the alteration in rumen microbiome and CAZymes profile with diet and host through comparative metagenomic approach. *Arch. Microbiol.* 201: 1385–1397. https://doi.org/10.1007/s00203-019-01706-z.

4 Purohit, H.J., Kapley, A., Khardenavis, A. et al. (2016). Insights in waste management bioprocesses using genomic tools. *Adv. Appl. Microbiol.* 97: 121–170. https://doi.org/10.1016/BS.AAMBS.2016.09.002.

5 Bohra, V., Tikariha, H., and Dafale, N.A. (2019). Genomically defined *Paenibacillus polymyxa* ND24 for efficient cellulase production utilizing sugarcane bagasse as a substrate. *Appl. Biochem. Biotechnol.* 187: 266–281. https://doi.org/10.1007/s12010-018-2820-5.

6 Grant, S., Grant, W.D., Cowan, D.A. et al. (2006). Identification of eukaryotic open reading frames in metagenomic cDNA libraries made from environmental samples. *Appl. Environ. Microbiol.* 72: 135–143. https://doi.org/10.1128/AEM.72.1.135-143.2006.

7 Srivastava, S., Dafale, N.A., and Purohit, H.J. (2020). Functional genomics assessment of lytic polysaccharide mono-oxygenase with glycoside hydrolases in *Paenibacillus dendritiformis* CRN18. *Int. J. Biol. Macromol.* 164: 3729–3738. https://doi.org/10.1016/j.ijbiomac.2020.08.147.

8 Srivastava, S., Jhariya, U., Purohit, H.J., and Dafale, N.A. (2021). Synergistic action of lytic polysaccharide monooxygenase with glycoside hydrolase for lignocellulosic waste valorization: a review. *Biomass Convers. Biorefin.* https://doi.org/10.1007/S13399-021-01736-Y.

9 Srivastava, S., Dafale, N.A., Tulsani, N. et al. (2021). Evaluation of designed consortium SNH-1 for efficient hydrolysis of agriculture waste to benefit bioethanol production. *J. Cleaner Prod.* 288: 125601. https://doi.org/10.1016/j.jclepro.2020.125601.

10 Srivastava, S., Dafale, N.A., Jakhesara, S.J. et al. (2020). Unraveling the camel rumen microbiome through metaculturomics approach for agriculture waste hydrolytic potential. *Arch. Microbiol.* 1: 3. https://doi.org/10.1007/s00203-020-02010-x.

11 Singh, R.S., Singh, T., and Pandey, A. (2019). Microbial enzymes—an overview, biomass, biofuels. *Biochem. Adv. Enzym. Technol.* 1–40. https://doi.org/10.1016/B978-0-444-64114-4.00001-7.

12 Kumar, K.R., Cowley, M.J., and Davis, R.L. (2019). Next-generation sequencing and emerging technologies. *Semin. Thromb. Hemost.* 45: 661–673. https://doi.org/10.1055/S-0039-1688446.

13 Meek, M.H. and Larson, W.A. (2019). The future is now: amplicon sequencing and sequence capture usher in the conservation genomics era. *Mol. Ecol. Resour.* 19: 795–803. https://doi.org/10.1111/1755-0998.12998.

14 Mat-Sharani, S. and Firdaus-Raih, M. (2019). Computational discovery and annotation of conserved small open reading frames in fungal genomes. *BMC Bioinf.* 19: 171–185. https://doi.org/10.1186/S12859-018-2550-2.

15 Gabler, F., Nam, S.Z., Till, S. et al. (2020). Protein sequence analysis using the MPI bioinformatics toolkit. *Curr. Protocol. Bioinf.* 72: e108. https://doi.org/10.1002/CPBI.108.

16 Michalska, K. and Joachimiak, A. (2021). Structural genomics and the protein data bank. *J. Biolumin. Chemilumin.* 296: 100747. https://doi.org/10.1016/J.JBC.2021.100747.

17 Wang, Z.J., Zhou, H., Zhong, G. et al. (2020). Genome mining and biosynthesis of primary amine-acylated desferrioxamines in a marine gliding bacterium. *Org. Lett.* 22: 939–943. https://doi.org/10.1021/ACS.ORGLETT.9B04490.

18 Luis, A.S. and Martens, E.C. (2018). Interrogating gut bacterial genomes for discovery of novel carbohydrate degrading enzymes. *Curr. Opin. Chem. Biol.* 47: 126–133. https://doi.org/10.1016/J.CBPA.2018.09.012.

19 Bombaywala, S., Dafale, N.A., Jha, V. et al. (2021). Study of indiscriminate distribution of restrained antimicrobial resistome of different environmental niches. *Environ. Sci. Pollut. Res.* 28: 10780–10790. https://doi.org/10.1007/s11356-020-11318-6.

20 Chaudhary, D.K., Khulan, A., and Kim, J. (2019). Development of a novel cultivation technique for uncultured soil bacteria. *Sci. Rep.* 9: 1–11. https://doi.org/10.1038/s41598-019-43182-x.

21 Leis, B., Angelov, A., and Liebl, W. (2013). Screening and expression of genes from metagenomes. *Adv. Appl. Microbiol.* 83: 1–68. https://doi.org/10.1016/B978-0-12-407678-5.00001-5.

22 Robinson, S.L., Piel, J., and Sunagawa, S. (2021). A roadmap for metagenomic enzyme discovery. *Nat. Prod. Rep.* 38: 1994–2023. https://doi.org/10.1039/D1NP00006C.

23 Berini, F., Casciello, C., Marcone, G.L., and Marinelli, F. (2017). Metagenomics: novel enzymes from non-culturable microbes. *FEMS Microbiol. Lett.* 364: 211. https://doi.org/10.1093/FEMSLE/FNX211.

24 Liu, Q., Xun, G., and Feng, Y. (2019). The state-of-the-art strategies of protein engineering for enzyme stabilization. *Biotechnol. Adv.* 37: 530–537. https://doi.org/10.1016/J.BIOTECHADV.2018.10.011.

25 Hemmerling, F. and Piel, J. (2022). Strategies to access biosynthetic novelty in bacterial genomes for drug discovery. *Nat. Rev. Drug Discovery* 2022: 1–20. https://doi.org/10.1038/s41573-022-00414-6.

26 Medema, M.H., de Rond, T., and Moore, B.S. (2021). Mining genomes to illuminate the specialized chemistry of life. *Nat. Rev. Genet.* 22: 553–571. https://doi.org/10.1038/s41576-021-00363-7.

27 Hover, B.M., Kim, S.H., Katz, M. et al. (2018). Culture-independent discovery of the malacidins as calcium-dependent antibiotics with activity against multidrug-resistant Gram-positive pathogens. *Nat. Microbiol.* 3: 415–422. https://doi.org/10.1038/s41564-018-0110-1.

28 Tracanna, V., Ossowicki, A., Petrus, M.L.C. et al. (2021). Dissecting disease-suppressive rhizosphere microbiomes by functional amplicon sequencing and 10× metagenomics. *MSystems* 6: https://doi.org/10.1128/MSYSTEMS.01116-20.

29 Santana-Pereira, A.L.R., Sandoval-Powers, M., Monsma, S. et al. (2020). Discovery of novel biosynthetic gene cluster diversity from a soil metagenomic library. *Front. Microbiol.* 11: 3138. https://doi.org/10.3389/FMICB.2020.585398.

30 Blin, K., Shaw, S., Steinke, K. et al. (2019). antiSMASH 5.0: updates to the secondary metabolite genome mining pipeline. *Nucleic Acids Res.* 47: W81–W87. https://doi.org/10.1093/NAR/GKZ310.

31 Skinnider, M.A., Merwin, N.J., Johnston, C.W., and Magarvey, N.A. (2017). PRISM 3: expanded prediction of natural product chemical structures from microbial genomes. *Nucleic Acids Res.* 45: W49–W54. https://doi.org/10.1093/NAR/GKX320.

32 Navarro-Muñoz, J.C., Selem-Mojica, N., Mullowney, M.W. et al. (2019). A computational framework to explore large-scale biosynthetic diversity. *Nat. Chem. Biol.* 16: 60–68. https://doi.org/10.1038/s41589-019-0400-9.

33 Koutsandreas, T., Ladoukakis, E., Pilalis, E. et al. (2019). ANASTASIA: an automated metagenomic analysis pipeline for novel enzyme discovery exploiting next generation sequencing data. *Front. Genet.* 10: https://doi.org/10.3389/FGENE.2019.00469.

34 Cimermancic, P., Medema, M.H., Claesen, J. et al. (2014). Insights into secondary metabolism from a global analysis of prokaryotic biosynthetic gene clusters. *Cell* 158: 412–421. https://doi.org/10.1016/J.CELL.2014.06.034.

35 Hannigan, G.D., Prihoda, D., Palicka, A. et al. (2019). A deep learning genome-mining strategy for biosynthetic gene cluster prediction. *Nucleic Acids Res.* 47: e110–e110. https://doi.org/10.1093/NAR/GKZ654.

36 van Heel, A.J., de Jong, A., Montalbán-López, M. et al. (2013). BAGEL3: automated identification of genes encoding bacteriocins and (non-)bactericidal posttranslationally modified peptides. *Nucleic Acids Res.* 41: https://doi.org/10.1093/NAR/GKT391.

37 Khaldi, N., Seifuddin, F.T., Turner, G. et al. (2010). SMURF: genomic mapping of fungal secondary metabolite clusters. *Fungal Genet. Biol.* 47: 736–741. https://doi.org/10.1016/J.FGB.2010.06.003.

38 Weber, T., Rausch, C., Lopez, P. et al. (2009). CLUSEAN: a computer-based framework for the automated analysis of bacterial secondary metabolite biosynthetic gene clusters. *J. Biotechnol.* 140: 13–17. https://doi.org/10.1016/J.JBIOTEC.2009.01.007.

39 Charlop-Powers, Z., Owen, J.G., Reddy, B.V.B. et al. (2014). Chemical-biogeographic survey of secondary metabolism in soil. *PNAS* 111: 3757–3762. https://doi.org/10.1073/PNAS.1318021111.

40 Kautsar, S.A., Blin, K., Shaw, S. et al. (2020). MIBiG 2.0: a repository for biosynthetic gene clusters of known function. *Nucleic Acids Res.* 48: D454–D458. https://doi.org/10.1093/NAR/GKZ882.

41 Hadjithomas, M., Chen, I.M.A., Chu, K. et al. (2017). IMG-ABC: new features for bacterial secondary metabolism analysis and targeted biosynthetic gene cluster discovery in thousands of microbial genomes. *Nucleic Acids Res.* 45: D560–D565. https://doi.org/10.1093/NAR/GKW1103.

42 Laursen, M.F., Dalgaard, M.D., and Bahl, M.I. (2017). Genomic GC-content affects the accuracy of 16S rRNA gene sequencing based microbial profiling due to PCR bias. *Front. Microbiol.* 8: 1934. https://doi.org/10.3389/FMICB.2017.01934.

43 Libis, V., Antonovsky, N., Zhang, M. et al. (2019). Uncovering the biosynthetic potential of rare metagenomic DNA using co-occurrence network analysis of targeted sequences. *Nat. Commun.* 10: 1–9. https://doi.org/10.1038/s41467-019-11658-z.

44 Pal, R.R., More, R.P., and Purohit, H.J. (2018). Bioinformatics tools for shotgun metagenomic data analysis. *Soft Comput. Biol. Syst.* 91–110. https://doi.org/10.1007/978-981-10-7455-4_6.

45 Almeida, O.G.G. and De Martinis, E.C.P. (2019). Bioinformatics tools to assess metagenomic data for applied microbiology. *Appl. Microbiol. Biotechnol.* 103: 69–82. https://doi.org/10.1007/S00253-018-9464-9.

46 Wang, Z., Wang, Y., Fuhrman, J.A. et al. (2020). Assessment of metagenomic assemblers based on hybrid reads of real and simulated metagenomic sequences. *Briefings Bioinf.* 21: 777–790. https://doi.org/10.1093/BIB/BBZ025.

47 Ayling, M., Clark, M.D., and Leggett, R.M. (2020). New approaches for metagenome assembly with short reads. *Briefings Bioinf.* 21: 584–594. https://doi.org/10.1093/BIB/BBZ020.

48 Kvist, T., Sondt-Marcussen, L., and Mikkelsen, M.J. (2014). Partition enrichment of nucleotide sequences (PINS) – a generally applicable, sequence based method for enrichment of complex DNA samples. *PLoS One* 9: e106817. https://doi.org/10.1371/JOURNAL.PONE.0106817.

49 Jain, M., Olsen, H.E., Paten, B., and Akeson, M. (2016). The Oxford Nanopore MinION: delivery of nanopore sequencing to the genomics community. *Genome Biol.* 17: 1–11. https://doi.org/10.1186/S13059-016-1103-0.

50 Hon, T., Mars, K., Young, G. et al. (2020). Highly accurate long-read HiFi sequencing data for five complex genomes. *Sci. Data* 7: 1–11. https://doi.org/10.1038/s41597-020-00743-4.

51 Risse, J., Thomson, M., Patrick, S. et al. (2015). A single chromosome assembly of Bacteroides fragilis strain BE1 from Illumina and MinION nanopore sequencing data. *GigaScience* 4: https://doi.org/10.1186/S13742-015-0101-6.

52 Bhende, R.S., Jhariya, U., Srivastava, S. et al. (2022). Environmental distribution, metabolic fate, and degradation mechanism of chlorpyrifos: recent and future perspectives. *Appl. Biochem. Biotechnol.* 194: 2301–2335. https://doi.org/10.1007/S12010-021-03713-7.

53 Jha, V., Dafale, N.A., and Purohit, H.J. (2022). Differential expression and cross-correlation between global regulator and pho regulon genes involved in decision-making under phosphate stress. *J. Appl. Genet.* https://doi.org/10.1007/S13353-022-00735-7.

54 Das, S., Bombaywala, S., Srivastava, S. et al. (2022). Genome plasticity as a paradigm of antibiotic resistance spread in ESKAPE pathogens. *Environ. Sci. Pollut. Res.* 29: 40507–40519. https://doi.org/10.1007/S11356-022-19840-5.

55 Jha, V., Bombaywala, S., Purohit, H., and Dafale, N.A. (2022). Differential colonization and functioning of microbial community in response to phosphate levels. *J. Environ. Manage.* 321: 115856. https://doi.org/10.1016/J.JENVMAN.2022.115856.

56 Lang, D., Zhang, S., Ren, P. et al. (2020). Comparison of the two up-to-date sequencing technologies for genome assembly: HiFi reads of Pacific Biosciences Sequel II system and ultralong reads of Oxford Nanopore. *GigaScience* 9: 1–7. https://doi.org/10.1093/GIGASCIENCE/GIAA123.

57 Guidi, L., Chaffron, S., Bittner, L. et al. (2016). Plankton networks driving carbon export in the oligotrophic ocean. *Nature* 532: 465–470. https://doi.org/10.1038/nature16942.

58 Zamkovaya, T., Foster, J.S., de Crécy-Lagard, V., and Conesa, A. (2020). A network approach to elucidate and prioritize microbial dark matter in microbial communities. *ISME J.* 15: 228–244. https://doi.org/10.1038/s41396-020-00777-x.

59 Neubauer, P.R., Widmann, C., Wibberg, D. et al. (2018). A flavin-dependent halogenase from metagenomic analysis prefers bromination over chlorination. *PLoS One* 13: e0196797. https://doi.org/10.1371/JOURNAL.PONE.0196797.

60 Nayfach, S. and Pollard, K.S. (2016). Toward accurate and quantitative comparative metagenomics. *Cell* 166: 1103–1116. https://doi.org/10.1016/J.CELL.2016.08.007.

61 Peretó, J., Bada, J.L., and Lazcano, A. (2009). Charles darwin and the origin of life. *Origins Life Evol. Biosphere* 39: 395–406. https://doi.org/10.1007/S11084-009-9172-7.

62 Robinson, S.L., Terlouw, B.R., Smith, M.D. et al. (2020). Global analysis of adenylate-forming enzymes reveals β-lactone biosynthesis pathway in pathogenic *Nocardia*. *J. Biolumin. Chemilumin.* 295: 14826–14839. https://doi.org/10.1074/JBC.RA120.013528.

63 Boeckmann, B., Bairoch, A., Apweiler, R. et al. (2003). The SWISS-PROT protein knowledgebase and its supplement TrEMBL in 2003. *Nucleic Acids Res.* 31: 365–370. https://doi.org/10.1093/NAR/GKG095.

64 Bui, H.Q., La, C.N.H., and Do, M.N. (2015). A fast tree-based algorithm for compressed sensing with sparse-tree prior. *Signal Process.* 108: 628–641. https://doi.org/10.1016/J.SIGPRO.2014.10.026.

65 Hendrikse, N.M., Charpentier, G., Nordling, E., and Syrén, P.O. (2018). Ancestral diterpene cyclases show increased thermostability and substrate acceptance. *FEBS J.* 285: 4660–4673. https://doi.org/10.1111/FEBS.14686.

66 Ashkenazy, H., Penn, O., Doron-Faigenboim, A. et al. (2012). FastML: a web server for probabilistic reconstruction of ancestral sequences. *Nucleic Acids Res.* 40: W580–W584. https://doi.org/10.1093/NAR/GKS498.

67 N. Lartillot. The Bayesian Approach to Molecular Phylogeny – Archive ouverte HAL, https://hal.archives-ouvertes.fr/hal-02535330/ (accessed 30 March 2022).

68 Montalbán-López, M., Scott, T.A., Ramesh, S. et al. (2021). New developments in RiPP discovery, enzymology and engineering. *Nat. Prod. Rep.* 38: 130–239. https://doi.org/10.1039/D0NP00027B.

69 Zhang, Y., Tao, L., Woods, T.J. et al. (2022). Organometallic $Fe_2(\mu\text{-}SH)_2(CO)_4(CN)_2$ cluster allows the biosynthesis of the [FeFe]-hydrogenase with only the HydF maturase. *JACS* 144: 1534–1538. https://doi.org/10.1021/JACS.1C12506.

70 Atkinson, H.J., Morris, J.H., Ferrin, T.E., and Babbitt, P.C. (2009). Using sequence similarity networks for visualization of relationships across diverse protein superfamilies. *PLoS One* 4: e4345. https://doi.org/10.1371/JOURNAL.PONE.0004345.

71 Colin, P.Y., Kintses, B., Gielen, F. et al. (2015). Ultrahigh-throughput discovery of promiscuous enzymes by picodroplet functional metagenomics. *Nat. Commun.* 6: 1–12. https://doi.org/10.1038/ncomms10008.

72 Akiva, E., Copp, J.N., Tokuriki, N., and Babbitt, P.C. (2017). Evolutionary and molecular foundations of multiple contemporary functions of the nitroreductase superfamily. *PNAS* 114: E9549–E9558. https://doi.org/10.1073/PNAS.1706849114.

73 Shannon, P., Markiel, A., Ozier, O. et al. (2003). Cytoscape: a software environment for integrated models of biomolecular interaction networks. *Genome Res.* 13.

74 Gustavsen, J.A., Pai, S., Isserlin, R. et al. (2019). RCy3: network biology using Cytoscape from within R. *F1000Research* 8: 1774. https://doi.org/10.12688/F1000RESEARCH.20887.3.

75 Harrer, M., Cuijpers, P., Furukawa, T.A., and Ebert, D.D. (2021). Doing Meta-Analysis with R: A Hands-On Guide, Doing Meta-Analysis with R. https://doi.org/10.1201/9781003107347.

76 Joachimiak, A. (2009). High-throughput crystallography for structural genomics. *Curr. Opin. Struct. Biol.* 19: 573–584. https://doi.org/10.1016/J.SBI.2009.08.002.

77 Jaroszewski, L., Li, Z., Krishna, S.S. et al. (2009). Exploration of uncharted regions of the protein universe. *PLoS Biol.* 7: e1000205. https://doi.org/10.1371/JOURNAL.PBIO.1000205.

78 Cramer, P. (2021). AlphaFold2 and the future of structural biology. *Nat. Struct. Mol. Biol.* 28: 704–705. https://doi.org/10.1038/s41594-021-00650-1.

79 Deng, L., Zhong, G., Liu, C. et al. (2019). MADOKA: an ultra-fast approach for large-scale protein structure similarity searching. *BMC Bioinf.* 20: 1–10. https://doi.org/10.1186/S12859-019-3235-1.

80 Akdel, M., Durairaj, J., de Ridder, D., and van Dijk, A.D.J. (2020). Caretta – a multiple protein structure alignment and feature extraction suite. *Comput. Struct. Biotechnol. J.* 18: 981–992. https://doi.org/10.1016/J.CSBJ.2020.03.011.

81 Carpentier, M., Chomilier, J., and Valencia, A. (2019). Protein multiple alignments: sequence-based versus structure-based programs. *Bioinformatics* 35: 3970–3980. https://doi.org/10.1093/BIOINFORMATICS/BTZ236.

82 Waterhouse, A., Bertoni, M., Bienert, S. et al. (2018). SWISS-MODEL: homology modelling of protein structures and complexes. *Nucleic Acids Res.* 46: W296–W303. https://doi.org/10.1093/nar/gky427.

83 Yang, J., Yan, R., Roy, A. et al. (2014). The I-TASSER Suite: protein structure and function prediction. *Nat. Methods* 12: 7–8. https://doi.org/10.1038/nmeth.3213.

84 Kelley, L.A., Mezulis, S., Yates, C.M. et al. (2015). The Phyre2 web portal for protein modeling, prediction and analysis. *Nat. Protoc.* 10: 845–858. https://doi.org/10.1038/nprot.2015.053.

85 Berman, H.M., Westbrook, J., Feng, Z. et al. (2000). The protein data bank. *Nucleic Acids Res.* 28: 235–242. https://doi.org/10.1093/NAR/28.1.235.

86 Labarre, A., López-Escardó, D., Latorre, F. et al. (2021). Comparative genomics reveals new functional insights in uncultured MAST species. *ISME J.* 15: 1767–1781. https://doi.org/10.1038/s41396-020-00885-8.

87 Ribeiro, A.J.M., Tyzack, J.D., Borkakoti, N. et al. (2020). A global analysis of function and conservation of catalytic residues in enzymes. *J. Biolumin. Chemilumin.* 295: 314–324. https://doi.org/10.1074/JBC.REV119.006289.

88 Shadish, J.A. and DeForest, C.A. (2020). Site-selective protein modification: from functionalized proteins to functional biomaterials. *Matter* 2: 50–77. https://doi.org/10.1016/J.MATT.2019.11.011.

89 Tian, W., Chen, C., Lei, X. et al. (2018). CASTp 3.0: computed atlas of surface topography of proteins. *Nucleic Acids Res.* 46: W363–W367. https://doi.org/10.1093/NAR/GKY473.

90 Ribeiro, A.J.M., Holliday, G.L., Furnham, N. et al. (2018). Mechanism and Catalytic Site Atlas (M-CSA): a database of enzyme reaction mechanisms and active sites. *Nucleic Acids Res.* 46: D618–D623. https://doi.org/10.1093/NAR/GKX1012.

91 de Castro, E., Sigrist, C.J.A., Gattiker, A. et al. (2006). ScanProsite: detection of PROSITE signature matches and ProRule-associated functional and structural residues in proteins. *Nucleic Acids Res.* 34: W362–W365. https://doi.org/10.1093/NAR/GKL124.

92 Di Donato, P., Buono, A., Poli, A. et al. (2019, 2018). Exploring marine environments for the identification of extremophiles and their enzymes for sustainable and green bioprocesses. *Sustain* 11: 149. https://doi.org/10.3390/SU11010149.

93 Yang, X., Wu, Y., Zhang, Y. et al. (2020). A thermo-active laccase isoenzyme from *Trametes trogii* and its potential for dye decolorization at high temperature. *Front. Microbiol.* 11: 241. https://doi.org/10.3389/FMICB.2020.00241.

94 Foroozandeh Shahraki, M., Ariaeenejad, S., Fallah Atanaki, F. et al. (2020). MCIC: automated identification of cellulases from metagenomic data and characterization based on temperature and pH dependence. *Front. Microbiol.* 11: 2646. https://doi.org/10.3389/FMICB.2020.567863.

95 James, P., Isupov, M.N., De Rose, S.A. et al. (2020). A 'Split-Gene' transketolase from the hyper-thermophilic bacterium *Carboxydothermus hydrogenoformans*: structure and biochemical characterization. *Front. Microbiol.* 11: 2752. https://doi.org/10.3389/FMICB.2020.592353.

96 Eom, S.H., Wang, J., and Steitz, T.A. (1996). Structure of Taq polymerase with DNA at the polymerase active site. *Nature* 382: 278–281. https://doi.org/10.1038/382278a0.

97 Parvizpour, S., Hussin, N., Shamsir, M.S., and Razmara, J. (2021). Psychrophilic enzymes: structural adaptation, pharmaceutical and industrial applications. *Appl. Microbiol. Biotechnol.* 105: 899–907. https://doi.org/10.1007/S00253-020-11074-0.

98 Daoud, L. and Ben Ali, M. (2020). Chapter 5 - Halophilic microorganisms: Interesting group of extremophiles with important applications in biotechnology and environment. In: *Physiological and Biotechnological Aspects of Extremophiles* (ed. R. Salwan and V. Sharma), 51–64. Academic Press https://doi.org/10.1016/B978-0-12-818322-9.00005-8, ISBN 9780128183229.

99 Ghosh, S., Kumar, S., and Khare, S.K. (2019). Microbial diversity of saline habitats: an overview of biotechnological applications. In: *Microorganisms in Saline Environments: Strategies and Functions. Soil Biology*, vol. 56 (ed. B. Giri and A. Varma), 65–92. Cham: Springer https://doi.org/10.1007/978-3-030-18975-4_4.

100 Desai, C., Patel, P., Markande, A.R. et al. (2020). Exploration of haloarchaea for their potential applications in food industry. *Int. J. Environ. Sci. Technol.* 17: 4455–4464. https://doi.org/10.1007/S13762-020-02773-2.

101 Karan, R., Mathew, S., Muhammad, R. et al. (2020). Understanding high-salt and cold adaptation of a polyextremophilic enzyme. *Microorganisms* 8: 1594. https://doi.org/10.3390/MICROORGANISMS8101594.

102 Yang, H., Huang, X., Fang, S. et al. (2016). Uncovering the composition of microbial community structure and metagenomics among three gut locations in pigs with distinct fatness. *Sci. Rep.* 6: 1–11. https://doi.org/10.1038/srep27427.

19

Microbial Gallic Acid Decarboxylase: An Overview and Advancement in Application Potential Study Through Bioinformatics

Ishita Biswas[1,3], Debanjan Mitra[1], and Pradeep K. Das Mohapatra[1,2]

[1] *Department of Microbiology, Raiganj University, Raiganj-733134, Uttar Dinajpur, West Bengal, India*
[2] *Professor A. K. Bothra Environment Conservation Centre, Raiganj University, Raiganj-733134, Uttar Dinajpur, West Bengal, India*
[3] *Department of Botany, S.B.S. Government College, Hili-733126, Dakshin Dinajpur, West Bengal, India*

19.1 Introduction

Gallic acid decarboxylase (GAD) (EC 4.1.1.59) included in the enzyme class lyases and, more importantly, carboxylases. The enzyme is also named 3,4,5-trihydroxybenzoate carboxy-lyase, gallate decarboxylase, and gallate carboxy-lyase [1]. They are highly sensitive to oxygen and require iron as a cofactor. GAD catalyzes the second step in the tannic acid degradation pathway, i.e., it nonoxidatively decarboxylates gallic acid to form pyrogallol and carbon dioxide [2, 3] (Figure 19.1). Enzyme tannase catalyzes the first step of the breakdown of tannin into gallic acid and glucose [4–6]. Tannins are plant secondary metabolites that perform an important function in plant defense mechanisms. They can precipitate proteins and other macromolecules. Gallic acids are used for the production of pyrogallol and the global antibiotic trimethoprim. They are well known in the pharmaceutical disciplines for their potential antioxidant and anticancer properties [3, 7]. Pyrogallol is used in a wide range of industries, including photography, garment manufacturing, leather staining, metallurgy, dying, and painting. It is also used as a mercury, silver, and gold salt reductant. Pyrogallol and several of its analogs are potent target therapeutics that inhibit quorum sensing in *Vibrio harveyi* via Al-2 (Autoinducer-2) [8]. Although the enzyme has industrial impotence, there are only a few reports that exist in the literature regarding GAD. This is the first work regarding the structure and functional properties of GAD through bioinformatics analysis.

19.2 Isolation and Selection of Gallic Acid Decarboxylase Producing Microbes

The enzyme GAD is exclusively present in a number of bacteria and yeast. Zeida et al. isolated *Pantoea agglomerans* T71 as a potential producer of GAD from the soil

Microbial Enzymes: Production, Purification, and Industrial Applications, First Edition.
Edited by Dinesh Yadav, Pankaj Chowdhary, Gautam Anand, and Rajarshi Kumar Gaur.

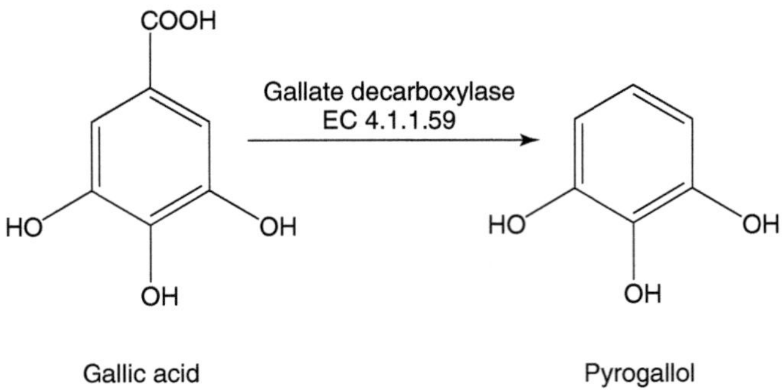

Figure 19.1 Decarboxylation of gallic acid by gallic acid decarboxylase into carbon dioxide and pyrogallol.

of an orchard near Okayama, Japan, using a selective gallic acid agar medium [2]. Soni et al. cultured *Enterobacter* spp. using 0.2% gallic acid as a sole source of carbon [8]. Yoshida et al. isolated and identified a pyrogallol-producing bacterium *Citrobacter* sp. 64-1 from soil [9]. Yoshida and Yamada used a basal medium incorporating 0.2% gallic acid for the synthesis of pyrogallol by *Citrobacter* sp. [10]. The list of microorganisms producing GAD has been presented in Table 19.1.

Table 19.1 Microbial sources of gallic acid decarboxylase (GAD).

Microorganisms	References
Pantoea agglomerans	Jiménez et al. [11]
Enterococcus faecalis	Jiménez et al. [11]
Klebsiella pneumoniae	Jiménez et al. [11]
Streptococcus gallolyticus	Jiménez et al. [11]
Lactobacillus plantarum	Jiménez et al. [11]
Arxula adeninivorans	Zeug et al. [3]
Enterobacter spp.	Soni et al. [8]
Klebsiella aerogenes	Meier [1]
Citrobacter sp.	Meier [1]
Eubacterium oxidoreducens	Meier [1]
Pleobacter acidigallici	Meier [1]
Azotobacter sp.	Meier [1]
Clostridium hydroxybenzoicum	Meier [1]
Streptococcus bovis	Osawa and Walsh [12]
Klebsiella oxytoca	Osawa and Walsh [12]
Intestinibacter bartlettii DSM 16795, *Anaerostipes hadrus* DSM 3319, *Hungatella hathewayi* DSM 13479, *Proteobacteria* (*Kosakonia radicincitans* DSM 16656 *Shimwellia blattae* DSM 4481)	Esteban-Torres et al. [13]

19.3 Purification of GAD Enzyme and Biomolecular Properties

Enzyme purification is an important step in predicting the enzyme's structural and functional aspects. Due to oxygen sensitivity, the stability of the enzyme GAD is quite low. By fractionating $(NH_4)_2SO_4$ with an overall yield of 100%, Nakajima et al. partly purified GAD from *Streptococcus faecalis* and *Klebsiella pneumoniae* isolated from rat feces roughly 16-fold over the crude extract [14]. Zeida et al. purified GAD from *P. agglomerans* T71 through ammonium sulfate DEAE-Sephacel column and FPLC Superdex 16-60 Hi-load gel filtration column [2]. Soni et al. purified *Enterobacter* spp. GAD from the DEAE-cellulose column with a yield of 14.48% and purification fold of 15.32 [8]. Biochemical properties of some bacterial GAD have been presented in Table 19.2.

19.4 Gallic Acid Decarboxylase Assay

The quantity of pyrogallol generated from gallic acid was used to estimate GAD. In a total volume of 4 ml, the reaction mixture contained 10 μmol gallic acid, 400 μmol potassium phosphate buffer, pH 6.0, and the enzyme. The reaction was carried out at 30 °C for 20 minutes with constant shaking before being stopped with 1 ml of 30% trichloroacetic acid. With the deproteinized filtrate, the amount of pyrogallol produced was determined. Under the assay conditions, one unit of the enzyme was defined as the amount of enzyme that catalyzed the synthesis of 1 mol of pyrogallol per minute. Specific activity was measured in units per milligram of protein [9].

The vanillin test is another technique. The reaction mixture, which included 2.0 ml of 50 mM acetate buffer of pH 5.0 and purified enzyme, was incubated at 30 °C for 10 minutes before being terminated with 2.0 ml of 1% vanillin in 70% (v/v) sulfuric acid. The absorbance at 500 nm was measured after incubation, and the amount of pyrogallol produced was calculated. The amount of enzyme that catalyzed the synthesis of 1 μmol of pyrogallol per minute was defined as enzyme activity [8].

19.5 Molecular Biological Aspects of Gallic Acid Decarboxylase with Special Reference to Human Gut Lactic Acid Bacteria

Jiménez et al. first reported on the molecular identification and characterization of the gallate decarboxylase enzyme of *Lactobacillus plantarum* WCFS1 [11]. The protein isolated was of 54 kDa. The protein was identified to be Lp_2945 and annotated as UbiD. The nonoxidative aromatic acid decarboxylases were found to be encoded by three genes, namely lpdB, lpdC, and lpdC. A study with recombinant *Escherichia*

Table 19.2 Biochemical properties of some microbial gallic acid decarboxylase.

Organism	pH_{opt}	$Temp_{opt}$ (°C)	Molecular weight (kDa)	Inhibitor	Activator	K_m	V_{max}	Enzyme activity	References
Pantoea agglomerans T71	6.0	50	320	K_2CrO_4, $(NH_4)_2S_2O$, H_2O_2, thiol-specific *p*-chloromercuribenzoate, Ag_2SO_4, $HgCl_2$, $CuCl_2$;	Iron	0.96 mM	150 U/mg	82%	Zeida et al. [2]
Enterobacter spp.	7.0	35	57	Detergents	Mg^{2+}	0.934 mM	0.167 U/ml		Soni et al. [8]
Citrobacter sp.	6.0	28				3.3 mM		265 units/1000 ml	Yoshida and Yamada [10]

coli cells demonstrated that only the LpdC protein yield gallate decarboxylase activity, while the remaining two are essential for gallate decarboxylase activity. Several other reports are also indicating the molecular mass of gallate decarboxylase through Sodium Dodecyl Sulphate-Polyacrylamide Gel Electrophoresis (SDS-PAGE) analysis. Purified gallate decarboxylase of *P. agglomerans* was found to have consisted of six similar subunits of 57 kDa as identified through SDS-PAGE [2]. Apart from *L. plantarum* several other lactic acid bacteria belonging to Firmicutes, Proteobacteria, and Actinobacteria have been reported as potent gallate decarboxylase producers [13]. Using high-throughput sequencing (HTS) technologies, these bacterial groups were identified by amplifying the catalytic C subunit of gallate decarboxylase (LpdC) encoding region of metagenomic DNA extracted from human fecal samples. The major bacterial genera included are *Anaerostipes*, *Klebsiella*, *Lachnospiraceae*, *Dorea*, *Clostridium*, *Blautia*, *Actinomyces*, and *Lactobacillus*. Studies on the genetic organization of gallate decarboxylases of *L. plantarum* indicate that genes are not grouped; rather, the lpdC gene, which codes for the C subunit, is adjacent to the gene that codes for tannase (tanLp1); however, the B (lpdB) and D (lpdD) component genes are separated by more than 1 MB. Alignment of LpdC protein sequences from the human gut bacteria indicates the presence of conserved amino acid domains, namely MAGIPTEA and VDEDVDIF, within the C subunit of the enzyme [13].

19.6 *In Silico* Aspects of Gallic Acid Decarboxylase

19.6.1 Insight the Sequence of Gallic Acid Decarboxylase

Understanding the amino acid sequence of proteins is essential for detecting mistakes throughout the biological data processing processes and distinguishing some unclear outcomes related to protein production. Currently, the UniProt database has 11 sequences of GAD.

Lactiplantibacillus plantarum (A0A7U1L1S8) showed the highest pI value (Table 19.3). The high pI indicates an excess of basic amino acids, which might trap H^+ and Cl^- ions in the intracellular microenvironment, resulting in the production of HCl. Acidic and basic amino acid residues showed higher abundance in *Aureobasidium melanogenum* followed by *Arxula adeninivorans. Pantoea brenneri* possesses the longest GAD (515 amino acids in protein sequence) in the database. The lowest instability index of *A. adeninivorans*, i.e., 20.49 indicated that its GAD is more stable than other organisms. A protein with a high aliphatic index is quite thermostable across a wide temperature range. In this regard, GAD from *Serratia* sp. is more thermally stable than other organisms. GRAVY (grand average hydropathy) of all organisms indicated that GAD is hydrophilic in nature. It can easily interact with water ions.

Multiple sequence alignment of protein sequences of the above organisms showed a conserved region with a significant amino acid variation (Figure 19.2). These variations occur on the basis of the nature of organisms. Evolutions in amino acid composition help an organism in adapting to different environmental conditions.

Table 19.3 Sequence properties like isoelectric point (pI), length, instability index (Ins), aliphatic index (AI), GRAVY of gallic acid decarboxylase sequences.

Organism name	ID	pI	% of (−)ve charged	% of (+)ve charged	Length	Ins	AI	GRAVY
Lactobacillus plantarum	F9US27	5.04	14.29	10.20	490	33.5	79.2	−0.373
Pantoea brenneri	A0A653XK74	5.54	12.43	10.10	515	42.65	89.59	−0.158
Ruminococcaceae bacterium	A0A6S6XG23	5.46	13.36	10.32	494	41.93	82.13	−0.189
Serratia sp.	A0A7S4LX67	5.62	12.70	9.88	496	40.1	90.69	−0.052
Enterobacter cancerogenus	A0A7R8N4G6	5.59	12.17	9.13	493	44.68	90.67	−0.127
Lactobacillus sp.	A0A5D0DDD0	6.17	9.56	8.09	136	44.18	81.84	−0.269
Lactiplantibacillus plantarum	A0A7X1N086	6.5	8.82	8.09	136	39.19	81.86	−0.272
Lactiplantibacillus plantarum	A0A856ZB78	5.89	10.29	8.09	136	43.32	81.1	−0.327
Lactiplantibacillus plantarum	A0A7U1L1S8	6.17	9.56	8.09	136	41.9	81.1	−0.327
Aureobasidium melanogenum	A0A5C2H6J1	5.39	15.79	13.88	209	35.38	63.01	−0.622
Arxula adeninivorans	A0A060TAG5	5.49	14.29	12.12	231	20.49	63.77	−0.583

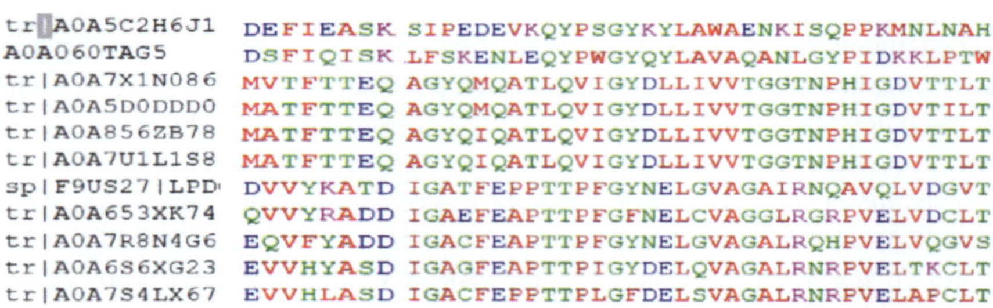

Figure 19.2 Amino acid conservations with variations in different sequences of gallic acid decarboxylase from different organisms.

19.6.2 Structure of Gallic Acid Decarboxylase

The crystal structure of GAD (PDB ID:7KD9) in a homotrimer revealed the binding sites for cobalt, potassium, and the substrate (Figure 19.3). Potassium is necessary for enzyme function and is found in the trimer's center, where from each monomer, with OD and the carbonyl oxygen of Glu88, it forms trigonal prismatic coordination. Through a twist in the beta-strand that connects them, it places the proximal and crucial His86, which is part of a catalytic dyad, at the substrate binding site. Cobalt assists enzyme activity even more. Its binding site, which is constituted by residues from two nearby monomers, is relocated away from the active site, implying an allosteric mechanism of activation. W35, R39, T60, H86, Y150, and

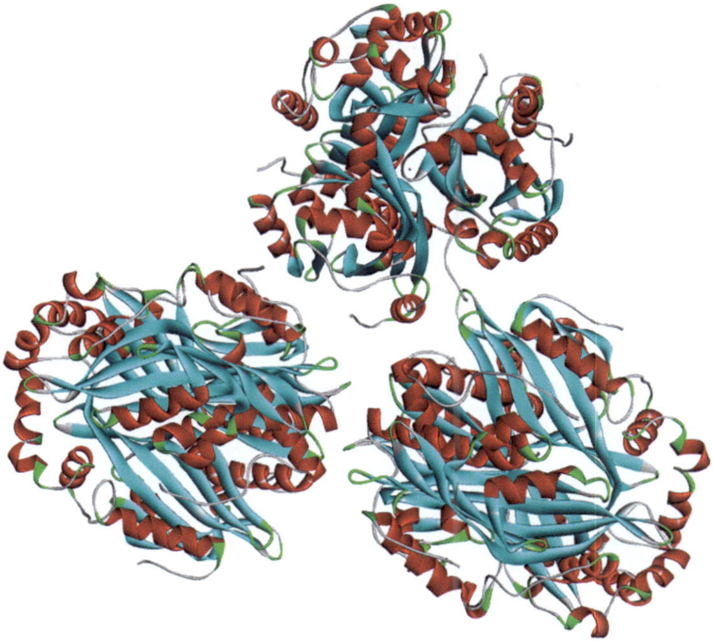

Figure 19.3 The crystal structure of gallic acid decarboxylase (homotrimer) (PDB ID:7KD9) from *Arxula adeninivorans*.

Q192 are all involved in a network of hydrogen bond interactions with the substrate analog 4-nitrocatechol. Mutations in any of these residues terminate enzyme activity. His86 being a part of a catalytic dyad with Asp 40, aids the process [3].

The hydrogen bonds that occur between the atoms of the polypeptide backbone are what give the secondary structure its form. In between the partially negative oxygen atom and the partially positively charged nitrogen atom, hydrogen bonds occur. Alpha helices, beta sheets, and turns are the three secondary structures that are most frequently seen in proteins. It has 1 sheet, 4 beta hairpins, 6 beta bulges, 6 strands, 7 helices, 8 helix–helix interactions, 18 beta turns, and 2 gamma turns as its secondary structure (Figure 19.4). Protein helices exhibit a predilection for having about an integral number of turns, increasing the stability of the protein. The main chain's CO and NH groups form a hydrogen bond that the alpha helix structure uses to stabilize itself. Each amino acid's CO group creates a hydrogen bond with its neighboring NH group, which is located four residues earlier in the sequence [15].

High-resolution crystal structure (1.50 Å) of GAD (6W54) from *A. adeninivorans* showed the effects of different intraprotein interactions after minimization in 1000 steps with a forcefield.

Aromatic–aromatic interactions have been involved in a variety of molecular processes, including protein folding, protein stability, catalysis, and drug creation [16, 17]. Because the local CH dipoles are in an antiparallel orientation, the electrostatic term in the benzene–benzene interaction stays extremely favorable at a considerable offset.

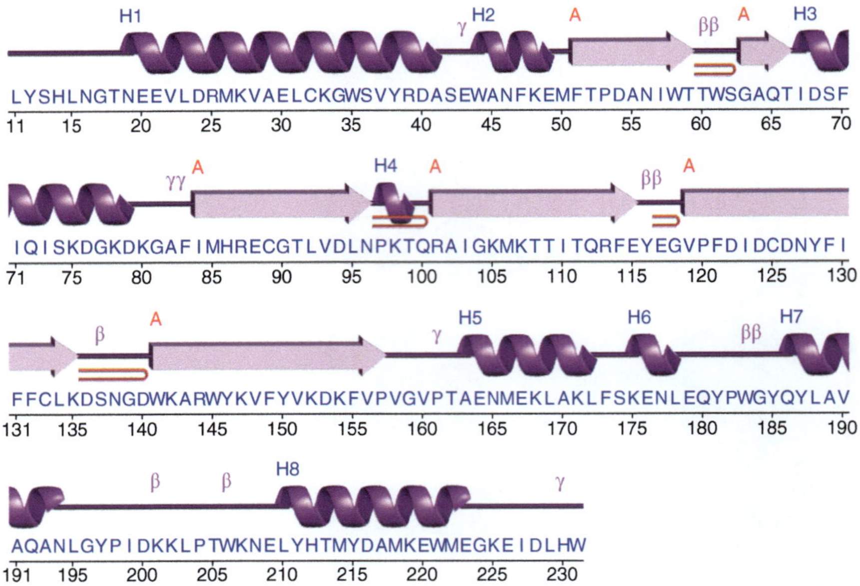

Figure 19.4 Secondary structure of gallic acid decarboxylase (PDB ID:7KD9) from *Arxula adeninivorans.*

GAD (6W54) from *A. adeninivorans* showed three networks and three isolated aromatic–aromatic interactions (Table 19.4). The 1st network of aromatic–aromatic interactions was formed by 14 interactions between multiple amino acids. Such a type of long network formation is not common in fungi. As *A. adeninivorans* is a thermotolerant fungus, this type of intraprotein interaction helps to increase its stability in extreme temperatures. The peculiar properties of *A. adeninivorans* make it particularly appealing for biotechnological uses.

Salt bridges in proteins are electrostatically attractive links between oppositely charged residues that are close enough to attract each other. They improve protein structure and the sensitivity of protein interactions with other biomolecules without increasing the free energy of unfolding. A salt bridge's net electrostatic free energy may be divided into three parts: charge–charge couplings, charge connections with permanent dipoles, and charge desolvation. Positively in terms of energy, unfavorable desolvation of interacting charges generally opposes Coulombic charge–charge interaction. Generally, it has two types: isolated and network.

GAD (6W54) from *A. adeninivorans* showed nine isolated and two network salt bridges (Table 19.5). LYS amino acids contribute majorly in forming of salt bridges than other charged residues. The improved thermostability of *A. adeninivorans* might be attributed to more salt bridges in its sequences, enhancing their contribution to protein stabilization [18, 19].

The structural characteristics that regulate the rate of exchange of ligands, ions, and aqueous solvents are protein tunnels linking functional submerged cavities with mass solvent and protein channels, which enable movement through biological membranes [20]. The structure of GAD (6W54) possesses five tunnels

Table 19.4 Isolated and network aromatic–aromatic interactions in gallic acid decarboxylase (6W54) from *Arxula adeninivorans*.

Position	Residue	Position	Residue	Types
58	TRP	145	TRP	Isolated
128	TYR	206	TRP	Isolated
150	TYR	185	TYR	Isolated
35	TRP	129	PHE	Network 1
35	TRP	131	PHE	
35	TRP	47	PHE	
35	TRP	51	PHE	
35	TRP	70	PHE	
44	TRP	47	PHE	
47	PHE	51	PHE	
47	PHE	70	PHE	
51	PHE	131	PHE	
61	TRP	197	TYR	
61	TRP	70	PHE	
129	PHE	131	PHE	
129	PHE	146	TYR	
131	PHE	146	TYR	
114	PHE	121	PHE	Network 2
121	PHE	155	PHE	
121	PHE	173	PHE	
155	PHE	173	PHE	
173	PHE	187	TYR	
149	PHE	211	TYR	Network 3
149	PHE	215	TYR	
206	TRP	211	TYR	
211	TYR	215	TYR	

with a maximum length of 8.9 Å. This tunnel is thought to improve catalytic performance by (i) promoting the direct passage of substrates and cofactors across consecutive active sites and (ii) minimizing excessive or undesired interim side reactions [21]. On the other hand, protein cavities are areas on the exterior of proteins where ligands (small molecules) can interact. These holes are thought to be ligand-binding sites for proteins. The placement of these cavities is crucial for better understanding the protein activities, which is required for structure-based drug discovery and development [22–24]. A total of eight cavities were identified with a high volume of 533 $Å^3$. These large cavities allow for quick transitions between

Table 19.5 Isolated and network salt bridges in gallic acid decarboxylase (6W54) from *Arxula adeninivorans*.

Position	Residue	Position	Residue	Types
33	LYS	88	GLU	Isolated
48	LYS	68	ASP	
54	ASP	144	ARG	
87	ARG	124	ASP	
94	ASP	105	LYS	
113	ARG	122	ASP	
124	ASP	154	LYS	
126	ASP	152	LYS	
164	GLU	168	LYS	
24	ASP	135	LYS	Network 1
24	ASP	27	LYS	
219	LYS	223	GLU	Network 2
220	GLU	225	LYS	
223	GLU	225	LYS	

physically diverse states by offering flexibility and alternate packing patterns. Voids are empty places within a protein that are surrounded by puffed atoms. A vacuum is sufficiently contained to prevent a probing ball from escaping [25]. This protein structure showed seven voids inside it with the highest volume of 329 Å^3. Tunnels, cavities, and voids in the structure of GAD from *A. adeninivorans* are represented in Figure 19.5.

19.7 Discussion

The present chapter covers the general features of GAD from microbial sources including its isolation, purification, biochemical characteristics, and assay methods. The enzyme is found to be very sensitive to oxygen; therefore, purification of it is quite tedious. The crystal structure of GAD from *A. adeninivorans* (6W54) showed heterotrimeric conformation. *In silico* analysis of the properties of 11 protein sequences of GAD has been performed. Among them, *A. adeninivorans* showed a higher abundance of acidic and basic amino acids. It also shows the lowest instability index indicating its more stability. Moreover, the presence of a large number of beta turns in the secondary structure of the protein provides additional evidence in support of the stability of the enzyme. Both isolated and network aromatic–aromatic interactions and salt bridges of GAD from *A. adeninivorans* (6W54) have been analyzed. It was found to possess three isolated and three network aromatic–aromatic interactions, with nine isolated and two network salt bridges in

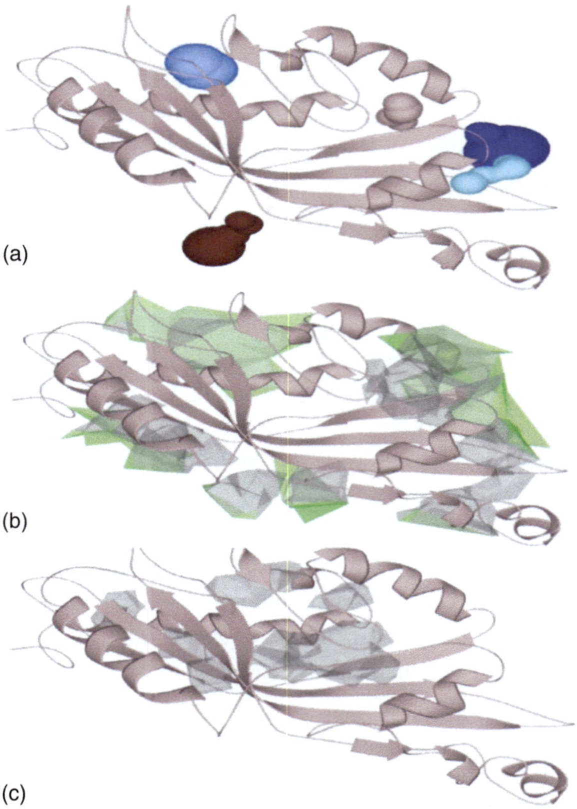

(a)

(b)

(c)

Figure 19.5 (a) Tunnels, (b) cavities, and (c) voids in structure of gallic acid decarboxylase from *Arxula adeninivorans*.

its sequence. Both these properties provide thermostability to the enzyme structure. Moreover, tunnels, cavities, and voids in the structure of GAD of *A. adeninivorans* have also been identified. The tunnels and cavities offer improvements in the catalytic accomplishment of the protein.

19.8 Conclusions

As the enzyme GAD is highly sensitive to oxygen, more attention should be given to searching for new and potential microbial sources for enzyme production and possible purification of the enzyme.

References

1 Meier, A.K. (2020). Identification and characterisation of gallic acid decarboxylase (Agdc1p) and catechol-1, 2-dioxygenase (Acdo1p) and their role in the degradation of tannic acid in the yeast *Blastobotrys (Arxula) adeninivorans*. Doctoral dissertation.

2 Zeida, M., Wieser, M., Yoshida, T. et al. (1998). Purification and characterization of gallic acid decarboxylase from *Pantoea agglomerans* T71. *Appl. Environ. Microbiol.* 64 (12): 4743–4747.

3 Zeug, M., Markovic, N., Iancu, C. et al. (2020). The crystal structure of gallic acid decarboxylase from *Arxula adeninivorans*. *Found. Crystallogr.* 76: a177.

4 Biswas, I., Mitra, D., Bandyopadhyay, A.K., and Mohapatra, P.K. (2020). Contributions of protein microenvironment in tannase industrial applicability: an in-silico comparative study of pathogenic and non-pathogenic bacterial tannase. *Heliyon* 6 (11): e05359.

5 Das Mohapatra, P.K., Biswas, I., Mondal, K.C., and Pati, B.R. (2020). Concomitant yield optimization of tannase and gallic acid by *Bacillus licheniformis* KBR6 through submerged fermentation: an industrial approach. *Acta Biol. Szeged.* 64 (2): 151–158.

6 Biswas, I., Mitra, D., and Mohapatra, P.K. (2022). Structural and catalytic advancement of fungal tannase: a proteomic contribution in industrial applicability. *Bioresour. Technol. Rep.* 19: 101103.

7 Mitra, D., Dey, A., Biswas, I., and Das Mohapatra, P.K. (2021). Bioactive compounds as a potential inhibitor of colorectal cancer; an in-silco study of gallic acid and pyrogallol. *Ann. Colorectal Res.* 9 (1): 32–39.

8 Soni, M., Sharma, K.P., Kaushik, S., and John, P.J. (2012). Purification and characterization of gallic acid decarboxylase from *Enterobacter* spp. isolated from a region in Rajasthan, India. *Int. J. Biosci.* 2 (12): 97–104.

9 Yoshida, H., Tani, Y., and Yamada, H. (1982). Isolation and identification of a pyrogallol producing bacterium from soil. *Agric. Biol. Chem.* 46 (10): 2539–2546.

10 Yoshida, H. and Yamada, H. (1985). Microbial production of pyrogallol through decarboxylation of gallic acid. *Agric. Biol. Chem.* 49 (3): 659–663.

11 Jimenez, N., Curiel, J.A., Reveron, I. et al. (2013). Uncovering the *Lactobacillus plantarum* WCFS1 gallate decarboxylase involved in tannin degradation. *Appl. Environ. Microbiol.* 79 (14): 4253–4263.

12 Osawa, R. and Walsh, T.P. (1995). Detection of bacterial gallate decarboxylation by visual color discrimination. *J. Gen. Appl. Microbiol.* 41 (2): 165–170.

13 Esteban-Torres, M., Santamaría, L., Cabrera-Rubio, R. et al. (2018). A diverse range of human gut bacteria have the potential to metabolize the dietary component gallic acid. *Appl. Environ. Microbiol.* 84 (19): e01558.

14 Nakajima, H., Otani, C., and Niimura, T. (1992). Decarboxylation of gallate by cell-free extracts of *Streptococcus faecalis* and *Klebsiella pneumoniae* isolated from rat feces. *J. Food Hyg. Soc. Japan. (Shokuhin Eiseigaku Zasshi)* 33 (4): 371–377.

15 Doig, A.J., Andrew, C.D., Cochran, D.A. et al. (2001). Structure, stability and folding of the α-helix. In: *Biochemical Society Symposia* (ed. Berry, A. and Radford, S.E.), vol. 68, 95–110. Portland Press.

16 Mitra, D. and Das Mohapatra, P.K. (2021). Cold adaptation strategy of psychrophilic bacteria: an in-silico analysis of isocitrate dehydrogenase. *Syst. Microbiol. Biomanuf.* 1 (4): 483–493.

17 Mitra, D., Paul, M., Thatoi, H., and Mohapatra, P.K. (2021). Study of potentiality of dexamethasone and its derivatives against Covid-19. *J. Biomol. Struct. Dyn.* 40 (20): 10239–10249.

18 Mitra, D., Pal, A.K., and Das Mohapatra, P.K. (2022). Intra-protein interactions of SARS-CoV-2 and SARS: a bioinformatic analysis for plausible explanation regarding stability, divergency, and severity. *Syst. Microbiol. Biomanuf.* 2: 653–664.

19 Mitra, D. and Das Mohapatra, P.K. (2021b). Discovery of novel cyclic salt bridge in thermophilic bacterial protease and study of its sequence and structure. *Appl. Biochem. Biotechnol.* 193 (6): 1688–1700.

20 Brezovsky, J., Kozlikova, B., and Damborsky, J. (2018). Computational analysis of protein tunnels and channels. In: *Protein Engineering*, 25–42. New York, NY: Humana Press.

21 Kingsley, L.J. and Lill, M.A. (2015). Substrate tunnels in enzymes: structure–function relationships and computational methodology. *Proteins Struct. Funct. Bioinf.* 83 (4): 599–611.

22 Dias, S.E., Nguyen, Q.T., Jorge, J.A., and Gomes, A.J. (2017). Multi-GPU-based detection of protein cavities using critical points. *Future Gener. Comput. Syst.* 67: 430–440.

23 Mitra, D. and Das Mohapatra, P.K. (2021c). Inhibition of SARS-CoV-2 protein by bioactive compounds of edible mushroom; a bioinformatics insight. *Int. J. Adv. Sci. Eng. Technol.* 9 (2): 84–88.

24 Mitra, D. and Das Mohapatra, P.K. (2022). In silico comparative structural and compositional analysis of glycoproteins of RSV to study the nature of stability and transmissibility of RSV A. *Syst. Microbiol. Biomanuf.* 3: 312–327.

25 Liang, J. and Dill, K.A. (2001). Are proteins well-packed? *Biophys. J.* 81 (2): 751–766.

20

Microbial Chitinases: Potential Applications in Agriculture

Rupali Gupta[1], Gautam Anand[1], Dinesh Yadav[2], and Maya Bar[1]

[1]*Agricultural Research Organization, Volcani Institute, Department of Plant Pathology and Weed Research, Rishon LeZion 7505101, Israel*
[2]*Deen Dayal Upadhyaya Gorakhpur University, Department of Biotechnology, Gorakhpur, Uttar Pradesh 273009, India*

20.1 Introduction

Chitin, a β-(1,4)-linked polymer of *N*-acetyl-D-glucosamine, is the second most abundant naturally occurring biopolymer after cellulose [1]. It is widely distributed in nature and forms a major constituent of the shells, exoskeletons, and gut linings of arthropods, mainly crustaceans and insects (Figure 20.1).

It is an important component of cell walls of a variety of fungi and makes up the structural components of certain protists as well as of nematode eggs [2]. Chitinases (CHIs, EC 3.2.1.14) enzymes that break down chitin are members of the family glycosyl hydrolases. They degrade chitin by hydrolyzing β-(1,4) linkages between *N*-acetyl-D-glucosamine units [3]. During the past decade, chitinases have gained importance because of their usage in medicine, agriculture, and the food processing industry [4]. Previous studies reported that the estimated amount of crop yield loss owing to biotic stress exceeded 40% during preharvest, and an additional ~15% after the harvest [5]. The main causes of these losses are bacterial and fungal phytopathogens, nematodes, insects, and plant viruses [4]. Currently, the cultivation of plants worldwide is highly dependent on the use of chemical pesticides to diminish losses caused by biotic stress. The major problem associated with these chemicals is the development of resistance in the target organisms, effects on non-target organisms and the hazardous effects of chemicals on the surrounding environment. Several human diseases have been linked to pesticide application in agriculture [5]. Therefore, it is essential to develop a substitute for the use of chemical pesticides that is environment-friendly, besides protecting the plants against pathogens. Chitin is found in the exoskeleton of insects and the cell walls of fungi. Therefore, chitin-degrading enzymes may be considered as a good substitute for chemical fungicides to protect crops and increase production without harming the host plant [6].

Microbial Enzymes: Production, Purification, and Industrial Applications, First Edition.
Edited by Dinesh Yadav, Pankaj Chowdhary, Gautam Anand, and Rajarshi Kumar Gaur.

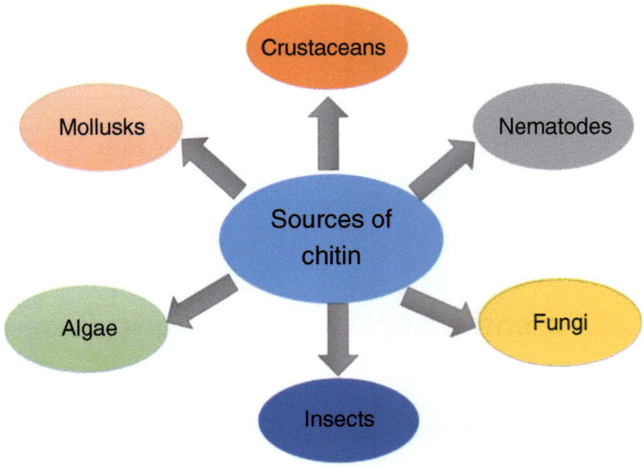

Figure 20.1 Some of the major sources of chitin.

This chapter talks about the importance and use of microbial chitinases as environment-friendly tools against plant pathogens. The chapter also discusses different types of chitinases, their source, and their application as biocontrol agents in agriculture.

20.2 Chitin Structure and Its Degradation by Chitinases

Chitin is a linear, unbranched polysaccharide made up of β-(1,4)-linked polymer of *N*-acetyl-D-glucosamine (GlcNAC). It is found in two crystalline forms; the α-form is the most abundant and is composed of antiparallel chitin microfibrils connected with intermolecular hydrogen bonds. The second form is β-chitin, which has parallel chitin chains [7]. Chitin is widely found in fungi and algae cell walls, cuticles of insects, exoskeletons of arthropods, and outer shells of crustaceans and nematodes, where it contributes to strength reinforcement [8]. Chitin has diverse applications in various food and chemical industries, and also possesses antitumor, antimicrobial, and anticholesterol properties [9]. Chitin can be a source of energy for chitinase-producing organisms, which can convert this polysaccharide into organic mixtures to be used as a source of carbon and nitrogen. Accumulation of chitin by living organisms is controlled by biosynthesis mediated by chitin synthase and hydrolytic degradation by the enzyme chitinase.

As glycosyl hydrolase enzyme, chitinases hydrolyze the polymer chitin at *N*-acetyl-β-D-glucosamine $(1 \rightarrow 4)$-β-linkages randomly producing different oligo- and monomeric forms. CHIs (EC 3.2.1.14) can be categorized into two types according to the position of the hydrolyzed bond. The breakdown of chitin into monomers of β-*N*-acetyl-D-glucosamine involves endochitinases and exochitinases. Endochitinases randomly cleave chitin at internal sites, producing chitototetriose, chitotriose, and diacetylochitobiose oligomers. The exochitinase

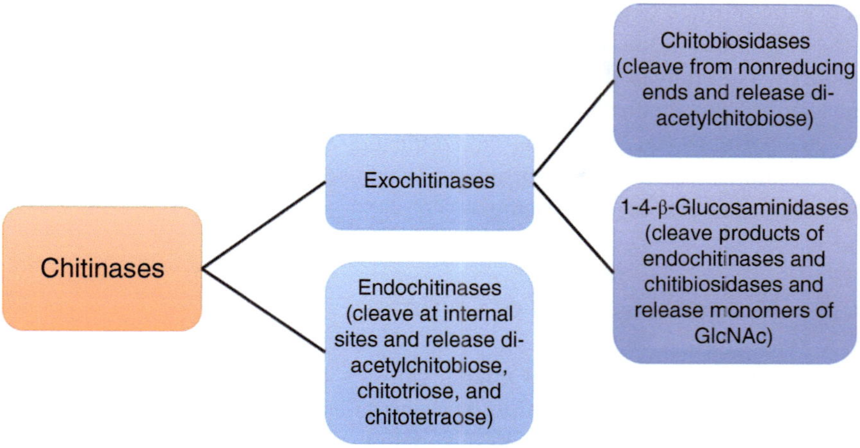

Figure 20.2 Classification of chitinases.

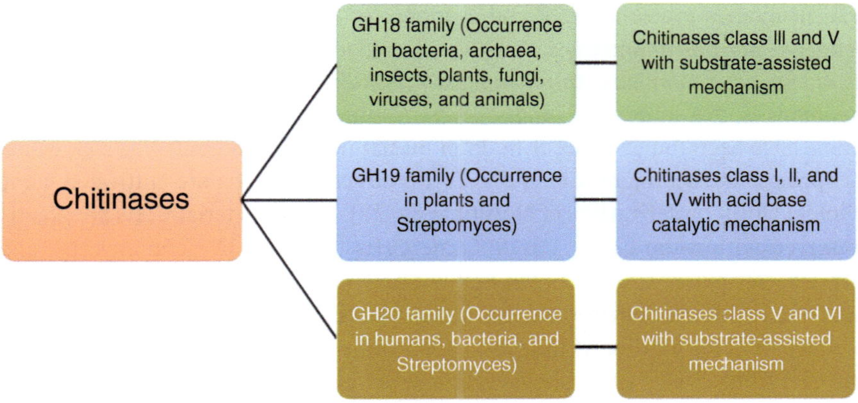

Figure 20.3 Chitinases belong to different glycosyl hydrolase families.

has two subgroups: chitobiosidases and β-*N*-acetyl glucosaminidases. Chitobiosidases catalyze chitin at the nonreducing end to produce chitobiose. Further, β-*N*-acetylglucosaminidases cleave the β-(1,4)-glycosidic bond of $(GlcNAC)_2$ to form monomers of β-*N*-acetyl-D-glucosamine [10] (Figure 20.2). According to the similarity of amino acid sequences, CHIs can be divided into three families: 18, 19, and 20 [6] (Figure 20.3).

Bacteria-derived chitosanase (EC 3.2.1.132) has recently been reported to deacetylate chitosan from chitin, eventually resulting in its transformation to glucosamine residues [11]. Although various CHIs have been found in bacteria, only some of them have wide-range specificity of the endochitinases, chitobiosidases, and β-*N*-acetyl glucosaminidases. These enzymes are able to resist environmental conditions of extreme pH and temperature; they are eco-friendly, versatile, and cost-effective for the synthesis of chitin and chitooligosaccharides. Effective application of these CHIs for marketable goals will be conceivable only pursuant to the acquisition of knowledge of the catalytic mechanism of the CHIs with high specificity. The study of the 3D structure of CHI produced by microorganisms [12] will form a basis for further understanding CHIs in relation to their structures, catalytic positions, and reactions with inducers and inhibitors. These research efforts could be assisted by exploring the benefits of protein engineering, *in silico* application, and genome sequencing.

20.3 Microbial Sources of Chitinase

It is broadly acknowledged, that microorganisms such as bacteria and fungi are the prevailing decomposers of chitin. Microorganisms are the best sources of CHIs owing to their immense richness in the environment and convenient cultivation, which assist in the cost-effective production of CHIs. Various sources for the isolation of chitinolytic microorganisms are given in Figure 20.4.

Bacterial chitinases are widely derived from various groups such as actinobacteria, firmicutes proteobacteria, and cyanobacteria [13]. Several bacteria, such as *Klebsiella, Serratia marcescens, Bacillus, Paenibacillus, Vibrio, Chromobacterium, Pseudomonas, Aeromonas, Xanthomonas, Clostridium, Arthrobacter, Nocardia*, and *Streptomyces*, are known to produce several different CHIs [3]. These bacterial strains have been found to occur in different natural environments like soil, water, hot springs, and sediment. Generally, CHI-producing bacteria are cultivated using colloidal chitin or derivatives of chitin media [12]. Many bacterial CHIs are greatly conserved within the family GH18. Some CHIs produced by actinomycetes and purple bacteria are assigned to the family GH19 [14]. CHIs isolated from bacteria occurring in different environments could possess distinct properties, making these enzymes valuable for diverse industrial applications. Sousa et al. [15] demonstrated that CHI from *C. violaceum* showed high activity at extreme temperatures, maintained hydrolytic activity at temperatures above 100 °C and showed antifungal activity against *Fusarium guttiforme* and *F. oxysporum*. In addition, Sun et al. [16] reported that the heterologous CHI from *Streptomyces* sp. F3 could resist extreme temperature and pH. Bacterial CHIs have displayed the efficiency to be used in different applications like depolymerization of chitin and chitosan for use as biocontrol agents against various phytopathogens and as an energy form [17].

Fungal CHI genes are found broadly across fungal genomes and belong to the CHIs family GH18, with the exception of CHI from *Nosema bombycis* [18]. Fungal GH18 CHIs were classified into four subfamilies: A, B, C, and D according to sequence similarity and domain organization [19]. Fungal chitinases are involved in morphogenesis, autolysis, and cell division [20]. They have also been found in mycoparasitic and entomopathogenic fungi [21, 22]. Deng et al. [21] reported that the chitinase Chit46 produced by *Trichoderma harzianum* impedes the growth of *Botrytis cinerea* and can efficiently hydrolyze colloidal chitin to GlcNAC with activities of up to 94.8%. Several species of *Trichoderma*, such as *T. harzianum*,

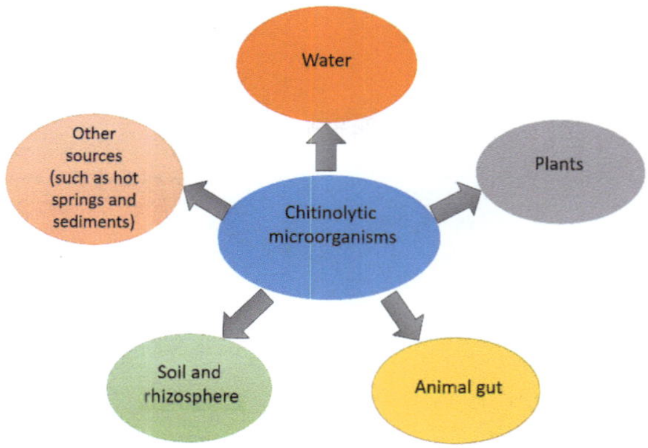

Figure 20.4 Different sources for the isolation of chitinolytic microorganisms.

T. longibrachiatum, T. atroviride, T. virens, T. erinaceum, T. lixii, and *T. asperellum*, are efficient chitinase producers [23–26]. Diverse species of *Aspergillus*, such as *A. carneus, A. terreus, A. niger, A. fumigatus, A. griseoaurantiacus, A. flavus,* and *A. niveus*, are also prominent chitinase producers [27, 28]. Some chitinase-producing fungi belong to the genera *Fusarium, Penicillium, Alternaria, Paecilomyces, Rhizopus, Acremonium, Verticillium lecanii, Beauveria bassiana,* and *Metarhizium anisopliae* [20, 29–33]. In recent years, several fungal CHIs have been identified for their possible applications in the development of potential biocontrol/antagonistic agents against plant pathogens and chitin hydrolysis [4]. CHI produced from thermophilic fungi display considerably high efficiency, thermal stability and survival under extreme conditions [17], which makes them an important candidate for various industrial applications. Mythili et al. [34] reported that engineered CHIs showed improved activity over the native enzyme in *T. harzianum*. Furthermore, use of genetically engineered CHIs has the potential to provide essential knowledge concerning the formation of bioactive chitooligosaccharides and the generation of more efficient approaches to fight against various diseases caused by phytopathogens. Currently, due to the limited knowledge of recognized fungal CHI sequences, our understanding of the molecular mechanism related to the applications of fungal CHIs is restricted.

20.4 Chitinolytic Microorganisms as Potential Biological Control Agents or Biopesticides

CHIs have numerous valuable applications in the field of biotechnology, including the management of chitin waste, pest or pathogen control in agriculture, and in pharmaceutical industries (Figure 20.5). In recent decades, agricultural production has increased, and farmers/growers have become highly dependent on chemical/synthetic fertilizers or pesticides for plant disease management [35]. The prevalent application of chemicals in current agricultural practice has jeopardized the use of agricultural produce and ecological stability all over the world. Biological management of agricultural pathogens is an effective and sustainable substitute for

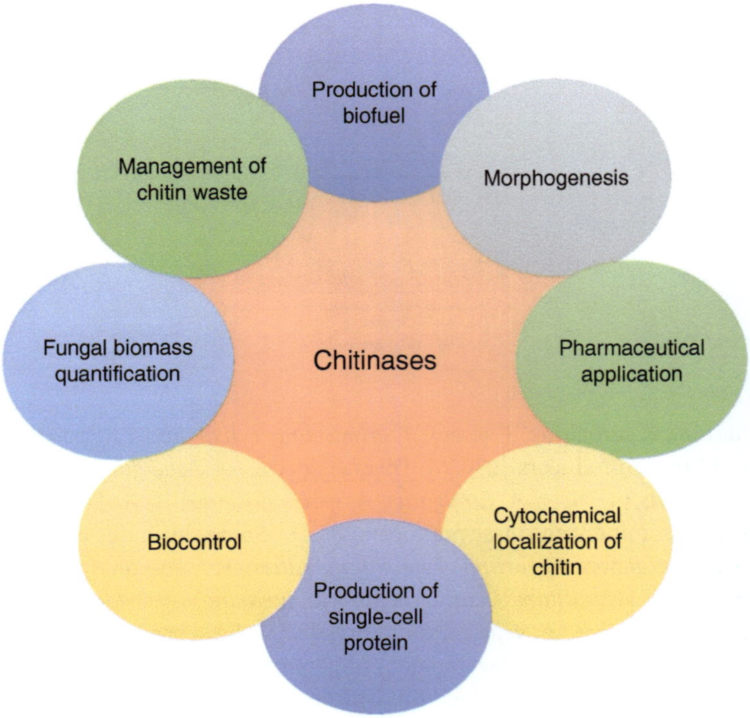

Figure 20.5 A schematic overview of applications of chitinase.

chemical control in farming. Among various mycolytic enzymes, CHIs produced by microbial communities are widely used as a biocontrol for inhibiting the growth of pathogens [36].

Microbial CHIs, used alone or in combination with other compatible microorganisms are antagonistic to various phytopathogens. CHIs derived from chitinolytic microorganisms, which are effective fungal cell wall-degrading enzymes, also act on different parts of complex fungal pathogen structures. The introduction of CHI synthesis genes both from bacteria and fungi into *Escherichia coli*, has aided in phytodisease management [37, 38]. Insect pests damage numerous ornamental and vegetable crops and diminish farming yields. The cuticles of the epidermis, the trachea, and the lining of gut epithelium of insects and eggshells of nematodes contains chitin. Hence, CHIs can play an essential role in the management of pests, pathogens, and insects. Some entomopathogenic fungi produce CHIs in the external environment to degrade the physical barrier, breach the exoskeleton, and induce plant defenses. Berini et al. [39] showed that metagenome-sourced 53D1 gene encoding CHIs can possibly be applied for the management of *Bombyx mori*. The results showed that the chitinase gene (*53D1*) was a potential enzyme applied as an insecticide. Table 20.1 provides a list of chitinolytic microbes that have been documented as potential biocontrol agents or alternatives to chemical pesticides against several pest and plant pathogens.

Table 20.1 Recent reports on the application of some microbial chitinases as biocontrol and biopesticides (cited 2015 onward).

Chitinase-producing microorganisms	Target plant pathogens	References
Bacteria		
Bacillus pumilus	*Scirpophaga incertulas*	[40]
Chitinophaga sp. S167	*Fusarium oxysporum*, *Alternaria alternata*, and *Cladosporium* sp. and *Meloidogyne incognita*	[41]
Streptomyces griseorubens E44G	*Fusarium oxysporum* f.sp. *lycopersici*	[42]
Streptomycetes	*Fusarium oxysporum* and *Rhizoctonia solani*	[43]
Streptomyces cellulosae	*Sclerotium rolfsii*	[44]
Bacillus subtilis TD11	*Rhizoctonia*, *Colletotrichum*, *Aspergillus*, and *Fusarium*	[45]
Pseudomonas fluorescens HN1205	*Meloidogyne incognita*	[46]
Paenibacillus sp. D1	*Helicoverpa armigera*	[47]
Chitiniphilus sp. MTN22 and *Streptomyces* sp. MTN14	*Meloidogyne incognita*	[48]
Bacillus pumilus RST25	*Fusarium solani* and *Aspergillus niger*	[49]
Bacillus subtilis ATCC 11774	*Rhizoctonia solani*	[50]
Pseudomonas GWSMS-1	*Verticillium dahlia* CICC 2534 and *Fusarium oxysporum* f.sp. *cucumerinum*	[51]
Pseudomonas aeroginosa	*Caenorhabditis elegans*	[52]
Pantoea agglomerans TD9, *Bacillus subtilis* TD11, and *Bacillus cereus*	*Rhizoctonia*, *Fusarium*, *Colletotrichum*, and *Aspergillus*	[53]
Stenotrophomonas maltophilia	*Coptotermes heimi* and *Heterotermes indicola*	[54]
Bacillus pumilus JUBCH08	*Fusarium oxysporum*	[55]
Serratia marcescens SEN	*Spodoptera litura*	[56]
Paenibacillus elgii HOA73	*Botrytis cinerea*	[57]
Fungi		
Trichoderma erinaceum	*Phytophthora meadii*, *Rhizoctonia solani*, *Curvularia lunata*, *Corynespora cassiicola*, *Rigidoporus microporus*, *Fusarium oxysporum*, and *Colletotrichum gloeosporioides*	[58]
Trichoderma sp. SANA20	*Botrytis cinerea*	[59]
Trichoderma spp.	*Meloidogyne incognita*, *Dematophora necatrix*, *Fusarium solani*, *Fusarium oxysporum*, and *Pythium aphanidermatum*	[60, 61]

(Continued)

Table 20.1 (Continued)

Chitinase-producing microorganisms	Target plant pathogens	References
Trichoderma viride	*Aspergillus niger*, *Fusarium oxysporum*, *Sclerotium rolfsii*, and *Bombyx mori*	[62, 63]
Trichoderma asperellum PQ34	*Colletotrichum* sp. and *Sclerotium rolfsii*	[23]
Trichoderma bissettii strains GJ-Sp1 and TOP-Co8	*Aspergillus flavus* and *Aspergillus niger*	[64]
Verticillium lecanii	*Fusarium moniliforme*, *Penicillium italicum*, and *Setosphaeria turcica*	[29]
Aspergillus terreus	*Aspergillus niger*, *Aspergillus oryzae*, *Penicillium oxysporium*, *Rhizoctonia solani*, *Candida albicans*, *Fusarium solani*, *Staphylococcus aureus*, *Salmonella typhi*, and *Pseudomonas aeruginosa*	[65]
Aspergillus awamori EM66	*Galleria mellonella*, *Spodoptera littoralis*, and *Agrotis ipsilon*	[66]
Aspergillus griseoaurantiacus KX010988	*Fusarium solani*	[67]
Aspergillus niveus	*Aspergillus niger*, *Aspergillus fumigatus*, *Aspergillus flavus*, *Aspergillus phoenicis*, and *Paecilomyces variotii*	[27]
Penicillium oxalicum k10	*Sclerotinia sclerotiorum* and *Mucor circinelloides*	[68]
Penicillium ochrochloron MTCC 517	*Helicoverpa armigera*	[69]
Fusarium oxysporum and *Ganoderma boninense*	*Trichoderma afroharzianum* JRE 1A and *Aspergillus fumigatus* JRE 4B	[70]
Cladosporium cladosporioides	*Curvularia lunata*, *Fusarium oxysporum*, and *Culex pipiens*	[71]
Monacrosporium thaumasium	*Panagrellus redivivus*	[72]

20.5 Metagenomic Approaches as a Tool to Unravel New Microbial Chitinases

In the last few decades, there have been many reports on microbial chitinases derived from cultivated microorganisms from various sources [6]. However, only a few of them have succeeded in applicability as a biocontrol or biopesticide in environmental conditions [39, 73]. This is mainly owing to the difficulties found in the natural conditions and instability of the enzymes used thus far. Another limitation of microbial enzyme investigations is the use of conventional approaches for cultivating the microbes on different culture media. The conventional approach restricts the type and number of microbes that can be used for enzyme research, since the majority of microbes are unculturable. However, the advancements in technology and the availability of new approaches allow scientists to search for novel enzymes without cultivation of microbes on culture media. Therefore, there is a snowballing demand for chitinases with enhanced properties such as improved stability, long shelf-life, and antagonistic activity against various pathogens under flexible (temperature and pH) field conditions. A potential substitute to accomplish these features would be the identification of novel CHIs having a special selectivity against the targeted destructive pests, which also possess preferred properties for commercial or industrial purposes. These attributes might be extended by the functional metagenomics in amalgamation with *in silico* methodologies. In recent years, there have been only a few findings reported on CHIs derived from uncultivatable microorganisms, and many of the present findings were derived from metagenomics data concerning CHIs from specific (marine and aquatic) environments [17, 74]. Thus, these chitinases are unlikely to have effects on cultivated plants when applied as bioinoculants, owing to the biological and physicochemical dissimilarities between habitats. There are some findings with CHIs isolated from soil [75], but these enzymes have not attained the standard properties for commercial/industrial application, and their findings have not been progressive. Although some studies have widely focused on the application of CHIs for several biotechnological and environmental purposes, not many have found effective practical applications [2]. Metagenomic approaches for environmental DNA preparations [76] from soil samples, can be an ideal source of novel and miscellaneous genes exhibiting CHI activities. However, the selection of methods of DNA isolation from soil samples is also a difficult task because soil DNA contains humic acid, protein, and carbohydrate contaminants. Thus, investigators need to apply distinct methods of sampling that have critical steps specific to DNA isolation from a particular habitat. Also, it is necessary to continue the current research for obtaining comprehensive and innovative screening approaches that increase the probability of finding novel CHIs of interest. Finally, the development in *in silico* biology coupled with the successes of metagenomic approaches could provide a novel outline to address these limitations [77, 78]. It is essential to note that metagenomic CHIs and their products are multipurpose and, simultaneously, under-investigation; hence, there are still several opportunities to be explored by researchers. With the upsurge in research on CHIs and their products, novel functions can be assigned to them for future applications. The advancement of metagenomics approaches will continue to assist scientists in isolating novel enzymes from diverse environments that are beneficial to agriculture and industries.

20.6 Conclusion and Future Perspectives

Chitinolytic microorganisms are important candidates with potential implementation in various industries like agriculture, pharmaceutical, biofuel, and waste management (Figure 20.5). In this chapter, the structure, classification, and application of microbial CHIs as promising biocontrol agents in agriculture is comprehensively reviewed in light of updated literature. Further, we also discussed various natural environments from where efficient CHI-producing microorganisms can be isolated. With the use of a metagenomic approach or activity-driven selections, there is a potential prospect for the exploitation of microbial CHIs from habitats that, to date, have remained elusive. These novel enzymes with unique properties are useful in various industrial setups. Herein, we have also reviewed how metagenomic approaches may lead to identification of new, efficient CHI microbes with enhanced potential for agricultural applications, particularly improving crop protection and yield. CHIs have numerous applications, not limited to the degradation of chitin. Thus, prospection of potent CHIs is vital for dealing with the rising interest in the management of chitin-enriched industrial waste products. Further advancement in the degradation of chitin will require the sustained exploration of novel enzymes, using value-added properties and high-throughput CHI activity.

Despite several discoveries in recent years concerning chitinolytic microorganisms, there is still a lack of information related to applications of chitin-degrading microbes, which could provide possible solutions for biocontrol and other associated issues. Further research is the need of the hour to enhance the commercial value of chitinolytic enzymes. Several findings highlighted the possibility of applying chitinolytic microbes as biocontrol agents in agriculture. In agriculture, the application of agents producing numerous metabolites of microorganisms, including CHIs, seems to be the most effective, since they display better antagonistic properties against pathogens than purified CHI enzymes. Thus, the application of these candidates, creating a consortium of chitinolytic microorganisms, appears to improve plant yield by fighting against various plant pathogens [35, 79, 80]. Further, these enzymes can generate a cascade of benefits throughout the production chain, producing good-quality food by decreasing the utilization of synthetic chemicals harmful to human health. The identification of new and potential chitinolytic microorganisms is crucial to lowering the second-largest natural waste chitin in the world. Positively, bioprospecting diverse and specific surroundings for novel CHIs with better activities is promising due to the current development in next-generation sequencing and systems biology methodologies.

Different genome sequencing databases have delivered a repository of CHI genes. Although, this has provided advances toward the identification of uncultivatable CHI-producing microorganisms and novel enzymes through synthetic biology studies, the enhancement in the properties of CHIs and high-throughput CHI assays still requires considerable attention. Further, knowledge of the metabolism of chitin-degrading microbes and desired genetic changes to develop the production of effective CHIs have to be joined to scale up their commercial practices. Developing unique bioreactors able to proficiently generate by-products from chitin remains a task that demands to be addressed from an industrial-scale perspective. To meet these challenges, the protein structure should be elucidated to accomplish the aim of augmented synthesis of enzymes in a cost-effective manner. The combined effort of various sectors (academic, federal, and industrial) as a group can be an effective solution to these challenges improving and implementing significant value drivers in the future.

References

1 Qin, Z. and Zhao, L. (2019). The history of chito/chitin oligosaccharides and its monomer. In: *Oligosaccharides of Chitin and Chitosan* (ed. L. Zhao), 3–14. Singapore, https://doi.org/10.1007/978-981-13-9402-7_1: Springer.

2 Oyeleye, A. and Normi, Y.M. (2018). Chitinase: diversity, limitations, and trends in engineering for suitable applications. *Biosci. Rep.* 38 (4): BSR2018032300.

3 Singh, R.V., Sambyal, K., Negi, A. et al. (2021). Chitinases production: a robust enzyme and its industrial applications. *Biocatal. Biotransform.* 39 (3): 161–189.

4 Gomaa, E.Z. (2021). Microbial chitinases: properties, enhancement and potential applications. *Protoplasma* 258 (4): 695–710.

5 Singh, A., Bhardwaj, R., and Singh, I.K. (2019). Biocontrol agents: potential of biopesticides for integrated pest management. In: *Biofertilizers for Sustainable Agriculture and Environment*, Soil Biology, vol. 55 (ed. B. Giri, R. Prasad, Q.S. Wu, and A. Varma), 413–433. Cham. https://doi.org/10.1007/978-3-030-18933-4_19: Springer.

6 Nayak, S.K., Nayak, S., Mohanty, S. et al. (2021). Microbial chitinases and their applications: an overview. In: *Environmental and Agricultural Microbiology* (ed. B.B. Mishra, S.K. Nayak, S. Mohapatra, and D. Samantaray) https://doi.org/10.1002/9781119525899.ch15, 313–340. Wiley.

7 Mohan, K., Muralisankar, T., Jayakumar, R., and Rajeevgandhi, C. (2021). A study on structural comparisons of α-chitin extracted from marine crustacean shell waste. *Carbohydr. Polym. Technol. Appl.* 2: 100037.

8 Gupta, R., Anand, G., Singh, S.P. et al. (2023). Harnessing beneficial Rhizospheric microorganisms for biotic stress management in medicinal and aromatic plants. In: *Detection, Diagnosis and Management of Soil-borne Phytopathogens* (ed. U.B. Singh, R. Kumar, and H.B. Singh), 283–308. Singapore, https://doi.org/10.1007/978-981-19-8307-8_11: Springer Nature.

9 Lv, J., Lv, X., Ma, M. et al. (2023). Chitin and chitin-based biomaterials: a review of advances in processing and food applications. *Carbohydr. Polym.* 299: 120142.

10 Poria, V., Rana, A., Kumari, A. et al. (2021). Current perspectives on chitinolytic enzymes and their agro-industrial applications. *Biology (Basel)* 10 (12): 1319.

11 Kaczmarek, M.B., Struszczyk-Swita, K., Li, X. et al. (2019). Enzymatic modifications of chitin, chitosan, and chitooligosaccharides. *Front. Bioeng. Biotechnol.* 7: 243.

12 Itoh, T. and Kimoto, H. (2019). Bacterial chitinase system as a model of chitin biodegradation. In: *Targeting Chitin-containing Organisms*, Advances in Experimental Medicine and Biology, vol. 1142 (ed. Q. Yang and T. Fukamizo), 131–151. Springer, https://doi.org/10.1007/978-981-13-7318-3_7.

13 Brzezinska, M.S., Kalwasińska, A., Świątczak, J. et al. (2020). Exploring the properties of chitinolytic Bacillus isolates for the pathogens biological control. *Microb. Pathog.* 148: 104462.

14 Lv, C., Gu, T., Ma, R. et al. (2021). Biochemical characterization of a GH19 chitinase from *Streptomyces* alfalfae and its applications in crystalline chitin conversion and biocontrol. *Int. J. Biol. Macromol.* 167: 193–201.

15 Sousa, A.J.S., Silva, C.F.B., Sousa, J.S. et al. (2019). A thermostable chitinase from the antagonistic *Chromobacterium violaceum* that inhibits the development of phytopathogenic fungi. *Enzyme Microb. Technol.* 126: 50–61.

16 Sun, X., Li, Y., Tian, Z. et al. (2019). A novel thermostable chitinolytic machinery of *Streptomyces* sp. F-3 consisting of chitinases with different action modes. *Biotechnol. Biofuels* 12 (1): 136.

17 Mathew, G.M., Madhavan, A., Arun, K.B. et al. (2021). *Thermophilic chitinases*: structural, functional and engineering attributes for industrial applications. *Appl. Biochem. Biotechnol.* 193 (1): 142–164.

18 Orlando, M., Buchholz, P.C.F., Lotti, M., and Pleiss, J. (2021). The GH19 engineering database: sequence diversity, substrate scope, and evolution in glycoside hydrolase family 19. *PLoS One* 16 (10): e0256817.

19 Yang, J. and Zhang, K.Q. (2019). Chitin synthesis and degradation in fungi: biology and enzymes. In: *Targeting Chitin-containing Organisms*, Advances in Experimental Medicine and Biology, vol. 1142 (ed. Q. Yang and T. Fukamizo). Singapore: Springer https://doi.org/10.1007/978-981-13-7318-3_8.

20 Thakur, D., Bairwa, A., Dipta, B. et al. (2023). An overview of fungal chitinases and their potential applications. *Protoplasma* 260 (4): 1031–1046.

21 Deng, J.-J., Shi, D., Mao, H. et al. (2019). Heterologous expression and characterization of an antifungal chitinase (Chit46) from *Trichoderma harzianum* GIM 3.442 and its application in colloidal chitin conversion. *Int. J. Biol. Macromol.* 134: 113–121.

22 Poveda, J. (2021). Trichoderma as biocontrol agent against pests: new uses for a mycoparasite. *Biol. Control* 159: 104634.

23 Loc, N.H., Huy, N.D., Quang, H.T. et al. (2020). Characterisation and antifungal activity of extracellular chitinase from a biocontrol fungus, *Trichoderma asperellum* PQ34. *Mycology* 11 (1): 38–48.

24 Erazo, J.G., Palacios, S.A., Pastor, N. et al. (2021). Biocontrol mechanisms of *Trichoderma harzianum* ITEM 3636 against peanut brown root rot caused by *Fusarium solani* RC 386. *Biol. Control* 164: 104774.

25 Shen, Z., Zhang, S., and Xu, B. (2022). *Trichoderma longibrachiatum* T6: a nematocidal activity of endochitinase gene exploration and its function identification. *Int. J. Biol. Macromol.* 223: 1641–1652.

26 Li, J., Kong, L., Ma, C. et al. (2022). A chitinase involved in the mycoparasitism of *Trichoderma atroviride* on aeciospores of *Cronartium ribicola*. *J. Phytopathol.* 170 (4): 209–213.

27 Alves, T.B., de Oliveira Ornela, P.H., de Oliveira, A.H.C. et al. (2018). Production and characterization of a thermostable antifungal chitinase secreted by the filamentous fungus *Aspergillus niveus* under submerged fermentation. *3 Biotech* 8 (8): 369.

28 Singh, G. and Arya, S.K. (2019). Antifungal and insecticidal potential of chitinases: a credible choice for the eco-friendly farming. *Biocatal. Agric. Biotechnol.* 20: 101289.

29 Yu, G., Xie, L.Q., Li, J.T. et al. (2015). Isolation, partial characterization, and cloning of an extracellular chitinase from the entomopathogenic fungus *Verticillium lecanii*. *Genet. Mol. Res.* 14 (1): 2275–2289.

30 Sonawane, K.D., Dandagal, N.R., Naikwadi, A.G. et al. (2016). Intergeneric fusant development using chitinase preparation of *Rhizopus stolonifer* NCIM 880. *AMB Express* 6 (1): 114.

31 Chung, D., Baek, K., Bae, S.S., and Jung, J. (2019). Identification and characterization of a marine-derived chitinolytic fungus, *Acremonium* sp. YS2-2. *J. Microbiol.* 57 (5): 372–380.

32 Guigón López, C., Muñoz Castellanos, L.N., Flores Ortiz, N.A., and González González, J.A. (2019). Control of powdery mildew (*Leveillula taurica*) using *Trichoderma asperellum* and *Metarhizium anisopliae* in different pepper types. *BioControl* 64 (1): 77–89.

33 Amobonye, A., Bhagwat, P., Pandey, A. et al. (2020). Biotechnological potential of *Beauveria bassiana* as a source of novel biocatalysts and metabolites. *Crit. Rev. Biotechnol.* 40 (7): 1019–1034.

34 Mythili, J.B., Chethana, B.S., Rajeev, P.R., and Ganeshan, G. (2018). Chitinase gene construct from *Trichoderma harzianum* proved effective against onion purple blotch caused by *Alternaria porri*. *Indian J. Biotechnol.* 17: 50–56.

35 Gupta, R., Singh, A., Ajayakumar, P.V., and Pandey, R. (2017). Chitinolytic microbes confer *Meloidogyne incognita* resistance and augment secondary metabolites in *Bacopa monnieri* (L.) Pennell. *Arch. Phytopathol. Plant Prot.* 50 (3–4): 178–196.

36 Gupta, R., Singh, A., Ajayakumar, P.V., and Pandey, R. (2017). Microbial interference mitigates *Meloidogyne incognita* mediated oxidative stress and augments bacoside content in *Bacopa monnieri* L. *Microbiol. Res.* 199: 67–78.

37 Abdel-Salam, M.S., Ameen, H.H., Kassab, A.S.M. et al. (2018). Enhancement of nematicidal potential through cloning and expression of chitinase gene from *Bacillus subtilis* subsp. subtilis BTN7A strain. *J. Genet. Eng. Biotechnol.* 16 (2): 305–310.

38 Luong, N.N., Tien, N.Q.D., Huy, N.X. et al. (2021). Expression of 42 kDa chitinase of *Trichoderma asperellum* (Ta-CHI42) from a synthetic gene in *Escherichia coli*. *FEMS Microbiol. Lett.* 368 (16): fnab110.

39 Berini, F., Casartelli, M., Montali, A. et al. (2019). Metagenome-sourced microbial chitinases as potential insecticide proteins. *Front. Microbiol.* 10: 464594.

40 Rishad, K.S., Rebello, S., Shabanamol, P.S., and Jisha, M.S. (2017). Biocontrol potential of Halotolerant bacterial chitinase from high yielding novel *Bacillus pumilus* MCB-7 autochthonous to mangrove ecosystem. *Pestic. Biochem. Physiol.* 137: 36–41.

41 Sharma, S., Kumar, S., Khajuria, A. et al. (2020). Biocontrol potential of chitinases produced by newly isolated *Chitinophaga* sp. S167. *World J. Microbiol. Biotechnol.* 36 (6): 90.

42 Rashad, Y.M., Al-Askar, A.A., Ghoneem, K.M. et al. (2017). Chitinolytic *Streptomyces griseorubens* E44G enhances the biocontrol efficacy against *Fusarium wilt* disease of tomato. *Phytoparasitica* 45 (2): 227–237.

43 Gonzalez-Franco, A.C., Deobald, L.A., Spivak, A., and Crawford, D.L. (2003). Actinobacterial chitinase-like enzymes: profiles of rhizosphere versus non-rhizosphere isolates. *Can. J. Microbiol.* 49 (11): 683–698.

44 Abo-Zaid, G., Abdelkhalek, A., Matar, S. et al. (2021). Application of bio-friendly formulations of chitinase-producing *Streptomyces cellulosae* Actino 48 for controlling peanut soil-borne diseases caused by *Sclerotium rolfsii*. *J. Fungi* 7 (3): 167.

45 Malik, M.S., Rehman, A., Khan, I.U. et al. (2023). Thermo-neutrophilic cellulases and chitinases characterized from a novel putative antifungal biocontrol agent: *Bacillus subtilis* TD11. *PLoS One* 18 (1): e0281102.

46 Lee, Y.S. and Kim, K.Y. (2015). Statistical optimization of medium components for chitinase production by *Pseudomonas fluorescens* strain HN1205: role of chitinase on egg hatching inhibition of root-knot nematode. *Biotechnol. Biotechnol. Equip.* 29 (3): 470–478.

47 Singh, A.K., Singh, A., and Joshi, P. (2016). Combined application of chitinolytic bacterium *Paenibacillus* sp. D1 with low doses of chemical pesticides for better control of *Helicoverpa armigera*. *Int. J. Pest Manage.* 62 (3): 222–227.

48 Gupta, R., Singh, A., Srivastava, M. et al. (2017). Microbial modulation of bacoside A biosynthetic pathway and systemic defense mechanism in *Bacopa monnieri* under *Meloidogyne incognita* stress. *Sci. Rep.* 7 (1): 41867.

49 Gurav, R., Tang, J., and Jadhav, J. (2017). Novel chitinase producer *Bacillus pumilus* RST25 isolated from the shellfish processing industry revealed antifungal potential against phyto-pathogens. *Int. Biodeterior. Biodegrad.* 125: 228–234.

50 Saber, W.I.A., Ghoneem, K.M., Al-Askar, A.A. et al. (2015). Chitinase production by *Bacillus subtilis* ATCC 11774 and its effect on biocontrol of *Rhizoctonia* diseases of potato. *Acta Biol. Hung.* 66 (4): 436–448.

51 Liu, K., Ding, H., Yu, Y., and Chen, B. (2019). A cold-adapted chitinase-producing bacterium from antarctica and its potential in biocontrol of plant pathogenic fungi. *Mar. Drugs* 17 (12): 695.

52 Chen, J., An, Y., Kumar, A., and Liu, Z. (2017). Improvement of chitinase Pachi with nematicidal activities by random mutagenesis. *Int. J. Biol. Macromol.* 96: 171–176.

53 Malik, M.S., Haider, S., Rehman, A. et al. (2022). Biological control of fungal pathogens of tomato (*Lycopersicon esculentum*) by chitinolytic bacterial strains. *J. Basic Microbiol.* 62 (1): 48–62.

54 Jabeen, F., Hussain, A., Manzoor, M. et al. (2018). Potential of bacterial chitinolytic, *Stenotrophomonas maltophilia*, in biological control of termites. *Egypt. J. Biol. Pest Control* 28 (1): 86.

55 Bhattacharya, S., Das, A., Samadder, S., and Rajan, S.S. (2016). Biosynthesis and characterization of a thermostable, alkali-tolerant chitinase from *Bacillus pumilus* JUBCH08 displaying antagonism against phytopathogenic *Fusarium oxysporum*. *3 Biotech* 6 (1): 87.

56 Aggarwal, C., Paul, S., Tripathi, V. et al. (2015). Chitinolytic activity in *Serratia marcescens* (strain SEN) and potency against different larval instars of *Spodoptera litura* with effect of sublethal doses on insect development. *BioControl* 60 (5): 631–640.

57 Kim, Y.C., Hur, J.Y., and Park, S.K. (2019). Biocontrol of *Botrytis cinerea* by chitin-based cultures of *Paenibacillus elgii* HOA73. *Eur. J. Plant Pathol.* 155 (1): 253–263.

58 Herath, H. (2015). Isolation and characterization of *Trichoderma erinaceum* for antagonistic activity against plant pathogenic fungi. *Curr. Res. Environ. Appl. Mycol.* 5 (2): 120–127.

59 Aoki, Y., Haga, S., and Suzuki, S. (2020). Direct antagonistic activity of chitinase produced by *Trichoderma* sp. SANA20 as biological control agent for grey mould caused by *Botrytis cinerea*. *Cogent Biol.* 6 (1): 1747903.

60 Sayed, M., Abdel-rahman, T., Ragab, A., and Abdellatif, A. (2019). Biocontrol of root-knot nematode *Meloidogyne incognita* by chitinolytic *Trichoderma* spp. *Egypt. J. Agron.* 18 (1): 30–47.

61 Mohiddin, F.A., Padder, S.A., Bhat, A.H. et al. (2021). Phylogeny and optimization of *Trichoderma harzianum* for chitinase production: evaluation of their antifungal behaviour against the prominent soil borne phyto-pathogens of temperate India. *Microorganisms* 9 (9): 1962.

62 Khatri, D.K., Tiwari, D.N., and Bariya, H.S. (2017). Chitinolytic efficacy and secretion of cell wall degrading enzymes from *Trichoderma* spp. in response to phyto-pathological fungi. *J. Appl. Biol. Biotechnol.* 5: 1–8.

63 Berini, F., Caccia, S., Franzetti, E. et al. (2016). Effects of *Trichoderma viride* chitinases on the peritrophic matrix of Lepidoptera. *Pest. Manage. Sci.* 72 (5): 980–989.

64 Chung, D., Kwon, Y.M., Lim, J.Y. et al. (2022). Characterization of chitinolytic and antifungal activities in marine-derived *Trichoderma bissettii* strains. *Mycobiology* 50 (4): 244–253.

65 Farag, A.M., Abd-Elnabey, H.M., Ibrahim, H.A.H., and El-Shenawy, M. (2016). Purification, characterization and antimicrobial activity of chitinase from marine-derived *Aspergillus terreus*. *Egypt. J. Aquat. Res.* 42 (2): 185–192.

66 Awad, G.E., Wahab, W.A.A., Hussein, M. et al. (2017). Sequential optimizations of *Aspergillus awamori* EM66 exochitinase and its application as biopesticide. *J. Appl. Pharm. Sci.* 7: 067–075.

67 Shehata, A.N., Abd El Aty, A.A., Darwish, D.A. et al. (2018). Purification, physicochemical and thermodynamic studies of antifungal chitinase with production of bioactive chitosan-oligosaccharide from newly isolated *Aspergillus griseoaurantiacus* KX010988. *Int. J. Biol. Macromol.* 107: 990–999.

68 Xie, X.-H., Fu, X., Yan, X.-Y. et al. (2021). A broad-specificity chitinase from *Penicillium oxalicum* k10 exhibits antifungal activity and biodegradation properties of chitin. *Mar. Drugs* 19 (7): 356.

69 Patil, N.S. and Jadhav, J.P. (2015). Significance of *Penicillium ochrochloron* chitinase as a biocontrol agent against pest *Helicoverpa armigera*. *Chemosphere* 128: 231–235.

70 Mendrofa, A., Munir, E., Yurnaliza, Y. et al. (2021). Chitinase and antifungal activity of endophytic fungi isolated from *Hedychium coronarium* J. Koenig. *Agric. Conspec. Sci.* 86: 131–137.

71 Al Abboud, M.A., Al-Rajhi, A.M.H., Shater, A.-R.M. et al. (2022). Halostability and thermostability of chitinase produced by fungi isolated from salt marsh soil in subtropical region of Saudi Arabia. *Bioresources* 17 (3): 4763–4780.

72 Soares, F.E.d.F., de Queiroz, J.H., de Araújo, J.V. et al. (2015). Nematicidal action of chitinases produced by the fungus *Monacrosporium thaumasium* under laboratorial conditions. *Biocontrol Sci. Technol.* 25 (3): 337–344.

73 Pasin, T.M., de Oliveira, T.B., Scarcella, A.S.d.A. et al. (2021). Perspectives on expanding the repertoire of novel microbial chitinases for biological control. *J. Agric. Food. Chem.* 69 (11): 3284–3288.

74 Thimoteo, S.S., Glogauer, A., Faoro, H. et al. (2017). A broad pH range and processive chitinase from a metagenome library. *Braz. J. Med. Biol. Res.* 50 (1): e5658.

75 Hjort, K., Presti, I., Elväng, A. et al. (2014). Bacterial chitinase with phytopathogen control capacity from suppressive soil revealed by functional metagenomics. *Appl. Microbiol. Biotechnol.* 98 (6): 2819–2828.

76 Prayogo, F.A., Budiharjo, A., Kusumaningrum, H.P. et al. (2020). Metagenomic applications in exploration and development of novel enzymes from nature: a review. *J. Genet. Eng. Biotechnol.* 18 (1): 39.

77 Guazzaroni, M., Silva-Rocha, R., and Ward, R.J. (2015). Synthetic biology approaches to improve biocatalyst identification in metagenomic library screening. *Microb. Biotechnol.* 8 (1): 52–64.

78 Dhole, N.P., Dar, M.A., and Pandit, R.S. (2021). Recent advances in the bioprospection and applications of chitinolytic bacteria for valorization of waste chitin. *Arch. Microbiol.* 203 (5): 1953–1969.

79 Gupta, R., Singh, A., Srivastava, M. et al. (2016). Augmentation of systemic resistance and secondary metabolites by chitinolytic microbes in *Withania somnifera* against *Meloidogyne incognita*. *Biocontrol Sci. Technol.* 26 (12): 1626–1642.

80 Gupta, R., Singh, A., Srivastava, M. et al. (2019). Plant-microbe interactions endorse growth by uplifting microbial community structure of *Bacopa monnieri* rhizosphere under nematode stress. *Microbiol. Res.* 218: 87–96.